THIS BOOK IS DEDICATED TO

## HENRIETTA STEWART

MY WIFE, WHO HAS GIVEN IT MONTHS OF EDITORIAL
LABOR AND MANY CONSTRUCTIVE CRITICISMS;

TO

## O. E. BAKER

WHOSE WORK IN THE ANALYSIS OF AGRICULTURE AND THE GRAPHIC
PRESENTATION OF ITS FACTS HAS BEEN THE GREATEST
SINGLE CONTRIBUTION TO THE MATERIALS OF
ECONOMIC GEOGRAPHY; AND

TO

## NEVIN M. FENNEMAN

WHOSE LABOR IN DELINEATING THE PHYSIOGRAPHIC PROVINCES OF
THE UNITED STATES IS A CONTRIBUTION WHICH HAS
PLACED ALL GEOGRAPHERS IN HIS DEBT

# PREFACE

NORTH AMERICA is passing through a crisis in its economic history. The population of the United States increased twenty-seven fold in the one hundred and thirty years between the first census in 1790 and that of 1920. This increase, without parallel in the history of the world, was accompanied by the use, waste, and destruction of resources at a speed also unparalleled.

That is past. What of the future? This is the concern of every intelligent citizen — a growing concern. It will be even more acutely an affair which the youth now being educated must face. Their education should give them a thorough knowledge of the continent on which they are to live. Hence this book.

# ACKNOWLEDGMENTS

As I let this book leave my hand I feel a profound sense of my obligation to many people — to the dozens who have actually helped me, to the hundreds who have labored on books, reports, and articles which in turn have been material from which I have tried to erect a new structure.

For twenty years I have taught a College course on the Economic Geography of North America. During that time I have been assisted by a number of younger men. I am sure that each of them has left some imprint on the book.

Of this group of friendly co-workers, I am especially indebted to Joseph H. Willits and Alfred G. White. Frank E. Williams also gave much aid.

For intimate and continuous assistance in the actual preparation of the book I am indebted to Mr. Howard Martin, of Columbia University, who aided in gathering material, and to Mr. Everett Rodebaugh, of Philadelphia, personal assistant, map editor and proofreader.

Parts of the manuscript have been critically read by persons (named below) who are especially familiar with certain sections of North America. I do not, however, wish to pass off to these friendly helpers any sense of responsibility for any mistakes of fact or philosophy which may have crept into its final form:

FRANK ADAMS, University California, College of Agriculture, Davis, Cal.

R. L. ADAMS, University California, College of Agriculture, Berkeley, Cal.

O. E. BAKER, Agricultural Economist, U. S. Dept. Agr., Washington, D. C.

N. A. BENGTSON, University of Nebraska, Lincoln, Neb.

ROBT. M. BROWN, College of Education, Providence, R. I.

R. D. CALKINS, Central State Normal School, Mount Pleasant, Mich.

A. B. CORDLEY, Oregon Agricultural College, Corvallis, Oregon.

O. S. FINNIE, Dept. Interior, Ottawa, Canada.

ALICE FOSTER, Mt. Holyoke College, South Hadley, Mass.

W. M. GREGORY, Cleveland Normal School, Cleveland, Ohio.

R. P. GREEN, State Normal School, Bowling Green, Ky.

W. H. HICKS, Dept. Agr., Agassiz, B. C., Canada.

BYRON HUNTER, Dept. Agr., Washington, D. C. (Bur. Agr. Econ.).

R. M. HARPER, University, Alabama.

E. C. JOHNSON, State College of Washington, Pullman, Wash.

H. L. KENT, College of Agriculture & Mechanical Arts, State College, New Mexico.

FRED A. MERRILL, 416 River St., Valdosta, Ga.

JOHN E. ORCHARD, School of Business, Columbia University, New York.

LEONARD O. PACKARD, Boston Normal School, Boston, Mass.
A. E. PARKINS, George Peabody College for Teachers, Nashville, Tenn.
EDWARD E. PHILBROOK, State Normal School, Castine, Maine.
GEORGE T. RENNER, School of Business, Columbia University, New York.
BERNARD H. SCHOCKEL, State Normal School, Terre Haute, Ind.
GEORGE SEVERENCE, State College of Washington, Pullman, Wash.
HOWARD E. SIMPSON, University North Dakota, Grand Forks, N. D.
S. SHEDD, Dept. of Conservation & Development, Olympia, Wash.
WILLARD SMITH, Phoenix, Ariz.
S. S. VISHER, University of Indiana, Bloomington, Indiana.
GEO. H. WHITCHER, New Hampshire Dept. Public Instruction, Concord, N. H.
ALFRED G. WHITE, University of Pennsylvania.
E. V. WILCOX, Agriculturist, Washington, D. C.
L. A. WOLFANGER, School of Business, Columbia University, New York.

I must give expression to my great sense of gratitude for the endless patience and ever-ready kindness of many experts in the United States Department of Agriculture. The members of the scientific staff of the Canadian Government differ from their brethren on this side of the line only in the somewhat smaller number of calls which I have made upon them.

And lastly I wish to acknowledge my indebtedness to Nathaniel S. Shaler, of Harvard, my unseen master. I knew him only through the printed page, which showed him to be a pioneer appreciator of the relationship between earth and man. I like to think that this book expresses his viewpoint to a generation which he cannot teach in person.

I wish to make public expression of my indebtedness to Isaiah Bowman's Book, *Forest Physiography*, — which is really a regional physiography, the only regional physiography of the United States. W. L. G. Joerg of the American Geographical Society has given valued counsel with regard to maps.

On most of the special regional maps in this book, the topography is adapted (with permission) from the physiographic diagram of the United States by Professor A. K. Lobeck, published by A. J. Nystrom Co., Chicago, Ill.

J. RUSSELL SMITH

COLUMBIA UNIVERSITY
NEW YORK CITY
    December 15, 1924

# CONTENTS

# CONTENTS

# NORTH AMERICA

# CHAPTER I

## THE GEOGRAPHIC ENVIRONMENT

HELL is hot. Did you ever wonder why? But not all Hells are hot. Among the pre-Christian Scandinavians Hell was encased in snow and eternal ice.

To the Norseman blue with cold, a hot Hell sounded too pleasant to be Hell at all. According to a story centuries old, a missionary to the heathen Northmen preached a Hell-fire sermon. " Now of course," said one of the cold ones, " we all want to go to that nice warm place you speak of. But tell us, do we *have* to be mean and kill folks and make a lot of trouble before we can? "

Hell is the theologian's attempt to portray in figurative language unpleasant things for the future. Figures of speech to be effective must come close home and speak of things that are well known.

The Old Testament Hebrew lived on the edge of the desert. To be lost in the desert and suffer there from heat and thirst was the most terrible thing imaginable. It was an effective mind that used this idea for the creation of Hell. With equal effectiveness cold, snow, and ice were used by those who sought to move the minds of the Norse, shivering most of the year, always short of fuel, and not infrequently getting frozen to death.

After a thousand years of war in Palestine, after a thousand years during which that country served as a highroad for peoples and as a football for empires, it was not unnatural that Revelation should have described Heaven as a walled city. The Koran, written by Mohammed in the center of desert Arabia, presents a Heaven abounding in cool shade and soothed by the sweet sound of running water, the natural opposite of the Hell of the neighboring Jews, which was also a desert product. A study of world literature and the world's peoples would yield a surprising variety of heavens and hells, each with a natural explanation.

As with religion so it is with each of the other great emotions, needs, and activities of man; to understand what man has wrought we must study the place, the environment, in which he has wrought. We are only beginning to see how profoundly human creations have been shaped by the stage on which the drama has taken place — the earth (the environment).

3

Here is man upon this earth, making his living under an almost un-believable variety of conditions. But with all this diversity in condi-tions, man everywhere has the same problems to solve. Everywhere he must eat, make fire, clothe himself, provide shelter and make tools. Everywhere he desires to procreate, to care for wife and children, to exercise powers, to express individuality through creative effort — art, music, social organization, building. Universal also is the feeling of reverence or worship, man reaching out toward a stone idol, a sacred bull, a socialistic state, a political party, the true God.

How does the Continent of North America influence man as he makes his living and lives his life upon it? This book is written to answer that question.

### Race and Form of Government

North America is fit to be the home of a great and powerful people. Why? The Fourth of July orator thinks he knows. For more than a century he has eloquently explained why the United States is great. For generations he has given two reasons: (1) that this country had the great luck to be occupied by ourselves, a people of amazing inherent qualities; (2) that the government had the great advantage of being a republic, whereas most of the rest of the world has had to worry along under the domination of kings, emperors and other inferior rulers. These explanations — the inherent qualities of a people and the inherent virtues of a form of government — will scarcely stand as paramount reasons if a scientific search is made for the fundamental causes of American power.

Are we not of the stock of Europe or a fusion of European races save in certain parts of our land where the negro is found? To him who would claim that the differences between North America and Europe depend on racial characteristics, I recommend a close study of the Arab. In his desert home where agriculture is impossible, the Bedouin (Arab) is an incurable nomad, contemptuous of all dwellers in houses, with the nomad's qualities of hospitality, laziness and a surprising willingness to rob, pillage, murder — none of which is forbidden by his code of morals. But this same Arab, when he broke into Spain in the eighth century, soon settled down in that good agricultural country. Nomadism be-came as invisible as the vermiform appendix. Fields, irrigation ditches and villages spread themselves over the plain. These erstwhile dwellers in tents moved into walls of stone, and in a few centuries they built that gem of architecture, the Alhambra. It took only seven centuries, in the fertile well-tilled valley under a good agricultural environment, for this once nomadic people to establish universities, develop sciences, and become in many essentials the most highly civilized group in Europe. The learned Moor (Bedouin) read philosophic books in his library, experimented in his laboratory, and made great discoveries in mathematics at the time when the rank and file of the Angles, Saxons, Celts and Teutons were more ignorant than Arab slaves. Then Christian Spain triumphed over the Moors and drove them back across the Mediterranean whence they had come.

Driven back to Africa many of them have again relapsed into nomadism, no other kind of life being possible in much of that region. This is clear evidence that environment is quite as strong as race as a determining factor in the actions and thoughts of man. Even his ideas of right and wrong are very strongly marked by geographic environment.

The Fourth of July orator's claim that the United States is thus and so because it has a republican form of government ceases to be plausible when we remember that Great Britain, for instance, is more democratic than the United States, more prompt in responding to the popular will, and that Switzerland exceeds Great Britain in this respect.

In the autumn of 1919 the paramount question in the United States, probably the paramount question in the world, was the American attitude toward the Treaty of Versailles and the League of Nations. The President wanted it with all the ardor of his spirit. The Senate had rejected it. The government was at a deadlock and the deadlock could not be broken until the statutory date of March 4, 1921, when by the machinery created by the Constitutional Convention of 1787 a change of administration was due. In England the government would have passed overnight to the group that had the votes, instead of waiting through seventeen months of deadlock created by a governmental mechanism designed to balance power rather than to enact the will of the people.

It is plain that the forms of government cannot be used as fundamental explanations of the deeper trends of man's activities, or of the achievements of the United States. Political affairs are, indeed, results, not causes.

### Economic Causes of Ideas

Political causes lie in industry and in other effects and results of the geographic environment. Politics are largely the attempts of men to adjust themselves to industrial and economic factors. The American tariff affords many examples of this. Without an understanding of the geographic factors, history may become merely a string of unexplained or personal episodes — interesting, dramatic, but facts without meaning.

What, then, is it that makes America fit to be the home of a great people? Since the explanation is not to be found in the settlement of the Continent by any particular race, or in any particular form of government, other causes must be sought. If we take a long view, the country's history is to be explained in large part, and its future may be predicted in large part, in terms of (1) *Resources* — the good opportunity for the production of food, clothing, shelter, fuel, tools, luxuries — six classes which include all of our material wealth; (2) *Climate* which (a) permits man to be healthy, (b) permits him to be energetic, (c) compels him to work and use that energy; and (3) *Location* and *Access*, which provide the opportunities for transportation and commerce and influence our relations with other peoples. These three great fundamentals — resources, climate, access — form the background of history and help greatly to explain society.

## Slavery — Economics and Ideas

Slavery shows us how geographical environment and industrial factors have worked together to influence both politics and morals. Slavery, an age-old and nearly or quite world-wide custom, seems to have been established in the early decades of colonial history along the entire Atlantic coast from Massachusetts to Georgia, and everywhere it was accepted without question. People felt that they needed slaves to work for them and they took them — Puritan, Quaker and Cavalier alike. By 1850 the right to hold slaves had become a moral question, and the men of Massachusetts were fiercely convinced that slavery was wrong. The men of Georgia contended with equal conviction that slavery was right. What was the cause of this change of feeling, and why did it end in civil war between the two sections of our country? Slavery did not pay in the North and it did pay in the South. The long cold winters of New England produced such a long, idle season, requiring so much food, clothing and shelter, that slavery in the North cost more than it yielded and it died a natural death in colonial days. Even in Maryland and Virginia slave labor did not pay at the time of the Revolution, and Washington and Jefferson, who were both slaveholders, along with most of the other dominant men of that region, regarded it as a dying institution and looked upon their slaves pretty much as we now look upon an old horse that has rendered us faithful service. We do not wish to see it abused, we have not the heart to kill it, and we therefore feed it at some expense and think of it as a kind of pensioner. These men regarded slavery as a thing to be got rid of as quickly as possible without injury to the negroes.

The Constitution of the United States specifically provided for slavery, but aimed to check it somewhat. The Constitution had recognized slavery because of the necessity of securing the votes of South Carolina and Georgia, the two states possessing the one important industry in which the negro could then make a profit for his owner: namely, raising rice in swamps in which white men would not work.

In 1793 a new factor appeared. The cotton gin was invented, and cotton, which then had about the same industrial importance in the

United States as the manufacture of radium has at present, suddenly became profitable because in two minutes the cotton gin could separate two pounds of cotton from the seed, a task which had taken the whole day's time of a diligent worker. The cotton industry rose in importance almost as suddenly as the automobile, the aeroplane and radio in this generation. Suddenly throughout the cotton belt the negro could produce wealth for his owner. It became profitable for the slave to cut down forests, dig out weeds, plow cotton and above all pick cotton, a task which afforded occupation for negro women and children, as well as for the men. In North Carolina, a cotton state, the desire for slavery became stronger; and this was the case also in the newly opened states to the west — Alabama, Mississippi, Louisiana, Arkansas, and later Texas. The border states of Maryland, Virginia, Kentucky and Tennessee found profit in selling their negroes [1] to the cotton states below them, and slavery, which was a dying institution in 1789, dominated American politics from 1820 to 1860 and finally produced the bloodiest war in American history.

If the growing season in the Southern states had been no longer than it is in New Jersey, there would have been no slavery question in American history after the establishment of the United States. Not only did slavery separate the different parts of the country into camps, but it made sharp divisions between different parts of the same state. For example, at the beginning of the Civil War, the state of Virginia split into two states over the question of slavery. Eastern (lowland) Virginia, with the warm climate and the better agricultural development of that day, was for slavery, while the hilly, poorer, colder, more sparsely populated part, West Virginia, had almost no slaves and was so opposed to the institution that she broke away from the mother-state and stayed with the other non-slave-holding states. In 1830 the Virginia Senate voted by thirty-one noes to twenty-nine ayes to abolish slavery. Then came the charge of immorality from the North increasing Southern bitterness and solidarity.

### Cool Climate and Human Energy

The greater work-habit and the greater working power of the man of the cool North as compared with the man of the warmer, less stimulating Southern climate is one of the keys of history, both in the old world and in the new.[2] If you compare groups of people living three hundred miles

---

[1] A "prime field hand" was only worth about $200 in 1790. Cotton, the best of the five slave crops, fixed slavery permanently on the South. In 1850, a prime field hand had come to be worth $2000. The up-keep of slave labor was low — food, shelter, and clothing for the slave often not running more than $15 a year per head. Eight cents per pound would easily pay for the expense of raising cotton, and the rest was profit.

[2] See E. Huntington, Civilization and Climate, for an interesting volume on this one great point.

north or south of each other in middle latitudes, you are likely to meet with a general belief among them that the Northern man is more energetic than the Southern. This is true in many parts of the United States. I have found it to be true in Spain, Portugal, Italy, and even in England herself.[3]

## Location and Liberty

The factor of location and accessibility is a most important influence, effecting sometimes most profound national differences. Thus it seems plain that prior to 1914 England and Germany had developed very different national concepts and ideals because one happens to be located in the middle of a continent and the other happens to be an island. The English civilization is renowned the world over for political liberty, free individualism, the chance it offers every man or every group to develop as it sees fit. England has been able to do this because, being an island, she could protect herself with a fleet. England being free from the fear of an invading enemy has not needed a strong army, and therefore her people have been free from the burden of military discipline and the necessity for mutual interdependence.[4] Germany, on the other hand, is located in an open plain in the midst of a continent, and exposed on every side to enemies. German soil has been a tramping-ground for marauding peoples from earliest antiquity, trampled in turn by the Swedes in the seventeenth century, the Russians in the eighteenth century, the French in the early nineteenth century. Here we find a people who naturally realized that they must arm and organize for defense. To defend land boundaries required not warships but soldiers, hence a great military system, a great army, and a degree of social solidarity perhaps before unknown upon this earth.[5]

These differing national factors were brought before the world's attention in the surprising contrast at the opening of the Great War in 1914. It took two full years of supreme effort and the sacrifice of tens of thousands of lives and almost unthinkable wealth before the free English could put their necks into the yoke of conscription and approach the degree of organization with which Germany began the war.

## Location and Social Ideals

The Chinese have often been held up to the world as a people who should be taken as a model for their unrivaled appreciation of peace. But

[3] The importance of a stimulating climate is steadily rising in men's minds as an explanation of human achievement. We see this truth reduced to a commercial form in the late James J. Hill's motto, to which, with all his millions, he absolutely adhered: "You can't interest me in any proposition in any place where it doesn't snow," or, more picturesquely, "No man on whom the snow does not fall ever amounts to a tinker's dam."

[4] In his novel, *Mr. Britling Sees It Through*, H. G. Wells calls the English an unincorporated people rather than a nation.

[5] See "Island and Continent at War," J. Russell Smith, *Century Magazine*, March 1916.

China, even more than England, has been so well protected by nature that war could scarcely be forced upon her. Pacifism of China is primarily a result of location. On three sides China has been surrounded by the most perfect natural safeguards — on the south by tropical forests, malarial valleys which are flooded and filled with jungle, and separated by snow-capped mountains; on the west by the arid plateaus of Tibet and Mongolia, impassable for large bodies of men; on the east by the Pacific, wide and empty, untraversable for ages. From the north alone was there any possibility of danger, and this the Chinese attempted to obviate by building the famous Great Wall. At times the country has been overrun from this direction by the Tatars and Manchus, but these invaders did little more than create a ruling dynasty and an official class. In the main China's history has been peaceful. China's environment has given her an opportunity to maintain peace, appreciate peace and therefore extol it. Now that the steamship has broken down that isolation, the more intelligent Chinese realize that their isolation is gone, and they are following as rapidly as possible the example of Japan, which has found that she must depend upon her own strength instead of relying upon the isolation of nature. This means armies, navies, and the other lamentable things that nations get when they feel a need for self-protection in a world where anarchy still prevails among nations.

China has been driven to this. Since 1900, despite her thousands of years of successful pacifism, she has made great strides in the development of armies and navies, merely because one phase of her environment (accessibility) has changed.

### Race or Place

Doubtless some reader will insist that, in spite of all, the qualities of the settlers of a region are the decisive element in the fate of a region. The point is not to be dismissed lightly despite the multitude of fairly plain cases where the conditions of the region seem to decide the fate of the settlers. The human stock of any country is a matter of great, perhaps vital importance; but the measure of that importance is very difficult to ascertain. It is appalling to think how little we know of what may be called racial qualities — if indeed such qualities exist. The inability of some races to survive in poor climates has been disastrously proved over and over again since the discovery of America and the sea-route to India.[6] The qualities of a people do not make much difference if the people themselves do not survive. If the people do survive, the "racial qualities" decline in importance with the passage of time because the longer a people remain in a particular environment the greater will be the influence of that environment on them. We see this in the case of the dark-skinned but finely featured people of India whose ancestors migrated

[6] See chapter on " Peoples on the Gulf and Caribbean."

from central Asia in historic times, while others not greatly unlike them migrated westward and became Greeks, Germans, Poles, etc.

Since natural resources, climate and accessibility are the stuff of which industry, trade, religion, national policy, and to some extent civilization are made, it is well to examine our North America to see how it is equipped in these respects, and to what state of development the resources and industries have come, and what prospects are still ahead.

# CHAPTER II

## THE CONTINENT OF OPPORTUNITY AND ITS CLOSING DOOR

"We are going to free the slave," cried Abraham Lincoln in a political speech at Madison, Wisconsin, in 1858. " I'm a free white carpenter," came a voice from the audience; " what are you going to do for me? " The practical Abraham quickly replied: " We will give you a farm. Uncle Sam has a farm for every one of us." Uncle Sam had, then, and Abraham did. After such campaign pledges as these, Lincoln was elected, and he carried out his promise about the farm in the Homestead Act of 1862, which gave one hundred and sixty acres of land to the settler merely for the settling. Free Land — that is the key to the history of North America in the nineteenth century. And the key to the history of the twentieth century is the fact and the results of the fact that the free lands are gone. The limitless lands of Lincoln's day have found limits. The limitless worlds of Columbus, and Da Gama, and Raleigh, and Captain Cook, and Lewis and Clark have been explored and settled and found to be not so big, not nearly so big in their good parts, as men once thought. And of the good parts of the new lands found by the great explorers, North America has the greater part.

Since the time of Columbus, the vigorous peoples of Europe have thrown themselves into the new lands from the Arctic to the Equator and then southward to where the Antarctic snow begins. They settled Iceland and Greenland, Newfoundland and New England, Virginia and Florida, the West Indies and the East Indies, Africa and South America. On all the coasts of the new lands the seed of these European peoples was planted almost everywhere. No important land was neglected. The early settlements in the West Indies and in parts of South America were as large and at first more promising than the feeble settlements of Massachusetts and Virginia. Yet the settlements in Massachusetts and Virginia survived, the people multiplied, and as a little seed sends its roots deep into the earth, so these tiny settlements on the shores of the cold Atlantic sent their penetrating threads of white men back into the continent and on to the shores of the Pacific.

Great cities smoke and roar in the middle of North America. But Africa and South America still contain great unexplored areas. These areas are unexplored because settlements made upon adjacent shores did not thrive. To make more plain the point of geographic influence, the

United States and Canada, which alone of all the new lands have become great powers, have at the north very large areas still unexplored and at the south large areas still almost unsettled.

### Easy Transfer of European Races

It so happened that the conditions of Central North America suited the new immigrants and they throve. In the tropics, which have not yet become a white man's land, settlers have dwindled or perished or have become simply scattered bands of half-breeds.[1]

In Iceland and Labrador, the rigor of a cold climate checked the food supply so that the white man has barely held his own in numbers, despite a thousand years of unusually favorable opportunity. A long cold winter and a short cool summer, compelling a short work season and a small crop yield has kept down the Icelandic population, but it has not hurt the vigor of the human stock, whereas in the tropics the climate has injured the white man's health and all but destroyed his racial stock.

It was in the middle region of North America that the white man found the real Eden of the new world. Here, and here only, has he increased and prospered, threaded the continent with railroads, seized upon its resources, built himself great cities with houses twenty stories high, and increased his numbers to more than 100,000,000. So much for this little strip of cool land between the parallels of 26° and 55° north. Yet with the same three centuries of opportunity, the new world lands with a tropical climate have not today one-twentieth of this number of white men. Why? North America, which is a triangular continent, is blessed by having the widest part, a large, rich, well-watered area, in the cool latitudes where the alternating summer and winter furnish (1) the warm season that permits man to grow fine crops, (2) the cold season that gives him the stimulus to activity and creates the necessity of saving for winter use some of the goods which he produces in summer, and (3) a climate that enables the white man to remain healthy as he cannot in the tropics. South America, while even more triangular in shape than North America, is very unfortunate in having its wide area blighted by tropic heat and moisture, while the part that is temperate in climate is so narrow that it has but a fraction of the area of the similar climatic region in the United States. But it is in the small temperate area of Chile, Argentina, Uruguay and Brazil that the energetic, machine-using white man lives.

The melting away of the British settlements in the West Indies goes to show how fortunate were those other English colonists who landed in the middle latitudes. No other area in the new world was so suitable in climate, soil, contact with sea and the chance of dominion over the whole

---

[1] The half-breed, or mestizo, as he is called in Mexico, Central America and South America, can survive the tropic climate better than the full-blooded European partly because the native blood (half or often more than half) gives him a better resistance to the evils of the climate.

continent. The gold-hunting Spaniards seized native wives and had the first pick of the lands, but the home-hunting English, bringing their wives and children with them, got control of the region which contains the real treasures. The Appalachian district of America was a particularly rich gift.

There are many other reasons why the white race has thriven in middle North America, for this new land was peculiarly advantageous to the settler. There were no new diseases to destroy. It is difficult for us to appreciate what this meant in the settlement of the continent, for despite the Spanish influenza or " flu " epidemic of 1918 we have not been ravaged by new diseases of a highly contagious character. We now think of measles as a juvenile affliction, yet it is a matter of record that when this disease spreads to a race that has never experienced it, measles is one of the most destructive of diseases, having destroyed 25, 40 and even 50% of the people on some Pacific Islands when first brought to them by white men. It may have done the same thing to a dozen different generations of white men at some remote time before selection gave relative immunity. When measles was new among ourselves there may have been five hundred or five thousand years when the population was reduced and humanity was at a low ebb until those white people whom the measles could kill were killed off.

While the white man got no deadly disease from the Indian, he brought new diseases (such as small-pox), which killed the Indian.[2] These two factors are of great importance in the rapid peopling of the continent by whites.

### Easy Transfer of European Crops

The colonists coming from Europe could transplant themselves, and what was almost as important, the climate enabled them to bring nearly all of their own crops; for wheat, barley, rye and oats, the main food supply of northern Europe, also grew well in America. They were not obliged to acquire a new agriculture or undergo the agonies of adjustment to a different food supply.

The grape furnishes a good example of the troubles that would have beset them if the crops had all failed to take hold of American soil. The European settlers came to America with the hope of establishing a wine industry. The Norsemen, centuries before, had named New England

---

[2] It is recorded that when the white men entered the Columbia Valley they found many Indian villages empty, with clothes and trappings still in the tepees, and fish-nets still swinging in the river. At first it was thought that the Indians had fled, but later it was found that they had been wiped out by the small-pox which they had contracted a few weeks before from a light case of varioloid in this same band of white men who were examining their blasted settlements. If it were not for white men's diseases, it is quite possible that the Indian might have held the white man back a century or two, and if he had had a couple of new diseases to give the white man and none to receive from him, it would be difficult to imagine just what the contest between the two peoples might have been.

"Vine Land" because the wild grape-vines climbing to the tops of the American forest trees were one of the most astonishing sights in the new world. The settlers brought with them choice grape-vines from Europe as they brought the seed of wheat, and barley, carrots and onions. The grape-vines soon blighted and died. The grape of western Europe will not survive in the eastern United States. The warm humid summer of our eastern states has no counterpart in western Europe, which is cool in the north, as in England, or dry in the south, as in Spain and Italy. Since heat and humidity are excellent for the development of fungi, there were varieties of fungi on the American grape which were relatively harmless to them, but promptly destroyed the foliage of all the European grapes that were brought here and caused them to die. Since the Virginia colonists had come here especially to grow wine, their prospects faded, and the return to England was being seriously considered [3] when they discovered another crop, namely tobacco, which they could grow and to which Sir Walter Raleigh gave some market-making publicity.

This little episode of the grape which nearly ruined the Virginia colony really serves to emphasize the richness and not the poverty of America, for on the whole the agriculture of the newcomers gained more than it lost through contact with America. The crop list was enriched by great new crops found growing on this continent.

### American Additions to Agriculture

In addition to all the European grains, America furnished two new food crops of almost unmatched value; namely, corn and potatoes. One has become the mainstay of America and the other the mainstay of North Europe. Corn, the king of American crops, was peculiarly advantageous to the early settler in this country. While the European small grains required carefully tilled and finely prepared land, corn, after the Indian method of primitive agriculture, could be grown among stumps and rocks and standing trees that had been deadened by axe or fire. Since wheat was planted in the fall and harvested the next summer, it took the settler who arrived in the spring nearly two seasons before he could eat the results of his sowing, while corn was ready for use in the form of ears for roasting, by July or August. Its yield was usually double that of wheat. Corn when ripe will stand for weeks on the stalk waiting to be harvested; meanwhile the men might be gathering other crops or might

---

[3] The reason for this large dependence upon the grape is found in the British trade conditions of that day. England was still an agricultural country. She was an exporter of wool and did not need to import wheat or corn, beef or pork, which are now the great staples of her import trade and which have long been the staples of the American export trade. Wine she did import. Wine was one of her chief imports, and the Virginia colonists, knowing that they had to have some basis of purchase in England, planned their future commerce with the mother country very carefully so far as economic need was concerned; but their plans failed to take into account the geographical environment of the grape.

go elsewhere upon hunting expeditions or be at war. No other grain can match corn in this ability to wait for the harvest. Its keeping powers are almost marvelous. In much of our country a part of the crop at least will stand in perfect condition on the stalk or in the shock until spring. It is excellent food for man and beast.

Few grains are used in such varied forms. The green corn is a prized midsummer vegetable; the hunter could parch the whole grains before his camp-fire and subsist if hunting failed. When the husk was peeled off by soaking the grains in lye and it was cracked between two stones, corn

made hominy, the stand-by of the Indian's diet; and there is no need to expatiate upon its use as meal, mush and bread in view of the practice of nations and the food lessons of the World War. Every one of the domestic animals eats corn greedily; so do rats and mice, birds and poultry.

Bundles of corn stalks (fodder) make a warm, dry roof for a shed or shack and later can be eaten by all the ruminant animals. The husks made the mattresses of the early settler's bed, and they are still used to some extent for that purpose.

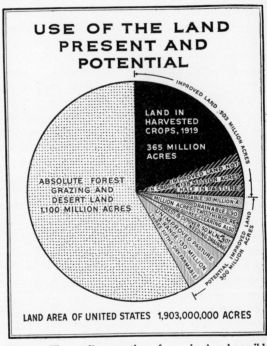

USE OF THE LAND PRESENT AND POTENTIAL

LAND IN HARVESTED CROPS, 1919
365 MILLION ACRES

IMPROVED LAND 503 MILLION ACRES

ABSOLUTE FOREST GRAZING AND DESERT LAND 1,100 MILLION ACRES

IMPROVED LAND NOT IN CROPS HALF IN PASTURE
IRRIGABLE 30 MILLION A
DRAINABLE 90 MILLION ACRES TWO-THIRDS REQUIRES CLEARING ALSO
FOREST & CUTOVER 50 MILLION NEEDING DRAINAGE UNIMPROVED PASTURE OR RANGE 430 MILLION
FIRE PATHS OR DRAINABLE

POTENTIAL IMPROVED LAND 300 MILLION ACRES

LAND AREA OF UNITED STATES 1,903,000,000 ACRES

FIG. 1 — The small proportion of crop land and possible crop land is usually a surprise. (Courtesy O. E. Baker, U. S. Dept. Agr.)

The potato, also a major American contribution, was not so important to the settlers as corn, chiefly because of the greater advantages of corn; but in northern Europe, where it is so cool that corn does not grow, the potato has met its great field of usefulness, being to Germany, Denmark, Ireland and other countries of northern Europe what corn is to America.

The colonial agriculture was also greatly enriched by tobacco. It is true that tobacco is a robber crop which destroys the soil; but it gave the exploiting colonists something to export to the mother countries in a day when they did not need any other American product. It was nearly two centuries after tobacco met this need of an export that cotton came forward in the warm, moist southland to revolutionize agriculture, trade, and politics, and to supply a staple which Europe lacked.

Thus the new settlers coming to America found not only a good climate, immunity from new diseases and conditions that made it possible for them to bring practically all their old crops with them, but they found also four other crops of importance; namely, corn, potatoes, tobacco and cotton. Altogether this gave a variety of crops richer, much richer, than that of Europe.

Precipitation, Inches, for the Week ending 8 a. m., May 24, 1921.

Fig. 2 — The maps of rainfall for a single week (see also Fig. 3) show that rainfall and drought are local in area. Each map shows the trail of at least three different rains of wide area. (Courtesy U. S. Weather Bureau.)

### Abundance of Land — Good Land

The country to which they had come also afforded an unexampled opportunity in land resources. Between the Great Lakes and the Gulf of Mexico and the Atlantic Ocean and the Great Plains is the choicest large block of homeland in all the world, with the possible exception of western Europe. From the St. Lawrence and Great Lakes to the Gulf the coast is rich in fish, well supplied with harbors, backed by a plain threaded with navigable rivers, rich in forests, rich in soil, rich in minerals — all these reaching inland to a distance which for more than two centuries seemed limitless to the inhabitants of this land of boundless promise.

It is true that the world is mostly waste land, nearly five-sixths of it either too cold, too dry, or too wet for crops, too steep and rough for tillage, or unhealthful for man. Despite its great virtue as a home for the European races, North America is not immune from the curse of waste land. A large part, perhaps one-quarter, is too cold for agriculture, another part, perhaps one-third, is too dry, and yet another large part to the south is too hot for vigorous white men. Even one-half of the United States is too-something for agriculture as we now see it. Only 40% seems destined to be productive. Yet there remains enough good land to make this the continent of unexampled opportunity.

Precipitation, Inches, for the Week ending 8 a. m., November 29, 1921.

FIG. 3 — See Fig. 2. (Courtesy U. S. Weather Bureau.)

One further advantage of this well-nigh matchless region needs to be mentioned — its immunity from drought. Read the book of Genesis and see the troubles of the Israelites as related in the famines that drove the sons of Jacob down to Egypt.

The drought-made famine, even in this century, as in many of the past centuries, has slain its millions in India, China and Russia. We have had no such experience on this continent. Drought we have and floods, plenty of them, but the drought is local in area, and so are the floods. Thus, while New Jersey burns, Virginia is sometimes too wet, and the plenty of one locality can supply the shortage of the other.[4]

[4] The variableness of the American climate within small limits of time and space and the local nature of our climatic troubles are well shown by the following reports:

Mr. O. L. Fassig, reviewing the Maryland weather for the year 1917, says:

Further than this, the drought east of the 100th meridian rarely if ever covers a whole season. Thus April and May may be dry, injuring the hay, but June and July may be wet, injuring the wheat but making good corn and pasture. Thus if the wheat crop and hay crops are poor, the corn and the summer pasture may be good, and the farmer is saved. A serious crop shortage has never menaced any large group of people in America until we reached western Kansas. There, long after the country was established as a great power, settlers attempted to make their farms in the western lands of little rainfall and met calamity.[5]

In India and China and also in Australia and parts of South America, the droughts are sometimes a whole season or even two seasons long and cover districts of wide expanse, so that death or (when possible) migration follows in their wake.

In addition to all these advantages of food resources and good climate the settlers in America had unprecedented advantages in forest and mineral wealth in which no continent can rival North America.

## Completeness of Resources

The United States alone has all the important minerals save tin and potash, and we now know that we can make all the potash we want if we are willing to pay a high price for it. The early settler found iron, the great indispensable metal, in many places up and down the eastern coast region, with plenty of charcoal to smelt it, and thus he equipped himself with the iron and steel tools necessary to subdue the great continent. In the United States alone there is half of the known coal of the world and most of the copper. The United States leads all the countries of the world in the production of phosphate, the greatest raw material of commercial plant foods, and iron ore, the great raw material for manufacturing. America was thus well-provided in the simple days of the colonist; and it is equally well-provided in the complex days of

---

"October was the coldest and wettest on record, with an average rainfall of 5.66, while November was cold and exceptionally dry" with an average rainfall of 0.6.

Mr. H. K. Bryson, Commissioner of Agriculture for Tennessee, reported, June 1, 1916, that "the eastern part of this state suffered from a drought of unprecedented severity, for from four to six weeks" (indicating local variations even within a part of a state), "while in the western portion a veritable deluge in some parts resulted in serious but not irreparable damage."

Mr. J. Warren Smith, Agricultural Meteorologist, in the National Weather and Crop bulletin, May 24, 1921, thus describes our climatic variability: "Frosts and freezing weather were general in the Northwest, with resulting damage to alfalfa, early truck and fruit; there was some frost damage in the central Lake region. It was too warm for truck in California, and the lack of moisture is being felt rather seriously in that State and in southern Arizona and New Mexico and western Texas; more rain is needed also in the extreme Southeast. The moisture conditions were favorable in most other sections of the country, except that there was too much rain in some central districts. Farm work was delayed by cool weather and wet soil in most Central and Northwestern States throughout most of the week."

[5] See chapter on "Great Plains."

the present, when civilization is based on mechanically produced energy derived from coal and water harnessed with iron and steel, copper and cement, all of which America possesses (for a time at least) in excess of any other continent.

The settler everywhere landed on the Atlantic Coast beneath the shade of the forest, which reached almost without a break from Quebec to Florida and westward across the Alleghenies to a place the white man scarcely saw for two centuries. Indeed, this timber, while it was very useful, even necessary in a cold climate, was really a serious bar to the rapid development of the early settlements. It is hard for the modern American farmer, and even harder for the city-dweller, to comprehend the toil and heavy labor that faced the settler as he felled with his axe the great trees of the primeval forests, rolled the heavy logs into piles to burn them and get them out of the way, and then with plow and mattock fought the roots and afterwards fought the up-springing shoots that tried to choke his corn. His ground was encumbered with great stumps for a generation before he had a smooth green field such as he had left in Europe and such as now clothes many million acres which were once the great deep forest, the hunting ground of the Indian.

## The Indian Civilization

Since America had all these advantages, all these useful things, why did it not develop a great civilization under the hands of the Indians long before the white man came?

One reason is that as human history goes, the Indian had been here but a short time. This fact is shown by the similarity of the Indians all over the American continent and by the resemblance they bear to people in the nearest part of Asia whence they came.[6] But they had probably been here long enough to have developed a civilization if all of the conditions *at their disposal* had been favorable. Civilization is a complex thing that has come very late in man's history. For the purposes of this book, civilization may be defined as a condition attained by men who have gained sufficient wealth to support a society that can be organized into large groups of people who live together under complicated relations, governed by laws of their own making.

A complicated civilization is a very new thing, as man's experience goes. It arrived for the most favored human groups only the day before yesterday — only in the last one or two per cent of the time that man has been man.

Despite the resources of a great continent, there were good reasons why the Indians in America remained relatively uncivilized after the Chinese, the Babylonians, the Egyptians and the Greeks had developed societies, made codes of law, written books and built libraries and temples.

[6] Authority of John C. Merriam — National Research Council, Washington.

All of these peoples had inherited much from those great but unknown benefactors who tamed and harnessed the beasts of the field. Perhaps the principal cause of the backwardness of America was the Indians' lack of beasts of burden to multiply the feeble strength of man by dragging the plow and hauling the crop, to enrich his food with meat and milk, and to enrich his apparel with leather and wool. The American continent was poor in tamable animals. It contained no wild horses, no wild cattle or buffaloes, no pigs; and the sheep of its mountains were long of limb and more fleet than deer. The nearest approach to cattle was the bison, an animal of mean disposition, which, by the way, has as yet baffled the white man's attempts to domesticate him. His towering stiff neck is perhaps spiritual as well as physical.

The alpaca and vicuña, two sheep-like animals of the Andes, were tamed and used in that region by the Incas, but their limitations are such that the white man has not thought it worth while to use them in competition with our other beasts. The dog was the only domestic animal common among the Indians and him they used as a sledge animal.

Not only did the Indians miss these animals as workers, as beasts of burden, as sources of milk, food, leather and cloth, but they also missed the developing and humanizing qualities which the care of animals instils into a people. The necessity of watching his sheep, of milking his cows, of storing food for them in the winter time would have tamed the Indian. It would have developed his staying power, it would have forced him to acquire a surplus; both of which are essential to civilization.

Indeed, the domestic animals might well have applied to the Indian the Darwinian law of the survival of the fittest. In the course of generations, the man who could not take care of animals could not be a successful farmer, and not being able to obtain a regular food supply for his children he would tend to become extinct, while those would survive who had the work habit and industrial dependability. Here then is a real racial difference between the industrious white man and the lordly Indian of Eastern North America. It is the ability to stand the pain of work, steady work — one of the great pains of the world, and one of the necessities of a dense population. The American Indian is a man of many splendid natural qualities. Witness his fine physique, his excellent athletic record, his good school record, his dignity, his native veracity, his loyalty. He caught the wild horses that ran away from the Spanish settlers and was making rapid progress in the utilization of horses. Given time and opportunity equal to that of the European races, he might have duplicated (essentially) their achievements. But he did not have the necessary thousands of years. Just as he was making a start, along came the white man, strong in organization, equipment and numbers, and brushed the poor Indian aside.

But the American Indian had one other obstacle to keep him from making a civilization. He had few safe nooks on the American continent where the course of peaceful living and building could be undisturbed for many generations. Reasonable safety from attack is needed for the development of civilization. Rome, you will recall, was built on seven hills, and in the near-by plain to this day towns occupy the whole crest of many of the sharp round hills which almost resemble the stumps of trees when one looks at them from a distance and notes the perfect wall still surrounding some of them. Thus were they defended through ages past. Greece developed her civilization on islands and in nooks like Sparta and Athens, protected by mountains from all marauders — witness the defense of Thermopylae.

In America the Indian made his greatest progress not in the parts of the country best suited for the production of food and supplies, but in the worst — the arid southwest where high mesas and almost inaccessible cliffs afforded a place for a protected dwelling and continuous peace. Here the peace-loving Hopi and other tribes, with their earthen jars filled with corn and water brought up by a toilsome climb from some little irrigated patch in the valley a thousand feet or so below, were able to hold at bay the marauding tribes of the open plain until they gave it up, and the successful pacifist could continue weaving his blankets, raising his children and worshiping his gods with snake-dances on his high, safe rock.

Through the open Mississippi Valley and the everywhere accessible East, the tribes and war parties surged at will, and no tribe had a chance to work out its destiny.[7] They were like Germany in Roman times. In that day Germany was the typical land of the barbarian, frequently overrun by migrant peoples who destroyed everything before them.

Thus, the Indian, despite his own virtues and the virtues of his continent, was neither numerous, nor highly organized, nor powerful. He was not sufficiently developed to absorb ready-made the civilization of the European settlers, so the latter pushed him easily aside, took his land and destroyed his simple society, which was much better than we make our school children believe. Having done the Indian unpardonable injury we try to save our faces by calling him names.

Some historians take comfort in our treatment of the Indian by pointing out that the Romans would have enslaved or slaughtered him, whereas we did neither. Our record with the Indian, judged by standards of honor, is not one of which the white man should be proud. The temptation was too great: the greatest thing in the world was involved — land, good land, the opportunity for a home, and we could not resist it; so we took it. The period of colonial history and the early years of American independence were marked by this struggle for the possession

---

[7] This openness of the middle of the continent results in the great advantage of easy communication, now that settled society gives man a chance to possess, produce and trade.

of the continent, not only between the white man and the Indian, but between the European races. England and France fought over it; England and Spain fought over it; the United States quarreled about it with France, with Spain, with England. Fortunately, these quarrels were settled by treaty or by purchase, sometimes vast purchases, as when we bought Florida from Spain and the vast reaches, then called Louisiana, from France; and finally, as the Anglo-Saxon flowed back against the weak Mexican, we took another realm by conquest, mollified by a small monetary payment.

### Immigration and the Passing of the Public Lands

Late in the nineteenth century the contest for the continent took new forms, the infiltration of the new races as immigrants and economic conquerors rather than as warriors and political conquerors. The old lands of the first settlers are being bought by the newly arrived peasant from Europe. Much more serious is the problem created by the arrival upon our western shores of the Chinese immigrant who, by his amazing industry, threatened to absorb an indefinite amount of the United States and Canada. By political edict and force of arms we exclude him, but the problem is not solved. America, this land of opportunity, is looked upon with yearning eyes by the Mongolian millions across the Pacific. So the future of America, like the past, promises to be influenced by the same great key of history — abundance of land.

The greatest single fact that lies behind American history to date is the fact that we have been a people living in the presence of a superabundance of land. For the 300 years down to the end of the nineteenth century, we have lived under the idea that " Uncle Sam has a farm for every one of us." In 1827, just before the beginning of the railroad epoch, the Secretary of the Treasury announced that it would take us 500 years to settle America, and he would probably have been right if man had continued to have only the axe, the sickle and the freight wagon. About the time of the settlement of Oregon, Senator Benton of Missouri declared that God himself had set the Rocky Mountains as the western terminus of American expansion. Throughout most of our past, western land has been abundant, and so free that anybody could take it. Before 1800 the view of the United States Government regarding land was that it was a source of revenue to be derived by giving the land in great blocks to companies that would sell it out to individuals. The government tried to sell land also at $2.00 an acre, with four years to pay for a 160-acre tract; but during the period from 1800 to 1820 when this practice prevailed, the government had the greatest difficulty in collecting its money, and by 1820 individuals were $21,000,000 in arrears for the payment of the land. Then the government reduced its price to $1.25 per acre cash for an

80-acre lot. This, too, was disregarded, and we have that interesting phase of American history in which the "squatter" figures largely. "Squatter rights" and "squatter sovereignty" were big questions in the middle West in the latter part of the first half of the nineteenth century. The squatter was a person who came into the empty territory that looked good to him, built himself a house, cleared the forest, fenced in a piece of land and said it was his. Why endure such injustice as to pay $1.25 an acre for it? In the '40's it was stated that only one-third of the voters of Illinois actually had good titles to their land. Squatters' associations were formed, like the Sun Prairie Wisconsin Squatters' Association. Their object was to keep out of the territory the man who was the legal purchaser. There were two very distinct sides to the question involved here. Who owned the land? Was it the people who had gone there and cut down the trees, hauled away the stones, plowed up the ground, tilled the land, perhaps driven out the Indians, or was it somebody else who came along a little later with the statement that he had paid $1.25 an acre for it to

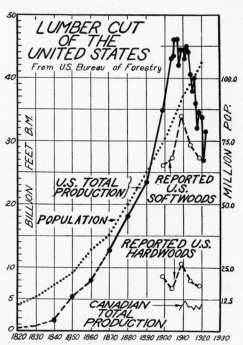

FIG. 4 — Population goes up but the production of lumber goes down despite increasing prices. Since we mine timber rather than produce it, the supply wanes.

a mysterious thing called government which had perhaps made some new rules since the arrival of the squatter. So numerous were the squatters, so strong their physical and voting strength, that in many ways the squatter-sovereignty claim won out. We see its legalized position in law in the homestead policy which is only a legalized form of squatter ownership because it gave land to anyone who would go and take it, live upon it and cutivate it.

During the period of the Civil War we took a new means of getting rid of land; namely, giving it to corporations that would build railroads through it.

The first railroad to the Pacific Coast, from Omaha to San Francisco, was partly financed by the government, which gave the company, for every mile of railroad, six square miles of land, every alternate square mile within six miles of the track. This method was extensively used to persuade capitalists to build railroads into unpeopled lands, the theory being that the railroads needing traffic would do their best to persuade settlers who needed land to come and take it. Within ten years after 1860 nearly 100,000,000 acres were thus disposed of, and altogether the government has given away for this purpose 155,000,000 acres of land, an area five times as great as Pennsylvania. The famous advice of Horace Greeley, " Go West, young man, go West," was followed by his generation as it had been followed by generations before him. In the seventeenth, eighteenth and nineteenth centuries, the young man of Massachusetts, Pennsylvania, Virginia or Carolina who could not find work on his father's farm had the choice of the city

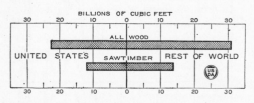

FIG. 5 — This chart of wood consumption is a measure of American riches in the era of free land, which is ending.

factory, the city store, the sea or the western land. If he went to the factory or the store, it was because the opportunity thus put to him seemed better than the land opportunity. The equipment of a young couple — horses, cow, pigs, clothing and blankets and quilts was the product of several years of *surplus* regularly furnished by a dependable climate. The majority chose the land, putting their young wives and their household goods into the farm wagon, tying the cow on behind, and joining the endless procession of settlers going out to the frontier to build the cabin, fell the forest and start the home.

### Resources Make High Wages

This abundance of cheap land has given us always high wages, because of the continuous presence of alternative opportunities. In 1914 the newly arrived immigrant who swept the streets in New York still had the choice of going on to Western Canada and receiving as a free homestead 160 acres of rich level prairie which the government begged him to come and take. Wages in New York had to be high enough to tempt him to stay in the East; this free land kept wages up.

Where land is plenty, it is cheap and a little work is very productive. Where land is scarce, it is dearer and man must dig more to get the same amount of output. This is by far the greatest factor that differentiates America from Europe or Asia as the home of man. It explains why the unskilled laborer in America before the Great War received from $1.50 to $2.00 a day, while in Europe he received from $0.30 to

$1.00, and in Japan and China from 10 to 25 cents. These differences do not correspond with any differences in the virtue of the individual or of the government, or of the language, or of the church. They measure the different ratios of men to resources.

This abundance of land has had many other results. Because of high wages and the necessity for getting work done more cheaply we have developed machinery as has no other nation. It is plain that a man can pay much more for machinery where it can replace labor at $1.50 to $3.00 a day, as it does here, than he can pay in Portugal where it replaces labor at 40 to 80 cents a day.

Often, however, it was not a question of replacing labor, for often there was an absolute lack of labor. It was a question of devising machines or going without production altogether. For the development of agricultural machines, we have had, in addition to abundant (and therefore cheap) land, the contributing factor of level land, which made the use of machinery easy. Some results of this agricultural development are shown by the fact that in 1840 the cradle and flail would cut and thresh a bushel of wheat for 18 cents, whereas some modern machinery does it for 3½ cents. The scythe and the rake would make hay for $3.00 a ton, whereas the modern mowing machines and hay rake and hay tedder and loader will help man to do it for half of that cost.

### Land, Slavery and Immigration

Other results of our abundance of land are seen in our slavery and our immigration. The enterprising European colonist in America in 1630 stood upon the edge of a great continent with forests waiting to be felled and fields waiting to be tilled to produce for him and for the markets in Europe. Being a man of brains and enterprise, he pined for a labor force that he might use to bring his industrial dreams to pass. But the laborers were few. His neighbors were busy with their own affairs, and were, like him, pining for helpers. There was no hired man to be had.

This vacuum was partly filled by indentured labor, a kind of temporary slavery conspicuous in colonial history. Men in England without resources who wished to come to America went into contract with ship captains, agreeing in return for free transportation to America to let the ship captain sell their services for a period of years to the highest bidder. The laws for the protection of indentured servants and the purchasers of their time were rather complicated and thorough in colonial days. But this supply of labor was inadequate, and thus came the next step; namely, the slave ship, the capture, enslavement and transportation of the African, a natural consequence of abundant resources and a scanty, energetic population. The putting down of slavery has not lessened our desire for labor or the coming of aliens. Our *pre-war* immigration of a million a year in good, normal times is a result of the attraction of the cheap lands of America. The young man leaves Holland, because he would have to pay $700 for an acre of newly reclaimed sea bottom, and comes to the United States where land, not so good as that of Holland but good land nevertheless, can be bought for from $40.00 to $100 per acre; or he leaves Italy where land rents at $25.00 an acre per year and comes to New England where he can buy fairly good land outright, sometimes with buildings on it, for $25.00 an acre.

Italian immigration usually comes from Southern Italy where there have been no new resources available, while in Northern Italy the development of Alpine water-power manufacture has afforded opportunity to the native who remains at home. It is quite natural that this immigration question in America should have produced its most acute results, the Chinese and Japanese questions of the Pacific slope, in the places where the contrasts in resources were the greatest and therefore the temptation to emigrate the keenest. The earth affords no greater contrast than that of the crowded fields of China and Japan with their hoe tillage and the wide and still almost empty plains of the Pacific slope with their large and all but untilled ranches, calling aloud for settlers.

These problems of immigration are types, not isolated episodes. They belong to the land hunger and land exploitation groups of questions which arise where a relatively empty land faces a crowded land.

Australia had a hot political fight about this matter. Here was the form it took. Should the few white people who owned big plantations in her tropic section be allowed to import colored coolie laborers or should the land remain idle? The latter idea won.

Among the many results of this abundance of land in America has been a lower cost of living, which has probably made it possible for the masses of people to be fed, clothed, and sheltered better and easier than has ever before been the case in the world's history.

### Lands End, High Prices and Conservation

Abundance of land has also made us the greatest of wasters. The continued throwing open of new lands in competition with the old has given us a recklessness in wasting material resources that has probably never been equaled in any such large area. Settlement swept the continent like a scorching fire. It was an exploitation that left great deserts where forests stood. "Here's a fine animal," said the frontiersman; "let's kill it. Here's a big tree, let's cut it down. Here's a thick sod, let's plow it up." [8]

We have had the attitude of reckless conquest in the presence of

[8] I am indebted to Dean Davenport of the University of Illinois for this motto of the frontiersman.

an indefinite plenty. But a change has come, forced upon us by hard facts. We have reached the end of an epoch. The free farm-land is gone. The era of preservation, conservation and scientific utilization has thrust its unwelcome problems upon us almost overnight. Between 1879 and 1889, the area put to cereals in the United States increased 66,000,000 acres; from 1889 to 1899 it increased but 45,000,000; and from 1899 to 1909 it increased but 6,000,000. Meanwhile, in that

| *Acreage Millions* | 1899 | 1909 | 1919 | 1922 |
|---|---|---|---|---|
| Corn........... | 95.0 | 98.4 | 97.1 | 102.4 |
| Wheat......... | 52.5 | 44.2 | 75.7 | 61.2 |
| Oats........... | 29.5 | 35.1 | 40.3 | 40.7 |
| Barley......... | 4.4 | 7.7 | 6.7 | 7.4 |
| Rye........... | 2.0 | 2.2 | 6.3 | 6.2 |
| Total........ | 183.4 | 187.6 | 226.1 | 217.9 |

(1919 is not a fair year for *wheat*, because of the war-bulge, caused by the hope of high prices.)　　　　　— *Yearbook,* U. S. Dept. Agr., 1922.

last decade of small acreage increase (1899–1909), the decade of the end of settlement, the population increased by 16,000,000, and it was 14,-000,000 in the next decade. There were almost four times as many people in the United States at the beginning of 1923 as there were in 1850, but the number of head of live-stock had not even doubled. In 1850 there were 134 hogs for every 100 of population; in 1923 there were only 58.

During the decade ending 1890, the population of the United States increased 25% while the area in crops increased 32%, and we had a period of prices that were

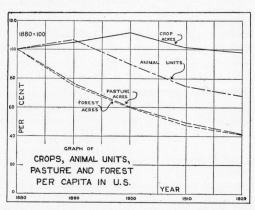

FIG. 6 — These significant lines point toward less wood, less meat, and more intensive agriculture.

discouragingly low to the farmer. During the decade ending 1900 the population increased 24% and the crop-area increased 29% so that down to the end of the nineteenth century the increase in food-production more than kept pace with the increase in population. But the new cen-

tury brought a new epoch. In its first decade, the population increased
21%, the crop-area less than 10%. This change in ratio has come to
stay.

At no place have we reached our limits more definitely than in the
matter of the lumber supply.
We passed the peak of production in 1907, the output
of the year 1920 being 27%
less than that of 1907. The
output declined in the year
1920 in 35 states and in-
creased in 12 states, 11 of
which were in the West
— our last timber-reserve.
The per capita consumption
dropped, astonishingly, from
500 feet per person to 316.
In 1924 the chief of the
Forest Service said: "Smaller and poorer houses are being built, timber is being
destroyed faster than it is
being replaced, quality is
growing poorer, and the
prices are becoming higher.
American living standards, particularly on the farm, are being threatened." Our easy westward flow of population to new soils has almost
ended.[9]

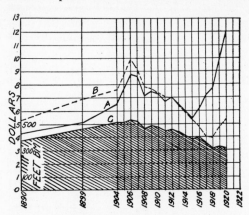

FIG. 7 — Three graphic ways of showing the increasing scarcity of lumber in the United
States: A, dollars per capita spent for lumber
in the United States; B, per capita expenditure
for lumber in terms of all commodities; C,
board feet of lumber consumed per capita in
the United States. (Courtesy U. S. Bureau of
Forestry.)

Since the scarcity of a thing makes its value high, we need look no
further to understand why between 1900 and 1910 the value of farms
in the United States doubled, while during this same period the actual
amount of grain increased 1.7% and its *value* increased 79.8%. That

[9] (Adapted from *Land Utilization in the United States,* by O. E. Baker;
page 4.) "Land area is of course limited; arable land in the United States is still
more limited. Because of climatic or topographic conditions only about 40% of our
land can ever be used for crops, and most of this is already in use, with the population increasing at the rate of a million and a half a year. During the nineteenth
century the population of the United States increased from five to seventy-six
millions, or fifteen fold, and during the first twenty years of the twentieth century,
the increase has been 40% of the increase during the previous century. The rate of
increase, however, has declined. From the Revolutionary War to the Civil War the
increase was at an almost uniform rate of 35% each decade; from 1870 to 1880
population increased 30%; from 1880 to 1890, 25%; from 1890 to 1910, 20%; and
from 1910 to 1920, 15%. Should even this low rate of increase during the past
decade, which included the World War and several epidemics of influenza, and also
six years without immigration, continue, our country would have in about a century
a population equal to that of China today. But our increase in population has been
based on extravagantly used and vanishing resources."

increased valuation of land and grain is not a measure of wealth (of increased goods) but a measure of scarcity, of approaching poverty. Between 1900 and 1914 the number of beef cattle in the United States decreased from 41,000,000 to 35,800,000, while, with this 12.9% decline in number, the value went up 42%. Since the nation can no longer offer land it offers education. The young man is now offered, not free land out West, but a night school or a trade school that he may become an artisan or clerk; an engineering school that he may become a manufacturer or a builder; a school of commerce that he may engage in foreign trade, or a school of business administration that he may increase his business efficiency.

The Census already brings us the record of these changes. The young men in America seeking their fortunes are no longer spreading over the farm lands, making new commonwealths in the wilderness.

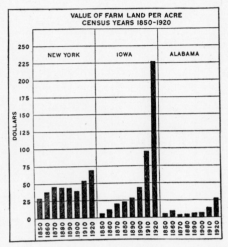

FIG. 8 — See Fig. 9.

Indeed, the case is quite the reverse. They are leaving the farm lands. The whole heart of the continent, the middle of the Mississippi valley, the region of the greatest agricultural riches shows almost everywhere a decline in rural population. The population

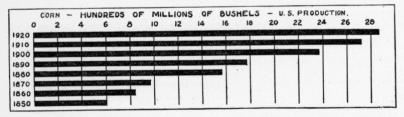

FIG. 9 — This pair of charts (See Fig. 8) shows how increasing production (through new lands) kept land values down prior to 1900, and how the check in production sent land values soaring. *Scarcity* makes prices high. (Courtesy U. S. Dept. Agr.)

of rapid increase is that of the cities — Los Angeles, Detroit, Seattle, New York, Chicago, the New England towns.

We have reached the end of one era and, what is more, we have entered upon another. Since the young man can no longer better his income by going to work on his own land he joins the labor union in order to obtain by pressure a greater share of the public wealth, and the Socialist vote grows steadily. England, with less land, has many more of these social consequences of land-shortage and of city and factory life than we have.

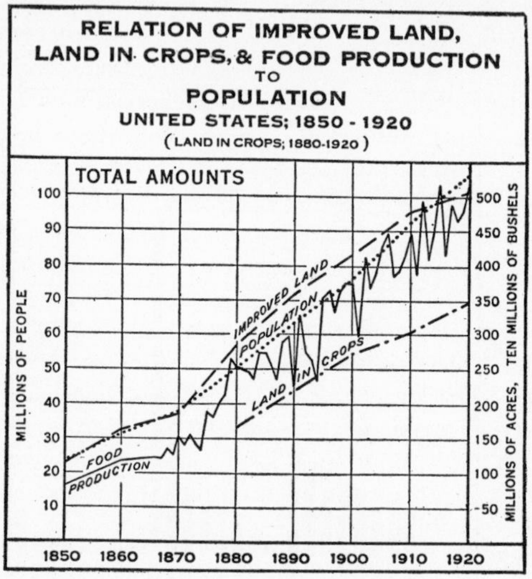

The decade, 1900–1910, which saw the doubling of farm-land valuation in the United States, saw also one of its results, the birth of the Conservation movement. It marked as well the end of the era of free land and the necessary beginning of the era of scientific utilization. We can get no more new land, so now we must work to produce more on the land we have. We must irrigate, we must drain, we must tame the rivers to prevent floods, we must fertilize and cultivate our lands better so as to produce larger crops. We are very properly becoming interested in plant breeding and scientific marketing. Our position is not altogether unlike that of Adam and Eve, who

RELATION OF IMPROVED LAND,
LAND IN CROPS, & FOOD PRODUCTION
TO
POPULATION
UNITED STATES; 1850 - 1920
( LAND IN CROPS; 1880-1920 )

FIG. 10 — See Fig. 11.

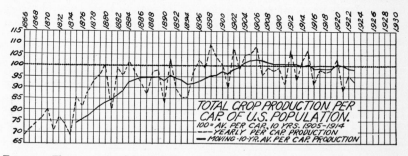

FIG. 11 — These two graphs (See Fig. 10) showing total and per capita production merit much reflection. Perhaps 1906, the per capita peak, is the most significant date in our industrial history. (Courtesy U. S. Dept. Agr.)

had lived on the free fruits of the trees in the Garden of Eden until Jehovah led them to the gate and drove them out into the treeless landscape, telling them to eat bread in the sweat of their faces.

### The Passing of the Frontier Type

The passing of the epoch of free land brings deeper changes [10] than those of price. It will cause the disappearing of old ideas and types and the coming of new ideas and new types.

The American frontiersman has been the picturesque follower of an unappreciated profession, the profession of conquering the wilds with small resources. It took these men generations to learn the art. They went into the woods with an axe and built cabins and raised families of sturdy children. They used twisted hickory branches (withes) for rope. They made their soap with lye leached from the ashes of the hearth-fire. They knew the habits of the wild animals that contributed to their supply of food and raided their granaries and hen-roosts. Every household possessed the knowledge of the trades that made clothes and food and tools and tackle. The frontiersman's life was a continuous application of self-reliance and inventiveness. This has helped to give us our marvelous output of mechanical devices. No nation approaches us in the number of inventions per man, although several nations are much more highly educated. It is an interesting question whether the passing of the frontier type will cause a decline in our inventive faculty. We do not yet know what will result from the habit of going to the store and getting standardized piece No. 002B and sticking it into the machine made in the standardized, specialized factory in the big city. Will it kill pioneering and inventiveness? Certainly the need of the pioneer is still with us. There are continents of human welfare of which we have penetrated only the coastal plain. The great continent of science is as yet unexplored save on its borders, and it is only the pioneer who will penetrate any frontier in quest of new worlds to conquer.

The passing of the frontier type will undoubtedly cause the passing of ideas and points of view.[11] The democracy of the nineteenth century was the individualistic democracy in which everyone looked out for himself, where free land produced a general financial equality, where there was no submerged class and serious social questions were few. The West, the frontier, has always been the seat of American democracy, the democracy of individualism.

[10] "The Influence of the Passing of Public Lands," an illuminating article in *The Atlantic Monthly*, 1914, by W. J. Trimble.

[11] From Frederick J. Turner's *The Frontier in American History:* "To the frontier the American intellect owes its striking characteristics. That coarseness and strength, combined with acuteness and inquisitiveness; that practical, inventive turn of mind, quick to find expedients; that masterful grasp of material things, lacking in the artistic, but powerful to affect great ends; that restless, nervous energy; that dominant individualism, working for good and for evil, and withal that buoyancy and exuberance which comes with freedom — these are traits of the frontier, or traits called out elsewhere because of the existence of the frontier."

This twentieth century of higher priced land brings with it the necessity of a social democracy where men work in groups, as in the labor union, the far-reaching corporation, the group action of companies, the farmers' land-bank, the co-operative creamery, the parcel post and the ever-increasing governmental and co-operative enterprises. Men are often driven by forces they do not recognize. It is to my mind highly interesting that the decrease in new grain-fields mentioned above and the building of the modern American navy occurred together, and that the decade of the virtual ending of free farms marked the beginning of our policy of acquiring foreign territory, that it has also been a period of great activity in commercial education.

This steadily increasing pinch has produced one of its natural results in the successive restrictions that we have applied to immigration. There is small prospect that these restrictions will ever be substantially lightened.

# CHAPTER III

## THE COASTS OF NEWFOUNDLAND AND LABRADOR

### *The Human Use Region*

THIS book describes North America as the home of man. Since a continent cannot be presented as a whole, it must be divided into parts. What shall be the basis of this division of the continent? It might be divided in many ways. The method chosen depends on our object.[1] If we were studying races, the map would show the location of the different races. If we were studying geology, the maps would present the areas of the different geological ages or formations. But this book presents and describes the continent as a land for human use. Therefore, the units need to have a unity that is based on human use. The colored map in the back of the book shows the continent divided into economic regions — regions whose boundaries result from the work of the cosmic forces that make climate, surface, soil, mineral deposits, land, lake and sea. The political units, such as Canada, Maryland or California, have their present boundaries because of the whims of chance and the accidents of history. As a result they are composed of areas that differ greatly in the kind of use that men can and do make of them. To understand Maryland, Canada or California as the home of man, it has long been the common practice to redivide the political units into regions each of which contains all of its kind of land within the state or group of states, as for example the Great Valley of California, or the Coastal Plain of Maryland and Delaware. On this basis of common conditions throughout a region the results of man's efforts, occupation, home and social organization tend to be alike over the whole of it.

### *A Fishing Coast*

The coasts of Newfoundland and Labrador are a good region with which to begin. Here we have a simple economic unit and one therefore that enables us most easily to see the method. (See map of North America, inside back cover.)

The people of the coast of Newfoundland and Labrador have one idea, one interest, and that is fish. Their lives are devoted to the sea and

---

[1] For a full discussion of this point see Smith, J. Russell, "The Elements of Geography and the Geographic Unit," *School and Society*, Volume 17, no. 441. Reprints may be obtained from the John C. Winston Company, Philadelphia, Pa.

its produce. The sea is particularly rich in fish and the land is particularly poor in the possibility of crops. Thus a natural specialization of activity centers the thought of a region upon fish.

An arctic current flows down the coasts of Labrador and Newfoundland. It is burdened in winter with pack-ice frozen in the open sea. In summer it is burdened with millions of tons of Greenland ice cast into the sea by the great ice-cap that covers hundreds of thousands of square miles, slowly flows to the sea-coast and floats away to the southward — a chilly curse upon the sons of men.[2]

The current hugs the shore of Labrador and eastern Newfoundland

FIG. 12 — A bleak-looking coast results from ice, cold seas, and glacial scraping on hard rocks. The coast of Newfoundland.

and creeps around to the western Newfoundland shore through the Strait of Belle Isle, carrying its arctic ice and cold into the Gulf of St. Lawrence. In May 1923 both entrances to the Gulf of St. Lawrence were completely blocked for a time.

Ice-water thus becomes the dominant fact of the shore environment — ice half the year and ice-water all of the year. The chill wind arising from ice makes the coast treeless. Since these coasts are high, rough and rocky, they have a peculiarly forbidding appearance. At the extreme south, on the little French island of St. Pierre, nineteen

[2] For the last ten years the United States has carried on an ice patrol off the Grand Banks of Newfoundland, to warn transatlantic shipping of the dangerous icebergs and floes. Two coast-guard cutters are usually detailed for ice patrol. Icebergs start in March and the patrol is needed until July. The patrol measured one berg which rose 248 feet above water and extended 1690 feet. This one berg had enough ice to fill every refrigerator in the United States for a year. — From *Science Service*, Feb. 16, 1923.

FIG. 13 — This map of natural forest areas should be examined many times by one who reads this book. (Courtesy Baum's *Atlas of U. S. A. Electric Power Industry*.)

miles from the coast of Newfoundland, one walks about in forests of evergreens that sprawl upon the ground less than knee-high. Thus they resemble tree growth at its extreme limit on high mountains. Sprinkled among the miniature and misshapen forests are laurels and goldenrod, only two to three inches high, but full of blossom.

The coasts, particularly the coasts of Newfoundland, are often wrapped in fog, because the warm waters of the Gulf Stream mingle off its shores with the cold Arctic Current, making the ideal condition for fog, namely, warm, moist air suddenly cooled. The fog, however, does not go far inland, at least in weather that would be otherwise clear, because the sun, shining on the land, warms it and melts the fog. Therefore a few miles from the shores of both Newfoundland and Labrador bright sunshine often smiles on the land while the shore and the sea are gray with fog.

Away from the chill waters, a few miles inland, the tree growth begins and the interior of both Newfoundland and Labrador is forested but mainly unsettled. The region we are now studying is the narrow strip of treeless coast whose people look to the sea for their chief means of livelihood. The sea is particularly rich in this region because fish are more abundant in cold waters than in warm, and can be caught more easily in shallow waters than in deep. The icebergs and floes keep the water cold, and wide shallows lie off the shores. The Grand Banks, lying about 100 miles southeast of Newfoundland, are one of the finest fishing grounds in the world. They have an area about the size of Pennsylvania, with waters so shallow that fish can be taken from the bottom of the sea with the lines. There are also fishing banks in the Gulf of St. Lawrence. The fact that the coast of Newfoundland, like that of Labrador, has recently sunk several thousand feet, means that it is a deeply indented fiord coast like that of Norway, which has had a similar history. The deep indentations make a multitude of good harbors for the shelter of fishing vessels. Naturally, therefore, fish mark the industry of these coasts and have dominated their history.

### Early Dependence on Fish

Newfoundland was discovered by Cabot in 1497 and within a decade was regularly visited by the fishermen of Brittany (France) and Cornwall (England). In 1578, 400 ships frequented Newfoundland. In 1583 Sir Humphrey Gilbert, the explorer, stopped at St. Johns to fit out his ships. He reported the place to be " very populous and much frequented." In 1600, 30,000 men [3] were there, a quarter of them British; the rest included French, Dutch, Portuguese and other Europeans. Strange to say, this wealth of fish and fishing did two contradictory things. It caused this to be the first part of the North American continent put to use and at the same time helped to delay and discourage permanent settlement.

For centuries Newfoundland was claimed in part by both England and France, yet both, through most of this period, discouraged its settlement. This was due to the desire to encourage their national develop-

[3] *Scottish Geographical Magazine,* March 1914.

ment at home in two ways: first, to give employment to the French and British fishermen; second, to encourage their navies and mercantile marines. For this the repeated sailings back and forth across the rough Atlantic were the finest possible training of men for hardihood at sea.

An English settlement was finally made in 1623, but in 1650 there were only 350 families in fifteen small settlements.

There are now about a quarter of a million people with a very free representative government much like that of Australia or Canada, from which they are entirely independent.

At the present time France, like every other nation, possesses free fishing rights on the Grand Banks, which are part of the open sea, but to aid her nationals, France, while relinquishing Canada, has managed in her treaties with Great Britain to retain not sovereignty, but a fishing right on much of the coast of Newfoundland. Here French fishermen (and also those from the United States, by a treaty of 1818) can land, camp for months, build sheds to dry fish and prepare them for the market, but they cannot make permanent settlements or fortifications. This is a fine distinction between economic and political empire. France also saved a fishing port out of the wreckage of her North American empire — the two little islands of Miquelon and St. Pierre, off the south coast of Newfoundland. The wooden shoes, the good Norman French, the dog-carts, the shop windows and the goods displayed therein all speak of France, the France of the past. The town of St. Pierre is a sad wreck with only 1000 people where it once had 3000, all because the Newfoundlanders passed a law forbidding the catching of bait along the Newfoundland coast. St. Pierre is a study in gray — gray rocks, gray houses, gray fog, lit up by windows full of bright flowers.

### Present Dependence on Fish

Political policy delayed settlement on the lands of Newfoundland, but this interference was less potent than the geographic conditions of the island. Even today it is well described as an empty shell with a fringe of shacks. There is a settlement on almost every fiord, because it is a natural harbor, and there is a system of 951 miles of railroad, mostly government-owned, connecting the capital, St. Johns (37,000 population) with most of the leading ports at the heads of the deeper fiords. There is also a fleet of thirteen steamers giving regular connection with Canada and the United States. It is, however, essentially true that a half mile inland Newfoundland is a wilderness, full of mosquitoes and black flies, and still occupied by a few Indians and the caribou. Its area is 42,000 square miles, about equal to that of New York, but the population of 259,000 (1921) is only one-fortieth that of New York.[4]

[4] The surface of Newfoundland would be unfortunate for the farmer even if the climate were favorable. The continental glacier that overrode the northern part of

The general dependence of this population upon fish is shown by the census of occupations (1914, last available): 67,000 fishermen, 5700 mechanics, 2900 farmers, 2300 miners. The foreign trade also reflects the dependence upon fish. The exports in 1920–21 were: dried cod, 13.33 million dollars; herring, .72; seal oil, .25; cod oil, .47; seal skins, .15; lobsters canned, .30; pulp and paper, 4.89; iron ore, .62 million dollars.

### The Dangers of Cod Fishing and Sealing

The opening of the cod-fishing season at St. Pierre is marked by the religious ceremony of blessing a dory. The boat is carried to the altar of the church by a solemn and reverent procession.

These coasts are no place for the timorous man. Catching cod may well-nigh be called heroic work, if danger makes work heroic.

FIG. 14 — The procession for the blessing of the dory.

Fishermen go to the banks in small schooners, each equipped with several row-boats called dories. In the front end of each dory stands a tub containing a line about 3000 feet long, called a trawl. To the trawl at intervals of six feet are fastened lines two feet long with baited hooks on the ends. The hooks are baited and the trawl is coiled in the tub while they are still on the schooner. Two men go out from

the American continent in the recent (geological) past found Newfoundland a land of parallel mountain ranges from 1000 to 2000 feet high. Before the glacier came they were probably soil-covered and forest-clad. When the glacier was gone, large areas were scraped down to bare rock; others had a thin and rocky layer of soil, the valleys were often dumped full of debris, natural dams of earth and rocks which produce many lakes, swamps and waterfalls. Even where the land is level, the glacial stones make tillage practically impossible over most of the land, although here and there are fine spots in the valleys.

the schooner in a dory. They drop overboard one end of the trawl with anchors to hold it down and with floats to show the location of its end. They row away in the dory playing out the line as they go, and afterwards spend the day going back and forth along this trawl, pulling it up and passing it over the boat, to take the cod off the hooks and put on fresh bait. The cod are taken to the schooner, packed in ice, and taken back to the mainland to dry, a process which causes them to lose one-third of their weight and marks the shore with great rows of sheds upon which the fish are spread to dry in the sun. The commercial codfish weigh from a few pounds to an occasional size of 100 pounds. The meat is one of the most easily prepared and will keep a long time if properly salted, smoked or dried. Codfish has been called the " bread of the seas," and finds a ready market, especially among the crowded and needy Catholic populations of southern Europe. It is of especial value in the tropics, where it keeps indefinitely, and has for centuries been a great staple of food and commerce.

When one considers the great land opportunities of the American continent, it is difficult to see why at present prices men keep on catching cod, unless it be some charm of the sea, some lure of danger. It holds no gambler's chance of great riches; indeed the chances are all in favor of a poor catch and death by drowning, with the certainty of a cold, mean job in the interval. Therefore I wonder why men risk their lives in this place where the waters are freezing cold, the winds are raw, icebergs often float about and the fog continually throws everyone into groping blindness on the rolling, tossing sea. To make the matter worse, this is the route of the transatlantic liners, which occasionally plow down the dories or the schooners in the fog. To cap the climax of terrors, it is the stormiest part of all the sea, for the St. Lawrence Valley is the great converging-point of the cyclonic storms that cross the American continent, whether their point of origin be British Columbia, Texas or the Bahamas.

Cod-fishers in their dories are continually getting lost in fogs and floating out to sea, or being driven off by sudden storms,[5] and it is no wonder that at some fishing-places Memorial Day is celebrated by throwing flowers into the sea, which is the last resting-place of so many fishermen.

The cod-fishing lasts from May until winter drives the fishers in. The seal season lengthens the fisherman's year by giving him a job from March until May. The Arctic seals come south with the current to give birth to their young on the ice-floes along the northern shores of Newfoundland and the southern shores of Labrador. Here, in Febru-

[5] I know an old man who keeps a shop in a fishing town. His hands are mere stubs, all that remained when he was rescued with his hands frozen fast to the oars, after floating in an open dory for four days driven by a biting blizzard that froze his companion stiff.

ary, over the miles of ice, a half-million baby seals may be heard giving their weird infant-like cries.

On a certain night early in March, the Newfoundland sealing fleet sails from St. Johns. This is an industrial event the like of which it is difficult to duplicate elsewhere. The whole city turns out to see the fleet off. It usually sails at midnight for the seal nurseries.

The sealing steamers approach the ice-pack along the shore. The sealers then leave their boats at the edge of the ice, go to the floes, kill the bachelor seals with a blow of the gaff and drag them to the edge of the ice, where small boats pick them up. The killer strips off the skin and a 2 to 4 inch layer of adhering fat. The good meat of the body is left to waste. Forty thousand is a good catch for a sealing steamer, and the expectation is to be home by the 10th of May. The seals are not the fur seals. Their skins make the leather used in motor-cycle seats and good handbags. Their fat is a substitute for cod liver oil, a material for soap, an illuminant for light-house lamps. There is danger in sealing, too, for occasionally a storm breaks suddenly upon the scattered sealers, breaking up the ice-floes and driving the pieces out to sea where drowning or freezing may be the sealer's fate.[6]

### Whaling and the Fight with Nature

The Newfoundlanders do some whaling. This was a great industry before 1860, at which time petroleum, by furnishing an oil for the family lamp, broke the price of whale oil, which before had been practically the only illuminant superior to the tallow candle. There was at that time much concern in the world over the darkness that was promised by the impending extinction of the whale. In those days they caught the whale by harpoons thrown by a strong man in the bow of the boat — another perilous task. By 1880 the harpoon gun reduced it to an artillery operation, and for a short time the whale-fishing industry was larger than ever, but it soon declined, again melted by the cheapening rays of petroleum, gas and electric lights. The whale blubber furnishes oil, the cracklings that remain make fertilizer, and the baleen makes commercial whale-bone, of which the price has been greatly reduced in recent years by

[6] The following news report describes the ever threatening tragedies of the sealer. "At least sixty-four members of the crew of the sealing steamer Newfoundland perished in a storm which caught them on the ice-floes near the Strait of Belle Isle last Tuesday. That number of bodies was recovered by other steamers in the fleet, which also picked up thirty-seven survivors, all suffering severely from frost bite. . . . The men lost were far from their vessels killing seals when the storm, with blinding snow, swooped down upon them. They were exposed forty-eight hours before assistance arrived, and in that time many succumbed. . . . When the blizzard came the crews of the other vessels managed to regain their ships, but the floes on which the Newfoundland's men were working drifted away from the main body of ice and when darkness fell that night not one had returned. The ship's crew consisted of 150 men, of whom 120 were on the ice. Captain Wesley Kean, his officers, engineers, stokers and cooks remained aboard."

improvements in the making of steel springs satisfactory to the corset trade.

Newfoundland seems to be a land of eternal warring and death. The furs from the interior have declined because of forest fires and too much hunting. The salmon of the rivers have declined because of the use of nets. The seals and whales declined because of excessive killing. The 1911–1913 average in the seal-catch was 250,000; 1918–20, 88,000. The Indian has declined in numbers because the white man has destroyed his food. Even the white man's great commercial stand-bys of herring and cod are not so regular as they once were.

Another important Newfoundland fish is the lobster, for which there are 600 canneries scattered along the coast. Some herring and halibut are caught; and the salmon ascends the streams in spring-time to spawn, affording sport to the tourist fisherman, although it is not an important commercial fish.

Suppose the fish supply failed.[7] Fish are really the result of a very delicate balance of nature. Little crustaceans as big as a pea or a grain of wheat or a mustard seed eat minute marine plants and animals. Codfish eat the small crustaceans. Anything that breaks any point of the series breaks the fishing industry. Man, of course, by continually catching the cod, tends to do this himself. Occasionally nature itself causes some overwhelming destruction. Thus, one spring, ships passing out from the Atlantic Coast of the United States found the surface of the water a few miles from the shore covered with tens of millions of dead fish. This continued for hundreds of miles up and down the coast. They were tile-fish, a good, edible species that lives in a rather narrow zone along the shores in water of a certain depth and within a certain range of temperature. Apparently there had been some change of temperature conditions that almost extinguished them, so that it took twenty years for them to approach plenty again. Indeed they have only begun to reappear in the United States markets as a result of the efforts of the United States Fish Commission in persuading the people that tile are good to eat.

The only marine dependence of Newfoundland to which man can give aid in propagation is the lobster. We can and do raise young lobsters in ponds and liberate them to fatten at sea. The basis of the main industry of Newfoundland and Labrador, therefore, does not appear to be as sound as might be desired. It should be pointed out at once that the resources of the sea are little known. In the scientific sense they are almost unexplored. We should be able to get great resources of food, oil, fertilizer, leather and other materials from the sea as land-limitation and increasing need drive us to it. Then these coasts will rise in importance.

[7] Back in the '60's one or two years of very bad fishing resulted in the necessity of government doles to stave off famine. The case became a sociological classic because of the long-drawn-out difficulty in getting the people back to work.

## Agriculture and Forestry

What are the other resources? Agriculture employs a small fraction of the workers and yields a total product worth only $3,000,000. The average Newfoundland fisherman does not even have a garden. The chief crops of the few farmers are hay, potatoes (6 bushels per capita), cabbage and turnips, all characteristic of the extreme northern agriculture.[8] Oats is the only grain that can be grown, and the actual production is negligible, $833 worth in 1921. There are on the island only 27,000 cattle and 74,000 sheep, less proportionately than we have in the United States, where sheep are relatively unimportant.

It is true that agriculture might be greatly increased by the development of more quickly ripening varieties that will endure the colder climate, as well as by such an intensive use of the soil as prevails in Italy; but there is no present prospect or need of such development.

The pulp mill is the most important new industry that has come to the Newfoundland coast in the last four centuries. It uses the product of the forested interior, which is another region.[9] Most of the Newfoundland interior that does not consist of lakes, bare rock or peat bog, is covered with black spruce forests, the best of pulp woods. The cool climate makes a slow growing tree, but the damp summer checks forest fires, and the small trees can be used for making pulp. The deeply indented coast permits paper mills to be built close to or on harbors and close to the woodlands. The lake-fed rivers furnish abundant water-power. The pioneer in this business was Lord Northcliffe, the English journalist, who secured 2500 square miles of forest land and built a huge paper mill at Grand Falls, with a capacity of 100 tons of paper and 240 tons of pulp per day, all of which were used by the Northcliffe papers in England. In 1922 the Newfoundland Government and the British Government were combining to finance an $18,000,000 plant on the southwest coast. Others are likely to follow. These mills promise to be a permanent industry on the Newfoundland coast as long as men want paper and the climate remains as it is. It is only necessary that the forests shall be kept in good production.

## Mineral Resources

The mineral resources of the island seem to be considerable and promise an industry that will increase largely, especially in iron ore. The iron is mined on an island, Belle Isle, in Conception Bay, on the east coast, which has a great deposit of iron ore estimated at 3600 million tons. From 600,000 to 1,000,000 tons of ore per year are mined. Most of it

---

[8] Lord Baltimore, founder of Maryland, showed his wisdom when he removed his Newfoundland settlement to the much more hospitable shores of the Chesapeake.

[9] See chapter on " Great Northern Forest."

is smelted at Sydney, Nova Scotia, although conditions for its export to the American ports are excellent and some is taken to Philadelphia. Some copper and pyrite ores are found, and there are extensive silver and lead deposits on the east coast.

## Labrador

If Newfoundland is a refrigerator, Labrador is even more truly one. The same Arctic Current flows down its eastern coast; and while it is possible for Newfoundland to receive a southwest wind from the not distant mainland the west wind of Labrador must cross Hudson Bay, which is always ice-cold and so blocked with ice that it is still a debated question whether or not commercial steamers can profitably pass in and out of it even for a space of six weeks at the end of summer.

In summer, 15,000 to 20,000 Newfoundlanders fish for cod along the coast of Labrador. Sometimes they stay in one place all summer and dry their fish there. These are called " Stationers," while those who sail up and down in their boats are called " Floaters." The permanent residents along the coast number less than 4000 and are known as " Liveyeres." There are some Eskimos to whom white men, some of them missionaries, have carried tuberculosis, Christianity, and education, with the result that their numbers are declining and their education is better than that of the cod-fisherman of British stock.[10] The Caucasians had no missionary for a long time, but at last their turn came. It came when Labrador and the "Liveyere" were discovered by Wilfred Grenfell, a fisherman's missionary, converted by the American evangelist, Dwight L. Moody. Grenfell sailed with the British North Sea fishing fleet, went with them to the Grand Banks, met the Newfoundlanders, became interested in them, went home with them, and found in their conditions the stimulus for a life-work of peculiar hardship, daring and interest. He found the scattered Labradoreans facing all the difficulties of the Newfoundlanders, with a more forbidding soil, a climate so cold that gardens were almost unknown, and the people often perishing for the lack of vegetable food to break up the ravages of scurvy.

The Labrador fishermen lived on rocky bays, many of which were unmapped when Grenfell came, and in many cases the fiords were full of hidden, uncharted rocks. The people lived a hard life. They were so isolated, so scattered, so few, that their outside connections depended upon occasional trading ships that came only once or twice a year. The arrival of the trading ship was naturally a great day; but the native was compelled to sell to men who bought at low prices, and then he had to buy from these same men who sold at dear prices.

The people were naturally poor. Cartridges were so expensive that the flint-lock gun still prevailed. There was no doctor. If they fell ill,

[10] H. Hesketh Pritchard, F.R.G.S., *Scottish Geographical Magazine*, May 1912.

they died or got well. Broken bones healed without care. There was no judge and no court. If they caught a thief, they hanged him. If they were out of food, they starved. Such was life and justice in an isolated land of hunger. If any people now living have lived the life of the Vikings, it is these. Only the hardiest could survive. They are said to eat only half as much as the Americans. Grenfell tells of a postman traveling fifty miles with only a piece of dry bread. It is said they will pour out gifts of cocoa behind your back, because they think that such stuff must be weakening.

Why did these deplorable conditions, so like those of the so-called barbarous peoples, continue into the twentieth century on the American continent, on land controlled by England? Partly because no one knew, but more because it did not pay to establish regular lines of steamers to trade with these people and give them the industrial basis for the support of a good community. Grenfell, who took up the life of a missionary to Labrador, has made the land known. Contributions of money have come to build hospitals, to establish schools, to build churches. He has mapped the coast and established a steamship line which carries their fish where they can get market-prices for them and which brings back goods for their co-operative stores. Grenfell is striving to free them from their dependence on the one resource of fish. This is done partly by introducing such hardy, rapid-growing vegetables as radishes, cabbage, lettuce, potatoes, which can be grown in selected spots. For a time his great hope was the reindeer, but his experiment failed for good reasons. The herd was too small, and it was preyed upon by fishermen's dogs and poachers. The half-starved Eskimo dog is a real terror. Grenfell's Jersey cows were protected by chicken wire, four sides and top, but the huskies made holes and killed them.

The remnants of Grenfell's herd of reindeer went to Anticosti Island in 1923, but it is only a matter of time before the Labradorean will look landward rather than seaward and become a reindeer farmer.[11] But that day is not yet. Reindeer packing plants should some day dot this coast.

### The Interior of Labrador

If you want to get your name on the map, the interior of Labrador offers an opportunity. It is the custom of geographers to name a river or a lake after the explorer who first comes out of the unknown with a good map of it. The map of the territory between Hudson Bay and the coast of Labrador shows blank areas in which states like Connecticut and Rhode Island could be placed by the half-dozen and still remain well within the bounds of the uncharted land. All you need to do is to land on either coast, go up some stream across the divide and down some other stream to some other body of water — a task that sounds simple

---

[11] See chapter on "Arctic Pastures."

but may cost the lives of those who attempt it, as it has done in the past. Living on the country has not been easy. This half-million square miles of land contains a few thousand Indians, mostly nomadic hunters, the majority of whom have never seen a white man.[12] Dr. Frank Speck, of the University of Pennsylvania, is authority for the statement that at least one tribe has always succeeded in running away when the white men have approached, although their camps have been found with water heated by dropping hot stones into bark vessels — a true survival of the Stone Age and of non-intercourse with the white man.

Roving bands of caribou may be met sometimes in thousands, and then again not at all for months, so that the problem of the explorer's food supply is a problem of transportation. If food and tackle are lost when his canoe overturns in the rapids, he probably starves as others have, for white men cannot catch fish, rabbits or birds with bare hands and stones.

### Water-Power

Much of the interior of Labrador is a plateau nearly 2000 feet in elevation dotted with lakes. These provide a natural storage of water, give an even flow to streams, and make the coast rich in water-power. In one fiord called Hamilton Inlet, in southern Labrador, a horse-power of two million is available. There has been talk of a great water-plant for the utilization of the near-by limestone, with electric current and air to manufacture the nitrates that are so important in both chemical manufacture and the production of fertilizers. This suggests the possibility of an enduring industry; and there is in the interior of southern Labrador enough forest growth for a considerable paper manufacture, with plenty of water-power to grind the pulp. This would only be a duplication of the well-established log-grinding industry on the north shore of the Gulf of St. Lawrence.

### World Trade and the One-Resource Man

The Labradorean waterfall, which now produces only mist, foam and noise, has the prospect of turning wheels and supporting a small town. A few decades hence, reindeer slaughter-houses should arise alongside power enterprises on this same coast to which the reindeer should be driven from the ranges of the interior. All this means only a population of a few tens of thousands of people, with the investment of corresponding tens of millions of dollars. These people, like the present Labradoreans, will be heavy purchasers of imported goods.

This emergence of the Labradorean fishermen from a hard condition of life which on its physical side may properly be called barbarous, is interesting as a type of world condition. The man of the land of one

[12] Dr. Truman Michelson of the Smithsonian Institution, *Washington Star*, September 30, 1923.

resource has a hard life, unless good transportation helps him to exchange his product on a fair basis for all of the six classes of goods. Thus the fisherman of Newfoundland, with his good steamer connections, sells dried cod and buys, from the Americans and Europeans, bread, meat, butter, sugar, fruit, fuel, clothing, lumber, practically everything that can be named.

Man's relation to the world has profoundly changed with the coming of steam transportation. In 1820, when people emigrated from the eastern part of the United States, they had to look at land pretty much as did Caleb and Joshua when the Israelites sent them into Canaan to appraise that territory. Land for the emigrant of 1820 had to have a complete list of resources, lumber for houses and fuel, suitable conditions for tillage, a climate to permit the maturing of crops, water-power to grind grain. Without all these, the agricultural community of 1820 could not hope to be comfortable. Therefore, the splendid grassy prairies of Iowa and Kansas lay empty save for roving Indians. Now one resource suffices. Fish or reindeer will do, or gold, or pulp for paper, or waterfalls to make nitrate. With this one thing that can be got to market and sold, the village store can have the products of every land, the home on the foggy shore can be comfortable, light and warm, men can be well-fed, well-read and civilized.[13]

As we study the American continent, region by region, we must use a very different standard of measurement from that used by the geographer or business man of 1820. One resource now suffices, but we must examine that one resource carefully. Will it endure? Perhaps it is gold, which in two years makes a feverishly prosperous city of shacks — shacks that in five more years may have become roosts for owls, because the gold and man have both gone. Perhaps it is whales — whales that will be well-nigh exterminated, leaving the wharf of the whaler to rot, as was the case in Nantucket. Perhaps it is agriculture. Agriculture can, with care, endure through unending centuries, as has been the case for 4000 years in China. The narrower the list of one's resources the more carefully must they be scrutinized.

[13] For example, see the section on Iceland in this book. The Falkland Islanders furnish another instance.

# CHAPTER IV

## THE ST. LAWRENCE VALLEY

### Character and Origin

THE shores of the lower St. Lawrence are high and bold like those of Labrador and Newfoundland. In many places the sheer cliffs are hundreds of feet high, with a village here and there busy with saw mills and fishing nestled at the mouth of a stream. Quebec marks the beginning of the lowland of the St. Lawrence Valley. The lowland came into being because its surface was composed of sandstones and shales which were softer than the hard, granitic rocks of the Laurentian upland to the north, the Adirondacks and the mountains of upper New England and lower Quebec to the south. The softer rocks weathered away faster and made the lowland in between the highlands. It is about seventy miles wide at Montreal and ends near the eastern end of Lake Ontario where the old, hard rocks swing across the valley to connect with the Adirondacks. This harder formation remains to make the hills, and in the river it remains as the Thousand Islands which so beautify the St. Lawrence River at this point. (See general map, inside back cover.)

The northern edge of the St. Lawrence Valley is sharply bounded by the steep hills. On the south it widens out to include the fertile valley of Lake Champlain. The neighboring hills of a part of Vermont and Quebec are also fertile and covered with farms.

The St. Lawrence River is really an arm of the sea, produced by the sinking of this region until the sea reaches far into the land. So great was this sinking that the Saguenay, a northern branch of the St. Lawrence, is in places eight hundred feet deep, and Montreal, the head of navigation, is a thousand miles from the ocean.

### Access and Settlement

There are four gates to this St. Lawrence Valley: up the St. Lawrence River, down the St. Lawrence River, the Ottawa Valley outlet to Georgian Bay and Lake Huron; and the Lake Champlain outlet to the Hudson Valley. These four outlets focus at Montreal, the natural site for the metropolis of that region.

Quebec, the first settlement, was a gateway fortress. It was located at the first place where the river was narrow enough for guns from the

Fig. 15.— The St. Lawrence Valley is a land of farms with small fields. (Courtesy Natural Resources Intelligence Service, Ottawa.)

fort to defend the region against the English ship of the eighteenth century. The site also offered the advantage of a certain amount of farming land, though not very much. The power that commanded Quebec has always commanded Canada. The city was besieged five times in five years.

The early days of the French colonist were hard. The forest was so thick that a man could clear only an acre and a half in a whole year. The climate was colder than any to which the Frenchman was accustomed. He could not bring his complete agriculture with him, corn would not ripen, and for a long time Quebec was little more than a fur-trading post.

The St. Lawrence is heart, highway and power for this valley.

The settlements on the northern shore, north of Quebec, have the advantage of river navigation but suffer from a peculiar isolation. There is but little farm-land. Ocean steamers pass up and down the river in front of these settlements, which are none the less isolated.

The river is shallow near the shore, and only small boats can come up. Winter ice keeps all boats away for five or six months. There is no railroad. " I should think life would be very dull there," remarked an American passenger on a St. Lawrence steamer. " Oh, no, madame, not so, not so! " replied a fellow passenger, a French-Canadian governess. " They have the consolations of their religion, and in summer their husbands' farm work to do." The farms here, even at the beginning of the twentieth century, were of the colonial type, producing most of the things the people used and selling but little. Eighteenth-century ideas naturally continued with the eighteenth-century life. A money crop of cheese is a twentieth-century innovation. So is an occasional pulp mill grinding logs that float down from the highland to the north. In summer many of the men are fishing.

At Quebec the St. Lawrence voyager meets the railroad and finds that the people have an interest in the outside world.

### Agriculture

The St. Lawrence Valley is a land of the snowshoe, the ski, the skate. The sleigh runs for months over the snow which steadily grows deeper and deeper until February or March. It is primarily an agricultural region with an agriculture that bears the stamp of the north-land. The short growing season prohibits corn and restricts the list of crops, but there is time enough fortunately for the development of all the small grains — wheat, barley, rye, oats, and buckwheat. The climate is suitable for wheat and other winter grain, for despite the rigors of winter the young plants, beginning their growth in early autumn, are kept warm by the blanket of snow which covers this region regularly and on melting fills the soil with moisture. Despite this climatic aid wheat is declining in relative and in absolute importance.

The farms here are small, and unfortunately much of the St. Lawrence lowland suffers from glacier-borne stones. Under such a severe handicap the region suffered greatly from the competition of West Canadian wheatlands with their vast reaches of rich, treeless, level, smooth, cheap land.

The acreage of oats exceeds all other cereals combined, and the hay production is greater per capita than it is in the United States.

As wheat has declined, there has been an increase in the growth of root-crops, such as potatoes, beets, mangels and turnips. Neither hay nor roots are exported to any extent. They are used as a food for cattle, especially for the dairy cow, for with the decline of wheat as an export crop and the inability to send abroad any other grain in its place, the Canadians have been compelled to intensify their agriculture by going into the dairy business.

## The Place of the Cow

The milk cow is often a sign of intensification of agriculture, a process whereby the same number of people get a greater yield from a given amount of land, although there may be no corresponding increase in product per person. Intensification of agriculture must finally reach a point where there is a decline in output per person but an increase in production per acre. Thus the acre that is in pasture would yield but 75 to 100 pounds of edible meat per year. The same acre in oats, roots and hay, all of which are fed to meat animals, would yield about 300 to 400 pounds of edible meat per year. But give the forage to dairy cows and the amount of milk produced may be several thousand pounds and a year-round job for the milk-maid. Hence dairying is more intense than meat production, meat production is more intense than grain growing, and grain growing is more intense than pasturage.

The natural outlet for the surplus of Canadian butter and cheese is the city markets of New York and New England, but from those they have been barred by the American tariff and the failure of reciprocity treaties. Accordingly, the Canadian was compelled to seek his market in Britain, wedging his way against the strong competition of the Dutch, Belgians, French, Swiss and Danes, and especially New Zealand.

The winning of the British cheese market is an interesting example of the success of associated activity where individual effort is helpless.

## Co-operation and the Farmer's Job

The perfect running of a farm requires a sort of intellectual and administrative Cyclops. The farmer who has several crops and several kinds of livestock needs a vast amount of technical knowledge about each one. In addition, the farm often has enough buildings to be a little village. The farmer has an ever-increasing number of machines and engines which he must keep in repair. A farmer is his own purchasing agent, often his own salesman, and to know how his business is running he must be his own accountant. Furthermore nearly every farmer must work on the land, or, if there are helpers, he must plan and superintend their work. Thus must a farmer often combine in one person the many functions that employ the whole administrative staff and working force of a factory. Verily the farmer should be a dozen men and a dozen scientists rolled into one. Now add to this burden the task of getting a foreign market, and you will see the basis of the new paternalism, government aid to agriculture, and also the basis of the new and rapid progress of co-operation in agriculture.

### Capture of the Cheese Market

The Canadian Government sent experts to study the exact requirements of the British cheese markets. When the desired color, flavor, composition and age of the cheese were known, schools were established to teach people how to make that kind of cheese, extension lecturers gathered farmers into groups and expounded cheese, cheese, cheese. Hundreds of co-operative creameries and cheese factories arose to handle the products of farmers' dairies. Quebec has 1700 cheese and butter factories, and in 1920 the province produced: 61,000,000 lbs. of cheese, 41,000,000 lbs. of butter, 60,000,000 lbs. of cream for other purposes.

The farmers of Quebec and Ontario banded themselves into co-operative breeding associations and cow-testing associations to improve the quality and products of their cattle, and in six years' time the selected Canadian cow gave 4400 lbs. of milk per year instead of 3800. Lastly, and perhaps most important of all for the conquest of a market, the cheese was branded by the government inspector, who certified that its quality was up to standard, so the buyer across the Atlantic

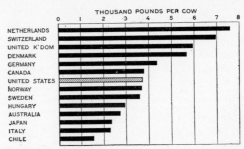

FIG. 16 — The place of Canada (and the United States) in this chart of annual milk production per cow should not be a source of pride. While technically a measure of cows, it is chiefly a measure of the effectiveness of human brains as applied to cows. (Courtesy U. S. Dept. Agr.)

could depend upon the quality of the cheese beneath that brand. The Canadian Government even keeps inspectors in Europe to see how the product arrives.

The success of this policy in comparison with the individualistic and unscientific method that was followed by cheese manufacturers in the United States is interesting and suggestive. In twelve years before the

World War the United States cheese export declined four-fifths, while Canada became for a time the leading cheese exporter of the world. Canada has recently been surpassed by New Zealand (using the same method), but her export is still a dozen times as great as ours even after the great boost that the World War gave to our cheese trade.[1]

When it comes to the detail of selling, the Quebec farmer does not bother with it; the co-operative association with thousands of members has *one* bargain, *one* distributer.

### The Champlain Section and the North Slope of the Adirondacks

The sections of Vermont and New York State that are in this region are as dependent on the pasture field and the dairy cow as are the neighboring sections of Quebec. The New York section, at the north base of the Adirondacks, is fairly dotted with cheese factories. Between 1905 and 1915 silos (using corn fodder — see next chapter) spread among the farmers here almost as rapidly as new styles in clothes. The Vermont section, the Champlain Valley, which has some rich limestone soils, makes butter and even ships fresh milk to New York and Boston by special trains. In ten years, 1909–1919, the amount of Vermont milk sold increased 62%. In 1919, Vermont, with $77.00 worth of dairy products per capita, led all the states of the United States. Wisconsin, the second, had $68.00 worth and Minnesota, the third, had only $32.00 worth.

This section is primarily agricultural, but the Vermont town of Winooski on Lake Champlain leads the world in the manufacture of wire window screens and doors.

### Mining and Manufactures

Eighty per cent of the world's asbestos is mined near the town of Asbestos about halfway between Quebec and the Vermont boundary. This industry, like several other Canadian industries, is largely owned and operated by American capitalists.

The mineral resources of the St. Lawrence Valley region, other than asbestos, are not large. It has no oil, no coal. This vital mineral is imported from two sources. It comes by boat from Nova Scotia, but the cost of transshipment from boat to rail limits the Nova Scotia coal to Montreal and other river points. Inland it is cheaper to get coal by

---

[1] Cheese exports in million pounds.

|  | 1903–13 *av.* | 1921 |
| --- | --- | --- |
| Canada | 167 | 137 |
| Netherlands | 127 | 115 |
| New Zealand | 55 | 153 |
| United States | 5 | 11 |
| World Total | 538 | 511 |

(British imports, 1921, 312 million pounds)
— From *Yearbook*, U. S. Dept. Agr., 1922.

rail from the mines of the United States. All the anthracite used must come from Pennsylvania, and those who live along the railroad that runs down the St. Lawrence River can appreciate the amount of this trade as, day and night, every thirty minutes, without ceasing, a long coal train, loaded with Pennsylvania anthracite, rumbles past, bound for Montreal.

Coal is usually a vital resource to a manufacturing state, but the St. Lawrence Valley rivals Switzerland in being as nearly independent of coal as any place in the world. Into this lowland from the highlands on both sides streams of wood and water-power are pouring, literally pouring.[2]

## Water-Power

When it comes to water-power, this region has few rivals except Africa[3] in either quantity, quality or convenience of this resource. The high plateau beyond the high hills at the north wall of the valley means that streams must make a swift descent. The fact that the plateau was overridden by the continental glacier means a blessing in water-power. This glacier pushed earth, rock and hills about as a child plays with sand on the seashore. When the glacier retreated no stream knew its own valley. Open valleys had become chains of lakes. Streams that had gone in an orderly way down their own valleys found themselves tumbling over precipices in strange places. Niagara Falls is an example of this. The ancient valley of the St. Lawrence was filled up and the river turned across a high limestone cliff, hence the great fall, one of the wonders of the world both in scenery and water-power. Although it is not in this region there are many falls of similar origin offering millions of horse-power to the men who will harness them.

To make matters yet better for water-power the plateau lakes produced by the glaciers serve as natural storage to give the streams an even flow.

The turbine water-wheel enables us to use great water powers. By this invention, twin of the electric motor in time of origin, a great amount of water can be brought to one small wheel; and when this is confined in pipes it can be brought from great heights, so that from 5000 to 15,000 horse-power per unit is now easy and common.

Electric transmission is the twin of the turbine in giving a manufacturing city access to the great water-powers. In the days of 1850 the mill had to stand immediately over the stream, with its wheels attached to the water-wheel by shafts or belts. Now we bring power by wire a hundred miles, two hundred miles, three hundred miles. Perhaps the

---

[2] For example: " There is available (undeveloped) within 45 miles of Ottawa 560,000 H. P. and within sixty miles 1,552,000 H. P. additional, making a total of 2,112,000 H. P. The city consumes about 75,000 H. P. in its sawmills, pulp mills and other wood-using plants. The name 'sawmill town' has often been applied to it."

[3] See *Atlas of Water Power*, U. S. Geol. Surv.

time is not far distant when it will be three thousand miles. The influence of these inventions is shown by the figures of Canadian water-power development: 300,000 horse-power in 1900, a million in 1910, two and a half million in 1920, and at the latter date it was really just getting under way.

### Wood-Pulp

It is a happy combination that Canada's greatest industry, wood-pulp, is a hog for power. It takes a hundred horse-power to make a ton of pulp a day. The fifty-four paper mills of Quebec used 312,000 horse-power in 1922, three of them using over 25,000 horse-power each. One Ontario plant at Iroquois Falls used 52,000.

Canada's wealth of pulp-wood has caused a great growth in her paper industry. In March 1923, Canada made more news print than the United States and furnished the United States with much of her material. In ten years' time the Canadian output of news print trebled while that of the United States almost stood still. The Canadian mills are often built on the St. Lawrence, where a branch stream can float logs from the northern forest to the mill. Some of these new paper mills are Canadian-owned, some British-owned, but more of them are owned in New York. Thus America has a double interest in the Canadian pulp business, first as a source of investment, and second as a source of supply. The two countries are in a curious reversal in this respect:

| Wood Pulp | Annual Production | Annual Use |
|---|---|---|
| United States ....... | 1,500,000 | 2,000,000 |
| Canada ........... | 1,150,000 | 180,000 |

### Government Aid to Water-Power

The governments of this region are actively aiding manufacturing by promoting its basal resource, water-power, which already supplies nine-tenths of all the power used. The government of Ontario began in 1906, with a hydro-electric commission that furnished transmission lines from private plants to consumers. In 1916 the government granted the commission the right to build plants, sell power and control private plants. Opponents of private monopoly point to its cheap rates as a successful example of government aid to enterprise.

The government of Quebec limits itself to storing water near the source of streams from which all users can benefit. As an example of this, a contract was let in 1923 for building a dam at Grande Decharge on Lake St. John at the head of Saguenay River. This lake drains 30,000 square miles and has an area of 400 square miles and a rise and fall of 20 feet. The dam at the outlet controls a flow, so that the minimum will be 22,000 cubic feet per second instead of 12,000 cubic feet. In five years they expect to develop 230,000 horse-power and eventually one million from these rapids, an excellent example of the value of upland lakes. In signing the contract for this dam, Monsieur Taschereau, Premier of Quebec, said this was another step in his dream that the province of Quebec should eventually be lighted and heated by electricity.

## The St. Lawrence Plan

All the water-powers, great as they are, seem small beside the stupendous plan for taming the St. Lawrence. This stream falls 222 feet between Lake Ontario and tide-water. For a long time this fall served only as an embarrassment to navigation, and forty-five miles of canal have been built to get boats around the many rapids. Now that the age of cement dams, hydro-electric power and great canal locks has arrived, there is a plan to build four great dams with locks, making the river a shipway, at the same time that 4,000,000 horse-power can be developed by the fall of the 241,000 feet of water per second.

The St. Lawrence is the king of water-power streams in respect to the evenness of flow, which only fluctuates [4] 25% because of the natural reservoirs of the Great Lakes, 91,974 square miles, in a total drainage basin of 565,000 square miles in which the rainfall is well distributed throughout the year. The Congo has vastly *more* power.

In January 1923, the Super Power Corporation of Buffalo filed application with the Federal Water Power Commission at Washington for permission to develop 1,600,000 horse-power at an estimated cost of $214,000,000. Such plans usually require years of thought and years of work before wheels begin to turn.

## Montreal and St. Lawrence Navigation

This improvement of the St. Lawrence navigation [5] will boom the trade of Montreal and perhaps make up for the present handicaps of the river. This city is located at the head of navigation; it is also at the focus of valley routes and at a point where an island furnishes much water-front. The port is well equipped with concrete docks, steel freight sheds, and the greatest grain warehouse facilities on tidewater anywhere. Her trade has grown rapidly. She is now the second port of America and the seventh in the world.

Despite its water route to the sea the St. Lawrence handles less than half the Canadian oversea wheat export that comes down the lakes. This is very surprising in view of the costs. Typical rates, November, 1911, were $.04½ a bushel by all-water route from Fort William on Lake Superior to Montreal. It was just twice that when diverted at Buffalo,

[4] The lakeless Potomac fluctuates 225-fold between highest and lowest.

[5] It is claimed that five cents per bushel will be added to the value of all grains in the territory tributary to the Great Lakes.

by rail to New York, yet that very season 48% of the lake-borne Canadian wheat went by Buffalo and New York, because of better steamship
service from New York, lower ocean rates and a lower insurance rate.
At that particular time insurance from New York was $.12½ to $.15
a hundred dollars; from Montreal $.65 to $1.10.  The fogs and rocks
of the twelve to fifteen hundred miles that lie between Montreal and
the fogless sea beyond the Grand Banks have sent many a good steamer

Fig. 17 — A part of Montreal Harbor.  (Courtesy Dept. Immigration and Colonization, Ottawa.)

to a rocky or an icy doom, a cost-factor for the ships that survive which
is measured in freight rates and insurance charges.

In the season 1920–21 St. Lawrence steamers carried 26 million bushels
of wheat, and those from United States ports 54 million.

### Slow Growth of Manufactures

Despite all the advantages of the St. Lawrence Valley, its manufacturing and city population has not increased as rapidly as that of Connecticut, Massachusetts, New York, or even Michigan.   There is a
varied industry producing shoes and other leather goods, cotton, iron
and steel products, ships, and many things for Canadian markets, but
commercially the St. Lawrence Valley is a land exporting dairy products
and wood products.  If it can maintain its supplies of wood, this industry, with its abundant source of power, may increase greatly.[6]

[6] American paper manufacturers are much concerned over the Canadian agitation
for the prohibition of the export of wood to the United States, amounting in 1922 to
over a million cords.  There are two reasons for this.  The Canadians would like
to have a home industry and they are beginning to be alarmed about their wood
supply.  "While Canada's resources of pulp-wood are being used at a startling rate,

### The Winter

In considering the future of this region, its long, cold winter looms up as a great handicap. Here is water-power by the million horse-power, adjacent forests by the hundreds of thousands of square miles, healthy climate and an industrious population of French-Canadian laborers, the great river for the highway, but a winter that shuts the highway half of the year, increases the cost of living, and makes the fighting of snow a positive cost-factor.

Canada has had some interesting mental reactions to this winter and this snow. For decades the people built at Quebec, Winnipeg and other places an annual ice palace, and they had coasting, skiing and other winter sports and made much of them. Then came the desire for immigration, particularly European immigration, and the Canadians thought that when people heard only of piles of snow and ice palaces and saw pictures of them they would not want to move to such a country.

About this time the Canadians were very much annoyed at Rudyard Kipling for writing his poem speaking of Canada as " Our Lady of the Snows." The business interests suddenly turned against the ice palace. For years it was abandoned. Then Americans took it up. Adirondack resorts and American railroads advertised winter sports, picturing them in every possible way, and Canada, seeing what she is missing, has at last returned to her ancient resource, the winter carnival.

FIG. 18 — Trying for the ski-jump record at a winter carnival, Quebec. Note the spectators. (Courtesy Canadian Pacific Railway Co.)

### Racial Friction

This region has a human handicap. It lacks the human solidarity that its open surface and electric transmission wires should produce. Here, as among no other North American Caucasians, we find one of

---

it is noteworthy that only two companies are doing anything in the way of afforestation. Meanwhile, natural afforestation is not keeping pace with the inroads of industry and fire loss. The Canadian Pulp and Paper Association has been urging the importance of adopting a definite afforestation policy, but it is difficult to obtain action, and the ' mining ' of Canada's forest wealth continues almost without restriction or thought for the future." — London *Times*.

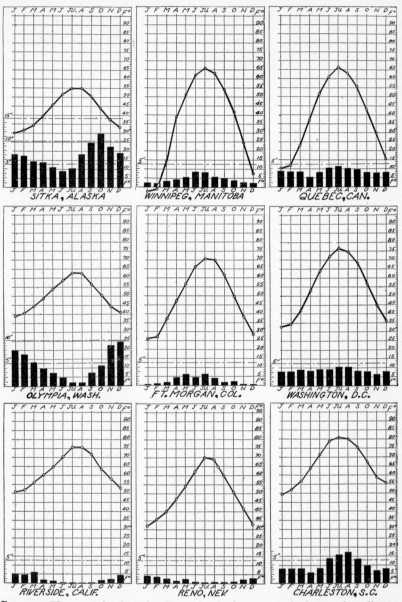

Fig. 19 — These graphs (see also Fig. 20), the best type of picture of a climate, show stations typical of regions. They are placed together for comparison, and merit careful study. Note the increasing rainfall, decreasing temperature, and low range of temperature in the Pacific Coast types: Riverside (Southern California); Olympia (Puget Sound); Sitka (North Pacific Coast).

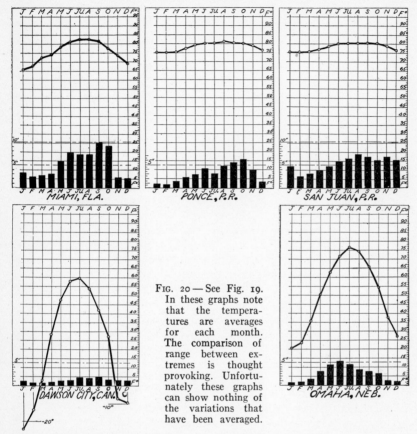

MIAMI, FLA.

PONCE, P.R.

SAN JUAN, P.R.

DAWSON CITY, CAN.

FIG. 20 — See Fig. 19. In these graphs note that the temperatures are averages for each month. The comparison of range between extremes is thought provoking. Unfortunately these graphs can show nothing of the variations that have been averaged.

OMAHA, NEB.

Reno (Arid Intermountain Plateau) shows same type of rainfall as Pacific Coast with greater range of temperature. Fort Morgan, Colorado (Great Plains), has still greater range with rainfall of entirely different type, the mid-continental.

Omaha (Corn Belt), Winnipeg (Spring Wheat), and Dawson (Yukon and Great Northern Forest) show variations of the same continental type. Comparison of Dawson and Sitka, not far apart in latitude, shows the extreme oceanic-continental contrasts.

Charleston (Cotton Belt), Washington (North Atlantic Coast Plain — Northern Piedmont), and Quebec (St. Lawrence Valley) enable us to compare the east and west sides of the continent. Miami (Florida peninsula) shows how near south Florida is to the trade-wind type. San Juan, rainy trade, Ponce, rainy-dry trade types. Compare the temperature with Riverside, Omaha, or Dawson.

the common troubles of Europe — conflicting racial solidarity. Four-fifths of the people of Ontario are British, while those of Quebec are four-fifths French, and the races are growing further apart, thus proving the error of the French publicist, De Tocqueville, who visited this region in 1830 and said that the French were " the wreck of an old people lost in the flood of a new nation." They have not been lost in the flood. The government reports of the province of Quebec are published in French and in English. There are two sets of schools, French and English. The French language is being deliberately purified of its Anglicisms, and the community is becoming more and more French. Someone has said that while England may claim to be the parent country, France is the real mother while England is but the stepmother. The old countries may say what they please; the mothers are forgotten. Quebec is a runaway child. She clings to French, but not to France. It is rather to her own individuality that she clings. The World War showed this clearly. In 1915, when the people of Ontario were enlisting by the hundreds of thousands to fight with the Allies in the European War, the people of Quebec did not enlist, not choosing to fight with either England or France. When Canada adopted conscription, Quebec resisted it hotly.

How does it happen that these are the only Europeans in all Central North America who have resisted the melting-pot? It may at once be said that they were not in the melting-pot. They were set off by themselves, surrounded on three sides by Gulf of St. Lawrence ice and by the empty forested highlands to the north and to the south. Here the French of the days of 1763 have been let alone in their agricultural isolation. In many ways the eighteenth century still continues. A student recently gathered up among these people a collection of ballads, verses and legends of old France including tales of the Round Table.

Farming is a conservative business. The French are a conservative people. The "habitant," as the rural French-Canadian is often called, has the land hunger of the French peasant. He loves it, he sticks. His children stick. They divide the farm and keep on as their father did. As the river-front is the desirable part of the river farm, the farms have been divided lengthwise until they are described as having their width measured in feet and their depth in miles. The house is on the river-front so that the south shore of the St. Lawrence seems like a village street, but it has no village organization. It is the parish that counts. Here the church of Rome still holds its eighteenth-century place as the center and control of men's lives. In thought, in education and in the press it still tells men where and how far to go. The people are still in the age of faith, simple faith; witness the pile of crutches at the shrine of Ste. Anne de Beaupré.[7] The mass is the great event of the week. Bad must be the weather to keep the farmer away.

A beautiful and charming novel, *Maria Chapdelaine,* by Louis Hémon,

[7] "I have spoken elsewhere of the effect of this isolation upon morals. The Church, aided by the encompassing hills, has brought to these people a peace of conscience and a moral sense which are sublime. Nowhere else have I seen such temperance and orderliness of life." — "The Isolation of the Lower St. Lawrence Valley," Roderick Peattie, *The Geographical Review* for February 1918, p. 116.

gives a sympathetic and understanding picture of this life of hard labor and this background such as no geographer can hope to rival.

In winter the habitant celebrates. Sometimes he postpones celebrations until the leisure of winter. He likes to celebrate. Betrothals, birthdays and anniversaries are a time of merriment, joy and high jinks.

The young people marry early. The Quebec couple usually christen their first child while still in their teens. The birth-rate is high, as it was in the United States in 1830.

BIRTH RATE, 1921

|  | per 1000 | Deaths | Gain |
|---|---|---|---|
| Quebec ........... | 37.1 | 17.5 | 19.6 |
| Ontario ........... | 25 | 14 | 11 |

In nearly every neighborhood you can hear a story of the widow with ten children who married the widower with twelve, or vice versa. The 80,000 French of the days of the Revolution have become three million, and they have also sent out many emigrants.

The Quebec French are overcoming the Ontario English by force of numbers. When young Protestant MacGregor comes home from school using French words, the farm is put up for sale because

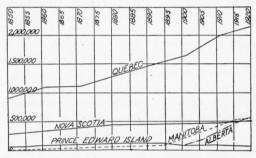

FIG. 21 — Suggestive increases and decreases of population in Canadian provinces.

of the fear of too much French association. Jacques Mercier buys it. Thus whole townships have passed from one race, one language, one religion, to the other, and old Protestant chapels stand in ruins by the roadside.

The misfortune of this is that the two groups keep up the friction and the separateness instead of mingling and rubbing along together as the members of the various churches do in England and the United States.

### Future

Perhaps the most significant thing about the industrial future of this region is the plan to export its greatest raw material — the power of the St. Lawrence — by wire to the United States. There is little doubt that the shores of the Hudson, of Long Island Sound and of New England are better places for manufacturing towns than the ice-bound shores of the St. Lawrence if the materials are easily movable, and the St. Lawrence power seems destined to go to the better place.[8]

[8] See index, " Super Power."

# CHAPTER V

## NEW ENGLAND–CANADIAN MARITIME REGION

### A Hard Land

SOUTH of the St. Lawrence Valley is a region of highlands which is still chiefly uninhabited forest. South of the highlands is the New England-Canadian Maritime District, comprising the lower lands (mostly below 1,000 feet elevation) of Nova Scotia, Prince Edward Island, New Brunswick, Maine, New Hampshire, Massachusetts, Rhode Island and Connecticut and extending from the suburbs of New York to the Gaspé Peninsula in the Gulf of St. Lawrence.

This is one of the most difficult regions in all North America to describe because it has so many minor variations. Therefore, we shall consider its major similarities and afterwards we shall call attention to the small areas of local variation.

Before cities and machines made life easier, this New England-Canadian Maritime Region was a land meant for hardy men. No others could survive and support families. It was a hard land — hard geologically, hard agriculturally, hard climatically. Most of its surface rests on rocks which are geologically old and very hard. Upon these rocks thousands of streams have worked for millions of years carving them into a land of rolling hills, whose elevation varies from sea level to a thousand feet. There is no soft flat plain beside the sea. The land has been submerged so that the sea flowed back into the valleys. Along the rugged coast of Maine and the deeply indented coasts of Nova Scotia and New Brunswick waves now beat upon the tops and sides of ancient hills.

### Glaciation

The glacier added numberless variations which helped to make the land a hard place for the home of man. The continental ice-sheet advancing across mountains wrenched off boulders and stones and strewed them over the lower lands. So varied are the results of glaciation that the meaning of the word is indefinite. The glacier made some parts of the region so rocky that they are hopeless for the plow. Elsewhere it scraped a few feet of soil from the tops of hills and left only bare rock. In other places streams rushed forward from the glacier and carried away all fine earth materials. Only stretches of coarse sand

FIG. 22 — Map showing part of New England-Canadian Maritime Region. Solid line — regional boundaries that are sharply marked. Broken line — a boundary that is transitional rather than sharp. See map in pocket.

("out-wash plain") were left.  Some of these areas absorb rain water so rapidly that the soil dries quickly and there is not sufficient moisture to make farming possible or even grass possible.  The people who live near them sometimes call these tracts "deserts" or "barrens," for even trees refuse to grow.  But the work of glaciers was not all bad.  In

FIG. 23 — Early mills at Pawtucket, a cotton-manufacturing center, located by water-power and navigable water.  (Courtesy F. W. Easton, Pawtucket, R. I.)

some places, they spread rich, glacial clays over the surface.  Elsewhere they brought fresh, unleached soils from great depths and mixed this more fertile material with the original surface soil.

### The Forest

It was hard for the settler to establish a home because the land of this region was covered with forest.  Spruce, pine, hemlock, oak, maple and hickory came down and met the salt spray of the ocean. The forest sheltered the wolf and the Indian and stood where the settler wanted to make a field. It took years of labor to fell the trees, grub the bushes, pry out stumps, roll away stones and make a farm. During the process men lost their reverence for the forest. In the time of Queen Elizabeth, England was almost deforested and generations of wood famine had caused the English settler to reverence trees.

### Climate

The region was further handicapped by climate. The winters were long and cold. Frequent storms occurred and often a deep mantle of snow covered the ground for three, four or even five months. Perhaps the Californian was right who remarked that if the United States had been settled from the Pacific coast New England would not have been discovered yet.

### The Pilgrim Fathers

But it was settled, and by a variety of hardy stocks seeking homes: Puritan English in New England, Scottish and German in Nova Scotia, Irish and Church of England English in New Brunswick.

The first settlers sailed for New Jersey but lost their bearings and landed on Cape Cod and from there sailed on to Plymouth. Since they thought that the hand of God had directed them, they accepted Plymouth as their home. The site had its advantages, for an old Indian clearing made a break in the forest and there was a good hill upon which to build a blockhouse. The settlers were not unmindful of drinking water and wood near at hand with which to build homes and feed the household fire.

The Plymouth colonists knew so little of the country to which they had come that they tried to raise indigo, rice and cotton. For decades they had no important agricultural staple to export. Their discouragement was extreme, and the letters they wrote in no wise praised the climate of the new land. But the Puritans were a superior stock of people. They had enough independence to resist the regularism of their day and to maintain their own church. They had enough courage to seek freedom in a distant wilderness. The Puritans were of middle-class working stock, sufficiently accustomed to labor to enable them to stand the necessary toil of the hard new land. It is natural that such hardy stock should later turn to manufacturing, and to the sea, and should be able to subdue the forest as they moved westward to settle new commonwealths.

In the early days these courageous settlers had two possible sources of income. They could farm. They could fish. They did both, but farming was the mainstay.

### The Colonial Farm Life

In what is now a territory of abandoned farms these settlers fought Nature and tamed enough of the rough land to make thousands of the small self-sufficient farms of the domestic epoch.

To understand the life of this time, we should think of the farm unit as a kind of little factory which produced its own raw materials and fabricated and consumed its own finished products. The wheat and corn of the little fields made the family's hominy, porridge and bread. The miller ground the grain for a share of it. The pig, sheep and cow, with the game that the people might catch, furnished all the meat they had. A patch of flax made fiber for thread and for linen. The homespun wool, dyed with the stain of walnut hulls, fed the hand-loom upon which were made the homespun cloth which illustrious men wore to the Continental Congress. The skins of the farm animals made the shoes. The wood-lot fed the fire and furnished lumber for the house, barn and fence. At the home forge the horse was shod and the wagon mended. Expenses for daily paper, telephone and gasoline were undreamed of. The plow-horse took the family on trips when traveling was not done even more simply, in the fashion celebrated by Longfellow in the romance of John Alden and Priscilla.[1]

### Environment and Political Experience

This was the era of small immigration from Europe, of the large family, of the rapidly increasing population, of a dense rural population in the lower areas of New England and Maritime Canada. The period has been justly celebrated as a precious time of preparation for political independence — whether formal like that in the United States, or informal like that in Canada and Newfoundland.[2] Their inability to migrate westward to large, new lands compelled the people of the maritime district to live close to one another. The new colonies were neglected by the mother country. Consequently, in the course of several generations, the people acquired the experience in self-government which was crystallized in the American Constitution.

The English colonists were schooled in self-reliance by many teachers. As fishermen they had fought with storms on one of the worst oceans. As farmers they had fought Nature to gain a piece of the earth on which to make a living. As interlopers in the Red Man's continent they had fought the Indian to the death that they might take his land.[3] Then

---

[1] A pamphleteer of 1786, a Massachusetts farmer, rehearsed these simple but manifold facts of the farm life at great length, and told how he lived comfortably by the expenditure of ten dollars a year, spent chiefly for metal, salt and gunpowder, and how he had one hundred and fifty dollars' worth of wheat money to save.

[2] Shaler, N. S., *The United States.*

[3] This conquest is a shameful story. I should hate to defend the white man's end of it before the Creator of mankind — unless the ownership of land is an offense meriting capital punishment.

came quarrels among the new possessors — the colonizing powers of Europe. Then, as now, European quarrels reached across the Atlantic. France and England fought each other at rather frequent intervals, struggling for mastery both in Europe and in America.

## The Struggle for Maritime Canada

The struggle between France and England for dominance in America made the eastern end of this region, the territory guarding the entrance of the St. Lawrence, very important. This river valley was then the only route from the Atlantic seaboard to the interior. Because the St. Lawrence Valley was the gateway to the continent, it became the seat of the French Empire in America. France was almost the dominating power in European affairs in the seventeenth and eighteenth centuries. So England, the up-coming rival, strove with France for the possession of this much-prized land. One of the great events in American history was the capture of Louisburg, 1759, by New England colonists. This victory helped the American colonists to realize their destiny. If farmers and fishermen could capture a great fortress from the mighty French, could they not afford also to look England in the eye? This awakening of national consciousness fostered the sense of independence that early ripened into the Continental Congress and Revolutionary War.

## The Rise of the Fishing Industry

The swiftly recurring generations of large families in a rough and meager land not only furnished political experience but strengthened the urge toward an economic dependence other than farming. The great piles of stone fences and the boulder-strewn little fields show that the population pushed the land hard in some places. The machine-tending farmer born on the rich, black, flat, stoneless prairies of Illinois wonders how his Yankee forbears made a living at all.

Migration, the great escape for restless and dissatisfied Americans and Europeans in the nineteenth century, offered small possibilities to New England in the eighteenth century. The man in Nova Scotia or Massachusetts saw the sea on the east and on the west a wilderness, rougher than his homeland. The sea, for three centuries the great rival of the land as a source of livelihood, offered fishing. And furthermore, as we shall soon see, it became the parent of two epochs in New England's history in the nineteenth century — the epochs of foreign trade and of manufacturing.

## Fishing

Save for the stormy climate, nature has conspired to make this a good place for fisheries.[4] The sunken coast, because it sank recently, is full

---

[4] The Indian had made much use of the sea. Fish were so plentiful that it was a common Indian practice to place one under each hill of corn, a device copied

of bays.  The rivers had wide estuaries.  These places are good alike for
catching fish and for sheltering ships.  Maine falls short of the full truth
when she calls herself " hundred-harbored Maine."

Fish are more plentiful in cold waters than in warm.  The cold winter
afforded an unlimited supply of ice with which fish could be stored until
wanted.  The cool summer permitted fish to be dried before they spoiled,

Fig. 24 — Codfish at Digby, N. S., drying beside the warehouse at the harbor
side.  Two-masted schooners.  (Courtesy Maritime Fish Co.)

which is impossible in warmer climates.  Not only were the shores good
for fishing but off the shores were the fishing banks, better (because
nearer) for the Canadians than for the Yankees.  East of Boston and
south of Maine is George's Bank.  South of Nova Scotia is Sable Island
Bank and farther east are the Grand Banks.

*Early Ship Building*

The British from their timber-hungry island were properly apprecia-
tive of the New England forest, for it contained pine.  Pine is the un-
challenged king of woods.  It is light, durable and buoyant; does not
warp, split, shrink or swell.  So the men of New England took pine and
some of the tougher oak for certain critical parts and built staunch
ships in which they went fishing.  Running in and out of their harbors,
they became great sailors.  It was these men who invented the schooner,
the most efficient of sailing ships.  While the sailors of Europe were

by the colonists.  Along the coast of Maine are heaps of oyster shells, four hundred
feet long, thirty feet high, said to be the largest in the world (*Literary Digest*, October 6, 1923).  These were left from Indian feasts — evidently oysters on the half-
shell have long been popular.

climbing aloft to take in rigging at peril of life and ship, the Yankee evolved the schooner. There was no dangerous climbing for him; he stood on the deck and worked the ropes and pulleys which, without waste of time and effort, sent his sails up and down. The Yankee sailor tacked his ship into the teeth of the wind and outsailed ships of every design and every land.

## Rise of Sea Trade

Sailing out to the Banks was a real sea voyage, on the stormiest of seas. The vessels that could go to the Banks, fish for a week or two and sail back, could go anywhere, and they did. Consequently the New Englander was soon engaging in trade.

He took dried cod and salt herring to the Mediterranean and the West Indies. Since wheat would not grow in the West Indies he took wheat flour and even bread; he took pine lumber and stuff from which barrels were made. The export of barrel-staves was an important factor in the colonial trade, since many barrels were required to hold West Indian sugar, molasses and rum, which, with other tropical produce, was a nucleus for the return cargo. These commodities were not only a welcome addition to the New England larder; their arrival planted the seed of future manufactures, for it was these ships which first brought to New England the cotton, rubber and cacao beans, which became the parent of important industries of the nineteenth century. The fishing schooner brought molasses-born rum which made distilleries so important in the colonial epoch.

Fish were carried to the Mediterranean. Thence it was not far to the Guinea coast for a return cargo of negroes. The New Englander brought most of the slaves to the South in the seventeenth century, and two centuries later his descendants spilled their blood freely to liberate the descendants of these slaves. For a time Boston and Newport were centers of the slave-trade, and Newport was for a time the greatest slave-market in America. A close relationship sprang up between the Newport traders and the Charleston, S. C., planters, which extended to a social intercourse between their families. It has lasted down to the present time: Newport is a favorite northern resort for Southerners, and there are many connections between Newport and Charleston society.

## The Clipper-Ship Era

The New England colonist, carrying his fish to market across the ocean, learned the ways of the sea and became acquainted with the people and ports of Europe and the West Indies. Soon more daring voyages were undertaken. There was never a time when the urge to make fast ships was greater. War between England and France, or England and Spain, or England and Holland then meant, among other things, privateers. Almost any ship was authorized to capture the ships of enemies. This was perhaps the golden age of piracy. Captain Kidd was neither a joke nor a myth; he was a daily menace. To distinguish between piracy and propriety was difficult and many a New England fortune was made or started by the success of her citizens as privateers.

If you were a privateer, you needed a fast ship. Also you needed a fast ship if you were trying to escape from a privateer or a pirate. Under this urge the schooner developed into the clipper-ship — an American product which unquestionably held the record for speed for three generations, or until it was displaced by the steamer. Possessed of the

triple advantage of the best design, the best woods, and an abundance of hardy sailors, it was not unnatural that the coasts of New England and Canada led the world in building and equipping ships for more than sixty years. In 1791 it cost France from $55.00 to $60.00 a ton to build ships. In New England it cost only $33.00 to $35.00 to build a better ship. Then the men of Salem, Boston, Glouces-

Fig. 25 — The residence of James Russell Lowell. Massachusetts trading cities have whole streets of such comfortable houses of the past. (Courtesy Boston Chamber of Commerce.)

ter and Marblehead loaded their ships with merchandise and sailed all seas, trading as they went and making a profit of several hundred per cent. The clipper-ship laid wealth on Boston's doorstep; many a fine old coast-town mansion and many a Yankee fortune dates from this period.

The half-century of the clipper-ship was a bright era for the coasts of New England and maritime Canada. Then their ports rang with the noise of the ship carpenter, while now only a few rotting logs attest an ancient prosperity that ended suddenly when England began to make steamers with iron hulls.

### The Rise of Manufacture

New England is a great manufacturing region for several reasons. Perhaps one of the most potent reasons is the accident of an early start. The same urge that drove the New England farmer to sea in quest of fish caused him to seek a market for the hand-made articles which the family could spare. As early as 1690 the wool produced by the New England weaver, fuller and dyer was exported to England. This her laws soon forbade. Then came the peddler — the man who went about seeking purchasers for his home-made goods.

## The Peddler

To sell his small surplus, the farmer-artisan often became a peddler, or he let a neighbor with a more roving disposition take his goods and seek to sell them. In the colonial times a man in Berlin, Connecticut, imported some sheets of tin from England. He hammered the tin into desirable shapes for cooking utensils and, taking a pack of the tin-ware upon his back, he set out to sell to his neighbors. This seems to have been the beginning of the famous Yankee peddling — a business which was favored by the long idle season of the New England farmer. The peddler carrying his wares upon his own or a horse's back, or in a cart or sleigh, became a well-known figure over wide areas. First he sold only tin-ware, then such common necessities as cow-bells, knives, platters, spoons, bolts, hinges, locks and round metal balls to put upon the ends of the sharp horns of the ox. The making of these things tended to develop the skill of the local blacksmith and was perhaps responsible for the tribute of Longfellow's poem, " The Village Blacksmith."

This peddler, far from home, with no reputation at stake and no expectation of developing a permanent connection with his customers, did not have a high reputation for honesty. The words " Yankee trick " originated from the peddler's mercantile practices. It was he who sometimes distributed basswood hams, white oak cheeses and wooden nutmegs. Connecticut is sometimes called the nutmeg state, regardless of the fact that real nutmegs grow only in the torrid zone. But despite the occasional shrewdness, trickery and immorality of this irresponsible pioneer of commerce, there seems to be little doubt that by making an outlet he helped to start manufacturing in New England.

## Ships and Manufacture

There were peddlers not only on land but on the sea as well. Ships went out seeking markets and the shipping industry contributed to manufactures in many ways.

The ships of Boston and Salem brought back many kinds of skins and hides from many distant places.[5] It was perhaps not entirely by accident that at Lynn, halfway between Boston and Salem, the shoemakers first applied division of labor to a job that had for ages been the work of a single artificer. At Lynn the sewing of uppers was handed over to the women, especially the women of sailors' families whose men were often away for weeks, months, and even (on whaling cruises) for years.

[5] Read Dana, *Two Years Before the Mast.*

## *The Epoch of Water-Power*

From this early hand-manufacturing and trade there came to be a surplus of capital. This made New England ripe for the mill-epoch. When the exciting news came across the Atlantic that machinery for spinning and weaving cotton had been invented in England, New England was ready.

With mercantile [6] sagacity, England prohibited the export of cotton-manufacturing machinery or drawings thereof, but she failed to prohibit travel. So one day, Samuel Slater arrived in Providence with a head full of knowledge concerning cotton-manufacturing machinery. He found financial backers and with their aid he equipped his cotton mills

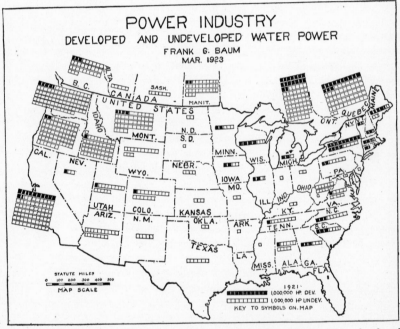

FIG. 26 — This map of water-power shows how fully New England has developed this resource, and how valuable Canada may some day be to her. (Adapted from Baum's *Atlas of U. S. A. Electric Power Industry*.)

at Pawtucket with machinery. Within twelve years (1802), twenty-nine other mills were started by men whom Slater had taught.

Thus began the first epoch of cotton manufacturing in New England. In 1814 a mill was built which was completely run by water-power. Capitalists then started inland in quest of more water-power. Fortunes accu-

---

[6] The government policy of encouraging a great variety of home industry and discouraging industry in other countries. See John Stuart Mill's *Political Economy*.

mulated at sea started the cotton-mills of Lowell, and Lawrence, Massachusetts; of Biddeford and Saco, in Maine; and of many other places. Only traders had the necessary capital.

Water-power has shaped New England's history and the distribution of her population much as a mold shapes hot metal which cools to its form. The entire region from western Connecticut to the tip of Gaspé was rich in water-power that was unusually dependable. The rainfall is well distributed throughout the year. Many of its soils are porous, because of the glacier, and therefore they absorb much rain, which they hold in storage and let run out gradually through springs. The glacier left upland swamps and thousands of lakes, of which there are one hundred and eighty within twenty-five miles of Boston. This combination

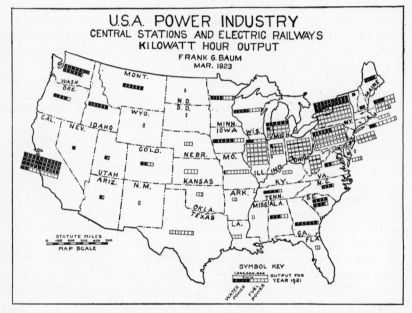

Fig. 27 — This map offers interesting comparison with Fig. 26. (Adapted from Baum's *Atlas of U. S. A. Electric Power Industry*.)

of even flow and plentiful supply meant that the country miller was not so often subject to having his dams washed out and his raceways broken as was the miller in Maryland or Virginia and in other places below the glacial belt. The even flow of the stream meant only a short period of shutdown during the summer drought, and therefore a longer working year.

The glacier had sent the rivers into strange courses, providing waterfalls. New England's factories were built near falls and were therefore pretty well scattered, though they were kept in locations near harbors, with which the coasts were everywhere supplied.[7]  It was natural, therefore, that Pawtucket should have been the first site of a power textile-mill in New England, for its location on the Blackstone River is at a point where the large stream plunges over a ledge of rock, below which the river is navigable. Lowell and Lawrence were but little farther away. As late as 1916 extensive surveys of the lower Merrimac were made with a view to making the river navigable to the foot of the great falls which made the city of Haverhill.

## Influence of Scattered Water-Power

Unlike the St. Lawrence, the New England-Canadian Maritime region has no place where a stream has power resources that are counted by hundreds of thousands of horse-power. There are, instead, hundreds of small falls. For this reason the manufactures of New England became widely scattered in many small towns in the period between the Revolution and the Civil War. This point will be clear when we see, by contrast, the great human hive of New York. Massachusetts alone has twenty-seven cities having more than 25,000 people. In New England, there are forty-two such cities, but New York State, with more population by far than all New England, has but twenty-two such cities.

It is a surprise to see what small waterfalls served to start New England enterprises which eventually grew to great importance. It is said that at Southbridge, Massachusetts, on a branch of the Quinnebaug River, a man began to grind lenses and to make other optical instruments with the power of a stream so small that when it went dry in the summer he used a horse for power. Once he even paid a stalwart negro ten cents an hour to take the horse's place and furnish all the power he needed in his little mill.[8]  Today on that very site is the great plant of the American Optical Company. This furnishes an excellent example of the growth of an industrial giant from a tiny industry which started beside a tiny brook. Most of these little mills have long since become picturesque ruins or have left scarcely discernible traces, but enough have survived to gather New England manufacturing into a host of little cities.

## The Influence of an Early Start

An early start often develops an industry in a place that has a relatively poor location. Once established the owner always faces a double dilemma: his plant is too big to move and too good to throw away. He can enlarge it but he cannot move it. If sites for plants were chosen

[7] Sixty-eight of the early settlements of New England were on or near these many harbors.

[8] Keir, R. M., " Some Responses to Environment in Massachusetts," *Bulletin Philadelphia Geographical Society*, July 1917.

today, many of New England's inland manufacturing towns would be situated elsewhere, doubtless on some of the many navigable waters, with a power-plant sending current over the hill.

### Influence of the Civil War Period on Manufactures

If names described the period, the Civil War should be spoken of in New England history as the Revolution. It changed men's lives both in the American and Canadian parts more than the Revolutionary War. This period marked (but did not cause) two industrial deaths and many industrial births. The deaths were the passing of the wooden ship and the whaling industry. For decades whaling ships had sailed from New England and Canadian ports. The voyages lasted from one to three years and extended to every sea where whales were found. Nantucket and New Bedford were the greatest whaling ports. New Bedford reached its peak of prosperity in 1857 when the fleet numbered three hundred and nineteen vessels. Petroleum made cheaper and better oil for the family lamp and marked the doom of the whaling industry at the very time when scientists, economists and ship-owners were becoming alarmed at the prospect of the early extinction of whales. In 1855 whale oil was worth seventy-nine cents a gallon. In 1858 the price had declined to fifty-four cents, and it fell even lower. In 1871, thirty-four vessels from New Bedford were caught in a storm in Bering Strait and all were wrecked. New Bedford's population declined between 1865 and 1870, but the old families, rich with whale money, shifted their interests from whales to cotton mills, for their city was well placed to take advantage of the third epoch of New England manufactures, namely the dependence upon coal. This epoch had begun about 1840. Then auxiliary steam plants were built, where one water-power after another proved too small for the growing industry to which it had given birth. This change threw the advantage back again to the coast cities. New Bedford, Massachusetts, typifies this growth. In 1860, she had 22,000 people; 1870, 21,000; 1880, 25,000; 1890, 41,000; 1920, 121,000. At this time she had sixty-eight textile mills, 55,000 looms, and 3,500,000 cotton spindles. The chief imports of her excellent harbor were fuel — crude oil and coal, of which her mills used 325,000 tons.

The growth of New Bedford is typical of the industrial revolution which the Civil War brought to New England. Then as now, although to a less degree, war was an economic struggle. Other things being anywhere near equal, victory went to the army that had the best supplies. The four years' struggle of the Civil War sent to New England factories sums of money which previously would have been considered almost unbelievable. These huge sums were paid for the rifles, the cartridges, the bits, spurs, buckles, bayonets, blankets, uniforms, overcoats, socks, shoes, caps, tents, flags and all of the other kinds of goods used and wasted by hundreds of thousands of men on the march, in camp and on the battlefields. Immigrants rushed from Europe into the El Dorado of good wages. Boston gained 40% between 1860 and 1870.

## Reciprocity with Canada

The Canadian provinces shared this manufacturing boom. They shared this luck because the United States in 1855 had enacted a reciprocity treaty with Canada providing for the free exchange of Canadian produce and of United States produce (reciprocity) for a period of ten years. Canadian industries boomed. Immigration increased three-fold. The valleys of Canada were cleared and turned into farms. She sent hay, potatoes and butter into American city markets. Her exports to America trebled in a year. Her fisheries and lumber industries throve and increased. This prosperity became all the more feverish owing to the insatiable demands arising from the American Civil War. In 1866, at the expiration of the treaty, the United States would not renew the reciprocity agreement. Canadian mills closed, people were out of work, immigration stopped. Black Friday had come and come to stay in the factory towns of the Maritime Provinces. Henceforth for forty years the people went upon their agricultural way. The different fate of the New England factory towns shows the marked potency of the political accident which gave half of this region to each of two different nations. The United States government passed heavy protective tariffs giving the factories of New England the advantage of markets from which the factories of Canada and other foreign countries were shut out.

## Influence of Western Lands

Then followed another of the accidents of history. After the reconstruction of war wastes, and between 1870 and 1900, the rush began to settle the western half of the Mississippi Valley. The Civil War had loosened men from their old places. The period before the war had equipped the eastern half of the country with railroads. We were then ready to equip the West. New inventions had made cheap steel. Plants that had manufactured war materials were ready to manufacture steel into farming equipment.

The prairies were level, treeless, most easy to settle. The stage was set for a post-war boom. It is doubtful if the history of the world elsewhere affords a parallel example of the speedy occupation of land. The Eastern States, particularly New England, scattered their sons and their grandsons from the East North Central States over an empire. They can be trailed by town names as well as by family history. Portland, Maine, and Salem, Massachusetts, reappear in Portland and Salem, Oregon. There are twenty-seven Salems, twenty-seven Manchesters, twenty-six Newports, twenty-two Plymouths, twenty Lexingtons in the United States, to the misery of postal clerks.

## The Era of Abandoned Farms

While New England's sons were settling the West, Boston financiers, with the accumulated profits of manufacturing, financed much of the railroad building. New England factories prospered from making tools and machinery for the new states to the west. Meanwhile a boomerang blow was preparing itself for New England. The rise of factory in-

FIG. 28 — When a little field yields as much stone as these fences show, the difficulty of competing with the stoneless West is apparent. (Courtesy John Clark, Hardwick, Mass., and S. B. Haskell, Director Agricultural Experiment Station, Amherst, Mass.)

dustry had taken manufacturing out of the home. The extension of railroads had given access to distant markets and had made possible the type of farm which sold one or two things and bought everything else. The rich new lands of the West dumped upon Eastern city markets and Europe a deluge of cheap produce. The American wheat-crop trebled between 1860 and 1880. The price of wheat in England declined from fifty-six shillings a quarter in 1877 to twenty-two shillings in 1894.[9]

[9] *Outline of Industrial History,* Edward Cressy.

The key position of wheat in consumption and in agriculture north of the Potomac and the Ohio makes it serve as an excellent key to agricultural conditions. If the price of wheat goes down and stays down, other produce follows it. If wheat goes up and stays, other produce follows the rise.

Since wheat went down and stayed down shortly after 1880, the New England farm ceased to be profitable. For the next thirty years the wide-awake sons of New England farmers had three ideas driven sharply into them — first, poor business on the old farm; second, tales of stoneless, level land, black with fertility, to be had out West for the taking; third, good wages in the factory towns in the valley, never far away. There followed another episode of industrial history probably without parallel. Thousands of families abandoned their farms. Sometimes abandoned farms characterized almost the whole of a community — the house with windows boarded up, sagging roof, rotting well-sweep, weeds and holly-hocks growing wild in the yard, and the fields grown up to wild roses, brambles, bushes and finally the young forest. The extent of this abandonment and the causes of it are shown by this table.

IMPROVED LAND BY GROUPS OF STATES EXPRESSED AS PERCENTAGES
OF 1870.  1870 = 100%

| Year | 1880 | 1890 | 1900 | 1910 | 1920 |
|---|---|---|---|---|---|
| New England ......... | 109.6 | 89.5 | 67.8 | 60.5 | 51. |
| East North Central .. | 137.7 | 143.5 | 157.9 | 162. | 160.1 |
| West North Central .. | 260.5 | 448.8 | 577. | 698.8 | 729. |
| West South Central .. | 276.3 | 444.8 | 578.9 | 848.1 | 934.3 |

The figures for New England are deceptively large. The Director of the Vermont Experiment Station told me in 1908 that about half of the so-called improved land of that State was then growing up in forest.

The 75% loss in the one sea-shore county of New Hampshire, immediately adjacent to the many mills of that section, is typical of the many counties where the factory offered its greatest opportunity to the farmer boy.

LAND UNDER CULTIVATION IN ROCKINGHAM COUNTY, NEW HAMPSHIRE

| 1870 | 235,605 acres | 1900 | 102,058 acres |
|---|---|---|---|
| 1880 | 223,544 " | 1910 | 113,573 " |
| 1890 | 179,402 " | 1920 | 86,336 " |

The census of 1920 shows many New England farmers over fifty-five years of age, and very few below thirty-five.

### The Present — A Land of Cities

In 1925, after the forces above enumerated had had a full half-century to work out their results, we find a great contrast between the Canadian and American ends of this region.  The Canadian part is rural, the American part has become, one might almost say, a collection of cities. The boom period of the World War helped to make this condition still more acute, as every Allied army called on New England for munitions and supplies.  Her factory workers [10] outnumber all other combined occupations.  Since these figures include rural Vermont, the importance of manufacture is still greater in the Maritime region.

Fifty-one per cent of the people of the United States live in cities, 79% of all New Englanders, and 37% of all those in the three Canadian Maritime Provinces.  Note the astonishing figures in Lower New England States, wholly or almost wholly within this region.

| | 1900 | 1910 | 1920 | Per cent, Urban, Last Census | Per cent, Increase of Population 20 Years |
|---|---|---|---|---|---|
| Massachusetts.......... | 2,805,346 | 3,366,416 | 3,852,356 | 94.8 | 37.4 |
| Rhode Island........... | 428,556 | 542,610 | 604,397 | 97.5 | 41. |
| Connecticut............ | 908,420 | 1,114,756 | 1,380,631 | 67.8 | 52. |
| New Hampshire (Hillsborough, Merrimack, Rockingham Counties) | 216,188 | 231,595 | 239,780 | 71.3 | 10.9 |
| Maine................. | 694,466 | 742,371 | 768,014 | 39. | 10.6 |
| New Hampshire (all counties except above)..... | 195,400 | 198,977 | 203,303 | 53.5 | 4. |
| Vermont............... | 343,641 | 355,956 | 352,428 | 31.2 | 2.6 |
| Iowa.................. | 2,231,853 | 2,224,771 | 2,404,021 | 36.4 | 7.7 |
| United States.......... | 75,994,575 | 91,972,266 | 105,710,620 | 51.4 | 39.1 |
| | 1901 | 1911 | 1921 | | |
| New Brunswick........ | 331,120 | 351,889 | 387,876 | 31.5 | 17.1 |
| Nova Scotia........... | 459,574 | 492,338 | 523,837 | 43. | 14. |
| Prince Edward Island.... | 103,259 | 93,728 | 88,615 | 21.5 | − 14.2 |

So great is the urban population, so meager is agriculture, that someone has estimated that Connecticut produces each year enough mutton to meet the needs of her people for only one day; only enough beef to meet their needs for eight days and only enough potatoes to meet their

[10] CENSUS OF 1920 — NEW ENGLAND WORKERS

| | |
|---|---|
| Manufacturing and Mechanical Industries ............ | 1,632,000 |
| Trade ............................................... | 329,000 |
| Agriculture, Forestry and Animal Husbandry .......... | 255,000 |
| Transportation ...................................... | 215,000 |
| Domestic and Personal Service ...................... | 260,000 |
| Professional Service ................................ | 175,000 |
| Public Service ...................................... | 66,000 |
| Extraction of Minerals .............................. | 4,800 |
| Total persons occupied ............................. | 3,234,000 |

needs for fourteen days. In Massachusetts the value of fisheries per capita in 1919 was $2.82; of farm produce, $28.35; of factory produce, $1041. This latter was a boom figure, replaced by $740 in 1921, but the forty-fold lead over agriculture shows the essentially urban character of the population. This urbanization is new, and it is a moot question if it can last. In 1790 New England had but 3% of her people in cities, and the figure had only risen to 20% in 1870.

## Boston

Boston is well called the " Hub " of this southern New England city area. Three of the spokes were the Boston and Lowell Railroad, carrying cotton to Lowell (1835); the railroad to Providence; and the railroad to Worcester and Springfield which was carried on to Albany in 1841.

Boston has three quarters of a million people within her limits, and the Boston Basin, a low plain surrounding the city, is dotted with towns, some of which are an unbroken continuation of Boston. The Boston " metropolitan district " has nearly 2,000,000 people, about one quarter of the population of all New England. Within a radius of fifty miles, there are more people than in any other territory in the United States, except in a similar radius around New York.

## Three Industrial Circles

Boston is the greatest wool market in the world, save London. It is a great market for hides and skins which ships bring from every continent. The city itself has varied industries and it is surrounded by three circles of specialized industry. The inner circle is the leather circle. In it are included Peabody and other suburban cities that contain great tanneries. Next comes the circle of the shoe towns — Haverhill on the north, which boasts of being the greatest center in the world for the manufacture of women's shoes and slippers, and Brockton on the south, with a similar renown for men's shoes. Lynn,[11]

[11] VALUE OF SHOE PRODUCTS IN MILLION DOLLARS, 1919. % OF U. S. PRODUCTION

| | | | | | |
|---|---|---|---|---|---|
| 1. Brockton, Mass. | 7.% | 81.54 | 1. Massachusetts | | 442.4 |
| 2. New York, N. Y. | 6 | 66.47 | 2. New York | | 190.4 |
| 3. Lynn, Mass. | 6 | 66.45 | 3. Missouri | | 109.2 |
| 4. St. Louis, Mo. | 5.5 | 59.85 | 4. New Hampshire | | 73.8 |
| 5. Haverhill, Mass. | 5.5 | 59.70 | 5. Ohio | | 71.3 |
| 6. Rochester, N. Y. | 3.1 | 35.91 | 6. Pennsylvania | | 65.4 |
| 7. Manchester, N. H. | 3. | 33.31 | 7. Maine | | 48.0 |
| 8. Cincinnati, Ohio | | 31.22 | 8. Wisconsin | | 44.3 |
| 9. Milwaukee, Wis. | | 30.00 | 9. Illinois | | 39.4 |
| 10. Boston, Mass. | | 27.52 | | | |
| 11. Philadelphia, Pa. | | 20.53 | | | |
| 12. Auburn, Maine | | 20.38 | | | |
| 13. Chicago, Ill. | | 17.59 | | | |

Four Massachusetts cities, Brockton, Lynn, Haverhill and Boston, together produced $235,000,000 worth of shoes in 1919.

in the midst of the shoe region, is the rival of both Brockton and Haverhill.

Walking the streets of Lynn one realizes what concentration an industry can have; the signs upon the places of business read — heels, welts, insoles, uppers, eyelets, thread, etc., etc.  It is an astonishing proof of the degree to which even a simple commodity like a shoe, so long made by one man, can be subdivided and become the work of scores of industries and thousands of people.

Textiles make the third industrial circle around Boston.  It reaches from New Bedford, Fall River and Providence around to Lowell and Lawrence.

Boston is often the center where business is transacted for factories located miles distant.  Three hundred shoe factories have sales offices located within a few blocks of each other in Boston.  Textile mills and machinery plants fifty, or even a hundred miles away, buy materials and sell the finished product in the Boston office to which the material is never sent.  Indeed material for export is sometimes made in Lawrence or New Bedford, sold through the Boston office, and exported by way of the export houses and the shipping lines of New York.

## The Textile Industry

The products of the whirling spindle and the noisy clanking loom overshadow all other New England industries, and employ one-fifth of all the factory hands of lower New England.  Ranks of looms reach across the wide floors of weaving rooms like rows of corn across the central plain, and the multitude of spindles tended by a single worker makes one think of perpetual motion and endless multiplication.  The section between Portland, Maine, and New York City produces nearly one-half (47.2%, 1919) of the cotton manufactures, and nearly three-fifths (58.3%, 1919) of the woolen goods, of the entire United States.  This fact explains Boston's wool market.  It also explains why the textile industry is the chief concern of the New England politician who, after all, must reflect what the public wants.  The textile industry even affects the curricula of the schools, as it doubtless should, for schools must strive to prepare young people for making a living as well as for being citizens.

Why is the textile industry so important here?  In the first place, it is indigenous to modern New England because, in the household epoch which prevailed until the beginning of the nineteenth century, the spinning wheel, now an heirloom, was used in almost every household.  Thus, when manufacturing for distant markets became possible, New England had the natural background for starting in the textile business.  The moist climate helped.  Moisture facilitates the manufacture of textiles by keeping the thread from getting dry and brittle, and it also reduces the amount of electricity in the thread, which often makes the thread snarl and tangle.[12]

### Concentration of Textile Industry

The textile industry, like the shoe industry, is concentrated. Thus, 20.4% of the total cotton manufactures in the United States, and almost one-half of the New England cotton manufacture, is centered in the five towns of Fall River, New Bedford, Lowell, and Lawrence, Massachusetts, and Pawtucket, Rhode Island.[13]

FIG. 29 — New England has many textile mills each large enough to support a town or small city — if the mill runs. (Courtesy Lockwood, Greene & Co., Inc., Boston.)

What are the qualifications of these towns for the cotton industry? Fall River may be considered as the mature type of a New England industrial town, in that it was started with the little water-power furnished by the Little Fall River (1813). In fifty years this power supply was outgrown and since 1865 production has been carried on chiefly in mills driven by steam generated by imported coal. The location of the

[12] At the present time this ancient advantage of climate is produced at will by controlling the humidity of the air in factories. Sometime we may become concerned to control humidity in buildings to make them most suitable for *people*. At present we are taking better care of our clothes than of ourselves.

[13] New Bedford, 8% U. S. production (1919); Fall River, 6.2%; Lowell, 2.7%; Pawtucket, 2.4%; Lawrence, 1%. These figures do not cover the whole production of these centers, because they pertain to municipal limits and do not include suburbs which, from the economic standpoint, should be considered part of the city. By this method of measuring these five cities have approximately 60% to 70% of the total cotton production of New England.

city upon a good harbor gives the best possible opportunity for importing fuels, although strangely enough the cotton comes by rail. The transformation of New Bedford has already been explained.

## The Woolen Industry

Lower New England also manufactures half the wool of the United States. The wool and worsted mills are scattered over more territory than the cotton mills. The cotton fiber was not abundant until after the beginning of the nineteenth century, so cotton spinning and weaving in the homes of New England was never widespread. When the cotton-gin was invented the industry developed not in the households of New England but primarily as a mill and city industry, whereas every village made wool, and when textile machinery came little woolen mills started where the village industries were. Thus woolen mills were scattered all up and down the valleys in remote places where small water-power would run a few machines, for example, in the Berkshire Hills country of western Massachusetts and the central upland around Worcester.

Despite this wide dissemination, the last fifty years have brought great concentration of wool manufacture in Lawrence, Massachusetts, which made 14% of the national production in 1910, and 10.1% in 1919. Lawrence is dependent chiefly upon the water-power of the Merrimac at a point where the river has the fourth fifty-foot cataract. This power resource attracted a man named Samuel Lawrence who, with a partner, bought the falls in 1843 and started the woolen business. This city now has the largest worsted mill in the world. The mills of one company in this one city turn out cloth so fast that the output would make a piece long enough to reach to England as quickly as an ocean steamer could get there. Providence makes 4% of the United States wool goods, and Lowell and Holyoke, Massachusetts, and Woonsocket, Rhode Island, are also important wool centers.

Holyoke, Massachusetts, is the product of a waterfall. The city is situated on the Connecticut River at a point where three ridges of hard (trap) rock cross the stream, making waterfalls high enough to permit the construction of three canals, one above the other, so that the water runs from the first canal, through a number of mills, then drops into the second canal and then into the third for the second and third power utilization in the same town. These many power-plants at one fall were built before the days of electric transmission. Now the method would be to make a central plant that would furnish power for all of the mills.

At Danbury, Connecticut, the fur from the rabbit skins of many lands is turned into hats, to the surprising extent of one-fifth of the total output of the United States. The hair of fur becomes felt by being beaten and rubbed until its tiny scales cling to each other.

### The Brass and Hardware Industries

The brass and hardware industries are good examples of Yankee skill, and like the textiles these industries are concentrated. Connecticut specializes in brass, making half the brass goods of the country. This is probably due to the peddlers of the early days who soon got to carrying brass-ware as well as tin-ware. The industry is centered in a string of small towns in the Naugatuck Valley, northwest of New Haven. From the brass industry developed the cheap clock, for which Connecticut has long been famous, and of which it makes a large proportion of the American supply. This state also makes three-fourths of the needles, pins, hooks and bells. Connecticut and Massachusetts make half the nails of the country and one-third of the tools. Over two-thirds of the firearms of the United States are made in Connecticut and in parts of Massachusetts adjacent to it — Bridgeport, New Haven, Hartford,[14] and Springfield, Massachusetts, being the great centers. The greatest center of hardware manufacture is the town of New Britain, which makes nearly one-seventh of the hardware of the country (1919), and before the World War celebrated its pre-eminence with the following statement in the paper of the local board of trade:

" This morning you probably arose from a comfortable night's sleep on a New Britain spring bed; you put on some attire furnished with New Britain buckles, some attire woven on New Britain looms; you visited a clothes-closet fitted out with New Britain hooks to which you gained access by unlocking a New Britain lock, turning a New Britain knob, then allowing the door to swing upon New Britain hinges. At breakfast you used New Britain cutlery, drank coffee from a New Britain percolator, read your mail brought you from a New Britain letter-box, slitting the envelope with a New Britain penknife. You walked through a hall built by New Britain tools and made solid with New Britain screws, opened a front door which was prevented from slamming by a New Britain doorcheck, and jumped into your New Britain automobile, or into a carriage drawn by horses with New Britain trimmings, to go to your office warmed by a New Britain register."

During the World War this town boasted that it furnished parts for airplane, battle-tank and submarine.

The peddler with his pack was a convenient means for the early distribution of jewelry, of which Providence and the near-by group of suburban towns known as the Attleboros, in Massachusetts, make one-half of the American output (1919). The variety ranges from the ten-cent store brilliants to the best of plate and solid metal.

[14] The people of Hartford, Conn., have a queer combination of dealers in life and death — firearms and life insurance companies. From the twenty-four insurance offices of this city $2,000,000,000 have been paid to beneficiaries in the last hundred years, and enough has been kept to support hundreds and help to make the city rich.

### Causes of Industrial Concentration

Why have the industries of New England been gathered into special centers? Some cities, like Worcester and Boston, boast the great variety of their industries. In contrast to this, Fall River has 87% of her workers engaged in making cotton, and New Bedford has 84%. In Brockton, 83%, and in Lynn, 50%, make boots and shoes. In Waterbury, Connecticut, 60% work on brass, bronze and copper products.

The rough surface of New England has undoubtedly helped to produce the specialization of industry. Much of the country is hilly, and the towns are scattered along the streams because of the water-power. In the early days hills made communication between towns difficult, unless the towns were in the same valley. Therefore, valley specialization resulted, until today some New England valleys are almost one long-drawn-out settlement with a common industry, such as the brass industry of the Naugatuck Valley of Connecticut, the textile industry of the Merrimac Valley (Lowell and Lawrence, Massachusetts; Concord, Manchester, and Nashua, New Hampshire). Other examples of valley industry are the paper industry of the Androscoggin and Connecticut Valleys.

Concentration has also come about because imitators have followed the lead of some successful pioneer. Often the son has followed the father, and other members of the family have taken up the business until all the mill-owners of a town may be more or less related. There are cases of mills that have been in the same family since before 1840.

The skilled labor of the established industrial center is a force tending to bring there other industries of the same kind. The skilled artisan is usually a permanent worker living in his home, and he expects to have his family with him. Such a man is hard to move, hence from the manufacturer's standpoint the greatest opportunity to obtain skilled labor is usually in an established center. The mechanical skill of the particular trades often goes from father to son. It may almost be said to be in the air. The knowledge of and the talk concerning the chief local industry makes an intellectual background for the people and they are apt to be a little more skillful than other workers. This is a reason why manufacturers who want to engage in this industry should and do go to an established center to start the new enterprise.

If the manufacturer wishes to establish an industry in a place where there is no trained labor force he meets difficulties, as was shown by the experience attending the opening of a new shoe factory in St. Louis. Workers from New England were transported on special contracts to do the work but they had to be paid more than twice the amount they had received in the great shoe factories of the home town in Massachusetts. It is thus plain that the many established manufacturing industries of

New England may be said to have their roots driven deep into her rock-bound soil.

## Results of Concentration

This concentration has a number of advantages. It is easier for the mill-owner who wishes to borrow money, because the financiers of the community know the condition of the industry and are able to estimate the risk. A banker would not be wise in lending much money to a man starting a new and untried industry in that locality. Buying the raw materials and selling the finished product are easier where there are many manufacturers. When machinery breaks down or needs repair, skilled mechanics who know how to do the work are on hand. The industry can divide and subdivide; for instance, one mill will spin, another weave, another finish, dye or print. By-product industries rise, like the glue industry around the fishing wharves or those mills of many kinds that use the shorter fibers which are waste to other mills. Finally, legislation and the education of the town can favor the one dominant industry. Textile schools are common in textile centers. Paterson, New Jersey, with 59% of its workers in silk mills, does not permit soft coal to be burned within its limits, because soot may injure fine fabrics.

Concentration also has its disadvantages.[15] When an industry becomes dull, the whole town is dull. A certain Massachusetts town lives from the payroll of two cotton mills. In 1924 one of the mills was shut down. This was temporary industrial death. Every merchant in town was scared about the credit accounts he was building up with the people who had no work and hence no money. Everybody felt blue. Men loafed and grumbled, women worried, and children were getting less to eat than they had been getting. The salesman of the closed factory came back without orders again and yet again. Then one day he packed his suitcase for a long trip. The whole town turned out in procession with songs and prayers to see him off on the night train. It was like cheering the departure of a college football team, but was much more serious. The salesman wired back an order for upholstery for Ford cars. The mill whistle blew again. The Chautauqua Association renewed its contract and there was again butter on the bread.

## The Manufacture of Machinery

The manufacture of machinery is the third industry in importance in lower New England. This industry belongs in this region by a kind of economic right. It is a kind of parasite, a hanger-on, or purveyor to the other manufacturing industries. For the textile, shoe, and other mills of New England many machines are needed. It costs a great deal more to ship the finished machines than to ship the raw materials used in making machinery — iron, copper, brass, tin and wood. Therefore there

[15] For a fuller discussion of the economics of concentration, see Keir, R. M., *Manufacturing Industries*.

is a natural tendency to make the machinery near the place where it is to be used.[16]  Furthermore, there is a great advantage for repairs and replacement of factory machines when the machine-producing factory is near the machine-using factory.  Once machines are in operation, it is the workers who discover defects and devise improvements.  New England has been the center of the inventions that have built up the machine design.  Thus shoe machinery has been perfected until every process is now a machine operation.

The natural results of these advantages appear in New England's production of 80% of the textile machinery of the United States (Massachusetts having over 50%), even though much of it may be used in new textile plants in the South or West where consumption is too small to start up machine manufacture.  One usually finds upon textile machines the names of Worcester, Lowell, Hyde Park or Whitinsville.  The same facts explain the great center at Beverly, Massachusetts, for the manufacture of shoe machinery, and also the centralization in New England of the manufacture of paper machinery for use in the paper industries of the upper New England forests.

### Tendencies and Future of New England Manufacturing

Lower New England lives by trade.  Her people live by selling manufactured produce which they make of imported raw materials in factories many of which are driven by imported coal;[17] meanwhile the operatives eat imported food and live in houses built with imported wood and heated

[16] Ohio ranks first in production of rubber machinery because of the great tire industry of Akron.  Oregon is leading state in the manufacture of sawmill machinery, Wisconsin second, Washington third, Tennessee fourth.  California makes peach-canning machinery; Massachusetts holds first place in manufacturing shoe machinery, with Missouri second.  The manufacture of cotton gins is largely centralized in cotton-growing states — seven having 89% of it: Georgia first, and Alabama second, the two states having one-half of total output.  (Census of Manufactures, 1919.)  Holyoke, Massachusetts, with dozens of water-power plants, was the natural place for the manufacture of the turbines for Niagara.

[17] WATER-POWER RESOURCES AND INSTALLED CAPACITY OF WATER WHEELS

| | Total Potential Water-Power | | Installed Capacity |
| --- | --- | --- | --- |
| | a Minimum h.p. | b Maximum h.p. | Water Wheels, h.p. |
| Maine.................. | 443,000 | 809,000 | 412,000 |
| New Hampshire......... | 135,000 | 246,000 | 217,000 |
| Vermont............... | 94,000 | 172,000 | 223,000 |
| Massachusetts.......... | 118,000 | 228,000 | 330,000 |
| Rhode Island........... | 6,000 | 13,000 | 43,000 |
| Connecticut............ | 72,000 | 137,000 | 156,000 |
| | Undeveloped Water-Power | | |
| New Brunswick......... | 300,000 | | 18,080 |
| Nova Scotia............ | 100,000 | | 34,323 |
| Prince Edward Island.... | 3,000 | | 1,933 |

— From *World Atlas of Commercial Geology*, Part II, U. S. Geol. Surv.
a Available for best 6 months of the year.
b Available for the best 50 weeks in the year, artificial storage may increase this greatly.

with imported fuel.   The particular facts show a condition almost without parallel.   The New Englander buys his fruit, his cereal, his sugar,
tea and coffee, bread and butter, meat and cheese, cotton, leather, iron,
indeed, every raw material he uses save a part of the wood.   Not even
the United Kingdom is so dependent upon material from some other
region.

The cost of freight is therefore an important factor in New England
life and it shows itself in the character of her industries.   The manufactured
product must be of high value to stand the freight charges in and out.
Therefore the freight cost must be small and the labor cost must be
high.   This means *skill*.   Indeed, in no section of the United States is
skill so conspicuously evident in every important industry.   Think of
the metal products of New England — rifle, skate, pocket-knife, hardware.   Consider the bar of silver which becomes the wedding gift of
silver plate, and the yet more precious bullion that goes out as jewelry.
Under the skillful processes of manufacture brass becomes the alarm-
clock that arouses the slumbering world to labor.   Compare the bulk and
weight of Pittsburgh's pig iron, sheet steel, rails, and skyscraper skeleton
with all this fine produce of New England.   A freight-rate of $10 per
ton on $50 worth of materials for skyscrapers is a very different thing
from $20 per ton on rifles worth $2000 or more per ton.

### Southern Competition

Can New England keep on buying everything and at the same time
increase in prosperity and human numbers?   The answer to this question
has caused much concern in the cotton industry.   Since 1880 cotton mills
have been increasing more rapidly between Richmond, Virginia, and
Montgomery, Alabama, than they have between New York City and
Augusta, Maine.   In Northern mills, the best month in the spring of
1923 showed a cotton consumption 23% less than the high record set in
the spring of 1916 during the war boom.   In contrast to this, the Southern
mills in this same spring of 1923 surpassed their wartime record by 4%.
Another measure of the competition between these two cotton-manu-

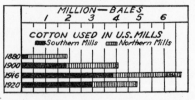

FIG. 30 — One of New England's alarms.

facturing sections is given by the
yarn output.   In twenty years, 1899–
1919, it more than doubled in weight,
but seven-eighths of the gain was
contributed by Southern mills.   A
few Northern mills had actually been
dismantled and the machinery taken
to mills in the South.

The chief explanation of these phe-
nomena, so alarming for the North, is to be found in the long hours and
lower wages of the Southern cotton operative.   In the North, union reg-

ulations have caused many Northern companies to build new factories in the South, rather than enlarge the old factory in the North.  Does this mean that the whole cotton industry is to go South and that New England will lose her major industry?  And will others follow, so that we will have abandoned factory towns, as we have abandoned farms?  The answer depends upon people, human energy, human skill.  In mere physical materials New England is on an unstable economic basis.

If an industry is capable of being completely standardized and carried on by workers who do not have to use much energy or intelligence, New England probably cannot hold her own in competition with places where food and raw material, power and living costs are cheaper than hers. Cotton machinery was the first manufacturing machinery made.  The industry is fairly well standardized, but it is extremely suggestive that it is the coarser yarns and the coarser cloths that are being made in the South, while the finer products are being made in New England.  The South is improving the quality of its output, however, and the final question is, can the Southern worker become absolutely as efficient as the Northern worker?  If so, the Northern worker may have to accept a lower standard of living because of the greater cost, or give up the competition with the South.

## The Place of Skill and Energy

This brings us back to the real question of human energy and human efficiency.  Men do not work with equal ease in all climates.  At the last census of the neighborhood of Boston the workers were receiving 80% more wages than the average of the people of the United States. These workers were doing the things which required skill, like operating shoe-machinery, and a larger proportion of these skilled operatives were well-educated natives instead of newly arrived foreigners.  If climate makes men hustle and makes their minds work, it is quite likely that the New Englander can keep on for decades, generations, perhaps even for centuries inventing things that others had not thought about and producing specialties that others cannot make.

If highly fabricated products are to be made, the disadvantages of New England are not so heavy as one at first might think.  Take the disadvantage of the absence of coal — the great base of modern industrialism.  A typical Fall River cotton mill, with a capital of a million and a quarter, sold, during twelve months, cotton goods worth $1,341,000, and used coal costing $37,485, or 2.8% of the value of the goods sold. Granted a handicap of 50% on coal in comparison with the mill in Appalachia, it figures out that this fuel-disadvantage for the factory was but 1.4% of the value of the produce.

The final question concerning the future of New England manufacturing is, can her workers maintain superiorities of brain, energy, and manual

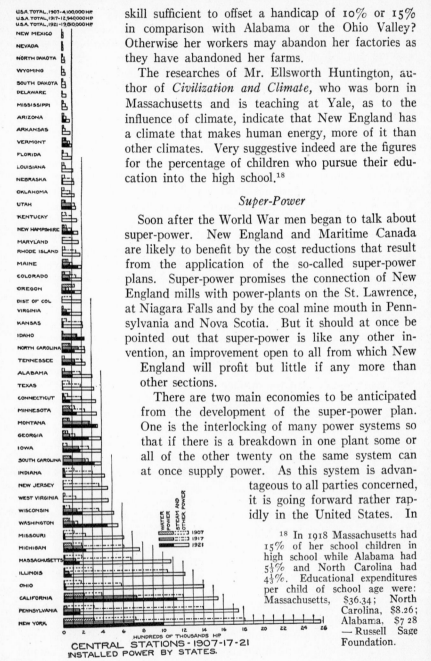

USA.TOTAL,1907-4,100,000HP
USA.TOTAL,1917-12,940,000HP
USA.TOTAL,1921-19,810,000HP
NEW MEXICO
NEVADA
NORTH DAKOTA
WYOMING
SOUTH DAKOTA
DELAWARE
MISSISSIPPI
ARIZONA
ARKANSAS
VERMONT
FLORIDA
LOUISIANA
NEBRASKA
OKLAHOMA
UTAH
KENTUCKY
NEW HAMPSHIRE
MARYLAND
RHODE ISLAND
MAINE
COLORADO
OREGON
DIST. OF COL.
VIRGINIA
KANSAS
IDAHO
NORTH CAROLINA
TENNESSEE
ALABAMA
TEXAS
CONNECTICUT
MINNESOTA
MONTANA
GEORGIA
IOWA
SOUTH CAROLINA
INDIANA
NEW JERSEY
WEST VIRGINIA
WISCONSIN
WASHINGTON
MISSOURI
MICHIGAN
MASSACHUSETTS
ILLINOIS
OHIO
CALIFORNIA
PENNSYLVANIA
NEW YORK

WATER POWER / STEAM AND OTHER POWER
1907
1917
1921

0  2  4  6  8  10  12  14  16  18  20  22  24  26
HUNDREDS OF THOUSANDS HP
CENTRAL STATIONS - 1907-17-21
INSTALLED POWER BY STATES.

skill sufficient to offset a handicap of 10% or 15% in comparison with Alabama or the Ohio Valley? Otherwise her workers may abandon her factories as they have abandoned her farms.

The researches of Mr. Ellsworth Huntington, author of *Civilization and Climate,* who was born in Massachusetts and is teaching at Yale, as to the influence of climate, indicate that New England has a climate that makes human energy, more of it than other climates. Very suggestive indeed are the figures for the percentage of children who pursue their education into the high school.[18]

### Super-Power

Soon after the World War men began to talk about super-power. New England and Maritime Canada are likely to benefit by the cost reductions that result from the application of the so-called super-power plans. Super-power promises the connection of New England mills with power-plants on the St. Lawrence, at Niagara Falls and by the coal mine mouth in Pennsylvania and Nova Scotia. But it should at once be pointed out that super-power is like any other invention, an improvement open to all from which New England will profit but little if any more than other sections.

There are two main economies to be anticipated from the development of the super-power plan. One is the interlocking of many power systems so that if there is a breakdown in one plant some or all of the other twenty on the same system can at once supply power. As this system is advantageous to all parties concerned, it is going forward rather rapidly in the United States. In

[18] In 1918 Massachusetts had 15% of her school children in high school while Alabama had $5\frac{1}{3}\%$ and North Carolina had $4\frac{1}{3}\%$. Educational expenditures per child of school age were: Massachusetts, $36.34; North Carolina, $8.26; Alabama, $7 28 — Russell Sage Foundation.

FIG. 31 — Among many other things this graph shows how greatly Massachusetts depends on imported fuel. (Courtesy Baum's *Atlas of U. S. A. Electric Power Industry.*)

the spring of 1924 it was announced that a thirty-mile unit would be built which would complete the connection between Detroit and Boston, 800 miles distant. This interlocking permits shifting of load factors whereby one district may use a surplus of power in the morning and another in the afternoon, according to demand.

The second great advantage of the super-power scheme is the utilization of large-scale units. A plant producing a quarter of a million horse-power requires per horse-power fewer pounds of metal to make the machinery, fewer cubic feet of building to shelter it, less man-hours to operate, less coal per horse-power hour than a smaller plant which would produce less power.

Large units well located would have also the advantage of diminished coal transport. Thus barges can carry West Virginia coal from Norfolk or Baltimore or Cape Breton coal to the giant power-plants of the super-power system on tidewater at New York, New Haven, Providence, Boston and Portland, much more cheaply than coal can be carried now by rail to the many scattered small plants of interior towns.

Super-power plans should make rapid strides. The knowledge has been in hand for years. The chief cause of delay has been and is conservatism and the fighting power of vested capital, some of which will suffer by the improvements.

### The Manufactures of Maritime Canada

New England and Maritime Canada are two parts of the same region, but they offer a strong contrast in manufactures because of the political factors. The eastern end, quite the reverse of the western, is poor in manufactures and at the same time rich in resources for manufacturing. During the Civil War period of reciprocity and the war boom there was little difference in the character or prospects of the two ends of this region. Then came the shutdown when the American tariff replaced free trade with Canada. To Canada this was a stinging blow in the face. Her abandoned factories now matched New England's abandoned farms. Canada could not believe that it was to last. For thirty-one years she begged and pleaded and hoped that reciprocity with the United States would come again. Then Miss Canada turned upon her heel and started to develop a policy of her own — protective tariff and development of foreign trade. So far as foreign trade was concerned, it amounted to little but dairy produce and wood-pulp. Like Maritime New England, Maritime Canada was not strong in foreign markets where she must compete with the older established industries of Europe.

Eastern Canada is also poorly placed to supply the Canadian market. The bad influence of geographic factors has been well summarized in the saying that this eastern Canada was the " land that was passed by." Canada is a strangely divided nation, economically and commercially. It

really is three lobes of good land projecting out from the United States
into the stony forests of the north. In the West, the wheat-lands of
Manitoba are a continuation of Dakota and Minnesota. To the east-

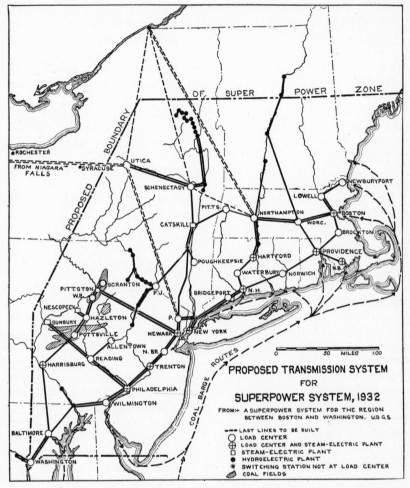

Fig. 32 — A piece of constructive imagination that is coming to pass — a number
of years late.

ward, across 900 miles of uninhabited forest, are the plains of Ontario,
a continuation of Michigan and Western New York. Other hundreds
of miles of uninhabited wild land separate the farms and factories of the
St. Lawrence Valley from the farms and factories near the Atlantic.
Through most of their history, the Maritime provinces have been worse

than an island, so far as access to the other parts of Canada is concerned. The St. Lawrence is frozen half of the year, and during that season, until 1897, the only way to reach the rest of Canada was by traveling through the United States. Since 1897 the impulse to Canadian independence has caused the construction of the Intercolonial Railway. It makes such a long detour around the lands of Maine that it is but little used and is financially unprofitable. This railroad renders the same kind of national service as a warship or a fort: it might be handy in war.

The result of these factors which discourage manufacture is shown in the well-nigh static population of the Maritime provinces. They are another New England without the factory towns. The largest city, Halifax, has less than one-tenth the population of Boston. This is true despite the possession of a finer collection of resources for the manufacture of iron than can be found anywhere in Europe, Asia or North America, save in the one district of Birmingham, Alabama. The iron and coal for Cape Breton are close together. Everywhere else something for iron manufacture must be carried a long distance. Pittsburgh smelts the ores of Lake Superior. England smelts the ores of Spain and Norway. But the island of Cape Breton has 200 square miles of coal on tidewater, with many of the deposits reaching far under the sea. On the cliffs

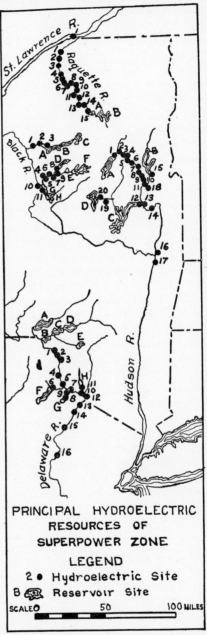

PRINCIPAL HYDROELECTRIC
RESOURCES OF
SUPERPOWER ZONE
LEGEND
2 • Hydroelectric Site
B ⬟ Reservoir Site
SCALE 0        50        100 MILES

FIG. 33 — Power can be wired to seacoast factory towns. (U. S. Geol. Surv.)

along Chignecto Bay, not far from Sydney, seventy seams of coal outcrop. Several are five or six feet thick and one is nine feet thick, with only two and a half feet of shale separating it from the next lower seam. Some of these coals are good for steam, others for gas, others for coke. Large deposits of limestone are near for flux, and a short ocean voyage brings the excellent ores of Newfoundland dug on tidewater to the iron plants on tidewater at Sydney, which is already called the Pittsburgh of Canada and has a growing iron industry. If we had in operation a reciprocity arrangement with Canada, this locality would furnish much of the iron and steel for the Atlantic seaboard, while the American plants on the Great Lakes would in turn supply central Canada. Cape Breton is a natural source for New England coal, and some is imported despite tariffs.

### Other Mineral Resources

Aside from coal, this region has few mineral industries, although it has three minerals most favorably located on tidewater and good harbors. These three are gypsum, limestone and building stone. In Cape Breton there are millions of tons of gypsum that can be quarried and loaded upon sea-going vessels. At times it is exported to the United States.

The whole rocky coast from Boston northward can furnish limitless amounts of building stone which can be loaded on ships with little effort. Rockport, Mass., located on Cape Ann, and Rockland, Me., have doubtless got their names from good natural reasons. At both places building stone is quarried almost at the ship's side, and Rockland has the advantage of limestone which permits the shipment of burned lime by water to many other coast towns. It is the largest American lime shipper.

Save the coast of Cape Breton, the most salient feature of the mineral equipment of this region is its poverty, although deposits of oil shale in New Brunswick may, in some era of scarcer petroleum, give rise to an industry that far outranks anything now in the Maritime provinces. It is reported to be nearly twice as rich as the Scotch shale which has already been worked at a profit. No other group of American States has so little mineral output as New England.

### Fisheries

The fishing industry in the New England-Canadian Maritime region has much more nearly shared the fate of agriculture than of manufacturing, although it has not actually declined. The New England fishermen catch between four and five pounds per capita for all the people of the United States, but the value is rarely as much as $3.00 per capita for the people of this region. The Canadian part has the better fishing resources, being nearer to the Grand Banks, but the number of persons engaged has remained almost static during the last ten years, although the capital invested has increased fourfold. This is largely due to the coming of the steam trawler and the motor, with which almost every fishing boat is now equipped. This marks the doom of the schooner, that great sailing vessel of the past.

The coasts of Canada have the richest lobster fisheries in the world, and the lobster, canned in the many canneries along these shores, is widely distributed throughout the world. Catching lobsters is a one-man job. In a rowboat the lobster fisherman visits the baited crates or lobster pots, which he has set in the shallow waters. He pulls up each crate to see if a lobster has crawled inside. Lobsters are almost in the class of domestic animals now that the eggs are artificially hatched and the young crustaceans are allowed to grow for some months in ponds on the shore before they are turned out into the sea to grow up and fatten. Over-fishing on the New England coast, in violation of the law that requires small lobsters to be thrown back, has greatly reduced the catch.

Gloucester, which has long been the most famed fishing center in the United States, devotes itself mostly to the preparation of fish for distant markets. Of late years Boston, with its large distribution of fresh fish, has actually received more fish than Gloucester, that is about a fourth of the New England catch. After the World War the combination of low prices and a fishing trust produced hard times for the Gloucester man. In 1922–23 Gloucester had but 200 fishing vessels in place of her old-time fleet of 400.[19]

This under-consumption of fish due to lack of selling organization is identical with the situation that prevents the fuller use of many farm-crops.

As this book goes to press, experiments are under way to adopt co-opera-tive fish selling, after the fashion of co-operative selling of farm produce. The organizers of fish markets have to reckon with a fickle wind. Thus on Monday, Oct. 17, 1921, Boston Pier had 1,000,000 lbs. of fresh fish. The next Monday it had but 112,000 lbs.

### Possible Fisheries

This story of the temporary decline in the fishing industry indicates the riches rather than the poverty of the American continent. What really happened was that with the post-war slump in agricultural prices

[19] "In the meantime, mackerel were selling for one, one and one-half and two cents per pound; more than one catch was dumped into the harbor for lack of any price. Consumers were at the same time paying as high as forty cents per pound for mackerel sold at retail stores. . . . There are in New England alone more than one hundred towns with populations ranging from 2,500 to 19,000 with no fish markets. Canadian dealers have learned the method of shipping carload lots of refrigerated fish to the Middle West, but no carload lots of refrigerated fish are shipped from Boston. In short, no sustained efforts have ever been made (scientifically) to study and extend the market." — "New England's Fisheries," by E. C. Lindeman, in the *American Review of Reviews,* 1924.

meat became cheaper and fish prices declined in sympathy. The sea has great unused, untouched, almost unknown resources if we study them carefully and use them scientifically.[20] America as yet is too rich in resources to bother much with such things as scientific tree-cropping or scientific study of the sea. Proof of this statement lies in the figures of fish consumption per capita year — United States, 16 lbs., Canada, 30 lbs., Sweden, 53 lbs., United Kingdom, 65 lbs., Japan (poor and hungry), about 200 lbs. (*Journal of Geog.*, May 1924, p. 200.)

## Population of New England

New England is the land of a passing race. Newspapers often speak of Massachusetts and other New England states as though Yankees were their dominant human stock and Puritanism the dominant faith. Time was when this was true, but that time has passed. New England, especially southern New England, the region of manufactures, is the land of the recent immigrant.

From the settlement of Plymouth until 1800, the population was almost pure British, chiefly English stock. During the first ten years after the settlement, 2500 British immigrants came. There was another large immigration after the Restoration of the Monarchy in 1660. For two and a quarter centuries, during the period of poverty and struggle, the Yankees increased, beat down the forest, won the fields, sailed the seas and went forth to populate Western commonwealths. Then came the era of manufactures, riches and prosperity. The Puritans, although they had dominated New England and most of the United States during nearly all of its history, ceased to bring forth many sons and daughters and have become a regretful but still potent minority in the land of the new immigrant.

## The Era of Modern Immigration

Since 1850 great changes have come to the New England population. First, the emigration of the rural population to the towns and to the West; second, the new immigration from Europe. The prosperity of the manufactures of New England has made her towns a labor market. In the '30's and '40's the New England textile mills were " manned " by farmers' daughters. Then the magnet of high wages drew in the foreigner, and the Irish and the French-Canadian jostled the Yankee girl at the loom and spinning machine. In three-quarters of a century before the World War the process made a new New England. Her population was increased by every wave of immigration from Europe, whether produced by prosperity here or hard times there. The greatest single rush of immigrants was due to the Irish famine of 1846. The failure of the potato crops in that densely populated island, which then had 8,000,000 people, and

[20] See Smith, J. R., *The World's Food Resources.*

now has about 4,000,000 (4,390,000 in 1921), caused deaths by starvation and large and sudden emigration to the United States, of which New England received a large share. The high birth-rate of French Canada and the lack of manufacturing development, has made her an important source of emigration to New England, and after the general revival of prosperity in 1898, people drawn by the opportunities of the mill-towns came by thousands and tens of thousands from southern and eastern Europe — Italians, Poles, Russians, Austrians.

The people have changed as much in racial composition as they have in distribution on the land. While the United States has 13% foreign-born, New England has 25.3% foreign-born, and those who have one parent foreign-born make the surprising total of 63% in comparison to but 7% in our Southern states. New England's population has been made over.

These figures, which are for all New England, do not fully cover the case, because the new immigrant has gone to the city, while the farm still continues to be the stronghold of the old stock.[21] The figures for Massachusetts and some of her cities show how completely the new arrivals have overwhelmed those whom they found in possession:

| Population given in 1,000's (From Census, 1920) | Total | Native White of Native Parents | Foreign-born | Chief Foreign Element |
|---|---|---|---|---|
| Fall River............ | 120 | 19 | 42 | Canada, 11.5 |
| Haverhill............. | 53 | 21.5 | 13 | Canada, 4.5 |
| Holyoke............. | 60 | 11 | 20 | Canada, 6.5 |
| Lawrence............ | 94 | 12.3 | 39 | Italy, 8.5 |
| Lowell............... | 112 | 24.6 | 38 | Canada, 13.8 |
| New Bedford......... | 121 | 20 | 48.7 | Portugal, 17 |
| Boston.............. | 748 | 181 | 238 | Ireland, 57 |
| Massachusetts........ | 3,852 | 1,230 | 1,077 | Canada, 262; |

Ireland, 183; Italy, 117; Russia, 92; England, 86; Poland, 69; Portugal, 53; Sweden, 38.

## Exit the Puritan

A colleague in Harvard tells me that on a Sunday afternoon in spring one may hear on Boston Common " every language but English." There are places in New England towns where the stores have signs, " English spoken here." An investigator spent an hour in the city hall in Woonsocket, R. I., during which time he heard no English except that which was addressed to him. The shop committee in a Peabody tannery in 1918 had the following rich variety: two Greeks, two Irish-Americans, one Pole, one Portuguese, one Italian, one Turk, two of unidentified foreign nationality. In the list of sons of New Britain, Conn., who died

[21] Maine, with a population of 768,000, has 107,000 foreign-born (the U. S. average), and of these 74,000 are French-Canadians from beyond the northern boundary.

overseas, the names beginning with S were as follows: Sarisky, Schade, Schleicher, Senf, Siomakevicz, Skorupa, Smith, Sokovich, Strohecher, Stunia, Sullivan, Sullivan.

The completeness of the passing of the Puritan in urban New England is well shown by the list of births and deaths recorded by the town clerk of a New England factory town in one month in 1915: [22]

It will take decades or generations for this transformation of stock to work out its final results, although many superficial results promptly appear. President Eliot of Harvard was merely observing the simplest fact when he remarked early in the twentieth century that Boston was a Roman Catholic city. It is estimated that the people are 80 or 90% of this faith because of the combination of English Catholics, Irish Catholics, of French Catholics from Canada, and of Italian, Portuguese and other Catholics from Europe. The editor of a Boston paper tells the new reporter from a distance to assume that every stranger to whom he speaks on the streets is a Catholic.

Early in the twentieth century the Boston School Board was composed of two old Puritan stock, two Irish, one Hebrew. We wonder who ruled. The Irish representation on this board was unusually small. Politically, most New England cities are completely governed by the Irish, who seem almost everywhere in the United States to have a genius for carrying elections. " Boston is filled today with O'Brien and Fitzgerald and Murphy ' Squares ' named after the boys who fell overseas — and the square which once bore the name of Edgar Allan Poe now bears the name of Matthew Emmet Ryan." [23]

[22] *Births*

A daughter, Ida, to Quintu and Amelia Perline.
A daughter, Vittoria Luigia, to Antonio and Luigian Musante.
A son, Albert Joseph, to John and Amelia Kottman.
A daughter, Hilda M., to John and Elsie Balster.
A daughter, Stanislawa, to Wlodslow and Mary Dictk.
A daughter, Annie, to Joseph and Mary Groszek.
A daughter, Helen, to Nikolay and Sophia Smey.
A daughter, Sophie Justine, to John W. and Louise F. Kempt.
A son, Joseph, to Redolf and Mary Govin.
A daughter, Katie Mary, to Nicholas and Joseph Moriscato.
A daughter, Victoria, to Mathew and Joanna Styfcka.
A daughter, Eugeniusz Jo, to Volente and Mary Borcz.
A daughter, Cecilia, to Peter and Anne Nasiadka.

*Deaths*

D. Wilbur Simpson, aged 59.
Sarah Anna Piper, aged 68.
Frederick G. Losee, aged 67.
Sarah Janet Goodall, aged 27.
Henry L. Wyant, aged 57.
Raymond Blum, aged 1 month.

In 1910 the foreign-born of Connecticut, numbering 30% of the population, gave birth to 63% of the children. Exit the Puritan, enter the Italian, Pole, German, Jew.

[23] "Massachusetts, a Roman Conquest," by John Macy, p. 236, in *These United States*, Boni & Liveright.

The ups and downs of the races were well described by an unsigned writer who published a long poem in 1880 in the *Hartford Courant*, quoted in 1895 by Charles A. Dana in *The Art of Paper Making*.

" Under the slanting light of the yellow sun of October,
  Close by the side of the car track, a gang of Dagos were working,

  .    .    .    .    .    .    .    .    .

  Then the thought came, why, these are the heirs of the Romans;
  These are the sons of the men who founded the empire of Caesar;
  These are they whose fathers carried the conquering eagles
  Over all Gaul and across the sea to Ultima Thule:

  .    .    .    .    .    .    .    .    .

  Yonder one pushing the shovel might be Julius Caesar —
  Lean, deep-eyed, broad-browed and bald, a man of a thousand;
  Further along stands the jolly Horatius Flaccus;
  Grim and grave, with rings in his ears, see Cato the censor.

" On the side of the street in proud and gloomy seclusion,
  Bossing the job, stood a Celt; the race enslaved by the legions,
  Sold in the markets of Rome to meet the expenses of Caesar.
  And as I loitered, the Celt cried out: ' Warruk, ye Dagos!
  Fill up your shovel, Paythro, ye hathen!   I'll dock yees a quarther,'
  This he said to the one who resembled the great imperator;
  Meekly the dignified Roman kept on patiently digging.

" Such are the changes and chances the centuries bring to the nations.
  Surely the ups and downs of the world are past calculation.
  ' Possibly,' thus I thought to myself, ' the yoke of the Irish
  May in turn be lifted from us, in the tenth generation.
  Now the Celt is on top, but Time may bring his revenges,
  Turning the Fenian down, once more to be bossed by a Dago.' "

In vindication of this prophet, a Connecticut manufacturing town had an Italian mayor in 1923.

Government in some manufacturing cities of New England has at times, especially in recent decades, been sadly corrupt.  It is easy, of course, for the outvoted Puritan to blame it all on the new immigrant, especially the Irish, but the population conditions of these cities make for boss rule.  The groups are diverse, many of them do not understand the language, the country, or the system of government.  The educational attainments of many of them are low and they are the natural material upon which political bosses thrive.  There result such rather surprising conditions as the discovery, shown by the Census of 1919, that child-labor had declined in every state in the Union except Rhode Island.

In the United States at large it declined 47%. In Rhode Island it increased 6%.

Yankee stock still has a few intrenched positions. Directors of banks are not elected by popular vote, and New England finance is in the hand of the old stock. So are most of the industries. So also is the long list of colleges and universities. No part of our country is so dotted with these visible signs of the effort to learn. State Universities have spread over the United States with many New Englanders in their faculties, but still hundreds of young people come each year from distant parts of the country to study in New England colleges.

The elementary schools of this part of New England are nationally famed for their excellence.

The Puritan is striving to hand on the torch of learning, to transfer the culture and traditions of New England to the sons of the immigrant down the street. Every small town provides free instruction to prepare the youth for any college, and if it does not have a high school of its own the town pays for tuition in some near-by town.

Nowhere else in the United States is the public library so universally a part of the village equipment. The Boston Public Library, second in America only to the Congressional Library at Washington, is the pride of the city and no other city can rival it, although Boston is only seventh in population among the cities of the United States. Nowhere are there so many historical societies as in New England. Nowhere are historic monuments so jealously preserved. Critics may say that the successful Bostonian flies away to New York, and may call Boston the abandoned farm of literature (Oliver Herford), but the report of *Who's Who* is highly suggestive of the continued vitality of New England. In the geographic classification, New York, the parasite of the nation, has twenty-seven pages, Massachusetts has ten pages, while such huge and weighty commonwealths as Pennsylvania and Illinois have but three pages each. Evidently there are still live brains, energy and ambition in Massachusetts.[24] Perhaps the climate gives men these qualities. Perhaps the Yankees can transfer to the new stocks all that is worth transferring. Perhaps, also, they cannot. The real danger seems to be that they will transfer too much by giving these people the ideas that will cause them also to die out as the Puritan is dying out.

### The Death of Brains

In recent decades education in America seems to have proved singularly fatal to the families of the highly educated. All statistical studies of the

---

[24] "An indication of the degree of interest which is to be found in science in a locality is brought out by my correspondence on nut tree questions. There are about three hundred names on the list. . . . I can find more enthusiastic correspondence on almost any scientific subject in a small New England town than in a whole southern state or in an entire South American republic." — Robert T. Morris, *A Surgeon's Philosophy*, p. 242.

birth-rates of recent American college graduates [25] show that their stock is melting away in New England and elsewhere in the United States about as fast as the Indian melted away before the white man's advance. Equally alarming are studies which show the excess of deaths over births of nearly all native American stocks in the United States, especially those living in the cities.[26]

It seems plain that success and education in America have within a short time produced voluntary limitation of numbers among the educated and well-to-do. This tends to the rapid decline in numbers of the offspring of the educated, the successful and the capable — the stock without which civilization is impossible. Our present attempt to educate everyone speeds up the elimination of the capable. We now know enough of the operations of heredity to know that this process of survival of the least able will almost certainly reduce the average of human intelligence to a low level in a few generations if continued.[27]

President Arthur E. Morgan, of Antioch College, thinks that the process of social organization, whereby a few brainy persons can control many, will enable us to get along with a smaller proportion of able people. Meanwhile he thinks that social need will develop a new morality, one which regards talent and brains as a public trust which must be passed on to a sufficient number of offspring to maintain the necessary average level of human intelligence, if not, indeed, to increase it. Thus far, humanitarianism (charity, medicine and education) has done much to save and aid the increase of the least valuable human stock, at the expense of the increase of the best — a service of most questionable ultimate utility to the nation and to civilization.

Now that we have almost prohibited immigration, New England's greatest necessity is that the present population shall not eliminate itself as her past population has done. This necessity of maintaining human resources presses upon New England especially because of her scarcity of material resources.

### Rural Emigration and Conservatism

The rural population of New England, still largely of Yankee stock, has for several generations been subjected to that selection resulting from the emigration, generation after generation, of those who elect to go away to better themselves. These are usually the more restless, the more imaginative, the more progressive. The conservatives stay at home and

---

[25] *The Racial Prospect*, S. K. Humphrey. *The New Decalogue of Science*, A. E. Wiggam.

[26] See " Urban Sterilization," *Journal of Heredity*, June 1917. (A recent study shows that equal numbers of city and country families in the United States had respectively 5,500,000 and 7,700,000 children in the same age-groups.)

[27] For the influence of heredity on selected human stock see *Journal of Heredity*, Vol. 15, p. 55, also Galton, Francis, *Hereditary Genius*.

become the parents of the next generation. From the island of Cape Breton comes the statement that one county with nine people per square mile has but two physicians and that nearly every person who goes beyond the grammar school migrates. This process, carried to the point where it has produced a sharp reduction of the total population in rural communities, has sometimes left the type of person who finds it difficult to adopt new and progressive ideas.

### The Population of Maritime Canada

Maritime Canada has been subjected to the same social forces that have influenced New England, save that of the development of the manufacturing city.

There are only three cities above 20,000 in the Canadian section, while there are fifty-four in the New England section. The Canadian city population is therefore comparatively small. This leaves a rural society much like that of New England. This rural population has been somewhat less subjected to culling by emigration because the youth of Maritime Canada has not been called to near-by city jobs as have New England farmers' sons and daughters. However, Maritime Canada has had a heavy migration to New England and to the Canadian West, and it displays plenty of conservatism.[28] In many localities the Puritan Sunday of Oliver Cromwell still prevails to the extent that trains do not run.

These three Maritime provinces have less uniformity of rural population than the United States part of this region. This is because large blocs of immigrants came in a body. Most of the northern coast of New Brunswick is settled by the French, south central Nova Scotia by the Germans, west Nova Scotia by the English, eastern Nova Scotia and eastern New Brunswick by the Scotch.

The Scotch went in such blocs to parts of Prince Edward Island that one county has 4000 people named MacDonald. Since the sole reason for a second name is to differentiate, the value of a second name disappears when everybody is named MacDonald. This difficulty of designation has been met in one case as follows. James MacDonald, the banker, was one of so many James MacDonalds that he was called " Banker Jimmie." His son, John, was one of the scores of John MacDonalds, so he was differentiated by being called " Banker Jimmie's John." Revering the family stock, this man named his son James, locally known as " Banker Jimmie's John's Jimmie."

---

[28] The reception of the automobile shows this conservatism. Motor vehicles were prohibited altogether on Prince Edward Island from 1908 to 1913. After 1913, autos were permitted on streets of Charlottetown and one other small town on three designated days per week. Finally in 1918, practically all restrictions were removed except prohibition from operating outside towns and cities during April when roads are soft from spring thaw. — U. S. Com. Reports, April 24, 1922.

## A Racial Comparison

The blocs of German and Scotch in Nova Scotia afford a puzzling contrast, the one cherishing education, the other neglecting, almost scorning it.[29]

## Agriculture and the Summer Visitor

The return of the pine tree has been the most conspicuous single change in the agriculture of all parts of this region. The pine returned when agriculture passed from the domestic epoch of the general farm to the commercial epoch of the specialized farm. In some places there have been interesting survivals of the old general farm system and in other places even more interesting revivals of agriculture through the development of specialties.

The survival of the general farm has usually been made possible through additional income derived from side industries, of which this region has three — fishing, lumbering and the summer boarder.

In the old days the winter was the time for making wagons, tools, harness, shoes and clothes. The farmhouse became a little winter factory. Now that this era has passed, many of the men go off to the woods for the season of wood-chopping. The women stay at home and take care of the stock, for which the New England building unit is conveniently arranged, namely, a string of sheds with the house at one end and the barn at the other. The buildings are connected, so that it is easy to go from the house to the barn without getting lost in the wild storms of winter. If the farm is near the shore (and Maine alone has 4000 miles of shore), a spare day in the warm season can be used for fishing. The possible combination of fishing and farming is better shown by the surprising fact that there are eight shore fishermen in the Canadian provinces to one who goes in a schooner to the Banks.

[29] " Pictou County is the center of the Scotch farming population, and this single county has supplied a list of college professors and college presidents that would do credit to a province. From this one county, nine men are now serving or recently have served as college presidents, and eighteen others as prominent college professors, not to mention educators of lesser standing. . . .

" In striking contrast to Pictou County with its Scotch population, devoted to higher education and producing in a generation or two twenty-seven college presidents and professors, is Lunenburg County on the Atlantic Coast, settled in 1752, mainly by German farmers from the Palatinate and Hanover. Of its 30,000 population, in 1891, 9000 could neither read nor write. They are an industrious, thrifty and fairly prosperous people but they are not making their sons into premiers or college presidents. The influence of the sea and of the fishing banks has made over a race of peasant farmers into the pre-eminent fishing population of Nova Scotia. And a people whose interests — created by their environment — seek occupation in fishing do not stress the intellectual side of life. It is a question which I ask and cannot answer: Suppose the same Scotch colonists who settled in Pictou County had, instead, settled in Lunenburg County, would they in that environment have produced the long line of illustrious men that they have produced in their present environment? " — " A Geographical Study of Nova Scotia," *Bulletin of American Geographical Society,* June 1914, pp. 417–18. R. H. Whitbeck, University of Wisconsin.

The summer boarder and the summer tourist now exceed both fish and forest as sources of income for the resident population. Men must live along the shore to get additional income by fishing. They must often go considerable distances to work in the forest. But to derive income from the summer tourist the farmer remains at home and develops whatever resources nature and his own industry provide. It is the tourist who does the traveling. He goes to the shore, to the inland farm, and also to the forest. This whole region has developed a keen sense of the value of the tourist and a knowledge of what interests and pleases him. The region has the attractions of beautiful landscape, climatic delight, the sports of hunting, fishing and sailing, and the richest collection of historical associations and remains to be found on the American continent. All of these things are jealously preserved.

### A Beautiful Land

In no other part of North America is there a similar area having such variety of physical beauty. South of Boston, the coast is sandy with soft landscape and with long waves rolling evenly upon the gentle beach. North of Boston, even to the extreme of Gaspé, red and gray granite is piled in endless variety of form. Upon this stern and rocky coast waves dash high and break into surging foam. The scene changes endlessly with every rise and fall of the tide. To many who watch this for an hour or for a day, flat sandy coasts become insipid, although they offer advantages to one who is keen about surf-bathing.

If the tourist goes inland he finds hundreds, even thousands, of lakes and ponds. Does he love especially the glade, the field, the farm, the quaint homestead, the wood, the hill or the almost untouched wilderness? He will find them all. The small proportion of cultivated land, even in the more populous States, as shown by the following table, makes it easy to understand the wilderness of New England landscape.

| | Per cent of Land Area in Improved Farm Lands | | | | Per cent of Area in Crops Other than Hay with Acreage Reports | Per cent of Area in Hay |
|---|---|---|---|---|---|---|
| Acres | 1920 | 1910 | 1900 | 1890 | 1919 | 1919 |
| Massachusetts....... 5,144,960 | 17.7 | 22.6 | 25.1 | 32.2 | 2.2 | 8.7 |
| Rhode Island....... 682,880 | 19.5 | 26.1 | 27.4 | 40.2 | 2.2 | 6.9 |
| Connecticut......... 3,084,800 | 22.7 | 32.0 | 34.5 | 44.7 | 3.9 | 1.1 |

The climate is cool. This is particularly true along the coast, for the cold waters come down from Labrador. When people swelter in Philadelphia, Chicago or Albany, tourists and summer boarders may be sitting by the fire on the coast of Maine or Cape Breton, or wearing woolen sweaters as they climb over the wind-blown rocks.

### Hunting and Fishing

As bait for the vacationist the resources of fish and game are carefully preserved.  As deer become scarce long periods of prohibition of hunting are decreed.  This has permitted the number of deer to increase until they are a veritable nuisance to farmers, for the deer loves to eat the

FIG. 34 — One of the delightful variations for the tourist.  (Courtesy Natural Resources Intelligence Service, Ottawa.)

bark of apple trees in winter. Every winter they walk into the suburbs of
scores of cities, even Stamford, Conn., suburban to New York, while
the visit of a wild bull moose in the streets of St. John, N. B., is expected
every year.

## Historic Attractions

The cultural and historic attractions for the visitor are utilized to a
high degree of perfection. Nothing of historic value is allowed to go
into needless decay or to be forgotten. The fact that Paul Revere rode
past a house is considered to be an asset. A Revolutionary bullet-hole is
a piece of property preserved more jealously than heirlooms. So are the
homes of those who have become distinguished. One is shown so many
houses where Washington slept that one receives the impression that he
must have been an inveterate traveler.[30]

In 1910 tourists spent $60,000,000 in New England, according to the
estimate of the Boston Chamber of Commerce, and the amount is now
probably nearly or quite double this. Many a farm, from Connecticut to
Cape Breton, would have to be abandoned if the family budget were not
rounded out by the cash that results from the sale of service and home-
grown produce in the highest of all retail markets — the home-table.
The hundreds of summer hotels and the thousands of summer cottages
that line the shores are another important local market and source of
employment. Thus does the New England-Canadian Maritime region
cash in its pleasant climate, beautiful countryside and landscape, sport
and historic places and the desire to please the guest.

## The Revival of Agriculture — Dairying

Fresh milk to supply the needs of millions of city-dwellers has been the
greatest single factor in the agricultural revival, especially in New England, with its large population. As fresh milk cannot be carried very
far, the cheap lands of the West cannot supply milk, although they can
supply butter, which is easily transported. The influence of these transportation factors is well shown by the small amount of butter-production
in New England and the great importance of market milk. It is shipped
long distances, some of it coming into Boston by express train from
upper Vermont and some even from lower Quebec.

Everywhere this region has well-watered lands and mostly there is good
grass, two factors that favor summer dairying. In winter the dairy furnishes more employment than any other form of agriculture; therefore
it is peculiarly well fitted to this region where the winters are long and
cold and prohibit outdoor farm-work for such a large part of the year.

---

[30] A person with a sense of humor had a sign in his yard somewhat as follows:
" This is the only house on the Lexington Pike in which Washington did not stay all
night." And another: " Paul Revere would have passed this house if he had returned
this way."

One measure of the predominance of dairying in agriculture is shown by the importance of hay among the crop-areas. Hay usually outranks all other crops combined. This figure is partly deceptive, for the reason that much of the New England hay can scarcely be called a real crop and therefore overstates in a statistical record. For instance, when a farm is abandoned a neighbor often pays a small rental for the privilege of cutting hay on the old fields, and finally, as the crop gets smaller and smaller, he is sometimes allowed to cut it for nothing, because the owner, hoping to sell the land, prefers that the field should be mowed once a year, otherwise it would grow up in brambles and forest. As a result, the New England hay-acreage is large, but the yield per acre is often low.

### The Revival of Agriculture — Canned Corn

" Maine canned corn! " In scores of cities these are the words by which the grocer assures you that his canned corn is the best. This superiority rests upon an interesting combination of climatic and economic factors. Southern Maine is dotted with canneries to which the ears of sugar-corn are brought, and for every cannery there are many silos in which the husks and stalks of the corn are stored for the dairy cow's winter food. The climate is too cold to permit corn to mature fully. But weeks before corn is ripe there is a stage when the ears are right for canning and when the stalks and husks are at the period of maximum edibility for cows. At this stage the Maine farmers can the corn and fill their silos.

The groceryman, though he may not know why, recommends Maine corn because it grows where the summers are cool. This causes the development of the corn to be slow, much slower than in the burning sun and hot winds of Illinois, where corn rushes speedily from blossom to roasting ear and dry, ripened grain. In the fields of southern Maine, where it is five or ten degrees cooler than Illinois, the corn lingers. If the weather is very cool the grain develops scarcely at all after the roasting-ear stage, and therefore it remains for many days tender and juicy and in prime condition. Under Illinois sun and wind corn would stay for perhaps only two days in really prime condition for canning. The Maine competitor has a great advantage in having a longer period during which he can deliver a large crop of fine corn to the cannery. The service of the fodder in the dairy is another factor which aids the canning industry. Thus canned corn from Maine is really a kind of by-product of a dairy-farm district, and amounts to a tenth of the national product.

### The Agricultural Revival Through Specialties

Although most of the area of this region is composed of old, hard rocks and thin rocky soils, there are six areas which are exceptions, and each of these areas of soft rocks and soft soils has developed an interesting and suggestive agricultural specialty.

### Nova Scotia Apples

The first of these soft spots is the Annapolis Valley of Nova Scotia, eight by eighty miles in length, running parallel to the south shore of the Bay of Fundy. The element of softness is afforded by red sandstone much softer than the hard, gray granite which rises on the south side of the valley and makes the main backbone of Nova Scotia. The north wall of the Annapolis Valley is a long ridge of trap-rock which separates the valley from the Bay of Fundy. This trap-rock is hardened lava which pushed through the other rocks in ancient times and now stands up as a high hill because it is so hard that it wears away much more slowly than the softer sandstone between it and the hard granite.[31]

The advantages which apples enjoy in the Annapolis Valley are due partly to climatic, and partly to locational reasons. On both sides mountain ranges protect the valley from strong winds. The Bay of Fundy furnishes the protection afforded by a body of water which by its warmth in winter keeps away extremes of temperature. Annapolis is five to six degrees warmer on the average in winter than Halifax, on the other side of the same peninsula. Ice remains in the Bay of Fundy until late in spring, the resulting coolness of the water-body delaying the growth of fruit buds until the danger of frost is over. By its warmth at the end of summer the water prevents autumn frosts, thus insuring a long harvest period. This climatic factor locates many fruit districts beside lakes and seas.

The Bay of Fundy goes yet further in providing a satisfactory temperature-control. The great danger from frost comes in the one or two still nights at the end of a cold wave. But the Bay of Fundy has the highest tides of the world, and the water rushes in and rushes out with such force that enough wind is produced to keep the nights from being deadly still.

The location of the Annapolis Valley, so close to ports, favors export to Europe, where the apples bear an excellent reputation. The crop is usually one to two million barrels. There is an official record of thirty-five barrels having been produced by a single tree in one year.

The abundance of natural ice provides cold storage without artificial refrigeration — a cost factor which must be borne by most commercial apple-growing districts of the United States.

### The Bay of Fundy Diked Lands

The second geologic soft spot — it is the softest spot of all — is the reclaimed tidal flats along the Bay of Fundy. When the tide, which

---

[31] This trap is the same material as the Palisades of the Hudson opposite Manhattan Island, and is one of the best of road materials.

is forty to fifty feet high,[32] goes out it leaves bare expanses of mud flat. Dikes have been built around the flats, and in the dikes there are auto-matic flood-gates. These gates swing open at low tide and let the water out. They swing shut as the tide comes in, and most of the water is kept out. Since the bottoms of these flats or bays have been made from good land which washed down from the hills, mixed with shells and other animal remains, the soil is unusually rich, and it gives annu-ally from two to four tons of hay per acre. If it shows signs of declin-ing in fertility, the sea is allowed to flood it again for a short time and thus to restore it. Such land sells for as much as $400.00 an acre. It is unfortunate that its area is not larger. This is the land that was settled by the Acadians and is commemorated by Longfellow's " Evange-line."

The Nova Scotia farmers on the Bay of Fundy like to talk about the excellence of their country as a bacon producer. The great virtue of bacon is to have a streak of fat and a streak of lean. For this they tell you with a twinkle of the eye that the Bay of Fundy has unusual re-sources. When the tide is low, wide areas of flats are exposed, and because the tide runs out so rapidly fish are often left flopping about. At low tide the pigs range the flats eating fish and getting fat. The tide returns with such speed that the pigs must run for their lives, and the effort makes them lean — a streak of fat and a streak of lean.

### Prince Edward Island

This island, half as large as Connecticut, a province all by itself, is the largest of the soft spots of sandstone and shale formation in the whole New England-Canadian Maritime region. In proportion to its area this is one of the finest pieces of agricultural land east of the Allegheny Mountains. The glaciers did not ruin it. They slid up out of the sea, bearing few stones with them to litter the earth. Nearly all of the island is arable, and half of it is under cultivation. The people, most of whom are Scotch, call it the " Garden of the Gulf," the "Emerald Isle of America," and many other complimentary pet names. The Maritime climate is thoroughly wholesome and approaches the northern limit of agriculture on the Atlantic coast. It is too cool for corn and too damp for wheat to thrive at its best, although the Prince Edward Islander produces enough wheat for his own use. Oats for the dairy cow exceed all other grains, and hay for the dairy cow exceeds all grains in area. Turnips and forage beets are grown. Thus do the crops tell the story of a main industry — forage crops and dairies.

Prince Edward Island has great value as an index of the pressure of men upon land in America. This index shows us that the continent

---

[32] At low tide, wharves stand higher than a house above wide flats. At high tide steamers scurry in, hastily unload and flee before they strand upon the flats.

is yet far from full.  Notwithstanding the advantages of climate and arability and excellent resources for fishing, there is a steady decline of population.  Farming is still chiefly of the general type, although the very high production of seventy bushels of potatoes per capita almost amounts to a specialty.  Two or three million bushels are exported [33] each year in schooners, and there are a dozen large factories for making potato starch.

But the really significant things about Prince Edward Island are its declining agricultural population in the midst of excellent resources which are rather remote from good markets, and its one great contribution to the new agriculture, namely, the development of fox-farming.

### Fox-Farming

The silver fox, denizen of the sub-Arctic areas of North America, sometimes has a black child.  This sport among fur-bearing animals has appealed to the sport among fur-wearing men to such a degree that these rare pelts brought $1000.00 to $2000.00 each in market.  In twenty years preceding the World War the supply of this fur had declined one-half and the price had advanced threefold.  A couple of shrewd Prince Edward Islanders succeeded in catching enough black silver foxes to start breeding them.  Some of the offspring were black.  The story goes that the canny Scots, to keep the new industry a secret, had their farm on a rocky, forested island.  They visited the island ostensibly to examine the lobster pots with which they had dotted its shores.  But one winter the sound froze, and a fox happened to get out of the enclosure and ran across the ice to the mainland.  Hounds trailed her back to the den, the owners of the hounds followed, the secret was out and a fox-farming furor arose.  Then the pioneers proceeded to make a fortune selling their foxes for breeding purposes for more than their weight in gold.  If a fox-skin sells for $1000.00, as it sometimes did; if a mother gives birth to seven offspring at a time, as she often does; and if she lives for years, as she may do, then the business looks good, so good, indeed, that from 1910 to 1914 a tremendous boom was on.  Silver fox pups of the best Prince Edward Island stock sold at from $12,000.00 to $16,000.00 a pair, and there was at least one sale of a pair of mature foxes of proved fecundity for $35,000.00.  As animals for breeding brought such prices that no one could afford to kill them, they bred foxes and sold them.  In 1915 the Silver Fox Breeders Association of Prince Edward Island was incorporated for the purpose of classifying, registering, and marking silver-black foxes, after the fashion of other live-stock breeders' associations.  Within a year a larger proportion of silver foxes were recorded than any other variety of live stock eligible for registration (*Scientific American*, December 16, 1916).  In 1919 the income of

[33] They sent 100 cars of seed potatoes to the U. S. in 1922 as a result of a start in 1919.

Prince Edward Island from foxes amounted to a million dollars, more than $10.00 per capita, an amount greater twice over than the per capita export of any single commodity from the United States.

| 1921 | No. Farms | Value Land and Buildings | Value of Animals and Fur |
|---|---|---|---|
| Prince Edward Island........... | 359 | $737,000 | $3,248,000 |
| Nova Scotia................... | 108 | 127,000 | 371,000 |
| New Brunswick................ | 62 | 130,000 | 598,000 |
| Quebec....................... | 109 | 173,000 | 430,000 |
| Manitoba..................... | 6 | 90,000 | 406,000 |
| Ontario...................... | 94 | 144,000 | 374,000 |

The industry spread even to British Columbia and the Yukon. In 1921 it is estimated that there were more than 22,000 foxes on fur-farms, that the income from that year had been a million and a half, and that the 3700 pelts sold had brought $153.00 each. In 1922, when the third annual silver-fox show of the National Silver Fox Breeders' Association was held in Muskegon, Mich., there were 500 American silver-

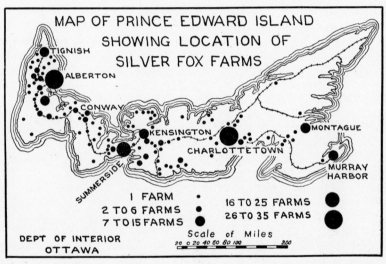

FIG. 35 — The success and spread of a new industry. There should be a hundred such new industries in the next hundred years.

fox farms scattered from Maine to California, and even as far south as New Jersey, Indiana and Kansas.

As the number of these animals increases, the value of their fur will go down and down until an equilibrium is reached, subject to *the fluctuations of style*. The high prices of the early days were a novelty which could not last long. This fox-farming is typical of fur industries which should be developed in cooler parts of North America. Why should we have domesticated so few animals? Already we have had several fur-farming bulletins from the United States Department of Agriculture (No. 1151 on fox-farming; No. 47, on beaver-farming). There is an appealing combination of economic qualities in the muskrat (not a rat at all). This rodent breeds as does the rabbit, about three litters per season. As in the rabbit the meat is edible, and like the rabbit muskrats are vegetarians and can live comfortably on the food that suits sheep or cattle. Moreover, they build their own houses. Therefore, as a new variety of cattle of the north they appear to have the maximum possible efficiency. One might wish that muskrats might become the rage. The area from Cape Breton to British Columbia and from the Chesapeake to Hudson Bay has thousands of lakes, swamps and streams where the animals are at home. Indeed, swamp-land in Maryland and Delaware is regularly rented, at a valuation based upon the price of muskrat skin and the catch of muskrats which the lessee is expected to make.

### Aroostook Potatoes

The fourth geologic soft spot in this region is in the Aroostook Valley in the northeastern corner of Maine, where there is an island of fertile, sandy loam soils surrounded on all sides by hard and inhospitable granites. The climate is too cold for corn, but admirably suited to potatoes. The

Fig. 36 — Aroostook potatoes as laid out by the digging machine. (Courtesy Coe-Mortimer Co.)

cool, moist, cloudy weather of upper Maine is apparently close to the ideal for potatoes.[34]   Settlers cleared the forest and began to raise potatoes among the stumps.

The potato does best in the moist climate where the warmest month is 65° F.   Northern New England has approximately these conditions.   Witness the national average potato yield for ten years of 98 bushels, of 60 bushels for Texas, of more than 200 for Maine.   For the exceptionally good crop-year of 1921 it was 298 bushels, a figure that approaches the good yields of northwestern Europe.   The uncertainty of potato-growing is shown by the yield of 160 bushels per acre in 1922.

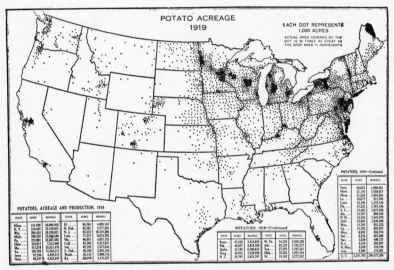

FIG. 37 — The potato seems to respond to sandy loams, cities (St. Louis, Louisville, San Francisco, etc.), and cool locations.   (Courtesy U. S. Dept. Agr.)

But the distance from market was such that the crop did not pay the first settlers.   In 1874 a New Hampshire starch manufacturer happened to come there and saw the opportunity for the potato starch industry.   If six tons of raw potatoes are cut in small pieces and soaked in water, a ton of starch will settle in the water.   It is easier to send one ton to market than six, especially as the dry starch is not subjected to injury from frost or decay.   Potato-starch factories increased, and Aroostook potato-growers prospered and produced more than half of the starch of the country.   They still hold this lead.

[34] Experiments have recently shown that potatoes do better in partial shade than in the full sunshine of such a climate as that of Louisiana.

In 1893 came railroad connection through Bangor with the American railway system and the shipment of seed potatoes.

Maine seed potatoes, chiefly from Aroostook County, are now in demand by the potato-growers from Massachusetts and Long Island to Florida and from Virginia to the Mississippi. The plants from the northern-grown seed are more vigorous and mature more quickly than the seed of the southern-grown potato. Every year a fresh supply is seeded from the original source of vigor. Thus the commercial hold and increasing prosperity of the Aroostook potato-growers is easily seen. Aroostook was the only county in New England

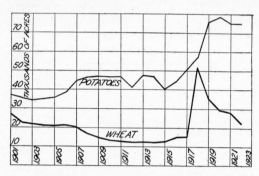

Fig. 38 — Acreages of wheat and potatoes in New Brunswick show the present superiority of the potato in this region. The World War influence on wheat is most plain.

where more land was cultivated in 1910 than in 1870. In 1920 it had made still further gains. The potato-farmers with their crop of 20 to 30 million bushels per year, commonly have a three-year crop rotation, potatoes one year, oats the second, hay the third, then potatoes again. The oats and the hay serve as food for the animals and may be called supply crops in contrast to the potato, which is a money crop — an excellent example of the development of an agricultural specialty.

### The Connecticut Valley

Red sandstones, much used at one time for building brownstone mansions, are much softer than granite rocks. Therefore they wear away faster. This faster wearing away of soft rock made the Connecticut Valley of western Massachusetts and northern Connecticut a wide open lowland surrounded by higher lands of harder rock. The continental glacier choked up the mouth of the Connecticut and turned this lowland into a lake, and then filled the lake with river deposits. Later, as the river cut its way out it has meandered back and forth, cutting the old lake deposits into a series of terraces at different elevations, and each with a different soil. These are the levelest land in New England. The early settlers called them " fields " and on them are all the towns of the valley — Springfield, Westfield, Pittsfield, etc. Some of these terrace soils are excellent for growing truck, and the two to three thousand acres of onions that are grown in the Massachusetts part of the valley make that state the fifth or sixth onion-growing state in the Union. Some of these soils, however, have special value for tobacco — the most particular of all crop plants with regard to its soil. On some of these terraces tobacco of excellent quality can be grown, but that grown upon the present flood plain of the river itself is almost worthless.

The tobacco industry of the Connecticut Valley was started a century ago and has grown steadily until it now covers about 40,000 acres of land, chiefly in Connecticut but partly in Massachusetts. About the year 1900, experiments in growing tobacco under the shade of cheese-cloth screens resulted in a leaf of unusual qualities. It was free from insect injury and hail injury. The uniform temperature and moisture gave a leaf of uniform quality and great toughness of fiber suitable for cigar manufacture, but the changed climate beneath the tent-screens required a different variety of tobacco. After experimentation, the Cuban tobacco was found to be the best. It sometimes sells for from five to ten times as much per pound as the tobacco grown in the open. The expense of planting posts and stretching laths covered with cheese-cloth is so great that this industry is now carried on chiefly by corporations. In 1920 Hartford, Conn., was the leading tobacco county in the United States.

## The Leda Clays

Portland, Maine, is the center of yet another oasis of good land, the sixth and last of the soft spots. It stretches in a narrow belt for fifteen or twenty miles up and down the coast from Portland and is called the Leda Clays. The chance traveler is struck by the excellence of the farms as he rides into this clay belt. Its origin is unusual. It was deposited on the bottom of the sea, a fact which permitted the fine particles of clay to become mixed with shells of sea animals, producing a limy clay, which is very rich and easy to cultivate.

## Blueberries

Extreme eastern Maine has what might be called a sub-industry in blueberries. They grow in what is sometimes known as the eastern spruce region. " A very large proportion of Washington and Hancock Counties, extending northward to the upper St. Croix, consists of granite. This particular granite is a hopelessly sterile and acidic rock, and in that part of Maine almost entirely denuded by glaciation, so much so that from the lower Penobscot eastward many areas are strewn with boulders often the size of a barn " (in a letter from M. L. Fernald). This was originally covered with spruce forest, most of which is gone by axe and fire, and many areas of old fields and old forest are alike given over to blueberries, which thrive in acid soils. The crop is cared for by having large bushes cut and the whole area burned every third year. This is one of the most destructive processes man can apply to

soil, but the blueberry thrives upon it for a time at least. The berries
are picked in large quantities and canned. They are a major industry
and an important source of income.

### Truck-Crops

The markets of the many cities make a local demand for truck and
garden-crops. Between 1895 and 1905 there was a rapid development

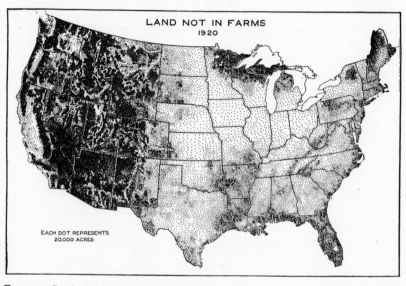

FIG. 39 — In the most comprehensive sense, this is a map of American Agriculture.
It shows the blueberry district of Maine very clearly by its absence of cultivation. (Courtesy U. S. Dept. Agr.)

of greenhouses near Boston for the growth of market-crops. Then the
greenhouses declined, because the express train service from Florida
improved so much that to bring the products of distant sunshine from
Florida became cheaper than to make a climate in New England with
fires. Most of the market-gardening is in the hands of newly arrived
foreigners, especially Poles and Italians. Near Boston some of them
have lengthened their growing season a little by building fences to
keep the north wind off their fields.

### Science and the New Agriculture

In one and a half decades New Bedford saw the wreckage and decline
of her whaling fleet and was again on the upswing as a cotton-manufacturing town. After four decades of agricultural decline most of the New
England farmland is still abandoned. Why the quick revival of manu-

facturing and the slow revival of agriculture?    Because agriculture is a much more scientific industry than manufacturing.    The ordinary factory uses one or two sciences and can have a specialist to attend to them. Thus it has a dyer or a chemist or an engineer or two.    The average farm requires the application of two or three times as many sciences as the average factory and the farm cannot employ any specialists at all. Take the complicated problems of soil management and fertilization. How would you fertilize a peach tree, apple tree, wheat crop, corn crop, hay crop?    For each of these questions there is a different answer.    What should a pig eat to produce pork most economically; what should a cow eat to make milk most economically; what should a horse eat to work most efficiently?    Good cow-feed will sometimes kill a horse.    The cow turns up her nose at pig-feed.    The answers to these particular questions are strictly scientific, and they are answered with varying degrees of error.    Suppose the American cows waste through inefficient feeding five cents every day for six months in the year.    Just a little waste like that rolls up to more than $10.00 for each of 24,000,000 cows, enough money to pay the total budget of every reputable university in the United States!

To find the right answer for these scientific questions requires careful study and experiment. The farmer is usually unable to do this.    Even if he had the necessary time and money he could not escape from the caprices of nature which vary the conditions and make experimentation very difficult.    Many of the agricultural experiments take years to reach a conclusion.    For example, the Agricultural Experiment Station of Arizona has started on a twenty-four-year series of experiments with date-palms.    Even if the farmer can carry on these experiments he is often unable to profit by them.    He might spend a thousand dollars on an experiment worth $100.00 a year to him and as much to each of another thousand farmers, but he cannot get the money from them to help him pay for the experiment.

## Science in the Factory

How different is the factory, where almost every condition can be definitely controlled!    Most of the experiments can be performed in a day or a week or a month.    Then before the year is out the factory can be profiting by the results; and in a decade, while the farmer is still conducting his experiment, the factory owner may be a millionaire. Recognizing these facts, we have created elaborate governmental machinery for the promotion of agricultural science and teaching for the benefit of all the people of the United States.    We have the national Department of Agriculture at Washington, with many bureaus (see annual report of the Secretary).    We have in every State one or more agricultural experiment stations, which carefully try out things which

may be of value to the State.  An example of this kind of work is the
experiments carried on in Connecticut to determine the food requirements
of animals, when growing, at rest, fattening or producing milk.  The
results are valuable to every State and every country in the world.

To carry the knowledge yet further, we have created the college of
agriculture, the agricultural high school and finally the county farm
bureau, which in more than one thousand American counties employs a
man to travel around the county, meeting the farmers face to face and
helping them to work out their problems.

The plight of New England indicates either that she is hopeless or that
agricultural science has not yet caught up.  The latter is the case.  New
England has great unused possibilities for increase of agricultural produce
when the need for it is so great that the farmer gets as good wages as the
factory worker.  As an example of New England's possibilities, I cite
fruit-growing, especially apple-growing.

### New England Fruit

Boxes of apples come to New England by hundreds of thousands from
beyond the Great Plains, often from beyond the Rocky Mountains.  The
freight cost is $1.00 or more per bushel box.  If the New England farmer
could produce apples at equal cost and have left as his share a freight
differential of $.50 to $.75 a bushel, it would be a profitable business.
There is no reason why he cannot do this.  The flavor of fruit grown in
New England is superior.  Apples can be grown on fertile but rocky
hills without plowing, provided the trees are well fertilized and otherwise scientifically cared for.  In fact, the apple grows wild in fields and
roadsides from Nova Scotia to the Mississippi and from lower Ontario
to Carolina.

One of the menaces to fruit is the destruction of buds by the late
spring frosts.  But if planted on hillsides, orchards may escape being
frozen when frosts kill the fruit buds in the valley.  This is explained
as follows: Cold air, being heavy, runs down the slope and settles on
the valley floor.  The valley may become full of air that has a temperature of $30°$, while the temperature of the air on the slope is $34°$ or
$36°$.[35]  Everywhere that frost comes hillsides, as compared with valley
floors, have an advantage for the fruit industry.

Thus the clayey and even the rocky hills of New England are suitable
places for the production of apples.  In some localities in Connecticut
peach-growing has been made successful by the utilization of this advantage of frost drainage, but the low temperature of the New England
winter often destroys the buds of peach trees whether they are on hill
or in valley.

[35] For a case so pronounced as to kill the buds on lower limbs only, see *United
States Monthly Weather Review*, December 1923.

### *Tree Crops — A New Agriculture*

Success in growing apples without tillage suggests the possibility of using other tree-crops in place of cultivated annual crops. New England has much fertile soil that is difficult, often impossible, to till with the plow. The great need of the New England-Canadian Maritime region, and also of many other parts of the world is for agriculture that does not depend on tillage, but is adapted to natural resources.

In agriculture we have been surprisingly uninventive. Little has been done to domesticate new animals or plants since the prehistoric primitive agriculturist (woman), seeking quick returns, planted annuals and developed the cereals from the grass family. She could not wait for trees to grow and bear fruit. But tree-crops could be made a part of agriculture because the yield is so great in proportion to the expense or effort.

We may search far to find a better nut than the American black walnut, which grows over the whole of this region. If we should find a better nut it would probably be the native shagbark. The butternut, hazel-nut, beech-nut, and a number of other wild, fruiting trees are natives of this region, and even hardy strains of the pecan and English (Persian) walnut thrive in southern New England.

During the first two decades of the twentieth century the technique of grafting nut trees has been perfected.[36] It is now easy and this century

FIG. 40 — The big insipid Japanese chestnut (left) was crossed with the sweet worthlessly small Chinquapin (right). The hybrid offspring (center) was sweet and of medium size. Hybridization has great possibilities. (Courtesy W. Van Fleet, Glenn Dale, Md.)

should see millions of trees grafted with twigs from the best stock that can be found. Already the patient pioneers have found rare specimen trees of black walnut, shagbark, hickory, Indiana pecan and other hardy northern trees which produce large crops of nuts whose kernels come out of the shells in halves like the kernel of the English walnut. Propagation from

[36] The whole technique of grafting your own nut-trees is explained and illustrated in *Nut Grafting*, Robert T. Morris. It works. Many have succeeded by it.

parent trees has begun in widely scattered locations.[37] This opens a wide vista of new crops through further plant domestication, plant introduction and plant breeding.[38] These three processes are to botany what the steam engine in 1800 was to mechanics.

Black walnut and hickory-nut meats are now very high-priced foods. This may induce the New England farmer to grow nut-trees in the rough brush-land or hilly pasture. Trees and grass grow well together. If cows do not need all of the grass, sheep-ranching might be developed, but the New England sheep-ranch requires the utter annihilation of the old system of small farming. A dozen farms must be combined to furnish upland pastures and valley lowlands for the intensive cultivation of corn for silage or hay for winter feeding, replacing gullied hillside and abandoned farm.

The order of intensification in the use of the grass should be first sheep, second cows, and lastly goats. I have seen such farms on the rough lands of Spain, Portugal, the Apennines, Sicily and the Atlas of Algeria.

The transformation of the untillable lands of the New England-Canadian Maritime Region into the tree-crop type of agriculture is a problem rather for the future than the present. Here and there a farmer will plant a few trees each year and protect them from animals. In a decade or two his farm will grow more valuable. The next generation will inherit a productive legacy and perhaps will plant trees enthusiastically. This type of agriculture continues to yield crops for generations, perhaps for centuries. There are numerous examples in Mediterranean countries.

## Forestry

Nature is not waiting for man to begin the task of reforestation, which is the immediate next call for most of the acreage of this region. Nature is always busy in the effort to restore most of the area to its original condition of forest. The immediate problem in the utilization of this land is to help Nature and then to protect the forest from fire and pest. In Nova Scotia and many other places natural pine forests have been destroyed by fire, which has so injured the soil that the less desirable spruce has taken the place of the pine.

The Gipsy Moth and the Brown-Tailed Moth have visited the region around Boston. These tree-killing insects were introduced from foreign countries, and temporarily freed in a new land from the checking influence of their natural enemies they have increased beyond reason. State and National governments have made large expenditures of money in the effort to check the ravages of these leaf-eating pests.

[37] Persons wishing further information should write to H. C. Spencer, secretary, Northern Nut Growers' Association, Decatur, Illinois.
[38] See J. R. Smith, "Agriculture of Future," *Harper's Monthly*, January 1913; "Agriculture of Garden of Eden," *Atlantic Monthly*, August 1914.

FIG. 41 — The ship in the North River and the sky line of stupendous New York office buildings which it helped to create. (Courtesy Cunard Line.)

## CHAPTER VI

## THE ERIE CANAL BELT — NEW YORK TO BUFFALO

### *New York City — Its Crowds*

In the spring of 1922 the New York *Tribune* reported that an old woman had died of fright on a subway platform in New York. After forty years of work she and her immigrant husband had sold their farm and were returning to Czecho-Slovakia to live in retired ease in their native village. They stood in a jam of people on a New York subway platform. The train rushed up with a roar and stopped. People surged out, others surged in. Our immigrant couple tried to enter, but the man could only get his foot inside the door. The station guard grabbed the old man, and with hand on shoulder and knee on hip, pushed him into the car, and held him there while dragging the door shut. Away went the train, leaving the frightened old woman on the platform in a mass of strangers, who like herself had not been able to get on the car. She saw the red light of the train fade away in the darkness and fell dead from fright. How could a poor immigrant woman know that in New York they always load trains in that manner during the rush hour when everyone is going to work? The inhuman pressure of crowds! That is New York.

New York is the most gigantic product of transportation. This is so because nowhere else in the world is there such a supreme focus of routes by sea and land. London is a close rival to New York, but London has Liverpool, Hull and Bristol as rivals. New York, being the gateway and market of the North American continent and having also one of the finest harbors in the world, has become the world's most important port.

From the top of one of the high buildings in lower Manhattan, the details of commercial life spread out before the eye like an animated map. Manhattan is an island thirteen miles long and a mile or two wide. To the west lies the Hudson (here called North River). Its broad stream flows southward to the widening bay and the yet wider sea. Northward the river is navigable through the highlands toward the rich interior. To the south and east of Manhattan is the East River, lined on both sides with docks and wharves, threaded by ferries and overhung with bridges which connect New York with Brooklyn, Manhattan's first overflow, and her present rival in population. Looking to the east and northeast you see the Harlem River dotted with boats. You look down upon innumerable piers and docks, some of which are a thousand feet long. Across the river in New Jersey at Hoboken and other points are other huge piers.

In all directions one sees boats — ferry-boats and the wide floats that carry freight trains from pier to pier; great transatlantic steamships, those queens of the sea which are really floating hotels; the lesser liners of the Atlantic; the white liners of the tropics; tramps, rusty with the sprays of the seven seas; Hudson River boats; Sound boats; coast steamers from Norfolk, New Orleans and Maine; even the humble four-master, remnant of the dying fleets of sail, and everywhere little tugs are puffing up and down and skillfully threading their way in and out among the multitude of craft. The tugs are busy pulling barges of coal, barges of lumber, barges of sacks, barges of everything, it seems.

New York is a commercial gold-mine, with the kind of lure that California had in '49. This rich, exacting gold-mine of business opportunity is the magnet that draws many of the able, the ambitious, the adventurous, and helps to empty the farmhouses of New England, of the South and even of the West.

So many people have come here to do business that the lower end of Manhattan Island has become terribly crowded. More space must be found. Where? Then someone invented the elevator, and buildings, instead of spreading out, shot up into the air and became higher and higher. The steel skyscraper piled men upon the land and condensed business upon this spot as never before in the history of the world. It aids business by letting so many people be near each other. New York now has about 250 buildings all of which are more than fourteen stories high, and some that are much higher than that. There are elevators which stop at every floor, and other elevators which give express service. "No stop to the 15th Floor" is a common sign. In one building two elevators are needed to reach the top; the first goes to the fortieth floor, where you change cars and take the second elevator, which will carry you to the fifty-eighth floor.

Some of the skyscrapers, cathedrals of commerce, are beautiful buildings. One, 758 feet in height, towers far above the Pyramids of Egypt, the Capitol and Monument of Washington or the Tower of London. When we look down at the street from the top of this building the people appear to be as tiny as ants; they move like ants in streams; like ants they come streaming out of the ground (subway entrances); like ants they press forward with a kind of relentless unheeding speed, for there is so much that one may do in this forty-storied metropolis if one moves fast enough; one can see more people if only one hustles more.

Fifteen thousand persons pour out of a single building into the streets, which are narrow because once they were lanes left between the cabins of the Dutch fur-traders of 1640 or 1650. So great are human numbers that if all the people got into the street at the same time they would fill it in some sections two layers deep.

This mass of humanity, drawn by the skyscraper, quickly overcrowded the surface cars.[1] Elevated railroads were built on every available street to lower Manhattan and trains roared and rattled past the second and third story windows and even on tracks built over the tops of houses. Soon they too became unable to carry the people. But passengers must be carried, so subways were dug underground and through them heavily laden trains rumbled and roared. In some places the subway has four tracks, with express trains and locals. The second subway soon followed the first, and the third followed the second, and still the crowds cannot be handled without such waiting and crowding and jamming as scared the old woman to death. Tunnels have been dug under the North River to New Jersey, under the East River to Brooklyn, under the Harlem to the Bronx. The streets are choked with automobiles. Nothing brings relief, for every new facility brings more people to share the matchless business opportunities in this most huge and most crowded of human hives.[2] The mere fact of numbers of people thus makes it the best possible place for many kinds of business. Every day three hundred and fifty people come to the city to live, and a hundred new telephones are installed.[3]

[1] In two ordinary minutes one February day in 1924 the following vehicles passed along Sixth Avenue at Forty-Second Street: motor vehicles 67, horse vehicles 4, street cars 7, elevated trains 5 (of 8 cars each). To many such streets a subway adds its quota.

[2] NEW YORK

Jazz, rattle, bang, crash, asphalt and cobblestones,
   Roar of the Subway — clangor of the El,
Battering the brainpan — shattering the consciousness,
   Some call it living, but I call it hell.
      — Baron Ireland, in *Saturday Evening Post*.
    (Copyright, 1922, by The Curtis Publishing Co.)

[3] W. J. Showalter in *The National Geographic Magazine,* July 1918.

### The Mohawk Depression and the Erie Canal

New York overtowers all American cities because for more than a hundred years it has been the only seaport of the United States served by an effective canal route to the Great Lakes.

The riches of the central region of the continent were known to the leaders of the Revolutionary period; to find a means of tapping its commerce was the dream of commercial prophets from the Revolution to 1830. Every important seaboard city had a plan, all unsuccessful except New York's. Her triumph was made easy because the Mohawk Valley provided the only break in the highlands which otherwise continue without interruption from the St. Lawrence Valley to the Gulf Slope.[4]

Before the Erie Canal was built the cost to haul wheat in the farmer's wagon over bad roads for a distance of 300 miles ate up the value of wheat. To haul one hundred miles ate up the value of corn. At one time sea salt from the Atlantic Coast cost $35.00 per ton in Pittsburgh. In April, 1822, corn brought $.08 a bushel in Cincinnati and $.80 in Philadelphia. There is a record of one boatload of flour taken from western Pennsylvania down the Ohio and Mississippi and around to Philadelphia. At that time, commercially speaking, the middle of the continent did not exist save for the fur-trader.

When the Erie Canal was opened in 1825 the freight-rate from Buffalo to New York dropped from $100.00 to $5.00 a ton and the freight-time

FIG. 42 — Canal locks of the nineteenth-century (Erie) canal, and the twentieth-century (Barge) canal, Waterford, N. Y. (Courtesy Funk & Wagnalls Co., New York.)

dropped from twenty days to eight. The traffic of the lake region poured into New York harbor. Instantly the Great Lakes became a part of New York's hinterland. The Lake States began to build canals into their own

---

[4] In its final form the Erie Canal, now called the Barge Canal, ascends from sea-level on the Hudson to an elevation of 420 feet; then it goes down to 360 feet at Syracuse; and up to 565 feet at Tonawanda, where it enters the Niagara River. The channel of the canal is 200 feet wide and 12 feet deep. The Barge Canal and its branches total 440 miles of canal, and 350 miles of canalized river and lake.

interior and thus New York, though distant many miles, became their port. Then in a few years railroads, reaching out from the Great Lakes, again extended New York's hinterland. Night and day the canal resounded to the yells of boatmen urging the mules which tugged the boats at four miles an hour along the greatest inland waterway of the Western world.

New York grew amazingly. The cities along the Erie Canal also began to grow. The first railroads in New York State, attracted by the towns, followed the Hudson River and the Erie Canal from town to town, and furnished more speedy communication. For hauling heavy freight the railroads had to meet the comparatively low rates of the canal boats. This influenced the railroads that later went more directly from Buffalo to New York; from Chicago to Philadelphia and Baltimore and even to Norfolk. Even the Grand Trunk Line of Canada which carries freight from the Lake Basin to New England ports had to keep its freight-rates low.

The Canal did New York City great service by carrying freight, and even greater service by drawing railroads to the port and by making them carry freight at lower rates than other railroads did to other ports.

Being the greatest port of export New York naturally attracted the most important steamship lines. The canal and railroads made ships come, and more ships made more railroads come. The Pennsylvania Railroad was built to bring traffic to Philadelphia and its main office was in that city. But, drawn by the magnet of the great port, Pennsylvania lines were extended to New York and the harbor became its terminus.

All these things made New York the gateway to the heart of North America. The Canal started this, but the railroads have actually carried most of the freight for many years.

The Erie Canal also made one of the most clear-cut regions in North America. I call the region the Erie Canal Belt, because of the predominating influence of this waterway in creating the long line of cities which has New York at one end and Buffalo at the other. This line of cities is almost uninterrupted and it extends from the ocean — the highway of the world, to the Great Lakes — the highway of the interior of the continent.

### Foreign Trade

A central position on the coast early made New York the focus of the coasting trade. On one side was New England with her manufacturing and fishing. On the other side was the agricultural South. Both regions sent their small boats to New York, to meet ocean vessels. In 1825 when the canal was opened, 4000 coasting vessels and 1400 foreign vessels entered New York Harbor. The Civil War clinched her hold upon the trade of the Middle States. The Mississippi and the Southern ports were closed for four years, during which time the railroads were consolidated and trade thoroughly established. Between 1860 and 1870 New York's share of United States exports increased from 24% to 50%.

New York has had a greater grip on our imports than on our exports, a fact which is explained by the differences in character of the two branches of commerce. A small city can handle exports of raw materials. Only a wharf and some dock laborers are necessary to export lumber, grain, cotton and phosphate rock.

Imports, however, are chiefly manufactured goods, or raw materials for manufactures which must be brought to developed cities, where there are storehouses, wholesale houses and adequate facilities for distribution.

FIG. 43 — At Bush Terminal, Brooklyn, one company operates piers with freight sheds where steamers load and unload; warehouses across the street for storage; cement structures at left where many manufacturers rent floor space with heat and light and power. Circulation is furnished by freight cars, trucks, wagons, barges, and belt conveyors. (Courtesy Bush Terminal Co., New York.)

Now that we have entered upon a period of export of manufactures, New York, with her many steamship lines, has the same advantage for the *export* of manufactures as she had at an early date for the *import* of manufactures.

### Manufactures in New York

Commerce was the scaffold and framework that started the city and held it up while a yet greater structure of manufacturing and local business was built upon the framework. It is interesting to see how one thing brings on another. All through the nineteenth century we were importers of fine goods from Europe, especially fine clothing and equipment. The goods landed in New York. Merchants from everywhere went therefore to New York wholesale houses and New York became the greatest wholesale market. If a local manufacturer tried to rival the popular European styles he took his produce to the same New York wholesale house. Hence the clothing industry naturally grew up in New York beside the wholesale houses. This proximity is a great advantage; clothing can be manufactured and displayed to better advantage and can reach the purchaser more quickly if the sales-room is on the first floor and the workshop is on the fifth or tenth floor of the same building, or just around the corner, as is now so often the case.

## The Clothing Industry

Immigration aided the growth of the clothing industry. The ships that carried exports and imports brought human imports too, and New York had the greatest non-agricultural labor supply in the country.

The clothing industry can endure the crowded conditions of a great city because small space is needed. About 1910 a private survey was made of New York industries and it was found that in one block in lower Broadway about 40,000 people were working at the clothing industry, housed in buildings ten or twelve stories high. The workers often sat as close together as students sit in school. This combination of market facilities and labor-supply has given New York more than half the clothing manufacture of the United States.[5]

The division of labor as applied to the clothing industry has gone so far that dozens now work on a single suit of clothes. An uneducated, non-English-speaking foreigner can quickly learn to do one of the simple processes in clothing manufacture.

The cigar industry, like clothing, is one that requires but little space for its prosecution and is therefore well suited to crowded city conditions and is important in New York.

## A Financial Center

The bankers of New York had to deal with the bankers of Europe whither her exports went. Also they had business with the bankers of the interior where her exports originated. This tended to make New York the financial center, although the quantity of her local business was also a sufficient reason. Certainly New York has now become the dominating financial center. Never in the world's history was so much gold stored as lies in her vaults or such collections of bonds signifying ownership of

[5] VALUE OF PRODUCTS FOR CLOTHING, 1921

| Rank | | Total | Men's | Women's |
|---|---|---|---|---|
| | | | (1,000,000 Dollars) | |
| | United States | $1,957 | $934 | $1,022 |
| 1 | New York City | 1,086 | 326 | 759 |
| 2 | Chicago | 208 | 165 | 42 |
| 3 | Philadelphia | 107 | 57 | 49 |
| 4 | Baltimore | 60 | 47 | 12 |
| 5 | Rochester | 50 | 50 | 0.2 |
| 6 | Cleveland | 42 | 16 | 25 |
| 7 | Boston | 36 | 20 | 15 |
| 8 | Cincinnati | 32 | 29 | 3 |
| 9 | St. Louis | 28 | 16 | 11 |
| | All other | 304 | 202 | 101 |

property in distant lands. The banks in little towns like those of Virginia, Iowa and Texas buy and sell securities through their New York correspondents and have deposits in New York banks. If an industry anywhere on the continent grows to a great size it nearly always has a New York office. Thus New York has become a great transaction center.

There are interesting examples of New York's control of more distant industries. A company which owns a railroad in Ecuador has men in a New York office who make bargains for steel rails shipped from Pittsburgh, for ties shipped from Oregon, for cement shipped from eastern Pennsylvania.

The Standard Oil Company, whose offices are on lower Broadway — though not a barrel of oil is produced within two hundred miles — is buying oil in a dozen distant states and nations, refining it in half a dozen distant cities and running steamers all over the world, but most of the stock is owned in New York and most of the larger business is transacted on Broadway. This concentration of finance has made Wall Street, a little strip of land thirty feet wide by less than a mile long, the best known street in the whole world.

New York sets the price for many commodities. In the Cotton Exchange, men who never saw a cotton-plant buy and sell cotton which they never see. Dealings on the New York Stock Exchange set the price each day for billions of dollars' worth of property. In a less conspicuous way, brokers and sales-agents sell the product of hundreds of distant factories and they also are price-setters.

So much has become centralized in New York that she has the same predominance in printing and publishing, as in finance and imports. Many of the books sold (published) in New York are printed in small towns in New England, New Jersey and Pennsylvania, where the cost of living is cheaper than in New York.

### A Travel Center

With the people going to New York on business trips and those going to and from Europe, the city has become the greatest travel center of the continent. Merchants from everywhere go to New York to make the rounds of the wholesale and manufacturing sample agencies. With so many visitors to be cared for it sometimes happens that in midwinter rooms in all the hotels are occupied and people have to go to Newark or even to Philadelphia to sleep. Tens of thousands of people in New York make a living by working in the hotels, restaurants and theatres that cater to the traveling multitude. Many of the hotels have an employee for every guest. Servitors of travelers are numerous enough to make a city far larger than was New York in the day when it was the capital of the United States.

To see plays, many of which never leave New York, tens of thousands visit the metropolis each winter.  Ten thousand actors and actresses entertain the audiences.  The theatres and moving-picture houses could seat 677,000 persons at a time in 1924.

It is often surprising to find what a small proportion of the workers in a city are actually engaged in the dominant industry and what a large proportion are engaged in taking care of the rest.  The butcher, the baker, the candlestick-maker — the people engaged in serving the city — are more numerous in New York than in any other city because of the difficulties of living in crowded New York.  Thousands, for example, have been busy for years building subways; other thousands are busy operating them.  New York is in constant process of being rebuilt.  Thousands are at work tearing down and putting up buildings, enlarging subways, renewing elevated railroads.  This kind of activity adds enormously to the number of people who are busy taking care of the rest and feeding them and adding to the cost of living.

New York has become so large that she is herself a market.  Scores of factories are required to keep her millions supplied with each particular kind of food, furniture and clothing.

## The People of New York City

The population of New York City is richer in its variety than any other similar group in the world.  Its people represent every race and tongue and culture.  If you wish to eat foreign food or study the idiom of a foreign language, you need not go to Europe — visit Little Italy, Little Slovakia, Little Lithuania or some of the other hundred foreign centers of New York.  In 1923 the National Council of the Episcopal Church made a study of the foreign-born groups in the congested portions of New York City and published a map locating 24 Polish centers, 23 Italian centers, 18 Greek centers, 13 Czech centers, 10 Magyar centers, 8 Russian centers, 8 Armenian centers, 6 Jugo-Slav centers, 2 Syrian centers, 2 Rumanian centers.  This survey classified the people of New York as follows:

Native-born of native parents ...... 1,500,000
Foreign-born .................... 2,000,000
Native-born of foreign parents ...... 2,300,000

Those of foreign birth or foreign-born parentage were of many nations.[6]

[6] Italians ........... 800,000       English ........... 137,000
    Germans ........ 670,000       Poles ............ 150,000
    Irish ............... 616,000

Approximate numbers of other nationalities as follows: French, 50,000; Swedish, 50,000; Scotch, 47,000; Norwegians, 40,000; Magyars, 80,000; Czechoslovaks, 80,000; Russians, 50,000; Greeks, 40,000; Syrians, 30,000; Latin-Americans, 30,000; Jugo-Slavs, 25,000; Armenians, 20,000; Danish, 18,000; Letts, 16,000; Swiss, 16,000; Finns, 15,000; Spanish, 10,000; Rumanians, 10,000; Chinese, 10,000; Dutch, 10,000; Lithuanians, 5,000; Ruthenians, 5,000; Japanese, 3,000; Welsh, 2,500; Belgians, 2,500; Flemish, 2,500; Turkish, 2,000.

Jew          Italian          Pole          Armenian

FIG. 44 — Representatives of a few of the races in New York's clothing industry. (English, and French dept.), *Fortschritt* (Yiddish), *Il Lavoro* (Italian), *Prace* Monthly: *Rabochy Golos* (Russian).

New York has more Irish than Dublin, more Italians than Rome, and it has turned out to be the Promised Land; for it has more Jews than Jerusalem had even in the most glorious days of King Solomon. It should be noted that although the Irish rank high in numbers the map showed no centers of Irish population. This is suggestive of the effectiveness of the American melting-pot. Irish immigration was the first to come in large numbers, and the Irish have become so thoroughly Americanized that they no longer live in centers but are scattered throughout the whole body. Their number in the city is attested by a list of 1530 Murphys in the telephone-book. Their influence in the city government is the same as it is in Boston. In 1924 the ruler of New York, Boss Murphy, chief of Tammany Hall,[7] died, leaving an estate of $400,000. At this time Mr. Ryan was secretary of Tammany Hall, Mr. McCooey was boss of Brooklyn, and the leading candidates for successor to Mr. Murphy were Surrogate Foley and Judge Olvaney. This dominance by the Irish is perhaps temporary. Americanization may bring others to the top. It is suggestive of future struggle for political supremacy that the most dangerous rival of Tammany Hall for leadership in New York politics in 1924 was Mr. La Guardia. He was of Italian descent, a Major in the A. E. F., a member of Congress and possessed of the fiery and sweeping eloquence that makes men agree with his opinions.

The city is filled with people of vigorous stock, for it is more often the stronger who migrate. Most of her people are the children and grandchildren of immigrants from Europe, or from the American farm. Seven out of every nine native-born children are of foreign immigrant parentage. The New York public school system, like that of Boston, is striving to transform the immigrant child into an American citizen. There is much

---

[7] This political organization, nearly one and a half centuries old, runs the Democratic party and in its periods of success completely governs New York by naming mayors, councilmen, judges, school directors, policemen, very much as the dominant political organization does in nearly every other city of importance in the United States.

| Hungarian | Russian | Slovakian | Ukrainian |

Publications of Amalgamated Clothing Workers of America: — Weekly: *Advance* (Bohemian), *Industrial Democracy* (Polish); Bi-weekly: *Darbas* (Lithuanian);

effort to train him for economic independence through vocational guidance and vocational training. The health of this population is good, as evidenced by one of the lowest death-rates in the world for cities of more than a million people.

The climate is wholesome. The nearness to the sea tempers summer heat. At Coney Island, within the city limits on Long Island, is a bathing beach, often thronged to the limits of its capacity in the hot season.

Opposed to these advantages is the increasing density of New York's population per square mile since 1865, but this has happened when our knowledge of preventive medicine was increasing rapidly, and its discoveries were applied by a vigorous health department. This has helped to bring about great improvement in the control of communicable diseases.[8]

### The Sister Cities West of the Hudson

In a geographical and economic sense the cities west of the lower Hudson [9] are as much a part of New York [10] as are the cities beyond the

[8] There were proportionately only half as many deaths from pulmonary tuberculosis in the decade from 1906 to 1915 inclusive as there were from 1876 to 1885. There were only one-third as many deaths from typhoid, one-fifth as many from diphtheria, one-sixth as many from scarlet fever, and only half as many deaths of babies under one year of age." — ("New York — The Metropolis of Mankind," W. J. Showalter, in *National Geographic Magazine*, July 1918.)

[9] Population in thousands, 1920:

| | | | | | |
|---|---|---|---|---|---|
| Newark | 414 | Bayonne | 76 | Perth Amboy | 41 |
| Jersey City | 298 | Hoboken | 68 | West Hoboken | 40 |
| Paterson | 135 | Passaic | 63 | Orange | 33 |
| Elizabeth | 95 | East Orange | 50 | | 1313 |

Trenton, Camden and Atlantic City are the only New Jersey cities in this class and not in this list.

[10] Population 1920:

| | |
|---|---|
| The Five Boroughs of Greater New York | 5,620,048 |
| Five near-by Counties in New Jersey | 1,951,277 |
| Two adjacent Counties in New York | 470,556 |
| One near-by County in Connecticut | 320,936 |
| | 8,362,817 |

Several thousand commuters go beyond the bounds of this area.

East River.  Like New York itself they have grown up as a result of the traffic focus.  Immediately across from Lower Manhattan is one city with three governments and three names, Hoboken, Jersey City, Bayonne. To the westward across the marshes is Newark, reached by barges and therefore industrially and commercially part of New York harbor.  The industries of these New Jersey cities are extremely varied, those of Newark, for example, ranging from lead pencils to locomotives, and including many machine-shops and electrical manufacturing plants.  The manufactures of enamel leather and patent leather are especially important. To the south of Newark is Elizabeth, claiming the production of half of the sewing-machines of the United States.  A little to the north of Newark is Passaic, with important wool manufacturing, and still farther north, where the Passaic River tumbles over the terminal moraine and makes a lot of water-power, is the city of Paterson, with a specialization in silk manufacture that rivals the dependence of Fall River upon cotton. Paterson now boasts that she makes more yards and more dollars' worth of silk goods than any city in the world, even Lyons.

## Buffalo

Buffalo stands at the other end of this region as the counterpart of New York, although only one-tenth as large.  New York commands the seven seas, Buffalo commands the east end of the Great Lakes.  The heavy lake traffic indicates the variety and abundance of the products and raw materials of the interior.  Thus Buffalo sends hemlock to New York and gets mahogany in return.  She sends grain and gets spices; flour and gets sugar; iron ore and gets diamonds; hides for imported cloth; iron goods and radiators for jewelry.

Buffalo's shipping in 1923 was greater than that of Liverpool, sixteen million tons having entered and cleared.  Through most of her career Buffalo has been a funnel pouring wheat, corn, oats and other produce from lake steamers to canal boats bound for New York.  In more recent years she has risen rapidly in manufactures [11] for which her resources are great and her industries are varied.  Buffalo's manufactured product reflects the character of her commercial location.  With her steamers

---

[11] The growth of cities in different sections of this region is very suggestive.

ERIE CANAL BELT CITIES OVER 25,000 — Per cent Growth, 1910–1920

New York ......................... 17.9%
Cities of Northern New Jersey .... 17. %
Buffalo .......................... 19.6%

| Hudson River Group | | Canal Group | |
|---|---|---|---|
| Newburgh................. | 9.2% | Schenectady ............... | 21.8% |
| Poughkeepsie ............. | 25.3% | Amsterdam ................ | 7.2% |
| Kingston ................. | 3. % | Rome .................... | 28.5% |
| Albany ................... | 13.1% | Syracuse .................. | 25.1% |
| Troy ..................... | 6.2% | Rochester .................. | 35.6% |

accessible to all the shores of the Great Lakes, near the Canadian forests, near the mines of Minnesota and Pennsylvania, she has a great advantage for the assembling of bulky raw materials — grain, lumber, coal, iron ore, and live animals for slaughter.  She has in addition the unrivaled power resources of Niagara.

Until 1885 Niagara was considered only as a spectacle, a world wonder. In 1890 work was begun on power-plants.  In 1895 power began to be

FIG. 45 — Grain elevators, tugs, barges, and steamers in Buffalo harbor.  Two grain-lifting devices slant down toward the ships.  (Courtesy Buffalo Chamber of Commerce.)

delivered in Buffalo, and now 870,000 horse-power is developed and transmitted by wire to points as far as Detroit, Toronto, Rochester, Syracuse, and Oswego.[12]

Since the users pay much less for this power than people pay for power in New York or Philadelphia, it is easy to see why the industries of Buffalo and the adjacent territory (see table of population increases) are increasing faster than those of the great metropolis by the sea.

[12] From "Water Power of World," *Geological Survey*.  Niagara Falls is the finest power site in the world.  Here are combined a high head that is easily developed, a large uniform flow and a market for the power.  The unique scenic beauty of the falls has prevented complete utilization, but plants in operation have capacity of 870,000 H. P., of which 385,500 H. P. is on United States side.  Power actually developed amounts to about 700,000 H. P.  To this total should be added 12,000 developed on Welland Canal, and 42,000 developed at Decew Falls, two miles from St. Catherines, Ont., from water diverted from the Welland Canal over the Niagara escarpment.  A license has been granted by Federal Power Commission that will

Manufactures in Buffalo actually doubled between 1900 and 1910, and again in the next decade.

Cheap power helped the flour milling industry to increase fifteen-fold between 1900 and 1923. Buffalo is now the second center in the world

FIG. 46 — Ten thousand horse-power of energy is flung out over the wires by each of these dynamos which is directly connected to its turbine. Power plant at Niagara Falls. (Courtesy Ontario Power Co. of Niagara Falls.)

and promises to be first. Because of transport factors, the output of this district tends toward coarse and heavy products in comparison to those of New York and New England. A very significant episode in the industrial life of this region was the transfer of the Lackawanna Steel Company's operations to Buffalo from Scranton. At Buffalo lake-boats deliver ore alongside the blast furnaces. There are many iron and steel plants which manufacture such things as radiators, automobiles and locomotives.

Being on the through route from the West to the East, Buffalo is a natural receiving-point for the grain which supplies her flour mills, of which there are so many that Buffalo is a close rival of Minneapolis. Its stock-yards are second in size only to those of Chicago. With the combined advantages of lake steamers and canal barges, Niagara power and cheap Pennsylvania coal, there is reason to expect that manufactures will continue to grow in this district.

increase to 500,000 H. P. the installed capacity on United States side. Hydro-electric Power Commission of Ontario is now constructing an additional plant at Niagara Falls which will have initial capacity of 300,000 and ultimately 540,000 H. P. Water is to be carried twelve miles through a canal and used with an effective head of 305 feet. Most of Niagara Falls power is obtained from a head of only 200 feet; the difference in level between Lakes Erie and Ontario is 327 feet. If total flow of River were used, the falls would furnish under favorable conditions about 6,000,000 H. P. A plan is being considered to use about 60% of the flow.

## The Intervening Cities

The transport advantages of the waterways from New York to Buffalo have caused that route to become a string of towns.[13]  From New York to Buffalo is 400 miles.  In that distance are fifty-five towns with more than 2500 people, thirty-one with more than 10,000, twelve with more than 25,000.

These cities have advantages of power and transportation that favor manufacturing.  The coal-fields of Pennsylvania are accessible to all of them.  Water-power is near at hand, especially in the Mohawk Valley, with the Mohawk River and Adirondack streams, and in the Buffalo-Rochester section with power from turbines at Niagara.  Everywhere the Hudson River Barge Canal waterway is an actual or potential factor of raw material supply and carriage to market.

These cities are much like those of New England in their dependence upon imported food and raw materials and upon exported produce.  They have superior advantages in transportation and the greater proximity to fuel and the center of population.  The market advantage is well illustrated by Albany.  Within 200 miles there are thirty million people.  The city has 680 trains a day and is at the crossroad of the routes from Buffalo to Boston and from New York to Montreal, with the Champlain Canal giving barge traffic through to the St. Lawrence.  But, after all, every other city between New York and Buffalo has almost as good transport facilities as Albany.

Undoubtedly Albany's excellent location helps to explain the varied character of her industries and their relation to densely peopled communities.  Her factories produce stoves, gas-heaters, gas-meters, car-heaters, writing-paper, adhesive paste, composition billiard-balls, chemicals, toys, caps and gowns, college badges, and a variety of other things.

[13] POPULATION IN THOUSANDS, 1920

| | | | | | |
|---|---|---|---|---|---|
| Newburgh | 30 | Fort Plain | 2 | Seneca Falls | 6 |
| Beacon | 11 | Dolgeville | 3 | Ithaca | 17 |
| Poughkeepsie | 35 | Little Falls | 13 | Waterloo | 3 |
| Kingston | 26 | Mohawk | 2 | Clyde | 2 |
| Saugerties | 4 | Ilion | 10 | Geneva | 14 |
| Catskill | 4 | Herkimer | 10 | Watkins | 2 |
| Hudson | 11 | Frankfort | 4 | Lyons | 4 |
| Rensselaer | 10 | Utica | 94 | Newark | 6 |
| Albany | 113 | Whitesboro | 3 | Fairport | 4 |
| Watervliet | 16 | Rome | 26 | Rochester | 295 |
| Troy | 72 | Oneida | 10 | Brockport | 2 |
| Green Island | 4 | Canastota | 4 | Albion | 4 |
| Cohoes | 22 | East Syracuse | 4 | Medina | 6 |
| Waterford | 2 | Syracuse | 171 | Lockport | 21 |
| Schenectady | 88 | Solvay | 7 | North Tonawanda | 15 |
| Amsterdam | 33 | Fulton | 13 | Tonawanda | 10 |
| Gloversville | 22 | Oswego | 23 | Buffalo | 506 |
| Johnstown | 10 | Baldwinsville | 3 | Lackawanna | 17 |
| | | Clyde River | 2 | | 1,876 |

The cities of the Hudson Valley and the canal have developed a number of manufacturing specialties, which illustrate the force of accident, that great factor in the location of manufactures. The Mohawk Valley towns have a great industry in knit goods, apparently because in 1831 an Albany merchant happened to operate in Cohoes the first knitting-machines ever driven by mechanical power. Today Cohoes has two-fifths of its workers engaged on knit goods. The same industry spread to the other towns of the valley: Little Falls, Rome, and Utica. One-third of Utica's workers are engaged in knitting industries, which indicates a high degree of concentration.

The city of Troy (72,000) shows another specialization; over half of its workers are busy making collars and cuffs, of which the city produces the astonishing proportion of nine-tenths of the American product. Why? The answer again seems to be found in an accident of history. In 1827 an incapacitated minister then engaged in the dry goods business concluded that collars separate from the shirts would be an advantage in the maintenance of cleanliness. His wife made some and started her neighbors making them for her husband to sell. In 1851 the sewing-machine started the real boom in the manufacture of collars and cuffs.

The accidental settlement of Scotch glove-makers in 1760 in Johnstown and Gloversville, a few miles north of the central Mohawk, started an industry which now produces about one-half of the gloves in the United States. They are made on motor-driven sewing-machines in the homes of the workers.

Schenectady, one of the early Dutch settlements and before the Canal was built a prosperous station on the trade-route to the West, has developed great concentration of its activities and of late acquired fame through the manufacture of machinery. Eighty per cent of its factory workers are in the great plant of the General Electric Company making electric appliances, or in the American Locomotive Works making locomotives. For the electric plant the location is especially good. The multitude of industries in New England and the Erie Canal Belt demand machinery and for its distribution few places could be better located than Schenectady with its through lines of railway connecting New York and New England with the West.

Mr. Henry Ford saw the advantage of this locality as a site for the distribution of machinery. In 1923 he bought a large tract of land just north of Troy, at the junction of the Barge Canal and the Hudson River, and announced plans for building an assembling and distributing plant to be second only to the main plant at Detroit. It is to be served by barges on the canal and river.

Poughkeepsie has several machine-shops that send machinery all over the world, and the town of Ilion, ten miles west of Utica, does the same with the Remington typewriter.

Rochester has a site marked by nature for a city.  Here the Genesee River tumbles 205 feet over the face of the same escarpment that makes Niagara.  This water-power early served to make Rochester an important flour-milling center.  The Erie Canal was a handy means of bringing the wheat and and taking the flour on to market.  A canal connecting the Erie Canal with the Allegheny and the headwaters of the Ohio at Olean early gave supplies of timber, oil, grain, and hemlock bark.  The bark started a tanning industry; perhaps that is why the shoe industry developed there.  Rochester is also a rapidly rising center for the manufacture of men's clothing.  The rise of a number of button factories is an interesting subsidiary development.

Rochester makes a quarter of the optical goods of the United States and is also well known for leadership in the manufacture of photographic apparatus, of which it produces a fifth of the American supply and more than one-half of the photographic materials.  This is an industry which undoubtedly requires skillful workers but its great concentration is probably due to the control of patents by a company that happened to develop there.  The city is conspicuous for the intelligent attention it is giving to a school of music and to industrial problems.  The city bought thirteen miles of the old Erie Canal right of way and converted it into a four-track interurban and freight-switching subway.

In 1907 Syracuse used 7.5 million kilowatt hours of power from Niagara central station.  The increase to 200 million in 1923 shows the

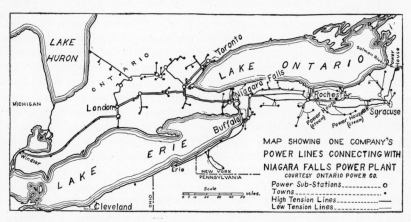

Fig. 47 — A step toward the scattering of manufacturing to good home spaces.

influence of Niagara Falls on the western canal cities.  Syracuse is unique among the cities of this whole region in having an important industry which depends upon local raw material.  Half of the soda in the United States is produced here.  The raw materials for this product are coal, limestone and common salt.  A stratum of salt underlies considerable areas near the city. It raises interesting speculations concerning the geologic past to remember that these deposits of rock salt can be made only by the drying up of the impounded arms of the sea or of salt lakes in a desert climate.

The other important mineral industries of this region are the brick and building-stone production of the Hudson Valley. Brick-making is an industry having a great physical restriction of area. Clay for making brick is found in many places, but because bricks are heavy to transport and are of low value they must be manufactured from clay that happens to be close to the market for brick. In the Hudson Valley good glacial clays furnish raw material, and the cheap barge the vehicle to the market. Scores of brick-works and stone quarries line the river bank. In the Hudson Valley there is necessity for much building and rebuilding and that explains the leadership in the world's brick industry.

### Agriculture

The agriculture of the Hudson and Mohawk Valleys is so much like that of Lower New England that it need not be discussed here. That of the territory west of the Mohawk is influenced by nearness to the Lakes rather than by nearness to the Erie Canal and will therefore be discussed in the chapter dealing with the Lower Lake Region, of which agriculturally it is certainly a part.

### Future of the Erie Canal Belt Region

The cities will probably continue to grow. The twenty-seven counties, which include the west end of Long Island, both sides of the Hudson, and a strip one county wide from the Hudson to Buffalo, contain 30.4% of the area of New York. In 1915 that area contained nearly 81% of the population of the entire State; in five years it increased to 83.1%. If the political divisions had been such as to allow us to include the cities of northern New Jersey, the predominance of this city belt in the midst of unused lands would have been even more pronounced.

These cities are in themselves a tremendous home market, but it is none the less true that between 1910 and 1920 only six of the twenty-seven counties showed an increase in rural population and some of them have been losing for twenty years. This neglect of agriculture is a result of the continuing richness of our continent; we do not yet have to use all of the available land. It puzzles an economist to see thousands of acres of undrained and entirely unused marsh-land between New York and Newark. This land is very fertile and if reclaimed by inexpensive diking would make truck-land of great value. Barges could carry the produce in a few hours from the field to the wharves on Manhattan. But it lies unused; the factory and the skyscraper are magnets which draw men from the land.

In predicting continued growth for the cities of this region we have to reckon with the fact that the Barge Canal is, as yet, almost unused since it was reconstructed. Figures for 1922 [14] show substantial increase over 1921, but the total is comparatively insignificant; for the canal cost $167,000,000.00 to rebuild and a million dollars a year to operate. Five per cent interest on the cost, plus maintenance, plus a very small sinking-fund, makes a high cost to the state. The canal, of course, represents a clash of interests. American railways have always fought canals and for a very natural reason. Railroads are more prosperous if the State-owned Barge Canal is unused. The canal has no boat lines upon it that serve the general public and that is one reason why it is so little used. Mr. Ford can build barges to carry his cars; a big brick manufacturer or a quarryman can have barges to market his own produce. So can the Standard Oil Company, or the big grain-carrier. But you and I cannot take a package down to a canal freight-station and leave it as we do at the railroad or post office, because there is no freight station and no public freight service. Some say that the manufacturer does not use the canal in summer because he is afraid that the railroad will not let him have freight cars in winter, when the canal is closed and he must depend on the railroad. It is probable that New York will in time use its canal with reasonable efficiency. It will then be once more a strong factor in city growth.

Meanwhile, during the twenty years of reconstruction and almost disuse of the Barge Canal, New York has continued to grow. A group of New York citizens are planning for continued growth and talking of the time when the city will have 30,000,000 people. Horror of horrors!

[14] PRINCIPAL COMMODITIES CARRIED ON NEW YORK STATE CANALS

| Commodities | 1921 | 1922 |
|---|---|---|
| | | Short Tons |
| Grain: | | |
| Wheat | 232,376 | 349,016 |
| Corn | 49,682 | 71,251 |
| Barley | 46,737 | 55,210 |
| Oats | 35,094 | 18,346 |
| Rye | 2,101 | 74,331 |
| Flaxseed | 34,597 | 33,560 |
| Sand, stone, and gravel | 294,860 | 460,933 |
| Petroleum products | 128,754 | 215,959 |
| Forest products | 127,680 | 198,380 |
| Salt | 60,539 | 50,177 |
| Metal manufactures | 52,477 | 125,311 |
| Cement and lime | 47,725 | 37,737 |
| Coal | 45,837 | 50,500 |
| Bricks | 36,436 | 68,358 |
| Sugar | 2,442 | 48,697 |
| Total, including all other commodities | 1,457,802 | 2,260,763 |

Source: Superintendent of Public Works, New York State, Annual Reports.

### The City Problem

New York is a perfect illustration of the social problem cycle. In 1830 the railroad began. Men used it in their business to make dividends. It has been well said that the railroads decided where there should be villages; what villages should become towns; what towns should become cities; what cities should become markets and what markets should become metropolises. Ninety-five years after the invention of the railway, we are still debating about the proper theory by which the railway shall be operated. It is only since 1870 that the public has even claimed the right to control the roads in the interests of the public welfare, and there is no agreement as to whether they shall be operated by private corporations or by the government.

The great city faces an extensive array of knotty problems. Take the problem of water. In the autumn of 1923 the people in many northern New Jersey towns prayed in their churches for rain. Thirty thousand factory workers had temporarily lost their jobs because there was no water in the mains. New York City appealed to the engineer and the money-lender, and borrowed hundreds of millions for water-works. She began her large enterprises with a great reservoir on the east side of the Hudson, the Croton Reservoir. Then came a reservoir on the south slope of the Catskills, but water shortage soon threatened again, and an eighteen-mile tunnel, the Shandakan, the longest tunnel in the world, has been dug to carry water under the mountains from a creek on the north slope of the Catskills to reservoirs on the south slope. There it connects with the aqueduct system that carries the water at great expense under the Hudson to connect with the older Croton system. While celebrating the opening of the Shandakan tunnel people were talking of an Adirondack water-supply. The Catskill system alone cost 180 million dollars.

The water problem is one of the simplest of the troubles produced by New York's increasing millions. Crowding, its costs and its results, are the greatest menace. Where people crowd to one place their presence makes high land-value and then the high land-value crowds them still more. So important is the site-value where people throng that a corner building may be worth $50,000.00 for stores, uptown on one of the main up-and-down avenues of the city, whereas a building of identical structure in the center of the same block may be worth only $35,000.00. The news-stand service will give some idea of the human swarm that surges in and out of the subway entrances. The station at 116th Street and Broadway, a residence and university station, has a news-stand on the station platform underground (one attendant), one at the street entrance in the middle of the street (two attendants), one on each sidewalk, one with two attendants. These six people are all busy selling papers and magazines to the throngs who hustle down to jam themselves into the cars which take them to the business part of the city.

"New York will be a nice place when they get it finished," remarked a man observing the tearing down and building up that continually goes on as population and land-values increase. For example, a plot of land at 103d Street, just west of Broadway, 100 × 160 feet, had on it eight solid stone houses, twenty feet wide, four stories high, built quite as substantially as the medieval houses of European towns which are still good. These structures were torn down in 1924 to be replaced by a thirteen-story apartment house, which will hold from fifty to a hundred families where eight once lived. Such a structure in the choice residence district of 35th Street and Park Avenue has a value of a million dollars. Its 225 rooms are divided into three- and four-room apartments, and the average annual rent is $825 per room. Apartments and skyscrapers, made possible by the elevators and the subway, create more congestion. It is estimated that 223,000 vehicles and 2,850,000 people

FIG. 48 — Each of the 225 rooms of this luxurious apartment house rents for $825 a year. Alongside are fine residences of the one-family type of forty years ago. (Courtesy Fred F. French Co., New York City.)

enter Manhattan Island south of 59th Street during twenty-four hours of a typical business day. The street traffic is so dense that the New Yorker is almost denied the pleasure of driving his automobile, unless he delights in delay, danger and manoeuvering in a jam.[15]

[15] Ninety-three people were killed by street accidents in New York City in one month, October 1923. If we erected markers at places where people have been

In 1923, some Fourth of July pleasure-seekers made an early start for a day on the New Jersey coast. They reached the ferries at lower New York at 7.30 and sat in the summer sun until 10.30 before they could get their turn at the ferry-boats. Others, avoiding ferries, crossed by bridge to Long Island, but the roads from the East River Bridge to the seacoast on the south shore of Long Island were solid with cars — two unbroken funeral-like processions, one going north, the other south, without room to turn out, except in emergency.

At ordinary times the vehicular traffic is so thick at the corner of Fifth Avenue and 42nd Street that five policemen are regularly on duty

at this one corner, and sometimes there are seven. When one considers the cost of these officers and the cost of delay in street traffic, it is easy to understand the recent estimate that street congestion costs a million dollars a day in new York and adjacent cities.[16] In 1916 Huntington estimated that with tunnels, ferries and bridges, the people of New York were spending $10.00 per person per year in traffic cost because Manhattan was an island, and that Manhattan rents were increased by $100 per family per year because of the resulting inability to travel.

FIG. 49 — Going to Grandma's. A cartoonist's fancy of life in the Manhattan tenements where there are many ingenious economies of space. (Courtesy *New York World*.)

All this pressure of human numbers on a body of land, complicated by the restrictions of an island, give us the high land-values and the consequent crowding which makes New York the most crowded city in the world. Each of four square miles has a quarter of a million people on it, for there are hundreds of thousands who cannot commute to the country and must live more nearly landlessly than men have ever lived before.

killed and injured several places in Manhattan would have a greater toll than some battlefields that are on the tongues of millions of school children. Someone, speaking of New York traffic and its fatalities, called it the " Battle of Manhattan."

[16] Huntington, Ellsworth, *Geographical Review,* September 1916.

This crowding is a great business advantage to the financier, the merchant, the publisher, to men of many, many callings who need to see people. To the mere worker it is quite otherwise. It may give him a job, but the wage is not proportionately high and there are many disadvantages for which there is and can be no compensation. New York is not a good place for the poor.

In and out the door of the East Side apartment-house fifteen or twenty or even twenty-five, and sometimes many more families pass to climb the stairs to their apartments.[17]  In 1924, one East Side block had 2421 people living in 1587 rooms. The New York *Tribune* (October 18, 1923) reported two million people living in tenements that had been outlawed but could not be replaced. Hundreds of thousands of children have no place to play but the street, where they must dodge pedestrians, push-carts, wagons and automobiles. They have no chance at the earth, no place to dig, no grass to play upon, no country in which to walk, no baseball diamond. They are denied even the boy's spiritual birthright — the companionship of a dog. The life is quite as far from nature as that of the animals in the zoo. Much has been done to better life conditions here,[18] but only a beginning has been made — an attempt to patch the unpatchable.

When we consider the suffering and physical injuries that result from this crowding,[19] it is appalling to think that anybody is planning for continued increase of numbers in New York. The great need of humanity and of New York is for a larger rationalism, which would distribute fac-

[17] " A woman came in the other day — had a husband who was earning $20 a week as a cigar-maker. She is paying $40.00 a month rent for rooms that used to rent at $15 a few years ago. You see that is a perfectly disproportionate rent, and she has been obliged to go to work. They have two children and she wanted to leave them in our day nursery. But so many mothers are going to work that we think a long time before we take any woman in a nursery whose husband is making more than $20 a week." (From the record of Commission of Housing and Regional Planning appointed by Governor Smith of New York, 1923; 1205 pages of testimony on New York alone.)

[18] " It is doubtful if any city does so much in the direction of welfare work as New York for its poorer citizens. Free sterilized milk for the children, free clinics of all sorts, free classes where mothers are taught to properly care for their children, evening classes for men, day nurseries and places where babies may be kept under competent care while their mothers go to work, free illustrated lectures for everybody. Lectures on preventable diseases and a hundred and one other aids are constantly at the service of these helpless persons. The famous Henry Street Settlement House is here; its methods and practices are copied in every city in the Union, and it is only one of the many such similar institutions all over the city." — (*Valentine's City of New York*, by H. C. Brown, p. 164. E. P. Dutton & Co.)

[19] " Out of about 400 children, 102 were so distinctly underweight that on examination we found most of them were underweight somewhere between five and seventeen pounds. Their ages were between five and twelve years. If a child were six or seven pounds underweight we would do nothing. It was the normal size or weight for an East Side child now. . . . I found that the cause of the children's condition was the housing condition foremost. We find that the children do not sleep. The usual family consists of five or six persons. There are no doors. There is no

tory-workers over the land so that they can live near their work and in the presence of green grass and fresh air. It would be of untold benefit if factory workers and their families could have access to earth, with room enough to dig. To have gardens, and a place to play is the right of every man.[20]

Unused land along the Hudson, the Barge Canal and other near-by territories offer plenty of room.[21] Constructive imagination is required — only that, everything else is already in the hand of man. England, further along in industrial evolution than we are, has already made a start in scientific city-building. It is a small start but a perfect example.

privacy. The gas is burning until 12 or 1 o'clock, especially if there is a baby. Everyone is talking. Everyone is walking. The street is noisy and the child does not fall asleep until 12 and half-past 12 and 1." (From record of Commission of Housing and Regional Planning, New York.) The New York *Tribune* calls New York " The City of Dreadful Noise."

[20] For an account of the scientific city, see Smith, J. Russell, *The World's Food Resources*, Chapter 27. Henry Holt & Co.

[21] See Digest of Report of Federal Engineer's Corps, *Nautical Gazette*, December 6, 1917.

Fig. 50 — Terminal station for Adirondack logs. Log boom in Hudson River, Glens Falls, N. Y. (Courtesy U. S. Forest Service.)

# CHAPTER VII

## NORTHEASTERN HIGHLANDS

The Northeastern Highlands lie between the St. Lawrence Valley on the north and the New England-Canadian Maritime region and the Mohawk Valley on the south. They include the Adirondacks of New York; a corner of Massachusetts;[1] most of Vermont; all of New Hampshire, except the southeastern corner; more than half of Maine; the greater part of New Brunswick, and that part of Quebec which lies to the south of the St. Lawrence Lowlands. They include the large Gaspé Peninsula which reaches north of Maine and New Brunswick far into the Gulf of St. Lawrence. Although this region includes part of five American states and two Canadian provinces, and covers more than 100,000 square miles of area, it has uniformity of resources.

The Highlands are a glaciated upland from 1000 to 2000 feet in height, peaks rising to 6000 in the White Mountains; to 4000 in the Adirondacks;

[1] People in Berkshire County, Mass., where county pride exceeds state pride, have a saying that "the best thing about Berkshire County is the chain of mountains to the east which shuts it off from the rest of the State." This chain of mountains, the southern tip of the Highlands, makes the Housatonic Valley tributary to New York, and most of the many summer residents are from that city.

to 3500 in the Shickshock Mountains of Eastern Quebec. The mountains and hills and the areas of boulder, swamp and lake, leave little land that is fit for the plow.

This upland differs from Lower New England in having no harbors, few cities and a scattered population. Unlike Lower New England it depends chiefly upon the production of raw materials for export. For manufactures it depends chiefly upon its own raw materials.

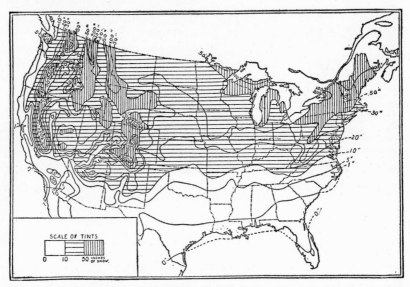

FIG. 51 — Annual average snowfall of the United States. The influence of cold winds blowing across warm Lake Ontario and against the high land is very noticeable. (Courtesy *Scientific Monthly*, Nov. 1919. C. F. Brooks.)

Being a plateau, it is cool, and frost drainage does not apply to plateaus, so summer frosts are common through much of the Northeastern Highlands. Being in the path of most of the winter storms, and cold enough to make snow rather than rain, its snowfall is far heavier than that of the Massachusetts coast. It is even heavier than that of the Laurentian Plateau beyond the St. Lawrence. A combination of factors makes agriculture difficult, and permits forests to grow. Therefore in this region great dependence is upon forest products. This always means a land of small and scattered population. Piscataquis County, Maine, has 3770 sq. mi. ($\frac{4}{5}$ as large as Connecticut) with a population of 5.5 per square mile. Two counties in northern New Hampshire comprise two-fifths of the state with but one sixth of the people. Hamilton County, New York, in the center of the Adirondacks, is nearly as large as Delaware, has 2.3 people per square mile and has steadily declined in population since 1900, having lost 20% of its inhabitants in twenty years.

## Forests

Forests have been and will continue to be the chief resource of most of this region. For more than half a century each autumn has seen bands of men going into the pine and spruce forests of this upland to build log cabins in which to spend the winter, while with axe and saw they fell the surrounding forest. With them are teamsters, and recently tractor operators, who drag the logs over the snow to the banks of the streams. There they wait until the spring freshet produced by melting snows carries the logs downstream.

In 1910 one thousand men and five thousand teams brought together on the upper Connecticut River 45,000,000 feet (board measure) of lumber, for the stream and lumber-jacks to take down to the saw and paper mills of Holyoke, Mass.

The effectiveness of the moderate and dependable spring freshet made easy the exploitation of these forests before the railroad came. Hence the virgin forest is practically gone and the lumber output is well instanced by the sharp decline in New York State [2] (partly Adirondacks and partly Allegheny Plateau).

The New York Commissioner of Forestry declared in 1924:

" We are using lumber in the State twenty times as fast as we are growing it, and are spending vast sums of money every year to import lumber from distant points that would not have to be spent if all the land suited to raising forests were producing crops. We have upward of four million acres of idle forest in the State. This means that we have an area three times the size of Delaware that is non-productive, and it is a serious economic menace." It is non-productive because of fire.

The situation in New York differs but little from that of the rest of the region.[3] After a few fires have killed the young growth and have destroyed the humus and leaf mold, the miserable aspen tree takes the earth where once stood the noble pine.

The total remaining stand of available timber in this whole region is insignificant; even Vermont imports some lumber. It is high time indeed for an era of tree-planting and scientific forestry; but it is unfortunate that the beginning has been so insignificant. The Bureau of Forestry re-

[2] NEW YORK STATE — LUMBER PRODUCTION

| | Rank | M. Board Feet |
|---|---|---|
| 1870 | 3 | 1,310,000 |
| 1880 | 4 | 1,184,000 |
| 1890 | 6 | 910,000 |
| 1899 | 17 | 875,000 |
| 1910 | 23 | 506,000 |
| 1920 | 23 | 410,000 |

[3] *Commerce Monthly*, Sept. 1922, National Bank of Commerce, N. Y., claims twenty-six million acres, 40,000 square miles, of potential but non-productive forest land accessible to our present starving pulp and paper mills.

FIG. 52 — The chief object of this picture is to show the stupendous size of a modern many smaller mills. (Courtesy Great

ports (1921) that we are having about 10,000,000 acres of forest burned each year and that we are planting about 28,000 acres. The futility of forest-planting in comparison with fire-prevention is shown by the slow growth of forest seedlings — only ten inches in the first six years. (U. S. Bureau Forestry.)

## Forestry

There is a double necessity for scientific forestry to begin in this region because such a large proportion of the timber now cut is for the pulp-mills which are scattered along the margins of the region from the Gaspé Peninsula to the western Adirondacks. This double necessity arises from the absolute scarcity of pulp-wood and from the great cost and difficulty to be encountered if a mill is moved to a new site. The paper mill is so expensive that the necessity of moving produces a much greater hardship than it does upon the owner of the sawmill, who can easily pick up most of his equipment and depart to other timber tracts, leaving the old site to wait for the destruction by fire which can wipe out in an hour the growth of half a century. The paper manufacturer can use small wood, so he cares much more for a cut-over forest than the saw-mill man does. A paper company built a railroad through the forest to Millinocket, Maine, and there, near a fine water-fall, erected a plant which cost millions of dollars. The company also built a town for their workmen. To keep the mill supplied with pulp-wood, the forests, which are owned by the company, are systematically managed so that they may yield pulp-wood for an indefinite time.

## The Oscillations of Agriculture

Most of this region has never had any agriculture, but the lower sections in Vermont and New Hampshire were occupied by the New England farmer in the period of his greatest activity. In New Hampshire the amount of improved farm-land has declined from 2,200,000 acres in 1870

paper mill. This particular mill now grinds the wood which formerly went to Northern Paper Co., Millinocket, Maine.)

to 700,000 acres in 1920. On a morning walk near Bellows Falls on the Connecticut River you could once count thirty houses, of which twenty-nine had been abandoned within twenty years. In a certain school district there were sixty children in 1870, while not a family was in residence in 1918. These people had been living on small farms which produced a part of the family support, the rest being obtained from work in the forest in winter. When the timber of the region was exhausted, the land alone could not yield a living and emigration was inevitable. The forest proceeds with quiet persistence to claim the land as it awaits an agricultural reconstruction with farming that will fit the land. Or it waits for fire.

On the slopes of the White Mountains at an elevation of 2000 feet there once was a type of farming suggestive of nice adjustment to local conditions, a type which may some day return if the population of the North American continent doubles or trebles. This farming at the highest limit of New England agriculture was distinctly the northern type, depending primarily upon grass for summer pasture and winter hay, eked out by a crop of oats. Each year the farmer had a cow or two to sell, and the money he received, by the rigid custom of the neighborhood, was put in the bank. The person who did not save his cow money was almost an outcast. The income for family support came from potatoes which were ground by water-power at the country mill, and sold as starch. Competition of Western meat hurt the price of cows, Aroostook potatoes hurt the price of starch, so the blueberries and the pine trees got the farms.

The agriculture of the Vermont upland has survived better than that of New Hampshire. The land is richer and the grass is better. Corn is grown on some of the land and is utilized by means of the silo. Root crops must be used at the higher elevation. The city markets to the southward give a good price for milk, and express trains carry the produce of the Green Mountain pastures of Vermont to Boston, as they do that of the Adirondack slopes to New York.

Maple sugar is an important crop of this region. The sugar maple tree grows wild everywhere. The sap from which the best sugar is made flows in the very early spring before the last snow has left the ground. During these periods of bright sunshine and frosty nights the sap seems to flow up and down the tree each day and produces much more sugar than is produced in southern lands where spring is warmer.

The province of Quebec conducts schools of maple-sugar making. Maple sugar is quite as important to the farmers of Vermont as to those of Quebec. The annual sugar-crop is about twenty million pounds. In

FIG. 53 — Sugar maple, sap buckets, sled, sap tank, and sugar house. Steam heralds work in the sugar house. (Courtesy *Nature Magazine*.)

this industry we see an example of native tree-crop agriculture already in full operation and capable of much extension.[4]

However, the numerous other sources of sugar, the low yield per tree,[5] the heavy labor involved in gathering and boiling the sap, make it one of the least productive of all the tree-crops. Also the trees are scattered and personal skill is required for sugar-making. These facts would all seem to indicate that the maple-sugar industry will remain in the hands of the individual instead of passing to the corporation.

In upland Vermont, free from cities, the rural Yankee still survives — an interesting and sturdy type of man thus described by one of his daughters: " Vermont, like some of the remote valleys of the Pyrenees,

[4] We acquired this industry from the Indian. The Algonquins were called " Tree Eaters." Maple sugar with powdered corn was a favorite hunting ration.

[5] There is reason to suppose that a test would reveal some trees that were several-fold more productive than others. These might be propagated and the sugar output increased without additional labor.

has always been too far out of the furiously swirling current of modern industrial life to be much affected by it or to dread its vagaries. For generations now, when times get hard and manufactures are flat and deflated and the mills in the industrial states around us are shut down, and the newspapers are talking about bankruptcies and bread-lines, the Vermont family, exactly as rich and exactly as poor as it ever was, remarks with a kindliness tinged with pride: 'Well, we'd better ask Lem's folks up to stay a spell, till times get better. I guess it's pretty hard sledding for them.' And when times get better, and Lem's family leave the poor little frame farm-house which has been their refuge, and drive off down the steep stony road which is the first stage of their journey back to wages and movies, the Vermont family stand looking after them, still with friendliness. . . . I am afraid there is an element of sinful pride in the granite-like comfort they take in the security given them by their plain tastes and ability to deal with life at first hand. No dependence on employers for them! . . . It is very rare when anybody in Vermont fails to secure a fair amount of shelter and clothing and food and education; and it is equally rare when anybody secures very much more than that. . . . Vermonters are not sentimental, articulate Celts, but hermetically sealed Yankees. But they live on this love for their homes and they have shown themselves quite ready to die for it." [6]

## Manufactures

Pulp-mills are the chief manufacturing enterprise of this region. The finer use of wood is shown by the manufacture at Orleans, Vermont, of most of the piano sounding-boards used in this country. Brattleboro, Vermont, boasts the largest pipe-organ factory in the United States.

This region has a really distinctive industry which seems to be linked with New England exactness and thrift. It is said that a farmer named Fairbanks, weary of being cheated by his neighbors, built himself a set of scales about 1830 so that he might know the actual facts concerning his business transactions. Then he made some scales for other people. Because Fairbanks refused to be cheated the largest scale factory in the world is located at St. Johnsbury, Vermont. A later rival in the near-by town of Rutland makes another famous brand of scales. At Rutland utensils to be used in making maple sugar are manufactured.

## Mineral Industries

The mineral resources of this region are like those of Lower New England, meager except for deposits of marble and granite. In the neighborhood of West Rutland are excellent and easily accessible deposits of hard marble. The machinery necessary for this industry is manufac-

[6] "Vermont, Our Rich Little Poor State," Dorothy Canfield Fisher, in *These United States,* Boni & Liveright, 1923.

tured in the neighborhood. The characteristic scene is one of deep holes, high derricks and piles of marble chips. Down in the great holes drills are busy cutting out blocks of marble, which are dressed at West Rutland and Proctor. This one locality furnishes half the marble of the United States, and distributes it over wide areas. This is an industry which it seems must decline here, because marble deposits are widely scattered over the United States. Vermont has a relative disadvantage because it is not easy to send the heavy, bulky marble long distances. But the energy and skill of her people in organizing the sale and distribution of her product have so offset the handicap of distribution that Vermont sends marble hundreds of miles and sells it almost on top of deposits which might be quarried if only Yankees were there to do it. The same conditions apply to her extensive exports of granite and slate (one-third of United States supply) which, like the granite, are produced in the neighborhood of the marble.

## The Vacation Industry

As the summer boarder is important in Lower New England, so is he important in the Northeastern Highlands. Along the lakes and mountains of the Adirondacks and Maine are numerous summer hotels, summer camps, summer homes and bungalows where tourist, fisherman, camper and other vacationists seek respite from the heat and the strain of city life. Mountain, forest and stream combine to give a variety of attractions to the man from the cleared land and the paved street.

The people of the Northeast Highlands make great efforts to save the deer to attract the tourist. Here vacations can have the touch of real wildness. For example, the Gaspé Peninsula has been crossed only about twice by educated white men. (*Geog. Review,* April 1923.) This involves canoeing up to the limit on one stream, carrying your stuff through a forest and over a mountain, and coming down another stream. It is easy to see why the activities of this region here tend to be limited to particular canoe routes.

The entrance of the ski and the toboggan into American life and the rapid increase of interest in winter sports are beginning to make these Northeastern Highlands a center of winter travel. Now that it ceases to be a hardship we are beginning to see beauty in the snow.[7]

Pictures of Dartmouth College winter sports in numerous Sunday supplements have helped to deluge this, the chief educational institution of the region, with an avalanche of students from all over the United States. Winter there is one long carnival. " Sledding is considered a rather puerile sport in this vicinity. Favor is given to skiing, snow-shoeing and

---

[7] " The extraordinary colors that one gets in snow. The shadows, the light shining through white birch trees, and the reflection of sky colors all give a constant variety to the colors in the snow itself. Our snow is nearly every color in the rainbow except white and the dirty brown slush of the cities." (Malcolm Keir.)

tobogganing, in the order mentioned. Snow is our cheapest and most
prevalent commodity. Yesterday we had a storm which filled our paths
and roads waist-deep with snow. Consequently snow-shoes and skis are
not only a sporting proposition but actually a household necessity. Children here in Hanover learn to ski during the first winter after they learn to
walk. Recently at our great Winter Carnival a six-year-old kid went
over our breath-taking ski-jump, a stunt which often the most experienced

FIG. 54 — This is a big fish in the Restigouche River, New Brunswick — bigger
if he gets away than if he is caught. (Courtesy Dept. Immigration and
Colonization, Ottawa.)

and hardy adult skiers hesitate to tackle. So for real sport, come up,
leave your sled and get upon a pair of skis." (Quotations from letter
from Professor Malcolm Keir, of Dartmouth College.)

### Future

The future of this region seems plain. If we ever come to regard
ourselves as custodians of our continent rather than its destroyers, this
upland will have careful forestry, systematic resort-development and
agriculture in selected spots on the lower levels. We may expect forest
products to be much more carefully saved and manufactured into lumber,
wood products and paper. Perhaps it may even take the extreme form
of printed paper and the paper-mill town will also become a printing
center for the great publishing houses of the metropolitan cities. The
agriculture will be much like that of Lower New England, which has
already been adequately described. The pastures and climate are espe-

cially suited to sheep. For many years Vermont merino sheep have been so famed that they have been exported to Australia for breeding purposes. The excellence of this country for sheep is a continual surprise to the sheep ranchers of the Western plains, and the revival of this industry may be expected. The government of New Brunswick started a sheep-promotion campaign in 1922. The ancient joke that sheep's noses had to be sharpened in Vermont so that they could reach in between the rocks to get the grass is not without significance both as to the character of the country and the adaptation of the sheep to it.

F IG. 55 — North Atlantic Coast Plain. Flat and exceedingly arable. A land of great possibilities as shown by this overhead irrigation of truck. Seaford Farms, Bridgeton, N. J.

## CHAPTER VIII

## NORTH ATLANTIC COAST PLAIN

I N the upper part of Manhattan Island much blasting of solid rock is necessary to get cellar space for a new building. In the lower end of Manhattan the builder, to get a solid foundation, spends thousands of dollars sinking piles or burying great masses of concrete in the sand, gravel and clay. This marks the difference between Connecticut and Long Island, between Philadelphia and Camden, between geologically old land and geologically new land. The softer, newer land is called the Atlantic Coast Plain.

### Coastal Plains of Eastern and Southern United States

Coastal plains are made of sand, clay and gravel that have been so recently washed down from higher land that the material has not had time to turn into rock. The line separating the older formations from the coastal plain formations of the Eastern and Southern United States runs from New York to Philadelphia, Baltimore, Richmond (Virginia), Raleigh (North Carolina), Columbia (South Carolina), Macon (Georgia), and swings around to the mouth of the Ohio, passes Little Rock (Arkansas), and crosses Texas into Mexico. Not long ago, geologically speaking, the streams flowing into the sea spread on the bottom of the Atlantic sands, clays, silts and gravels, which make up the surface of the Coast Plain, 341,000 square miles in extent, 11% of the United States.

As is the case with most shores, the Atlantic coast-line has alternately risen and fallen. The present sea margin, as in New Jersey, is about midway between the edge of the old continent at Philadelphia and the edge of the continental land mass, which is marked by a great precipice several thousand feet deep at the edge of the so-called continental shelf which extends the gentle slope of the Coast Plain as a platform fifty miles out to sea. The evidences of advancing and receding sea are found in the

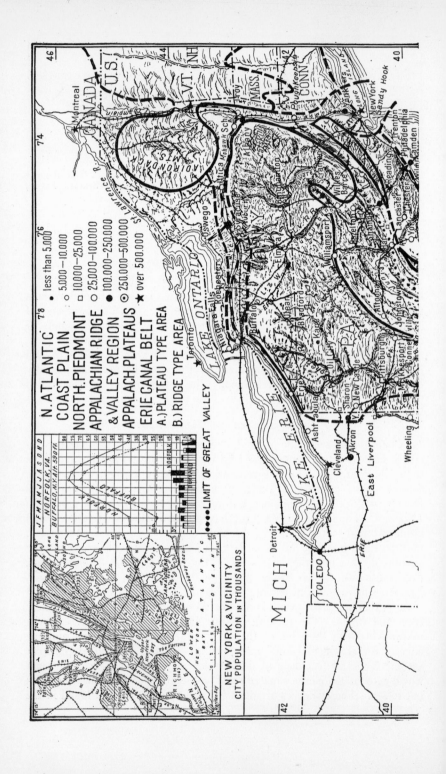

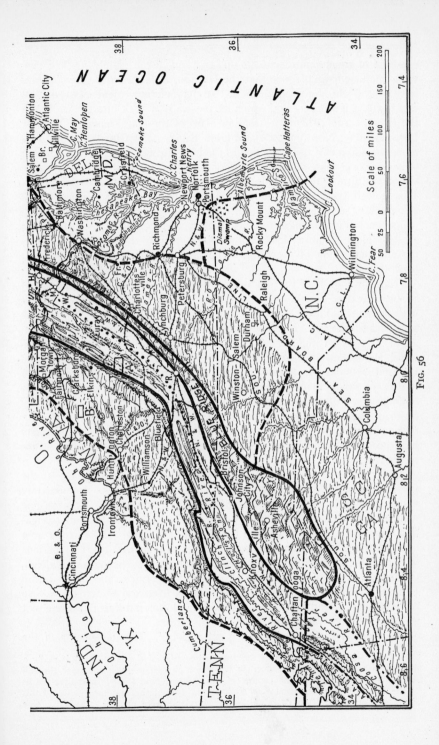

Fig. 56

presence of recent marine fossils on land and in the plainly marked canyons which soundings prove that the Hudson, Delaware and other streams have cut in the continental shelf. In its last movement most of this coast sank a few dozen feet, which let the sea flow back into the valleys of the rivers, turning them into shallow arms of the sea — Chesapeake Bay, Delaware Bay, New York Bay, Hudson River, Long Island Sound. This moderate sinking of the coast makes the best harbors if the stream is large. Otherwise over most of its length the coast offers no good harbors, because the waves always tend to pile up a strip of sand called a barrier beach. This is well typified by the conditions on the New Jersey coast where the resorts, such as Atlantic City, stand upon the narrow sand-beach which encloses the characteristic tidal lagoon behind it. At intervals shallow inlets in the barrier beach are kept open by the continuous inflowing and outflowing of the tides. The lagoons are excellent harbors for small boats.

From the mouth of the Hudson to the mouth of the Rio Grande, and on into Mexico, the shore is nearly everywhere a barrier beach, fringed with lagoons and with bedrock deeply buried. The Coast Plain widens as it goes southward. It includes the Florida peninsula, most of Alabama, all of Mississippi and Louisiana, corners of Tennessee, Kentucky, Missouri, a substantial slice of Arkansas, and a large territory in Texas. Its land boundary is always the line between the old hard rocks and the recent sands, clays and gravels brought down by the streams. This boundary is most clearly marked on the rivers by rapids or falls, or by series of them where the stream crosses the easternmost ledges of solid rock, which wears away but slowly. Having passed the rocks, the rivers have been able to cut deep, wide channels in the soft coastal plain strata to the east.

As far south as Richmond, the streams are tidal estuaries up to the falls, and navigable sometimes even for ocean-going boats. Immediately above these falls the streams are difficult even for canoes. This fall-line with its double charm of falls for power and industry and head of navigation for commerce, is the natural location for the largest cities in the area between the mountain and the sea. This fact is proved by the locations of Trenton, Philadelphia, Baltimore, Washington, Richmond, Raleigh, Columbia, Augusta, Macon and Columbus (Georgia), and even Austin (Texas). South of Richmond the fall-line is from 100 to 200 feet above sea-level, the streams are not navigable and the fall-line cities are not so large as those farther north.

The Coastal Plain has soils of great variety.[1] The movements of the

----

[1] This variety increases one of the many difficulties of the farmer. It is really a difficult task to know just what crops will grow on certain soils, and how the soil should be treated. Hence the coming of soil surveys, now one of the major works of the United States Department of Agriculture. One of the first surveys found this significant situation: Two communities in Maryland were on the same soil. One

water that placed these deposits were sometimes swift, carrying away everything but the coarser sand. In other places the less swift current left finer sand; and in yet other places it left clay, or nearly pure clay. Sometimes there was deposited an abundance of shell, giving a high lime content, and again fossil beds (marl) were formed. So rich in plant food were the marl beds that they were quarried for fertilizer. In other places the lagoon behind the barrier beach has been filled by a mixture of humus from river mud, animals and plant remains and sand from

Fig. 57 — The process of making coastal plain has not ended. In Thomas Jefferson's time the entire American navy was anchored here — the site of the harbor of Bladensburgh, on a side estuary of the Potomac, near Washington. Now it has become a shallow stream. In a few more years it will become dry land — so fast have hill farms on the near-by Piedmont washed into the streams in the process of their speedy ruin by erosion. (Courtesy William Pickett Helm, Washington, D. C.)

the barrier beach. This makes soil of the finest kind. In many places, especially in the South, the sea retreating across the plain left its legacy of ancient beaches, which made the land surface very sandy. There are also areas of upland marshes, characteristic of level land having abundant rainfall.

Upon the whole, the process whereby the soils of the Coastal Plain were

was prosperous, had good schools, good roads, good churches; the other was unprosperous, with poor roads, poor buildings and despairing people. Why this difference? The people were not to blame. One community grew the series of crops for which the soil was good, namely truck. The other was trying to grow grains, for which the soil was not good. The application of this lesson is nation-wide, as is the work of the soil survey

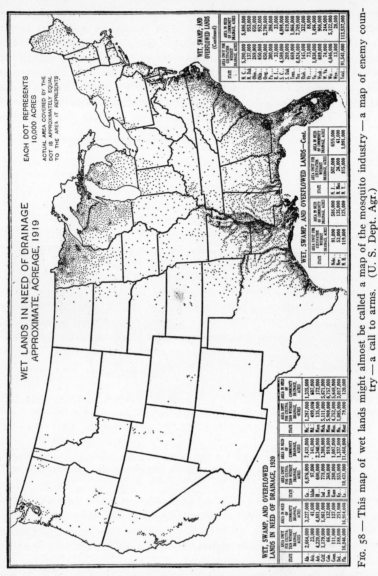

Fig. 58 — This map of wet lands might almost be called a map of the mosquito industry — a map of enemy country — a call to arms. (U. S. Dept. Agr.)

made tended to take out the soluble elements, which are plant foods, and left too much sand which is always of low fertility. That is one reason why parts of the Coastal Plain remain unsettled [2] — despite the fact

[2] I have walked through the woods, seventeen miles in a straight line, parallel to and a few miles north of the railroad connecting Philadelphia and Atlantic City, without seeing a human habitation or even a field or a good saw log. This is a part of a 3000-square-mile area of forest, or would-be forest, gutted by axe and fire.

that it is so level, soft and stoneless that plowing is most easy and roads could run in any direction. There are whole counties without a natural stone large enough to be of use in killing a snake, yet many gravel-banks make excellent road material.

Throughout its length, the Atlantic and Gulf Coastal Plain has the curse of level lands with good rainfall. The water stands on the land until it becomes stagnant and raises a pest of mosquitoes — one of the great handicaps of the entire region.

### Bounds and Character of the North Atlantic Coast Plain

If the boundaries of regions were based on geology or soils alone we should have one region running from Vera Cruz, Mexico, around the shores of the Gulf of Mexico and the Atlantic Coast up to Long Island and Cape Cod. All of it is coastal plain having similarity of soils, but nature has spread dissimilarities of climate over these similarities of soil. It is so nearly a desert near the mouth of the Rio Grande that agriculture must wait upon irrigation. The lower Mississippi is wet, with a long, hot, summer; so wet that agriculture must often wait upon drainage of the land. In the Florida part of the plain they pick oranges and bathe in the sea when on Long Island there is skating and Cape Cod may be ice-bound. These differences of climate cause the Coastal Plain to fall naturally into several regions; one of which, the North Atlantic Coast Plain, is the part under consideration. The North Atlantic Coast Plain has its southern boundary at the place where cotton becomes an important crop. The same line marks the northern boundary of the Cotton Belt. (Figs. 19 and 20.)

The North Atlantic Coast Plain is not a land of cities because there are no great mines, as in Pennsylvania, and no important waterfalls, as in Massachusetts. Because it is level no place has distinct superiority, so there are no great commercial foci, as at New York. Norfolk is the nearest approach to a commanding commercial location. The Coastal Plain, therefore, remains a land most of whose people are farmers. The sandy soil was not well suited to the needs of the colonial settler, because it was not good for grass. The early settler wanted pasture and hay as well as wheat and corn. For this reason much of the Coastal Plain has never been cleared and settled, and as in New England some of its settled areas have been abandoned.

### The Trucking Industry

It is fortunate that although the sandy soils of the Coast Plain and elsewhere are unsuited to grass they are admirably suited to the production of watery products — melons, tomatoes and nearly all of the truck crops. The sweet potato reaches its perfection in soil so sandy and so poor that it would bring despair and bankruptcy to the growers of wheat and corn. The Coastal Plain is therefore an admirable region for truck farming, and recently there has been an agricultural revival that promises permanence. The changes which caused the revival are, first, the application of lime and chemicals (commercial fertilizer) to soils of low natural fertility, thereby making them highly productive; second, the establishment of express-train service which carries truck crops to Northern markets for several weeks or months before the local supply is ready; third, and most important, the development of the canning industry and the increased demand for canned foods. If a crop is canned its *period of consumption* is prolonged a whole year, or even two years, and its *area of consumption* embraces almost a world.

The truck industry tends to develop in centers because different types of soil suit different crops and because centralization has advantages to the grower both in production and in marketing. If scores or hundreds of farmers around a certain town are growing strawberries or cantaloupes there is a personal stimulus in keeping up with the procession, and personal aid through the spread of knowledge and technique. Every laborer in the community knows how to help. The merchants in the town keep every possible supply. In marketing it is easy for producers to take the advantages of co-operation and carload shipment with its faster service and lower freight-rate. It is easy to fill a car where the produce of many growers can be brought to one station, whereas it would often be impossible to ship in carload lots if producers were scattered. Once a center is established another advantage often appears. The buyers come and buy from the growers and ship full carloads to points where there is a good market.

Farmers' co-operative associations are a potent reason for the existence and development of this centralized production. The product is graded and packed according to association rules and a standard package is then put on the market. Confidence is created and people buy almost without looking. This has occurred conspicuously in three places in the North Atlantic Plain: the Cauliflower Growers' Association of eastern Long Island; the Monmouth County Potato Growers' Association in northern New Jersey; the Eastern Shore of Virginia Produce Exchange. Each of these organizations came into being because conditions were hard for the individual farmer. Farmers, acting separately, would consult current price-reports to see which market gave highest returns. Everyone would send his produce to that market; this would over-supply and glut the market and sometimes cause the goods to sell for less than the freight cost. At the same time some other equally accessible markets would be bare. This, unfortunately, is an experience which all independent truck-growers who ship by rail have met many times in a decade. When an association has been formed among farmers its chief purpose is to sell all the cauliflowers or potatoes, or whatever it may have, through one sales agency, which can watch the markets of the whole country and distribute supplies to cities and towns where truck is needed, thus avoiding the glutting of any market. This guarantees a better supply to the city and a better price to the farmer. The keystone of this operation, however, is the guaranteed standard package. Thus, a basket of cauliflower with the Long Island Association brand is so well known in many markets that its contents do not need to be examined. The tag tells

FIG. 59 — This map shows well the northward march of the seasons, the way both seed time and harvest swing up the coast — a vital factor in the truck industry. (Courtesy U. S. Dept. Agr.)

the story. So does the mark of the Monmouth County Potato Growers' Association, or the Eastern Shore of Virginia Produce Association.[3] Naturally, the localities whose farmers have reached this degree of efficiency are sections of unusual prosperity.

This development of trucking centers throughout the Coastal Plain gives

[3] An inspector of this Association stopped his Ford, sprang to the platform of a railway station, ripped the burlap from one barrel of a shipment of outgoing potatoes, rolled them out on the platform, and looked them over with a merciless eye. That barrel had on it the Red Star of quality, and it was the inspector's job to maintain that quality. A bystander remarked: "With some o' these here potato growers the fear of the inspector is greater than the fear of the Lord."

great diversity of production in different sections. At one place the whole town and countryside revolves around potatoes as surely as the Labradorean settlement does around codfish. At another place, perhaps only a few stations away, the people may buy even the potatoes they eat while they grow strawberries or cantaloupes or even cucumbers by the trainload. Near the cities greater diversity is produced because the grower has the advantage of being able to haul a succession of produce to the near-by market in his own wagon or truck.

The North Atlantic Coast Plain is divided by rivers and bays into six natural subdivisions: Cape Cod, Long Island, New Jersey, the peninsula between the Delaware and Chesapeake Bays, the "Western Shore" or the tidewater lands of Maryland and Virginia, west of the Chesapeake, and the Norfolk district.

### Cape Cod and Its Berries

Cape Cod has a sandy, gravelly surface, made partly by glaciers. At this point the glacier stopped for a long time and the melting waters rushed away from its front, strewing sand and gravel all over the plains to the south and leaving rather steep slopes to the north. The islands of Nantucket, Marthas Vineyard and Block Island have a similar origin. As the ice melted it left pockets, ponds and swamps in the midst of the sands. Most of the area between Buzzards Bay and Cape Cod Bay, including the three islands above mentioned, is scrubby bush or forest land without much good timber.

Fig. 60 — Scoops with teeth, like large combs, pick cranberries much faster than bare hands. (Courtesy United Cape Cod Cranberry Co., Boston, Mass.)

This unpromising-looking land is developing two agricultural specialties — cranberries and strawberries. The surrounding water gives protection from spring and fall frosts. The marshes of Cape Cod are the natural home of the cranberry, which is a marsh plant. To help to keep down weeds in the cranberry bogs, and to keep the berries out of the mud, it is customary to put a layer of sand over the top of the muck. This is usually done in winter, when sand can be hauled over the frozen ground or ice. Weeds are kept down by temporary flooding. Dikes and other devices are built to control water to be used for that purpose.

This little.section is the leading cranberry district of the United States. The growers are organized into a co-operative association which might almost be called a trust, and which spends several hundred thousand dollars a year in creating a demand for cranberries by advertising. The industry has spread to Nantucket, which claims to have the largest single cranberry field in the world — 240 acres.

Since 1900 commercial strawberry plantations on dryer lands have taken advantage of this special climate.

### Long Island

Long Island gives us our last glimpse for a time of the work of the continental glacier. Two terminal moraines stretch the whole length of the island (Fig. 22). It is their bulk which gives the two projecting ends to the eastern part of the island. Throughout their length these moraines are marked by the characteristic irregular hills and sinks (or kettle-holes) which, in the sandy soil, can rarely hold enough water to become lakes. The moraines are a mass of boulders and stones which seem strangely out of place as they lie upon the soft sands of the island. The surface is mostly composed of the sand and gravel washed into its present position (out-wash plains) by the outrushing glacial waters.

Considerable areas are of almost pure sand marked by uninhabited wild barrens covered with a poor growth of pitch pines and scrub oak. Wild deer still live here, although this uninhabited region is almost within the sound of the great metropolis at the mouth of the Hudson.

The western third of the island is covered by Brooklyn and its suburbs (well over 2,000,000 people) and by market-gardens intensively cultivated by new immigrants, chiefly Italians and Poles. The suburbs, like a slowly rising tide, are gradually spreading to the eastward.

In the central third of the island, sand plains and wilderness predominate. On the eastern third the soil is better and there is an intensive agriculture which shows interesting recent readjustments. In 1885 this territory sent 1,500,000 gallons of milk to the cities at the western end of the island; in 1895, 500,000 gallons; in 1900, 4000 gallons, and now there is *none*. Instead of cows at pasture, there are fields of potatoes, tomatoes, cauliflowers and other garden vegetables, especially cabbages. This locality produces almost the national supply of cabbage seed — a natural development of a specialty in a region where much attention has been given to the crop. This shift of agriculture from an animal industry to a vegetable industry has been made possible by the recent great increase in the use of commercial fertilizer which permits sandy soils when abundantly fed to yield heavily of garden crops.[4]

[4] The intensity of Long Island agriculture is well shown by average county expenditures of fifty dollars per cultivated acre per year for labor and forty dollars for fertilizer. Compare this to the great world staple of wheat, with a gross value of twelve dollars to fifteen dollars per acre.

The autumn frost immunity of the narrow east end of the island gives the farmers there a monopoly in selling ripe tomatoes late in October after the mainland crops are frozen.

### The New Jersey Section

The contrast between agriculture on the clay lands to the west of Philadelphia and the sandy lands to the east of it shows clearly how soils can differentiate regions. There is practically no trucking on the Pennsylvania clay lands; instead there are dairy farms.

Late in the nineteenth century many of the farmers on the sandy loams east of Philadelphia were also chiefly dependent upon the sale of milk,

Fig. 61 — Truck and apples. Two crops growing at the same time. Possible over wide areas. Horace Roberts Farm, Moorestown, N. J. (Photo J. Russell Smith.)

but the dairy business has now almost entirely disappeared. In its place enormous quantities of fruits and vegetables are grown to meet the demands of the two million people in and around Philadelphia. About 1910 one lone milk-shipper continued to send his cans of milk to one of these stations and his driver was quite unhappy because the men who shipped vegetables mooed like a cow when he came to the station. The stone roads leading to Philadelphia are thronged with wagons and trucks loaded with vegetables. Fifteen hundred vehicles have crossed the Delaware in a single day and many others stayed in Camden to leave their product at the canning factories that operate there to handle the surplus that cannot be immediately consumed.

The possibilities of the truck industry, aided by fertilizers, are typified by the history of a particular piece of sandy upland about twelve miles east of Philadelphia. A man born in 1800 cleared the land and tried to grow grains. His son, born in 1830, allowed it to grow up to pines and forest because it did not pay to raise wheat, corn or hay. The grandson, born in 1865, has again cleared the land, and planted it to truck. His first crop was watermelons, and he raised a thousand of them on an acre of land and sold the crop for more than $100.

He planted an orchard of peaches and apples along with the watermelons, and the melons and wood (resulting from the clearing) paid all the costs down to the end of the first year. The next year other truck crops made income in the young orchard.

The greatest single feature of the New Jersey section of this plain is an area of three thousand square miles of pine forest in the southeastern section. Here and there are settlements, often miles apart. The traveler wending his way through pines in New Jersey will suddenly come to a wide green opening as flat as a floor, as smooth as a lawn, and as large as a small farm. It is a cranberry bog, one of many in this vicinity. New Jersey is second only to Massachusetts as a producer of cranberries, and soon she may be first.[5] For a time certain fungi injured the crop in New Jersey, but two sprayings of bordeaux mixture controlled the fungi and the natural advantages of New Jersey over Massachusetts may now be expected to make themselves gradually felt. These advantages are nearly level and less swampy land. It is, therefore, easier to use machinery to prepare the soil for planting.

The cranberry industry brings hundreds of transient laborers to the pines in the early autumn. The workers are Italians, Poles and other foreign-born. They spend the winter in the cities and the summer in going from place to place picking berries and vegetables. They begin with strawberries in late May, and proceed to peas, beans, tomatoes, peaches, summer apples, pears and finally to cranberries. They then return to the city until spring comes again. On some of the truck and fruit farms are rows of shacks, each of which is occupied, for a time, by a family of berry-pickers.

At Hammonton, a railroad junction down in the pines of South Jersey, there is a great concentration of raspberries, blackberries and dewberries, while a few miles away at Glassboro are hundreds of acres of apples.

This region affords good illustrations of a distinction that needs to be

[5] CRANBERRIES

| Acreage | 1920 | 1922 |
|---|---|---|
| New Jersey | 10,000 | 11,000 |
| Massachusetts | 13,000 | 12,000 |
| Average yield in barrels per acre. | | |
| New Jersey | 13.3 | 18.2 |
| Massachusetts | 21.5 | 23.4 |

— From Yearbook, U. S. Dept. Agr.

made between American and European agriculture.  In this country we usually think of intensive agriculture, especially growing garden crops, as a hand agriculture.  This is only partially true.  We have developed a kind of agriculture which may be called extensive-intensive.  With the aid of machinery it shuns the laborious hand methods of Europe and as far as possible plants large areas of garden crops, instead of small garden patches.  As an example of this type of agriculture, a single farmer living ten miles from Philadelphia operates eleven truck farms which he manages by telephone and automobile.  For one year he reported the following astonishing yields per acre:

> Corn, 80 to 100 bushels.
> Hay, 3 tons.
> String Beans, 175 bushels.
> White Potatoes, 250 bushels.
> Sweet Potatoes, 300 bushels.[6]

## The Eastern Shore

The peninsula between the Chesapeake and Delaware, known throughout Maryland and adjacent States as the Eastern Shore,[7] is like the corresponding western shore of the Chesapeake and the tidewater territory of Virginia in being unusually favored because the far-reaching arms of the Chesapeake make water transportation possible over a large area of which the great focus is Baltimore.  Steamers come from many places in the interior of Delaware, like Smyrna, and from Fredericksburg and Richmond in Virginia.  For a long while there was no other transportation service for this area.  Ten counties located in the long peninsulas of Eastern Virginia are still without a mile of railroad, chiefly because the streams are so numerous and the boats are so satisfactory.  Every farmer lives within a few miles of a boat-landing.  Many farms have a private boat-landing, and it is not uncommon for a man to own his boat. This was even more common in Colonial times.  Shaler has pointed out that these self-contained plantations prevented the development of town life in Virginia and Maryland and hindered the building of roads.

In southern Delaware and the adjacent part of Maryland, everywhere there are fields of tomatoes, peas, beans, potatoes, melons, and, at almost every railroad station is the canning factory.  This region is one of the four great canning centers in the United States, the other three being the Ontario plain of western New York, Wisconsin, and California.

Baltimore is the greatest single canning center in the country, because the steamboats afford a cheap and easy way of gathering the produce

[6] "A Fortune from Sand Without Livestock," Smith, J. Russell, *Country Gentleman,* July 27, 1912, p. 2.
[7] It is a sacrifice of social efficiency that this peninsula, now divided among three states could not be one state with uniform interests.

from widely scattered localities.  In times of dearth the boats even go
through the Chesapeake and Delaware Canal to Delaware Bay, ascend
the rivers of western New Jersey, and take the peas and tomatoes to
the factories in Baltimore.

The two Virginia counties at the extreme southern end of the Eastern
Shore are the seat of the Produce Association previously mentioned.  In
some parts the sands are quite infertile, but this happens to be exactly
the type of soil required for the sweet potato, whose quality is ruined by
soil of high fertility.  The farmers have a most unusual system.  A part

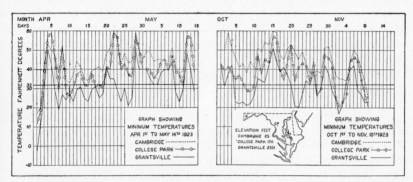

Fig. 62 — The study of the spring and fall low temperatures shows what a difference
the water body gives to Cambridge as compared to College Park.  Grantsville
shows the Plateau climate.

of each farm is in pine trees whose needles are gathered up and thrown
into the barnyard to be trampled by the horses, mules and cattle.  In the
spring the mass is spread upon the fields where white potatoes are planted.
The next year after the crop has partially exhausted the soil, sweet potatoes are planted; the next year white potatoes and so on indefinitely.
White potatoes are sent to all parts of the United States in their season,
which is limited to a short period from late in May to early July.

### The Western Shore and the Norfolk District

In Colonial times the western shore of the Chesapeake in both Maryland and Virginia depended greatly upon the tobacco crop, and upon
the labor of the negro slave.  It will be recalled that tobacco probably
saved the Jamestown colony from failure, because it was the only thing
that could be produced to sell in Europe.[8]  So important was it in Colonial times that tobacco served as money for over a century, even the

[8] N. S. Shaler says that the demand for tobacco in Europe laid the foundation
for American commerce.  It made Virginia prosperous, a leader in the Revolutionary
War, and in national affairs.  But — tobacco fixed slavery on America and cotton
extended it.

minister receiving his salary in tobacco.[9] The commercial prominence of this crop helped to impoverish the territory where it was grown, because tobacco is one of the worst soil-robbers known to agriculture. Land upon which tobacco has been grown for a time usually becomes exhausted.

The emancipation of the negro interfered with the tobacco industry. A great deal of hand-labor is required to care for the microscopic little plant, to hoe it, to pick off the worms which will eat holes in its leaves, to pick off the buds to prevent blooming, to break off the young shoots so that only a single stalk will remain, and finally to strip the leaves from the stalk and prepare them for market. The slave women and children were an adequate labor supply while slavery lasted. Soil exhaustion, emancipation and the decline in the price of corn, due to the opening of the West, are the chief explanation of the surprising fact that some counties in the Western Chesapeake Basin, including the site of historic Jamestown, had only about half as many people in 1920 as were there in 1820.

The emigration has been so great that many communities did not have enough energetic people left to maintain satisfactory community life. Many old fields are grown up in pines. The land is cheap, easily worked, and awaiting the scientific farmer. Around the Norfolk district is a veritable agricultural boom with high land-values based upon facilities for marketing truck crops for which the harbor and location of Norfolk offer unusual advantages. In twelve hours the boat from Norfolk reaches Baltimore; in twenty hours, Philadelphia and New York; and in thirty-six, Boston. These facts explain the enormous concentration of truck-growing in the immediate vicinity of Norfolk, where the soils are admirably suited to it.

Tributary also to Norfolk and a few miles back of the truck center is the greatest peanut center in the United States. This nut was introduced to the people of the North when the army returned from the Civil War. Since then there has been a steady increase in consumption of peanuts and several counties on both sides of the Virginia boundary back

---

[9] Witness the interesting Virginia statutes of 1662 in which tobacco seems to have been a great aid to godliness. " Every person who refuses to have his child baptised by a lawful minister shall be amerced 2,000 lbs. of tobacco; half to the parish, half to the informer." " In actions of slander occasioned by a man's wife, after judgment passed for damages, the woman shall be punished by ducking, and if the slander be such as the damage shall be adjudged at above 500 lbs. of tobacco, then the woman shall have a ducking for every 500 lbs. of tobacco judged against her husband, if he refuses to pay the tobacco."

" Enacted that the Lord's Day be kept holy, and no journeys be made on that day, unless upon necessity. And all persons inhabiting in this country having no lawful excuse, shall every Sunday resort to the parish church or chapel, and there abide orderly during the common prayer, preaching, and divine service, upon the penalty of being fined 50 lbs. of tobacco by the county court." (Surface, G. T., Bulletin Phila. Geog. Soc., Oct. 1907.)

of Norfolk have almost their sole commercial dependence upon this crop, many farms selling nothing else. The remarkable food-value [10] of this leguminous plant combined with its adaptability to sandy soils of low fertility mark it as one of the greatest crops of the future. Not only is it richer than meat in protein, the tissue-making food, but it is also rich in both carbohydrates and fat, two essentials of nutrition. A bushel of peanuts, weighing thirty pounds (hulls included), will produce a gallon of edible oil when crushed, and twenty pounds of cake, a stock food high in protein and especially suitable for dairy cows or growing animals. The uncooked peanut keeps in perfect condition for an indefinite time.

## The Agricultural Future

What will be the agricultural future of this region? Unfortunately, or fortunately, according to the point of view. there is a demand for only a fraction of the truck this region can grow. In fact, 2% of the

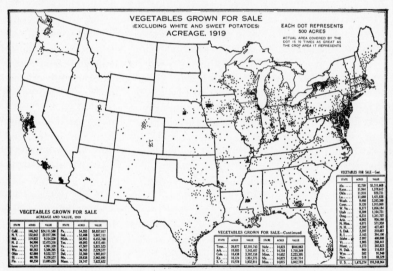

Fig. 63 — This map shows the importance of the North Atlantic Coast Plain in the vegetable industries. (Courtesy U. S. Dept. Agr.)

area of good truck-land in the United States suffices to supply at the present time all the commercial needs of the nation. The chief reason why the region has remained unsettled is that every time the farmer has tried to extend the truck area, glutted markets have discouraged him and stopped the spread of the industry. Production can increase only as demand increases.[11] Thus far the people have strangely ignored the

[10] See table of Food Values.
[11] Innumerable examples might be presented showing that fine crops of vegetables have been grown but could not be sold even when the farmer took them to market

opportunity to develop an agriculture which would produce staples for which there is a steady demand and a reasonably steady price — namely, animal industries.

It has been demonstrated time after time in every county of this region that an application of phosphorus and lime and a little potash to the sandy soils of the Coastal Plain will make them produce splendid crops of legumes such as clover, alfalfa, vetch, peas (several varieties), beans (several varieties) and corn.

Once the sandy soil is filled with vegetable material and a little commercial fertilizer is applied, it yields splendid crops of corn. In some localities fifteen crops in succession have been grown by the following method: — at the last cultivation of the corn a legume, usually crimson clover, is sown. This plant, which is a native of North Europe, grows in the autumn and early spring, blooms in April and furnishes a great mat of vegetation which, to enrich the corn crop, is plowed under before the corn is planted in late May or early June. As far north as Trenton, N. J., two crops are regularly grown on this sandy soil by progressive farmers. One combination is peas, to be picked for market or canning by June first, followed by corn, in which a legume such as vetch, crimson clover or cow peas is sowed to gather nitrogen for the next season's crop. Another two-crop combination is early peas, tomatoes, and crimson clover planted among the tomatoes to live through the winter and enrich the land or to be cut for hay at the beginning of the next season.

The need of this region is for another discovery of the land, and why it has not been discovered by more people is difficult to understand, especially now that good farm-land is worth $200 and upwards in the Corn Belt and can still be had for a fraction of that in the Coastal Plain. Interesting examples of this discovery are furnished by a very successful alfalfa farm run by a California man near Fredericksburg, Va., and the great success of a colony of Scandinavians who tired of the cold winters of Dakota, settled near the site of the original Jamestown and soon turned the old pine fields into productive stock farms.

Dairying takes almost nothing from the soil if butter is the export, because the manure of the animal returns all the phosphorus, potash and nitrogen to the earth, and butter, which is chiefly carbon, is taken freely from the air by plants that help to make the cow's food. Thus the sandy soils of the Coastal Plain, like the sandy soils of Denmark, might yield annually vast quantities of milk and butter, but this being an advanced stage of agriculture, would not be the first stage of the animal industry.

---

in his own wagon. The sale of California tomatoes, wrapped in paper, at $.25 per lb. in Broadway stores in early autumn, when they were bringing $.75 per half-bushel in Washington and could still be harvested in many Coastal Plain locations, indicates the need of better market organization for Coastal Plain produce.

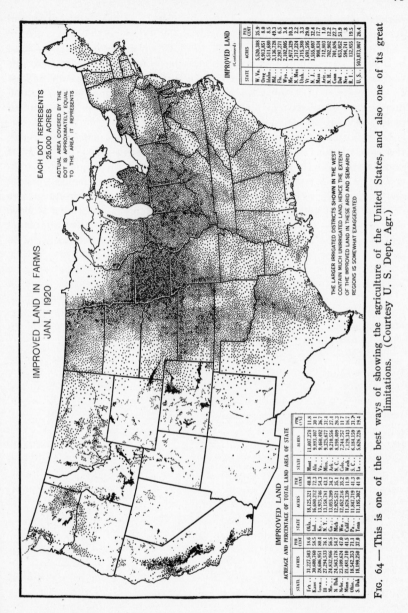

IMPROVED LAND IN FARMS
JAN. I. 1920

EACH DOT REPRESENTS
25,000 ACRES

ACTUAL AREA COVERED BY THE
DOT IS APPROXIMATELY EQUAL
TO THE AREA IT REPRESENTS

THE LARGER IRRIGATED DISTRICTS SHOWN IN THE WEST
CONTAIN MUCH UNIRRIGATED LAND. HENCE THE EXTENT
OF THE IMPROVED LAND IN THESE ARID AND SEMI-ARID
REGIONS IS SOMEWHAT EXAGGERATED

IMPROVED LAND (Continued)

| STATE | ACRES | PER CENT |
|---|---|---|
| W. Va. | 5,520,308 | 35.9 |
| Ore. | 4,913,851 | 8.0 |
| Idaho | 4,511,680 | 8.5 |
| Md. | 3,136,728 | 49.3 |
| Fla. | 2,297,271 | 6.5 |
| Wyo. | 2,102,065 | 5.4 |
| Ariz. | 1,957,229 | 10.3 |
| N. Mex. | 1,717,224 | 2.2 |
| Utah. | 1,715,380 | 3.3 |
| Vt. | 1,691,595 | 29.0 |
| N. J. | 1,555,607 | 32.4 |
| Mass. | 988,634 | 17.7 |
| Ariz. | 712,803 | 1.0 |
| N. H. | 702,902 | 12.2 |
| Conn. | 701,684 | 22.7 |
| Del. | 653,582 | 51.9 |
| Nev. | 594,741 | .8 |
| R. I. | 132,855 | 19.5 |
| U. S. | 503,073,007 | 26.4 |

IMPROVED LAND
ACREAGE AND PERCENTAGE OF TOTAL LAND AREA OF STATE

| STATE | ACRES | PER CENT | STATE | ACRES | PER CENT | STATE | ACRES | PER CENT |
|---|---|---|---|---|---|---|---|---|
| Tex. | 31,227,503 | 18.6 | Okla. | 18,125,321 | 40.8 | Mont. | 11,007,278 | 11.8 |
| Kans | 30,400,760 | 58.5 | Ind. | 16,680,212 | 72.3 | Ala. | 9,933,407 | 30.1 |
| Iowa. | 28,606,951 | 80.4 | Ky. | 13,975,746 | 54.3 | Minn | 9,460,492 | 36.7 |
| Ill. | 27,294,533 | 76.1 | N. Y. | 13,158,781 | 43.2 | Wash | 9,235,677 | 21.4 |
| Mo... | 24,832,966 | 56.5 | Ga. | 13,055,209 | 34.7 | Ark. | 9,210,556 | 27.4 |
| N. Dak | 24,563,176 | 54.7 | Mich. | 12,925,521 | 35.1 | N. C. | 8,198,409 | 26.3 |
| Nebr. | 23,109,624 | 41.5 | Wis. | 12,452,216 | 35.2 | Colo. | 7,244,757 | 11.7 |
| Ohio. | 21,481,710 | 71.1 | Calif | 11,878,339 | 11.9 | Wash | 7,129,343 | 16.7 |
| S. Dak | 18,199,250 | 37.0 | Pa. | 11,847,719 | 41.3 | S. C. | 6,184,159 | 31.? |
| | | | Tenn | 11,185,302 | 41.9 | La. | 5,626,226 | 19.4 |

FIG. 64 — This is one of the best ways of showing the agriculture of the United States, and also one of its great limitations. (Courtesy U. S. Dept. Agr.)

A more natural beginning would be the production of meat, and in this industry the most promising line of development would be that of pasturing pigs. Pigs could be allowed to harvest a succession of crops —

perhaps winter grain with vetches and clovers, cow peas, soy beans, and even corn.

The sandy soil, ever dry enough to plow, smooth and nearly as level as a floor, offers admirable opportunities for tractor-plowing and permits the use of the most complicated machinery. This land, proof against erosion because of its physical features and the absorbing power of sand, invites man to the extreme of cultivation. With the present high price of meat and high price of land elsewhere, it seems impossible that this territory shall much longer contain unsettled wilderness growing up in pines. It is one of the richest unused resources of America. One of the great drawbacks is doubtless the mosquito — product of the abundant marshlands. Marshes could, with profit, be drained if science, capital, energy and imagination were applied. To be effective against the mosquito, this drainage would have to be undertaken over large areas. We need to have well organized campaigns against this enemy of man's comfort and satisfactory progress, but we have yet to realize that it takes an army to oust him.

FOOD VALUES OF CROP AND LIVESTOCK PRODUCTS *per acre*
From W. J. Spillman

| Food Products | Yield per Acre | | Calories per Pound | Pounds Protein per Acre | Calories per Acre | Acres to Equal One Acre of Corn in Calories |
|---|---|---|---|---|---|---|
| | Bushels | Pounds | | | | |
| Sugar Beets....... | 12 T. | | | 0 | 5,565,000 | .56 |
| Sugar Cane....... | 20 T. | | | 0 | 8,750,000 | .36 |
| Corn............ | 35 | 5,960 | 1,594 | 147.0 | 3,124,240 | 1.00 |
| Sweet potatoes..... | 110 | ª5,940 | 480 | 53.5 | 2,851,200 | 1.10 |
| Onions.......... | 300 bu. | | | 189 | 2,565,000 | 1.22 |
| Irish potatoes..... | 100 | 6,000 | 318 | 66.0 | 1,908,000 | 1.64 |
| Rye............. | 20 | 1,200 | 1,506 | 118.8 | 1,807,200 | 1.73 |
| Wheat.......... | 20 | 1,200 | 1,490 | 110.4 | 1,788,000 | 1.75 |
| Cabbage........ | 9 T. | .... | | 214 | 1,760,000 | 1.77 |
| Rice, unpolished... | 40 | 1,154 | 1,460 | 55.4 | 1,684,840 | 1.85 |
| Rice, polished..... | ... | 1,086 | 1,456 | 50.0 | 1,581,216 | 1.98 |
| Soy beans........ | 16 | 960 | 1,598 | 294.7 | 1,534,000 | 2.04 |
| Tomatoes........ | 7 T. | .... | .... | 100 | 1,330,000 | 2.35 |
| Peanuts.......... | 34 | 524 | 2,416 | 126.2 | 1,265,018 | 2.47 |
| Oats............ | 35 | ᵇ784 | 1,600 | 89.4 | 1,254,400 | 2.49 |
| Beans.......... | 14 | 840 | 1,337 | 157.9 | 1,123,080 | 2.78 |
| Cowpeas......... | 10 | 600 | 1,421 | 116.4 | 852,600 | 3.66 |
| *Dairy Products* | | | | | | |
| Milk........... | ... | 2,190 | 325 | 72.3 | 711,750 | 4.39 |
| Cheese.......... | ... | 219 | 1,950 | 56.7 | 427,050 | 7.32 |
| *Meat* | Live Pounds | Dressed Pounds | | | | |
| Pork........... | 350 | 273 | 2,465 | 22.7 | 672,945 | 4.64 |
| Beef........... | 216 | 124 | 1,040 | 18.5 | 130,000 | 24.00 |
| *Poultry Crop* Meat and Eggs | 66 lbs. and 111 eggs | | | 27.5 | 149,000 | 21.0 |

ª 54 pounds per bushel.          ᵇ Hulled kernels.

This table of food values per acre of various crops, especially vege-tables, shows the great potential service of this region as a producer of vegetable food.

### Population

It should be noted that in the southern part of this region about one-third of the people are negroes to whom the spasmodic labor of the truck-farm is more welcome than the continuous labor of dairying. In some sections August is an almost continuous picnic. The remainder of the population is chiefly native white.

### Forests

The proportion of the Coastal Plain that is in forest is larger than that in improved land, but the good timber has all been cut once or twice

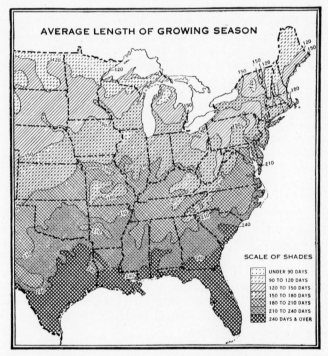

Fig. 65 — The longer growing season permits double cropping and the rapid growth of forest trees. (Courtesy U. S. Dept. Agr.)

and unfortunately large areas are repeatedly burned. It is a land well suited to the short-leaf or old field pine, a timber tree of so much value that lands exhausted and abandoned have, in fifty years, produced pine trees large enough for saw-logs. In many such forests the furrows left from the tillage of the last crop of corn can still be seen.

The schooner, reaching into nearly all parts of the Coastal Plain from ocean lagoon or inland bay, was the great vehicle that aided in the early exploitation of the forests.

## Fisheries

Fisheries have been important in the economic life of this region, especially so on Cape Cod, Nantucket and Marthas Vineyard. It was from Nantucket that one of the great whaling fleets sailed in the days when the oil lamp furnished illumination. No other part of this region has had such dependence upon fish.

The off-shore fisheries of mackerel and bluefish are of some importance, but the shad and herring, which come in from the sea to spawn in bay and stream, are more important. The herring has done much to make the cost of living low in this region. In the spring herring enter the streams in such quantities that they can be caught by countless thousands. It has for generations been the custom for people on the Atlantic slope to salt down a year's supply of herring. Five dollars or even less a thousand has long been a common price. When the negro field-hand comes to do a day's work he often brings a salt herring and cold corn-bread for the midday meal — not particularly appetizing food, but explanatory of a low cost of living.

The oyster industry in the partially enclosed waters of Long Island Sound, Delaware Bay and Chesapeake Bay now furnishes the main salt-water income of this region. The dredging of natural beds has resulted in their serious depletion. The oyster, helplessly fast in her shell, lays eggs which float through the water and hatch in the drifting current where the young oyster swims for a time and finally makes fast to some firm substance and there must die after living for a time on what fate brings. He cannot live in the mud, but clean sand or gravel are ideal. By putting down shells and brush men make artificial resting-places and artificial oyster-beds. If the full resources for this industry were utilized the output of these three bays would be many times its present product.

As oysters can easily be stolen from the oyster-beds, the Virginia part of the Chesapeake Bay is more productive than the Maryland part because of better police protection.

The canning factories of Baltimore, busy in summer with fruit and vegetables, are partially employed in winter with canning oysters.

## Manufacturing and Trade

The Coastal Plain is strangely lacking in local raw materials for manufacturing. It has neither coal nor water-power to use in fabricating

imported raw materials. It is true that it could have imported coal
more easily than New England, but it lacked the established centers of
manufacture, such as those created by New England's water-power[12]
The one Coastal Plain industry, save canning, is the glass industry of
southern New Jersey, for which the unlimited stretches of white sand
furnish ideal raw material. Charcoal from the pine forests was used
in the early days to melt the sand, and New Jersey held the first
place in glass manufacture in 1860, with the chief centers at Salem,

Fig. 66 — Preparing beans for canning in a Baltimore factory. (Courtesy W. F.
Assau Canning Co.)

Bridgeton and Millville — towns near the edge of the pine-forest area.
The exhaustion of the charcoal supply compels the New Jersey glass
manufacturer to use Pennsylvania coal, and the industry survives only
by making very fine products such as laboratory glass. The most of
the glass factories have gone to the natural-gas fields of Western Pennsylvania, West Virginia, Ohio, Indiana and Illinois. The New Jersey
industry has increased but little since 1860 and now ranks sixth among
the States, producing in 1919 only one-fifth as much as the first State,
Pennsylvania.

Baltimore, lying at the edge of the Coastal Plain, is both a commercial

12 I omit the consideration of Philadelphia in this chapter, it being more nearly
dependent upon the interior of the continent than upon the Coastal Plain, but I
include Baltimore, a city which seems much more than Philadelphia to be the
product of the plain and of the sea.

FIG. 67 — The towns on Hampton Roads properly boast that this deep natural
(Courtesy Chesapeake

and a manufacturing city. It is the most southerly of the large (pop.
733,826) northeastern cities, while to the south of it there is no other
city approaching its size save Washington (437,000), until New Orleans
(387,000) is reached. Partly because of its size and partly because of
the excellent steamboat service to the Chesapeake territory, Baltimore
early developed an important distributing trade. The country merchants
not only of Maryland, but also of West Virginia and Virginia and even
points farther south, depend chiefly upon Baltimore as a source of
supply. This makes it somewhat like New York in being able to distribute consumption goods such as clothing, of which the manufacture
is twice as valuable as any other product in Baltimore, amounting, in 1921,
to $60,000,000, or about one-eighteenth that of New York. Other than
this, no other single industry predominates. The canning of vegetables,
fruits and shell-fish is important. The city is not insignificant as a
publishing center. Being the terminus of one of the trunk-line railways,
the Baltimore and Ohio, it has shops for repairing and building cars.
As the commercial center of the Coastal Plain, Baltimore is the natural
place for the manufacture of fertilizers; the amount manufactured increased from five to ten million dollars' worth between 1900 and 1910,
and jumped to thirty-two million in 1919. In a suburb of Baltimore,
Sparrow's Point, are large steel works using Cuban ores, and admirably
fitted for making iron and steel for coastwise and export trade.

The Chesapeake Bay permits freight-ships of all sizes and liners of
medium size to reach Baltimore and there are a number of lines to Europe
and some to other foreign countries. Her chief imports are fertilizer
materials, copper, iron ore, manganese ore and wood pulp. Her exports,
which are several times as valuable, are chiefly of grain, flour and tobacco
(these three comprising half the total), iron and steel manufactures and
coal.

The most important city lying entirely within the North Atlantic

harbor will hold all the ships in the world.   Water front at Newport News.
and Ohio Ry. Co.)

Coast Plain is Norfolk (pop. 115,000).   The cities of Portsmouth
(54,000) and Newport News (35,000), just across narrow arms of the
Bay, bear the same relation to Norfolk that Jersey City and Brooklyn
do to New York.   Since 1880 these towns have grown as rapidly, in
percentages, as New York itself.   The sunken coast at the mouth of the
James makes Hampton Roads a harbor of supreme excellence, capable
of sheltering all the ships of the world with room to spare.   Three railroads, — the Norfolk and Western, the Chesapeake and Ohio, and the
Virginian, bring coal almost by gravity from the coal-fields of Virginia
and West Virginia, and give access to Pittsburgh, Cincinnati and Chicago.
The superior excellence of Hampton Roads over all south Atlantic harbors makes Norfolk a natural foreign-trade center for the Carolinas and
an export point for railroads coming up the coast.[13]   These roads can
either forward their produce by water or by car-ferry across the mouth
of the Chesapeake to the main-line railroad going up the peninsula to
Philadelphia and the North.

When one compares Norfolk with New England, the cost of living
appears to be less because it is nearer to food supplies and coal and
because it has a milder climate.   Thus the reason for its recent growth
appears to be plain.   The real puzzle is, why is Norfolk not larger?

### Seashore Resorts

On or near the beaches of the North Atlantic Coast Plain are the
summer homes of thousands of families.   There is the prospect of its
becoming the home of many thousands more.   Nearly all of the coast,
from Cape Hatteras to Sandy Hook, is excellent for bathing.   From the
mouth of the Chesapeake to Atlantic City the coast is everywhere backed
by a bay, the Chesapeake or Delaware, which makes it impossible for

[13] In 1923 the Ford Motor Co. erected in Norfolk a plant for assembling and
for local and foreign distribution.

railroads to run without long detours from the interior to the coast. To
Atlantic City, however, there is a straight, uninterrupted railway line
from Pittsburgh via Philadelphia to the sea. Here enterprising capitalists built railroads, so that fast trains could take the people to
Atlantic City, which became the largest resort in the world. The experiment paid. Visitors come by thousands, by tens of thousands. The
city claims to be able to shelter 350,000 over-night guests. The permanent population of Atlantic City is 50,000; it is estimated that it receives

FIG. 68 — The beach — a playground of the Nation — the reason for Atlantic
City's existence. (Courtesy Atlantic City Publicity Bureau, Inc.)

10,000,000 yearly visitors. The average daily population in the month
of August is about 300,000.

The hotels, of metropolitan sumptuousness, have all the solidity of re-
inforced concrete despite the fact that they rest upon sand. The boardwalk which extends for miles up and down the Atlantic City beach front
is a kind of national parade-ground.

The Jersey Coast, from Sandy Hook at one end to Cape May at the
other, is dotted with smaller resort cities, and promises, at no distant
date, to be an almost unbroken line of cottages or cities, so rapidly is
the vacation habit growing in America and so accessible is this good
bathing coast.

### Future

For fifty years the population of the world has been separating itself
into manufacturing regions and raw-material-producing regions — witness
the cities and the abandoned farms of our Northeastern States. Few
parts of the world rival the North Atlantic Coast Plain as a site for the

scientific creation of manufacturing cities, — cities which shall be healthful and efficient for both machines and men, for dividends and for living.

Within a short time we have seen the United States Steel Corporation conceive and create Gary, a city which suddenly spread over the sand dunes at the south end of Lake Michigan. Similarly the Lackawanna Steel Company made a new suburb of Buffalo where a lake-front site offered better advantages for making steel than did Pittsburgh or any other inland city. Suppose the same or slightly larger constructive imagination should start out to make a manufacturing city or a string of manufac-

FIG. 69 — The conflict — nature forever moving the beaches and man wanting them for building sites. The sandy beach is often a moving, not a fixed, thing. Building the sea wall. This last device nearly bankrupted the little town of Longport, N. J., where the sea had swallowed a boardwalk, many houses and acres of land. (Courtesy Lewis M. Haupt.)

turing cities that would house many industries instead of one. Where should a city be located to be a good place both for the worker and the owner? It should be, indeed it must be, in a healthful climate, a climate that makes energy rather than a climate of ease. Certainly some part of this region has a climate of achievement. Ellsworth Huntington says that it is the northern part, and history seems to agree with him, although Captain John Smith said of the southern part: " Heaven and Earth never agreed better to frame a place for man's Habitation."

The ideal manufacturing city should have a climate which stimulates men to achievement, and the city should be located in a place of easy access. In this respect, the whole of the North Atlantic Coast Plain is richly endowed. The estuaries of the Chesapeake have water-front enough to afford ideal transportation for cities housing millions of operatives. If it should be desired to make the cities at the northern rather than the southern end of this region, it would be a simple matter to make ship canals that would connect with New York Harbor, reach across New Jersey to Trenton or the Delaware, or down the coast to Cape May. Along such a coastwise waterway, factory towns on the inside of the lagoons would be swept each hot day of summer by the cool sea-breezes. While Philadelphia and Baltimore sweltered, these cities would be comfortable, and barges running back and forth between the Delaware and New York Bay would give the transport advantages

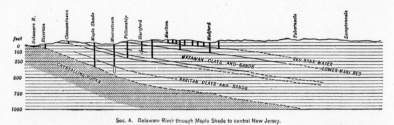

Sec. A. Delaware River through Maple Shade to central New Jersey.

FIG. 70 — Layers of porous sand alternating with layers of tight clay are ideal for the formation of artesian wells, which furnish cheap and excellent water supply for the cities on the New Jersey shore. (U. S. Geol. Surv.)

of New York. Upon the level sand plain railroads and highroads could be built at a minimum of cost and could go in all directions with the maximum of freedom. The productivity of the plain promises abundant fruits and vegetables, and the nearness of the sea brings fish. The underlying strata are full of artesian water and could doubtless supply water to many cities as they now do to Atlantic City and every other town of importance on this coast. Super-power lines can serve the entire region with electricity from mine-mouth power-plants.

All this requires no new invention, merely the application in times of Peace of that large imagination and a small part of the forceful energy that we use in times of War. The same constructive imagination could drain all the swamps, drive out the mosquito and make the coast plain an entirely different kind of place.

FIG. 71 — One of the great agricultural inventions. Mr. Lawrence Lee of Leesburg, Va., lays off horizontal terraces on Piedmont hills. With a Martin grader and a tractor the terrace is made deep enough to hold water at time of rain so that it soaks into the earth instead of running away and carrying earth with it (Fig. 110). By this means trees planted below the terrace or ditch get the chief benefit of cultivation without its cost *and they grow.* At present the cultivated hills of the United States are rapidly being turned into deserts. Here is an effective cure of great possibilities if used with intelligence. (Photo Lawrence Lee.)

## CHAPTER IX

### THE NORTHERN PIEDMONT

FROM the Hudson River southward a belt of hilly or rolling clay land resting on hard rock lies between the Coastal Plain and the Blue Ridge Mountains. The meaning of the word Piedmont is " the foot of the mountain." The soils of the Piedmont differ from those of the plain because they are residual; that is, they are made of broken parts of the rock that lies beneath them. As these rocks are often granite and gneiss, the resulting soils are usually rather heavy, composed largely of clay and in the main of good fertility. In this respect, the soil is a pronounced contrast to the Coast Plain soil. The Piedmont is separated from the Coastal Plain by the Fall Line Belt which is often a transition zone a few miles in width.

The western limit of the Piedmont throughout most of its distance is very plainly marked by the steeply rising eastern slope of the Blue

Ridge Mountain. In the Carolinas the mountain widens out into a plateau. Through most of Virginia and Maryland the boundary is a clear-cut ridge. In Pennsylvania it is not so clearly marked because the ridge happens to be absent for a short distance in the southern part of the state, but the geological and soil formations and the general type of country continue through Pennsylvania and New Jersey to the suburbs of New York. The Piedmont belt is about 50 miles wide in Maryland, but increases in width to 125 miles in North Carolina. The total area is about 80,000 square miles.[1]

The elevation of the Piedmont is from 300 to 500 feet on the east and from 500 to 1200 feet at the foot of the mountain. Originally it seems to have been worn down by the streams to a plain whose surface was uniform, but in comparatively recent times the mass was raised somewhat and consequently the streams have cut valleys which increase in depth as they go from west to east. Thus a road that follows the Blue Ridge near the foot of the mountain goes across an almost level plain, while a parallel road ten or fifteen miles to the eastward would have to descend at frequent intervals into the rather steep-sided valleys of streams that have cut 50 or even 200 feet below the general level of the hilltops. The southern part of the Piedmont has the long warm summer that permits the growth of cotton. This part of the Piedmont area will be considered as a part of the Cotton Belt and the present chapter will discuss that part of the Piedmont which is north of the Cotton Belt.

## Agriculture

The northern Piedmont, lacking minerals, except lime and building stone, with scant water-power, and having no harbors save on its eastern edge, is of necessity primarily an agricultural region. It falls naturally into three divisions because of the different types of agriculture in each: (1) the tobacco section in the south; (2) the apple and livestock section in the northern half of Virginia; (3) the general farming and dairy section in the north.

## The Tobacco Section

Tobacco dominates the agriculture of this region in northern North Carolina and southern Virginia up to and slightly beyond the James River. The tobacco territory is a disheartening sight to the traveler who is accustomed to well-kept fields and a neat countryside. The first impression is that every one has recently moved away save a few who cultivate a patch of corn and tobacco here and there. This is so because of the system of cultivation. The man who may own 100 acres

[1] New Jersey .......... 2,500    North Carolina ....... 20,000
Pennsylvania ......... 5,000    South Carolina ...... 12,000
Maryland ............ 2,500    Georgia ............. 18,000
Virginia ............. 18,000    Alabama ............. 5,000

of land will derive all of his money income from three to eight acres of tobacco. This, with a patch of corn for his work-animal or animals, comprises his entire cultivated area. After a few crops, the land is so impoverished and gullied that it is allowed to rest. During its vacation, the land grows up to blackberries and other bushes until finally the young forest may re-establish itself. The impression of abandonment is well-founded. Most of the land has been temporarily abandoned to

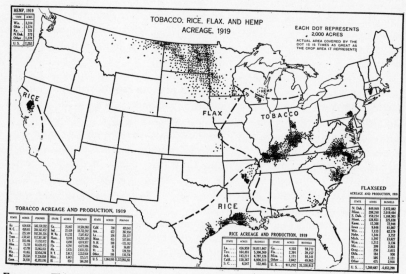

FIG. 72 — This map shows that tobacco (and also rice) tends to remain in concentrated areas. (U. S. Dept. Agr.)

await the time when it will be subjected to another series of robber-crops and gullying.

The Virginia State Agricultural service is endeavoring to establish " independence week " — a time for the preaching of the doctrine of varied crops, pigs, chickens, cows, sheep, clover, peas and good gardens and less dependence on canned goods and the country store. Tobacco, the raw material of this section, dominates the manufacture of nearly every important near-by town. Durham and Winston-Salem, North Carolina, have large factories for the manufacture of chewing and smoking tobacco. Lynchburg, on the James, has some tobacco factories and Richmond has many more. These towns produce half of the tobacco manufacture of the United States.

### The Apple and Livestock Section

The northern edge of the tobacco belt merges gradually into one of the best-known apple sections of the United States. It reaches from the James River northward to the Rappahannock. Fifty years ago, farmers began to plant apple orchards in the small, moist, fertile valleys, called coves, immediately at the foot of the mountain ridges. These orchards succeeded. Then many others were planted, until now it is said that one may walk for seven miles along the foot of the Blue Ridge Mountain in Albemarle County, and pass directly from one apple orchard to the next. The varieties grown are chiefly the Winesap and Albemarle Pippin, many of which are exported to Europe.[2]

There is no reason why this particular locality should have an advantage over other parts of the Piedmont or other parts of the United States, except the fact that the apple industry has been established here.

Owing to the large yield of orchard crops, it is very unusual for the trees to cover a large proportion of the area in any territory. This is particularly true of the apples in the Piedmont. Nearly all of them are along the western edge. The rest of this region is a land of beautiful rolling hills and the main crops are corn, hay, pasture and wheat. This is almost the southern limit for wheat because farther south wheat is injured by fungus and decay due to warm, damp weather in early summer.

That most excellent pasture grass, known as blue grass, covers fields wherein fat cattle and fine horses feed.

For a long time this part of Virginia was famous for its horses, but the business has diminished since the automobile came.

Before the World War the United States War Department bought a large farm across the ridge, near Fort Royal, and established there a base for the supply of cavalry remounts. They even bought breeding stallions for the use of farmers, so that the good quality of all the horses may be continued. Jumping horses for the fox hunt are still produced here.

In this locality it is probable that the English country-gentleman type of society of 1640 has survived more fully than even in England itself. The cavalier type which fled before Cromwell's persecutions settled back there in the hilly country somewhat removed from the arteries of travel, and therefore the agricultural basis which is necessary for survival has been less disturbed than in England. The people still ride to hounds, delight in outdoor life and horse shows, and maintain a social consciousness which tends toward the exclusion of men who are not landowners. Since 1900 the fox-hunting avocation has been strengthened by the process of selection — persons of wealth from New York and elsewhere have bought estates, established kennels and stables and nurtured foxes.

---

[2] It is commonly believed that the trade was established about 1840 by the minister to America from Great Britain. He was a plantation owner in Albemarle County, and he presented some Albemarle Pippins to Queen Victoria. The Queen liked the pippins and they became popular.

### The General Farming and Dairy Section

In the middle of Loudoun, the most northern county of the Virginia Piedmont, is a sharp line between North and South. It is not a climatic line but a social and industrial line. The southern end of the county is cavalier, aristocratic, fox-hunting, traditionally of the Democratic party. During the Civil War it re-cruited the famous Colonel Moseby's guerrilla Regi-ment. The northern end of the county was settled, not from the Chesapeake, but from the north by Pennsylvania Quakers and Germans w h o migrated southward in their wagons during the last half of the eighteenth century. These people were willing to work with their hands, were op-posed to slavery, were dem-ocratic in their social out-look, and at the time of the Civil War were with the party of liberation. This end of the county raised a volunteer regiment to de-fend the Union.

These northern types of people, with the Swedes who settled along the lower Delaware, and the Dutch who settled along the lower Hudson, comprise the population of the Pied-mont from the Potomac to the Hudson. Their farms are small, fifty to one hun-

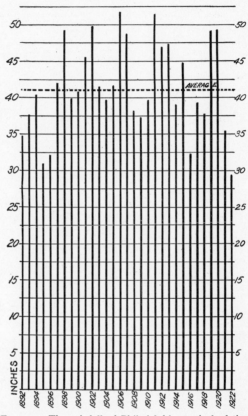

Fig. 73 — The rainfall of Philadelphia, typical of the Piedmont and indeed of eastern United States, shows small annual fluctuation and is therefore favorable for agriculture.

dred acres, while the farms of the country-squire sections from Loudoun County southward tend to be large, 200–500 acres or even more. These small farms yield more per acre and are well tilled. The county is dotted with large, well-built barns indicative of thrift.

Throughout the entire belt, from the Potomac to the Hudson, wheat is a money-crop grown on almost every farm. Corn is an even more universal dependence, but is chiefly used to feed the livestock, which is the chief agricultural output of the region. In districts less accessible to the towns, farmers are fattening cattle or swine, and occasionally they keep sheep or sell horses. But the presence of large cities, Washington, Baltimore, Philadelphia, New York, tends to make a heavy demand for dairy products, and the map of the location of creameries and dairy cows shows this influence very plainly.

The United States Department of Agriculture made a study of farming operations on 378 farms in Chester County, Pa., a well-cared-for part of the Piedmont near Philadelphia. These farms averaged 90 acres in size, and derived 44% of their income from dairy products and cattle; 14% from hay sent to the city and sold at high prices to feed city horses; 8% from wheat; 8% from poultry and eggs; 9% from potatoes.

The tendency of the future was indicated by the fact that on the smaller farms of the Chester County district the portion of income derived from poultry and eggs, an intensive kind of agriculture, was much larger than upon the average of the farms. It was found that the shipment of butter had declined six-sevenths between 1890 and 1915, because of increase in the demand for fresh milk from the growing city population near by. Truck was absolutely insignificant — an interesting fact when one considers the great production of truck on farms that are equally distant from Philadelphia, but situated upon the sands of the Coastal Plain to the eastward.

These Chester County farms are fairly typical of all that part of the Piedmont that lies in upper Maryland, Pennsylvania and New Jersey. The small well-tilled farms respond to the steadily increasing demand of the city population for dairy products. Agriculture becomes intensified to meet urban need. This is particularly true in the Pennsylvania districts where a large proportion of the people have German blood. The Pennsylvania German seems to be essentially conservative. He has not emigrated so much as the other Eastern stocks. Therefore he has stayed upon the land and developed an agriculture so intensive that eastern Pennsylvania is very conspicuous in the maps of agricultural production.

### Lancaster County Germans

This intensive agriculture by the farmer of German stock is best seen on the plain near Lancaster. In the hands of these diligent farmers a belt of limestone rock and soils has become a fat land. It is like Europe, with European land-values, European yield, European appearance save for the fences and the huge barns, of which nearly every farm has two — one barn for the forage and the livestock and one for tobacco. This carefully tilled tobacco-section contrasts strangely in appearance with that of southern Virginia and North Carolina.

The Lancaster County tobacco-growers have a systematic four-year crop rotation — wheat, clover, corn and for the fourth year potatoes and tobacco. The farmer sells the wheat. He feeds the straw, clover, corn, fodder and some bought grains to cattle which he sells for beef. Great quantities of manure are a by-product of stock-raising and this serves to maintain the fertility of these farms, which have sale-values from $200 to $500 an acre,[3] and a tobacco yield of 1400 lbs. per acre, while the yield is only 600 lbs. in North Carolina.

FIG. 74 — Field of tobacco on well kept Lancaster County (Pennsylvania) farm. (Courtesy U. S. Dept. Agr.)

### Cities

The northern Piedmont is a region having no reason to possess large cities, for no spot has any great advantage over any other locality. In its 500 miles of length there are but five towns which have more than 20,000 people.[4] In the north, Lancaster and York, both on main lines of the Pennsylvania Railroad and centers of rich farming localities, have developed machine shops, textile mills and rather diverse manufactures. At Winston-Salem, with a nucleus of tobacco, manufacture has had a similar development. Lynchburg, the largest Piedmont city between the Pennsylvania boundary and the Carolina boundary, was at one time the terminus of the James River Canal and the Lynchburg-Knoxville turnpike, which marked it as a distributing center in the pre-railroad days. Lynchburg, which has cotton mills and tobacco factories, has become a basing-point[5] for railroads and is therefore a considerable distributing center. Charlottesville, situated at the crossing of the main line of the Southern Railway going south, and the Norfolk and Western Railway going west, is the center of the Piedmont apple belt and the site of Thomas Jefferson's famous democratic University of Virginia. Nevertheless, it is only a small town of 11,000 people, indicative of the limitations of the Piedmont as a place for cities.

At the edge of the Piedmont are tidewater harbors and waterfalls. These are factors which cause cities to grow, and here on the boundary

[3] It should be remembered that these values are based upon a small tract of land, from 50 to 100 acres, with almost a small village of good buildings.

[4] Lancaster, Pa. ........ 53,000    Durham, N. C. ...... 21,000
York, Pa. ............ 47,000    Winston-Salem, N. C. .. 48,000
Lynchburg, Va. ...... 30,000
[5] See index.

of the Coastal Plain and the Piedmont are Richmond (171,000), Washington (437,000), Baltimore (733,000), Wilmington (110,000), Chester (58,000), Philadelphia (1,823,000), Trenton (119,000).

Richmond is at the edge of the great tobacco belt, and has enormous manufactures of tobacco. It has boats that run to Norfolk, and two railroads, the Norfolk and Western and the Chesapeake and Ohio, coming from the West, give access to the Appalachian coal-field; and it is not far distant from the iron furnaces of the Great Valley. Richmond, being on the Fall Line, has water-power and therefore the possibilities of varied

Fig. 75 — Airplane view showing a part of architectural Washington — the Washington Monument, the Lincoln Memorial, with the Potomac River and Virginia in the distance. (Courtesy U. S. Army Air Service.)

manufacture, as is evidenced by the location there of an important locomotive works and wood-working industries.

Washington, D. C., is a city unique perhaps among the cities of the entire world because of its almost complete lack of any economic basis. Its sole reason for being is political. When the early congresses of the United States could not agree on any important city for the national capital, they compromised by planning a new city in the marshy woods along the Potomac near the home of President George Washington, for whom the new city was named. Washington has a firm basis for growth because this nation is rapidly increasing in numbers and in wealth. Also a greater number of things are being done by government. A single law, the Soldiers' Bonus Bill, gave work to 4100 additional Government employees, most of whom lived in Washington. The World War increased the number of Government employees in Washington alone from 38,000 in 1917 to 111,000 in 1918. The proximity of Washington to the South is indicated by the fact that 25% of its population is negro. Persons who are interested in political affairs like to live in Washington in order that they may be near the center of governmental activity.

Washington is unique among cities of its size in having been planned before it was built. General Washington had Major L'Enfant of the French Army draw up the scheme of right-angle streets, diagonal avenues, and abundant breathing spaces, all of which make the city comfortable and distinctly the most beautiful city in America. The architecture of Government buildings is better than that of most public buildings in America, the Congressional Library indeed being one of the most beautiful buildings in the entire world.

Baltimore was discussed with the Coastal Plain, but Philadelphia seems to partake more of the inland than of the Plain and is presented with the Piedmont. It is a great manufacturing city with more than 2,000,000 people, if we consider its industrial suburbs, which may properly include the thriving city of Chester (58,000), ten miles to the south, Camden (116,309), across the Delaware, and other scattering mill-towns. The census of 1919 showed a total of $1,996,481,000 manufactured products for Philadelphia.

There is no single predominating reason that explains the origin and development of this great city. It is true, however, that it has a number of advantages — it is at the head of ocean navigation; it has two rivers that give good and ample water-front; it is situated at the Falls of the Schuylkill, which made water-power of much relative value in the early days; it is near the anthracite coal-fields and early built a canal and railroad up the Schuylkill Valley to tap these coal-fields; and therefore, Philadelphia was one of the first cities to have a good fuel supply. This same Schuylkill Valley was, until 1870, an important center of iron manufacture, furnishing a basic raw material. The city was settled by thrifty and industrious Quakers and Germans [6] who also settled the surrounding territories, where for two centuries they have tilled the soil and have furnished an abundant food supply. The results of these combined advantages make Philadelphia a city of varied manufacture with,

[6] Philadelphia's population is less foreign than that of cities farther north: — Population, 1,823,779.

| | |
| --- | --- |
| Native white of native parents | 698,000 |
| Foreign-born white | 397,000 |
| Native white of foreign parents | 447,000 |
| Native white of mixed parents | 144,000 |
| Negro | 134,000 |

however, a strong preponderance of textiles,[7] although machinery, leather, shoe and publishing industries are very important. It has the largest loco-motive plant in the world, and an important ship-building industry.

The Delaware River has two great advantages for ship-building. It is ice-free almost every day of winter, and it is near the machine shops

Fig. 76 — A machine tool, boring and turning mill, machining a safe door. The platform on which the man stands revolves, carrying with it the piece of metal in the center and pushing it against the two pieces of tool-steel which can stand the terrific strain of shaving off the chips visible in the picture. Tool-steel with its well-nigh miraculous cutting power is one of the bases of this age of machinery. The machine can handle larger pieces than it is now working. (Courtesy Wm. Sellers & Co., Inc., Philadelphia.)

and steel mills, the capital and trained labor of the North. It was there-fore natural that in the great ship-building rush of the World War the

[7] Value of Products in Millions of Dollars (1919)

|  | Worsteds | Cotton goods | Woolen goods | Total |
|---|---|---|---|---|
| Philadelphia | 88 | 37 | 36 | 161 |
| Lawrence | 125 | 21 | .. | 146 |
| Fall River | .. | 135 | .. | 135 |
| Lowell | 4 | 60 | 5 | 69 |
| New Bedford | .. | 177 | .. | 177 |

supreme effort should have been centered in the Hog Island Yard, just below Philadelphia. This was by far the largest shipyard ever built. But it was a war activity, for whose product there was no demand in peace. So the shipyard is no longer used and has become a scrap-heap — merely another offering to the great god War.

Wilmington, Delaware, has advantages similar to those of Philadelphia and is rising in importance as a manufacturing center for machinery, cars and vulcanized fiber. But it is better known as the headquarters of the manufacturers of gunpowder, dynamite, and an endless list of chemicals and allied Dupont Company products.

Numerous suburbs of New York are located on the Piedmont hills, but they are pre-eminently dependent upon the commerce of New York harbor and have been discussed in a preceding chapter.

### The Future of the Piedmont

Plainly this district must continue as a land of agriculture. But to prevent deterioration there must be a readjustment of agricultural methods, or soil erosion will reduce it to the condition of a second-class forest. If one compares the rate at which soil is formed with the rate at which the plowed earth is gullied and carried away during a thunderstorm anywhere in the southeastern part of the United States, it becomes plain that the Piedmont farmer must readjust his farming to suit his land. Agricultural readjustments are very slow and hitherto the Piedmont has suffered greatly from soil erosion because men have kept the level-land type of agriculture on rapidly eroding hills.[8] The 378 Chester County, Pa., farms examined by the United States Department of Agriculture showed that only 70% of their land is arable; and many parts of the northern Piedmont are more hilly than Chester County. Therefore if it is to retain the beauty of its landscape and the fertility of its soil, only the more level parts must be intensively cultivated, the steeper parts must be left in pasture or in

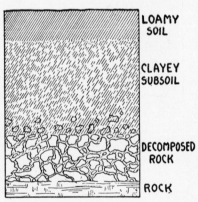

LOAMY SOIL

CLAYEY SUBSOIL

DECOMPOSED ROCK

ROCK

Fig. 77 — In the Piedmont, as in most hill regions, all man has is a thin mantle of earth material between the living plants and the dead bones of bedrock. This thin earth mantle is most difficult to keep. The bedrock yields soil *very slowly*. After plowing begins the gully takes soil away *very rapidly*.

trees. Its fertile soils and good rainfall make it admirable for the development of a tree-crop agriculture in places where now the plow and

[8] The erosive power of water increases 32-fold with doubling of its velocity.

the gully are making ruin with alarming speed.[9]  The wholesome climate of the Piedmont, the absence of the swamps, mosquitoes and malaria which curse parts of the Coastal Plain, make it an attractive place for the homes of men.

The value of the land in the southern part of the Piedmont, namely, the cotton and tobacco belts, is very low, partly because of the damaged condition of the soil and partly because of the continuance of unscientific agriculture.  In the northern Piedmont farm-lands have an unduly

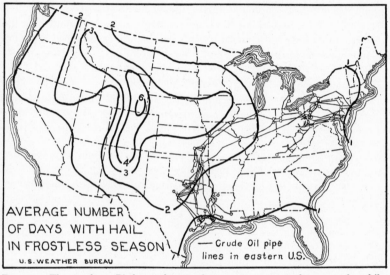

AVERAGE NUMBER OF DAYS WITH HAIL IN FROSTLESS SEASON

U.S. WEATHER BUREAU

— Crude Oil pipe lines in eastern U.S.

FIG. 78 — The northern Piedmont has good access to our petroleum supply while it lasts.

low sale-value because of competition with cheap Western produce and because the young men have gone to work in the cities.  As a result, both before and since the World War Piedmont farms in many localities have been for sale at prices sometimes less than the cost of the buildings.[10]

This is undoubtedly a region where the best type of rural community life should and could be developed.  There is a neighborhood fifteen miles north of Washington, in Montgomery County, Md., that has been

[9] I have evaporated five inches of June gully-water from a Virginia corn-field and had it yield one-half inch of the richest soil in the field.  Careful study of crop-yield on the hillsides and level land of almost any hilly farm anywhere will show great and significant differences in yield.

[10] In 1924 a Pennsylvania farm was sold for $9500.00.  It has seventy-five acres of fertile, tillable land, five never-failing springs; a three-story, fourteen-room stone house of mansion proportions, with running water; commodious barn, with quarters for twenty-five cows and half a dozen horses, a granary and spacious loft; springhouse and other outbuildings.  It lies within one hour by train or automobile from the center of Philadelphia; within half a mile of one railroad station and within

studied by the United States Department of Agriculture as an example of a good community having a satisfactory rural organization.

Why is it a model community? It is not because the soil is better than elsewhere, or that it has superior opportunities for markets. The soil was originally rather poor, and in 1840 was in the same state of ruin as much as the Tobacco Belt today. There was something else that entered into the spirit of the neighborhood and made it something that commanded the interest of the government of the United States. The place was settled by a group of thrifty Quakers with a few college graduates who settled down to be good farmers and to develop a good community. They built stone roads, established good schools and were among the first to install rural telephones. The women's club is the oldest in the United States, and there are now several other women's clubs, four farmers' clubs, and various musical and other social organizations.

The people there can enjoy suitable social contacts without having to go to the cities to get them. What this neighborhood has done can be done anywhere in the Piedmont. It is just a question of the application of intelligence, and the chief task for intelligence today is to adjust life to one's environment.

The good living conditions of its small towns should give northern Piedmont many more small manufacturing towns (2000–10,000 pop.) in the coming era of the universal distribution of electric energy.

---

two miles of three others, all reached by improved roads. The house is only a few rods from a concrete highway, with an hourly bus service.

A man of wide experience in building and real estate asserted that the buildings could not be replaced today for less than $25,000.00. It is true that farms bring more money in this region 150 miles from a big city than they do 30 miles from it.

The $9500.00 paid for this seventy-five-acre farm, with its substantial buildings, would barely buy a two-story dwelling on a sixteen-foot lot in the residential district of Philadelphia or its suburbs. Such facts are causing some migration of farmers from the middle West to the Piedmont, especially to the northern Piedmont.

FIG. 79 — A well-kept farm on the fat lands of the Valley of Virginia. In the background, an Appalachian ridge. (Courtesy Norfolk & Western Railway Co.)

# CHAPTER X

## THE APPALACHIAN RIDGE AND VALLEY REGION

THE Appalachian uplands lying between the Piedmont and the Ohio Valley are divided naturally into parts. The western part, through the Allegheny-Cumberland Plateau (next chapter), has layers of rock nearly horizontal and streams cutting back into it in all directions. The eastern part has its strata folded so that the surface has become a multitude of ridges and valleys. This region will be described in the present chapter.

### PART I. THE GREAT APPALACHIAN VALLEY

One of these Appalachian valleys is much wider than the rest and also longer. Many generations have called this valley the Great Valley. It is a remarkably long valley extending for more than a thousand miles from the St. Lawrence Valley to Central Alabama. The geologist and the physiographer maintain that the Champlain and Hudson lowlands are a part of this Appalachian Valley, but the geographer shows that man cannot use these two parts of the valley in the same way. Access and use make a different economic or geographic region of the part south of the Hudson. It includes a part of seven States (New Jersey, Pennsylvania, Maryland, West Virginia, Virginia, Tennessee and Alabama) but the total area is only about 20,000 square miles, because in all its thousand miles of length, the Valley rarely exceeds twenty-five miles in width and often it is less. While it is properly spoken of as one valley, the Great Valley has different local names because it is drained by a number of streams — the Delaware, Lehigh, Susquehanna, Potomac, Shenandoah, James, Roanoke, New, Holston, Tennessee and Coosa. In northeastern Pennsylvania it is known as the Lehigh Valley; near the Susquehanna, as the Lebanon and Cumberland Valleys; and in northern Virginia as the Shenandoah Valley or the Valley of Virginia. Except for the small area in southeastern Pennsylvania where the Blue Ridge disappears (Fig. 56), the valley is plainly walled in on both sides by sharply rising ridges, known to people in the valley as North Mountain and the Blue Ridge. In some places the valley floor is cut by ridges near its middle which run parallel with the enclosing mountains. At the divides between the various rivers that drain it, such as the Shenandoah, the James, the Roanoke and the Tennessee, the Great Valley rises to nearly 2000 feet, but the ascent is always gentle, and the passage from one river basin to another is so easy that in some cases the traveler would scarcely notice it.

## A Great Highway

This continuity has marked the valley as a great highway. In early times, when the Indians held the plains of western New York, it was the only break in the Appalachians open to the English settlers, and was therefore the highway across the mountains. This explains the fact that Kentucky and not Ohio was the first state west of the Alleghenies. The migrating settlers from Pennsylvania, Maryland and Virginia, and even from North Carolina, drove their wagons down the Great Valley to the boundary of Tennessee. There, at the extreme western corner of Virginia, a break in the western wall called Cumberland Gap gave access to the headwaters of the streams flowing toward the Ohio. Through this passage Daniel Boone and other settlers of Kentucky entered this unknown region of wonders, dangers and good soil.

It is estimated that more than 300,000 people passed through the Great Valley and Cumberland Gap between 1775 and 1800 on their way to settle the West.[1] Back through this same gap later on came the droves of horses, cattle and hogs walking to the Eastern markets. There were so many hogs that the road was known locally as the " Kaintuck hawg road." Because of its access to the north, the valley as far south as the headwaters of the James was settled by people from Pennsylvania. Most of them were Germans but some were Quakers; and many were Scotch-Irish, the people who settled all central Pennsylvania. On the less accessible Piedmont these people got only a short distance south of the Potomac. The Pennsylvania settlers of the northernmost corners of

---

[1] Salisbury, Barrows and Tower, *Elements of Geography*, p. 360. This figures out at something like 12,000 people a year, or 2,000 per month during the open months, or fifteen or twenty wagons a day. It must indeed have produced a sensation of endless moving for those who lived on that road to see a wagon go by every half hour for six months of every year, each with its family of settlers from the little-known East going into the less-known West.

Virginia came in by way of the Harper's Ferry Gap from the Great Valley.

The service of the valley as a highway came sharply to the fore during the Civil War. As the armies of the North and South strove to menace and protect Richmond and Washington, they found the Coastal Plain chopped by tidal estuaries and the Piedmont hilly and bad traveling for the army wagons, but the Great Valley offered opportunity to travel in a straight line over almost level country where the stone roads were better than those of any other part of the United States. These geographic factors made the Great Valley the chief avenue for the rapid advance of large bodies of soldiers from the North and South. In 1862 and again in 1863, the two great invasions of the North were by way of this valley; that of 1862 was checked at Antietam, in the edge of the Great Valley in Maryland. In 1863 the Southern scouts reached the Susquehanna, and the main army was checked at Gettysburg, a few miles outside the limits of the valley in southern Pennsylvania at a place where the Blue Ridge [2] almost fades away and made easy the possible turn toward Washington. Armies between Washington and Richmond were constantly exposed to the danger of a flank movement up or down the valley and more than once were compelled by this cause to retreat. The importance of the topography of the Great Valley during the Civil War is graphically told in the record of the Great Valley town of Winchester, Va., three miles from the boundary of the Confederacy and the Union. This town changed hands seventy-two times during the four years. It was a few miles south of Winchester that the battle of Cedar Creek occurred, celebrated in verse because of Sheridan's ride. Sheridan had been sent to the valley with a large army because, even in the weakened condition of 1864, the Confederacy had been able to alarm the North and almost able to take Washington by sending the daring raid of General Early through the valley into Maryland and Pennsylvania while Grant's army was hammering Lee before Richmond.

The most direct railroad line from New York to New Orleans traverses the Tennessee-southern Virginia section of the Great Valley.

### The Influences of Limestone

The Great Valley is remarkable because it can be so nearly described in the terms of one geological fact — underlying limestone rock. Because the soft limestones of the region have dissolved and worn away more rapidly than the shales and sandstones upon its edges, the Great Valley was slowly carved, while the harder rocks, because of their resistance, now remain as the ridges of the Blue Ridge and the Allegheny Mountains.

[2] The Northern Army was victorious partly because of its position on a low ridge which the Southern Army had to attack. Note the military influence of the ridge.

Limestone is the best material for making good stone roads; this fact also helps to explain the service of the valley as a highway. It has per county or per thousand people several times as much good stone road as equally rich districts occupied by the same kind of people in the Piedmont but a few miles away. So excellent is the main valley turnpike that for a number of years the best automobile highway from New York to Savannah and Florida was by way of the Great Valley from Harrisburg to Chattanooga, Tenn. The beauty of the country, with its fertile fields, well-kept farms, big barns, productive orchards, and ever-present mountains, makes it a delightful territory for the touring automobilist.

As is usually the case with soils made of decomposed limestone, the valley from end to end is justly famed for its fertility.[3] This fertility enabled it to compete successfully with the cheap lands of the West in the latter part of the nineteenth century, although it was the only section in the East that was able to do so. Here the epoch of abandoned farms so common in many other parts of the East has not come. The valley has not had the same decline of land-values, and as one stands on the top of the Blue Ridge and takes a panoramic view of the Piedmont to the east and the Great Valley to the west, the contrast in the appearance of the country is marked. The Great Valley is conspicuous by its wheatfields and the almost complete absence of forests, while the Piedmont is conspicuous by its woodlands and pastures.

The limestone soil is excellent for wheat, corn and clover, which are, north of Georgia and Alabama, the chief crops of the valley, leading to an export of grain, cattle and dairy produce. It is a prosperous land with tilled fields, neat fence-rows, well-painted houses and big barns. The section of the Great Valley near the Virginia-Tennessee boundary is much intersected by sharp ridges, and the portion of arable land is small, but, as is the case everywhere throughout the valley, the limestone soil produces splendid pastures which are here devoted largely to sheep and cattle. The animals, however, are not prepared for market here, but are shipped off as " stockers " to finish their preparation in localities where a greater proportion of arable land gives crops of grain and hay.

In its southern part, the part in Alabama and Georgia, the climate of the Great Valley is warm enough to permit the growth of cotton. (The agriculture of this part of the valley is presented in the chapter on the Cotton Belt.)

The limestone is not without its disadvantages. It weathers unevenly and the fertile fields are often surprisingly obstructed with outcropping knolls or long rows of projecting stones left from a harder stratum. These

[3] It is not universally composed of limestone, for shale formations of much lower fertility occasionally cover the valley floor and give sharp contrasts of fertility and poverty of soil, crops and farm buildings.

stone patches are usually dotted with trees and matted with blue grass.
The valley farmer has developed much ingenuity in working modern
machines around stones.   The solubility of limestone means that here,
as in nearly all other limestone localities, the country is underlaid with
a series of caves and underground passages which carry the water away
from the surface, so that in comparison with the near-by Piedmont it is
strangely devoid of springs and streams.   The water table is not so near
the surface, so that the farmers and towns also often suffer from water
shortage.[4]   The caves are not without some value, for at Luray and
Shenandoah Caverns and at Natural Bridge we have scenic phenomena
of increasing interest to travelers.   The Natural Bridge is a section of
cave-roof that has not yet fallen in.

FIG. 80 — Orchards on top of Apple-pie Ridge are almost continuous for miles
between Winchester, Va., and Martinsburg, W. Va.   This is a low ridge in
the Great Valley.   In the orcharding business the East has much to learn
from the West.   (Courtesy Berkeley County Fruit Growers' Assn., W. Va.)

### Apples

The lower part of the Shenandoah Valley is developing a specialty of
apple-growing, with the chief centers near Winchester and Martinsburg.

[4] The rainfall is slightly less than in the Piedmont, because of the enclosing
mountain walls.  Frederick, alt. 275 on Piedmont, 40 inches; Hagerstown, alt. 560,
Great Valley, 36 inches.  It is 32 inches 40 miles S.W. of Hagerstown in enclosed
valleys.

A few miles west of the railroad connecting these places is a low ridge which for a century and a half has been called Apple-pie Ridge. It is now so nearly covered with apple orchards that one may travel along its crest for many miles and never be more than 100 yards from an apple orchard. This locality has four million apple trees and cold storage plants that hold a million barrels of apples, but it has no natural advantage for the production of apples not shared by many other Eastern localities.

Concentration of this industry gives us another good illustration of the method whereby a center of agricultural production develops. About the time of the Civil War a farmer planted a twenty-acre field of apples on the slope of the Apple-pie Ridge. His neighbors laughed at him, and at times he himself thought that perhaps he was, as they said, a fool. Nearly twenty years later he sold a crop of apples for $6000.00. Two years later he did it again. A few of his neighbors began to plant orchards. They prospered, and like ripples in a pond of water the planting of apple orchards spread until by 1900 the third circle of converts was beginning to make good profits, and hundreds of acres of apple orchards were being planted.

### Manufacturing

In its manufactures the Great Valley again shows the influence of the limestone, for it lies at the base of two great industries.

Fig. 81 — Scooping Great Valley limestone in 8500 pound bites — material for cement mill, iron furnace, or road-builder. (Courtesy Atlas Portland Cement Co.)

Limestone furnishes a raw material for the cement industry. Cement is made of limestone and shale, burned, ground and intimately mixed. Thus the native rock of the valley and the closely associated shale formations provide these two raw materials for cement in almost every county for the whole of the valley's length. Coal of the near-by Appalachian Plateau or of the valley itself, as in Alabama, furnishes the other necessary raw material. Since the valley is close to the great centers of population it has long had leadership in cement manufacture. The chief center for its production has been the Lehigh Valley district of eastern Pennsylvania, which has the combined advantages of being equally near the anthracite coal useful for fuel, in a district populous with diligent Germans, and near the ports for the arrival of the new immigrants. Allentown, Easton and Phillipsburg, Pa., are the chief cement towns of the Lehigh Valley, which has at times made as much as one-third of the cement output of the United States. But the amount is relatively declining because of rising centers elsewhere, even in the Great Valley itself, as at Hagerstown, Md., Roanoke, Va., Chattanooga, Tenn., and Birmingham, Ala.

In the cement district of Pennsylvania there are also important slate quarries which produce half the product in the United States, chiefly between Slatington and Bangor, where an intensely worked deposit is the largest slate quarry in the world.

The limestone causes the deposits of iron ores which mark the valley formation from Alabama to Lake Champlain. When a stream of water with a little iron in solution flows across limestone it dissolves enough limestone to cause the water to precipitate the iron as ore. Thus limestone and iron-ore are associated throughout the world, and the Lehigh and Schuylkill valley sections of the Great Valley were early centers of modern iron manufacture in the United States. At the present time iron is made in this valley at Harrisburg, Bethlehem, Lebanon, Pa.; at Roanoke, Va.; several places in eastern Tennessee, and especially in Birmingham, Ala. Birmingham is unique among the world's iron centers. There, and there only, do we find within the same township an abundance of the three great raw materials of iron ore, limestone, and coal, which explains the superiority of this over all other districts for making iron cheaply. For these reasons the site of a cornfield in 1870 is now a city whose population increased from 132,000 in 1910 to 178,800 in 1920.

With the exception of Birmingham, no Great Valley city has enough superiority over any other to produce great leadership in size. The valley is long and narrow with a tendency to have a string of towns near its center, each of which is a kind of local commercial capital of a fertile district but is not able to command a large territory. Where a plateau stream crosses the valley, giving access on the east to the Piedmont and the ocean and, on the west, to the Appalachians, we find a crossing of the ways, with some advantage of access and consequently a town larger than its neighbors.[5]

[5] With a railroad map one can easily see the location factors; in Bethlehem (50 thousand), Harrisburg (75), Hagerstown (28), Martinsburg (12), Staunton (10), Roanoke (50), Chattanooga (57).

For manufacturing resources and opportunities towns are much alike save for the cement advantage of the northern end and the iron advantage of the southern end. Chattanooga, Knoxville and other smaller towns between them on the Tennessee River will have barge and steamboat transport down the Tennessee to the Ohio and Mississippi as soon as the Muscle Shoals improvements are completed. Railroads have easy grades to the cotton-fields and New Orleans. Coal-mines in the plateau to the west of them are so close that trucks sometimes haul the coal from mine to factory. Copper and bauxite are mined near by. Marble is abundant. There is much unused water-power. Taking it altogether, this resembles the Ruhr Valley of Germany, differing only in that its material resources are richer and far less developed. Knoxville doubled its population between 1910 and 1920. The reasons are plain.

Throughout its whole length the valley has the raw materials of lime-stone, shale, and coal from near-by Appalachia, as well as the wood from the Appalachian forests. The influence of the abundant wood supplies of the near-by Appalachians is shown in the small city of Hagerstown where eighteen manufacturing plants use wood in carload lots. Being on through lines of the railroads from the South, the valley is the highway for the passage of cotton from the Gulf plains to the port of New York. The industries are primarily cement, iron and steel, machinery and wood manufactures, with an increasing attention to textiles, chiefly silk and cotton.

## Future

The future of the Great Valley seems to be plainly marked in the continuation of its present. Everywhere it is a region of beautiful landscape, healthful climate, fertile soil, with abundant supplies of the raw materials that mark its present industries. It will soon be supplied with electric power from mine-mouths and water-power plants. It seems to be plainly destined for a continued growth in manufacture which will dot it from end to end with a succession of small cities. These will have the great advantage of not becoming metropolises in size, and for that reason will have better opportunities to get food, raw material and space to live. It is a beautiful land. Everywhere the refreshing mountain will be in sight, beckoning man to climb and enjoy vistas of charming landscapes. This increasing city population in many units will intensify the agriculture.

The limy soil of the valley is especially suited to the walnut tree, and the rocky pastures and the untillable rough spots in Great Valley fields offer sites for enough walnut trees to add millions of income without interfering with any other crop. The fertile but unplowable rocky pastures that nearly everywhere abound offer an unusually favorable opening for a tree-top agriculture with such crops as the walnut, hickory, pecan, persimmon, and mulberry, of which excellent native or imported varieties have already been domesticated. The list of such possible tree crops may be indefinitely extended through selection, breeding and importation of desirable strains. The semi-suburban character of the valley settlement affords an excellent background for such an agriculture, requiring high intelligence.

## PART II. THE APPALACHIAN RIDGE COUNTRY

West of the Great Valley, and extending from East Central Tennessee almost to the Delaware River, is a district like the Great Valley in geologic origin but different in that it is such a succession of ridges and valleys that its surface has much more of ridge than it has of valley. In this ridge country the rock layers have been so much folded that in the territory west of Harrisburg, Pa., geologists have come to the conclusion that eighty-one miles have been compressed into sixty-six, showing eleven principal folds and many more ridges. In bygone millenniums, this area was worn down by the streams almost to a flat plain with its surface near the tops of the present ridges. Then the whole area was raised. This gave the streams a chance to wear it down again, and they cut the present valleys where the rocks are soft and left the hard rocks, chiefly sandstones and conglomerates; and these make the present ridges. Irregularities in folding made the hard layers produce parallel ridges, zigzag ridges and ridges that surround canoe-shaped valleys.

One such valley, that of the Kishicoquillas Creek, is fifty-three miles by four miles, with only one outlet, which is near Lewisburg, Pa.

Particular ridges of this Appalachian Ridge district are usually twenty-five to fifty miles long, although there is one that has been traced for more than 300 miles.

This mass of ridges and valleys has a sharp western boundary at the place where the folding of the rocks stopped and the beginning of the

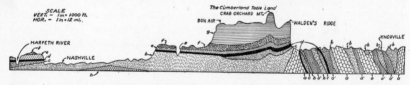

FIG. 82 — Cross section from the Carolina Mountains through the Great Valley of East Tennessee, the Cumberland Plateau, the Nashville Basin, and the eastern and western Highland Rim. The letters show the appearance and reappearance of the various strata and explain how the Great Valley soils have islands of less fertile shale. (Tennessee Dept. Agr.)

horizontal formation makes the eastern edge of the Appalachian Plateau. This is one of the most clearly marked plateau fronts to be found anywhere, and is known for hundreds of miles as the Allegheny Front, a mountain with an ascent 1000 or 1500 feet from the east. At the top the nearly level plateau reaches far to the westward.

The chief streams of the region had their locations before the last great uplift started them to cutting out their present valleys. Therefore they flowed across both hard and soft rocks. Some streams have been able to saw their way through the layers of hard rock that remain as mountains, producing such well-known features as the Delaware Water Gap, the gap at Harpers Ferry, W. Va., and many other gaps often called wind-gaps in which streams no longer flow. All the smaller streams now run lengthwise of the smaller valleys, giving a trellis effect to the map of the rivers (Fig. 83). The district as a whole is therefore a gigantic corrugation, a collection of long narrow ridges and long narrow valleys sharply separated from the neighboring valleys by steep, sharp-topped ridges which often run past county after county without a break. A colored county map shows how uniformly these ridges have become the boundaries of counties in central Pennsylvania.

Fortunately for man, the master streams that cross the whole series, Susquehanna, Potomac, James, New Kanawha, have made it possible for the railroads to get through the ridges in the narrow gaps. Often the track is close to the stream on one side, and cliffs of jagged rock overhang it on the other side.

### Varied Conditions

Its method of formation makes the Appalachian Ridge Country almost as varied in economic opportunity and economic and social develop-

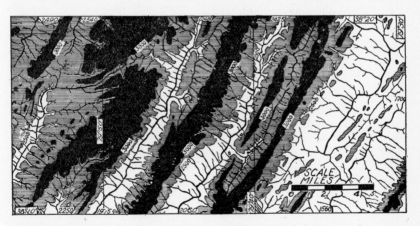

Fig. 83 — Section of Appalachian Ridge and Valley. Black areas are above 3000 feet; white, below 2500 feet. For location see A, Fig. 56.

ment as is New England itself. Often the valleys are so narrow as to be almost V-shaped gorges. There the farmer must wrestle with the slopes of shale hills or at best find but a small field or two on the valley floor. In other places the limestone formations appear and the valleys are rich like small sections of the Great Valley. A few of them widen out into fertile areas locally famed for their rich farms and prosperity. Thus in southwestern Virginia such a limestone pocket [6] known as Burke Garden is regarded as one of the natural curiosities of the State. In Bedford County, Pa., another limestone valley occupied by thrifty Quakers and known as Friends' Cove, offers a marked contrast to the poverty of some adjajcent shale formations of steeper slope, low productivity, soil erosion and farm abandonment — a feature which in some localities makes the Ridge Country a close rival to parts of New England.

## Agriculture

Farming is the chief support of the people, and it is upon the whole in a rather decadent condition, with notable exceptions previously mentioned. Because of the complete absence of cities over most of its area,[7] there is no near-by market for hay and milk as is the case in New England or the Great Valley. General farming is the rule — some wheat, some corn, some cattle, occasionally some hogs, with a small amount of dairying. Satisfactory dairying requires a scientific agriculture and more dairy cattle than are possessed by most localities in this rather ill-developed region.

Transport is most difficult. The narrow valleys support a few people, but not enough to build or maintain good roads. The winding stream that drains the valley often swings from side to side so that the main valley road must cross and recross. I recall twenty-seven such crossings in thirty miles in one valley, and all the crossings were fords which became uncrossable after rain. The cost of twenty-seven good bridges on that stream would have bankrupted all the people in this little valley. The people in hundreds of localities have from five to forty miles of such dirt road between their homes and the freight station. For evident reasons most of this ridge and valley country is without railroads save for the main lines which, at great expense, have been built as through lines to reach the plateau on the west.

All these difficulties of soil and surface seem to be almost a conspiracy of nature against the farmer with his plow and reaper. This is not a land of the big red barn as in the Great Valley. The soils, usually shale, usually hilly and of but medium fertility, have in many cases been

[6] This little valley, 5 × 6 miles, has the same limestone formation as the best of the Great Valley. Its splendid blue grass pastures, like those of other such Appalachian valleys, fatten cattle without a grain ration. " Raising export cattle is about the only industry. It is hard to say what this land is worth as it is not sold. The only way to get it is to inherit it or marry it, and it is hard for an outsider to do either." (R. J. Holden, *Virginia Polytechnic.*)

[7] Aside from the anthracite coal towns, the only cities in this region are Cumberland, Md., Altoona and Williamsport, Pa. They are all close to the Allegheny Front and chiefly dependent upon the pay-roll of railroad repair-shops on through-line railways.

made very unproductive for grain and grass by unscientific cropping and by washing. As a result almost whole townships are for sale at a few dollars an acre. With these rather dispiriting conditions, many localities have suffered because many of their people capable of leadership have gone to Eastern cities or Western farms or plateau mines. When their natural leaders are gone, neighborhoods stagnate. Such communities offer a great opportunity for commercial fruit-growing, for which the land has unusual resources.

The succession of ridges rising several hundred feet above the near-by valleys affords excellent frost drainage. This explains why the peach

FIG. 84 — Typical mountain farm, log buildings, rail fences, split palings about the yard, split shingles on the roof, and hillsides that will be eroded and ruined by plow culture. (Courtesy *North and South Magazine*, Louisville, Ky.)

crops in farmers' orchards on some of these ridges have come with un-failing regularity at times when there has been a great scarcity of peaches because of the general destruction by cold waves which kill the crops of commercial orchards in less protected locations.[8]

The second factor is the market location. That part of the Ridge Country in the drainage basin of the Potomac combines the contrast of elevation for frost drainage with a location on two trunk railways; namely, the Baltimore and Ohio, and the Western Maryland, each of which goes from seaboard cities to Pittsburgh and the Middle West cities. At sundown the fruit shipper can decide whether he will have his car of fruit the next morning in Pittsburgh or New York.

The shale soil merging into the rotten, deeply fissured rock is excellent for both peaches and apples, and the very low prices of from $5.00 to $25.00 an acre are a pronounced advantage in comparison with $100.00 to $200.00 or more in western New York, the Great Valley or the Pacific

[8] Mr. H. W. Miller, operating large orchards on ridges near the Potomac, reports frequent frost damage at 1500 feet, the bottom of his orchards; occasional freezes at the top 2800 feet, and frost immunity between.

Slope.   The fairly numerous population furnishes an excellent labor
supply for the spasmodic work of orcharding, if scientific supervision is
provided.   This combination of conditions has attracted a number of
men of energy and capital from outside districts, so that along the Potomac between North Mountain and the Allegheny Front (the eastern and
western edges of the Ridge section) there are more than 50,000 acres of
peaches and apples.   As evidence of the influence of the human element,

namely, leadership, I cite
the case of three families,
controlling a n d operating
about 2000 acres of peach
and apple orchards, in which
some of the work is often
done by the men who sold
the land to the enterprising
newcomers.

This district is n e a r
enough to Washington to
be selected by a number of
government officials w i t h
horticultural instincts as
places for corporate enterprises in which they are
part owners and consultants.
The fruit industry is still in
its infancy with large acreages of young orchards. It
is much the most important
agricultural industry in the

FIG. 85 — Fire-killed forest typical of the west
(windward) side of thousands of miles of
Appalachian Ridge. (Courtesy Anthony
Euwer, Portland, Ore.)

Ridge Country. With steepness, rocks and isolation,
most of the surface of this
area is or should be in forest.

Unfortunately most of the forest is a ruin because of repeated fires.
Many fires are deliberately but mysteriously started to burn the young
trees so that huckleberries may grow — huckleberry deserts they should
be called.   Since huckleberries come best with a fire every two or three
years the fires are expected with the regularity of the returning seasons.
Since huckleberries here are public property and waste by millions of
gallons, the landless starter of fires gets all the berries he wants for himself and his children (especially the children) to pick.   Meanwhile the
timber famine looms.

There is no reason to expect that orchards will occupy even a large
proportion of the soil suited for this purpose.   The reason is not far

to seek. The good fruit ridges are so much more extensive than the market for their product that over-production is the ogre of the peach-grower and even of the apple-grower. When all the peach districts have a good crop, the price is so low that few make money. Thus a certain fruit farm in the Appalachians shipped a car of Belle of Georgia peaches in the scant year 1916, and received a check for $1015.00, while the year before a car of the same fruit from the same orchard did not bring enough money to pay the freight and commission, leaving the farm with the whole cost of growing, picking, packing, hauling to the station, as an additional dead loss.

It is a shame that this land of beautiful ridges cannot be put to uses that suit it rather than to uses that gut it. The Swiss example shows us what it may become when we have adjusted our industries to our resources. This land is naturally more productive than Switzerland. The climate is warm enough for corn — king of crops. Switzerland has well-tilled valleys, slopes with terraced orchards and vineyards, upland pastures producing cheese from cows and goats, and finally forests that hold the rough land and yield wood as regularly as any other crop yields harvest.

While there is no market for great extension of peach and apple growing, there is an indefinite market for meat, and a tree-crop agriculture might be developed to furnish food for hogs and poultry.[9] The frost immunity of the shale ridges makes this country peculiarly suitable for tree crops subject to injury by spring frost.

### Anthracite Coal

Near the place where the ridges merge into the plateau, in the extreme northern end of the Ridge and Valley country, is a concentrated raw material of national importance — Pennsylvania anthracite coal. In certain down-bending strata, the processes of erosion have not yet reached some 480 square miles of anthracite coal which is but a remnant

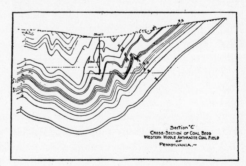

FIG. 86 — The bent and slanting strata show why anthracite coal is expensive to mine.

of a vast amount that has long since gone down to the sea. It is expensive to mine because the bending of the strata has made the coal layers bent

---

[9] The nutritious mulberry ripens its fruit for ten weeks in summer and is considered by many Carolina farmers to be as valuable as corn, acre for acre. The persimmon is equally valuable in the autumn. Acorns, beech nuts, and hickory nuts are mast — the natural food of swine in the primeval home.

and crooked.  The great demand from the heavy populations of the Eastern States has built up a great mining industry in the valleys of the
upper Schuylkill and the eastern branch of the Susquehanna.  Here we
have a collection of cities.  Population, 1920: Scranton, 137,000; Wilkes-
barre, 73,000; Plymouth, 16,000; Pittston, 18,000; Pottsville, 21,000;
Shamokin, 21,000; Hazelton, 32,000; Mahanoy City, 15,000; and numerous small towns whose sole cause for being is anthracite coal.  The
total population, depending in one way or another upon these deposits, is
at least a million people, many of whom are recent arrivals from the
old world.  This locality seems to be one of the great magnets to attract
the newly arrived immigrant.  In the middle of the nineteenth century
the coal was dug by Welsh and Irish miners, especially Welsh.  Then
came Irish, then Italians, and later East European Slavs, so that the
language spoken in the anthracite region is a mixture like that of Central Europe where the late empire of Austria-Hungary had eleven languages officially recognized.

The 80 million tons of freight that come out of these mines make the
anthracite district a traffic magnet to which seven railroads have been
built to carry the precious smokeless house fuel to its scattered market.

Much labor is needed to separate this coal from the slate and prepare
it for use.  This is done in buildings called breakers, huge structures,
tall, gaunt and black and rising from a blackened landscape.

A journey through the anthracite coal district brings forcibly to the
mind the name of " robber industry " which Europeans have applied to
mining.  It destroys, and can neither preserve nor restore.  We see this
in the great black banks of culm (or mine refuse) that encumber the
surface of the earth, in the holes which follow the cessation of mining,
and the falling in of mine roofs.  The earth suddenly opens and in falls
your cellar, your house, your church, your locomotive, your cow, your
child, even the bodies of your dead in the cemetery.

The practice of selling mineral rights separate from the land has
caused parts of cities to be undermined, to the peril of the buildings
above.

It is estimated that 800 million tons of good coal underlie the town of
Pottsville.  The Arabs build their villages *outside* of the *date* oasis.

A group of secondary industries followed the development of mines.
Cars, wire cable and machinery used in the mines are made near by.
But the most conspicuous industry above ground is the textile industry,
especially silk.  This industry gives work to the women of the families
whose male members are engaged in the heavier industries.  This complementary relationship of the textile mill and the machine shop and
mine has made Pennsylvania important in silk manufactures also.

The future of the anthracite town is an interesting puzzle.  The mines
must be worked out in a few generations.  According to some estimates

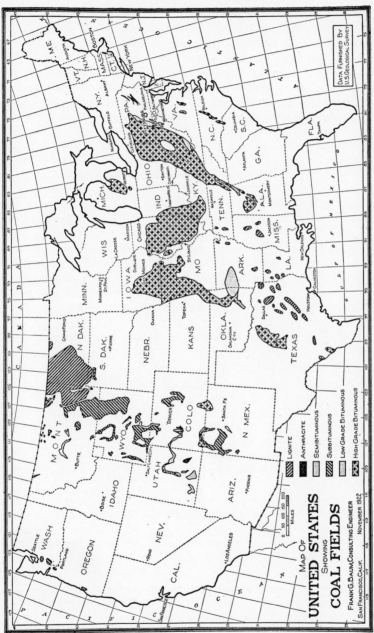

FIG. 87 — This map shows the small area of the anthracite fields and makes it clear how a few companies can control it all. (Baum's *Atlas of the U. S. A. Electric Power Industry*).

it will be 150 years at the *present* rate of production. The most accessible mines were opened first and the increasing cost of mining the anthracite may before long cause the output to decline in competition with
the cheaper and much more abundant bituminous coal. People in these
cities must then develop other industries or move away. But there is
great staying power in established industry, and it should be remembered
that these cities are as well placed as many New England cities for
manufacturing imported materials.

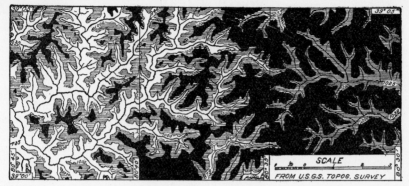

Fig. 88 — A section of the dissected plateau showing how the streams have eaten a labyrinth of valleys. Black areas are above 1200 feet, white, below 1000 feet. For location see B, Fig. 56.

# CHAPTER XI

## THE APPALACHIAN PLATEAU AND THE CAROLINA MOUNTAINS

WEST of the Allegheny Front the rock strata, so contorted in the Ridge Country, lie in almost horizontal layers which slope gently to the west. This is the Appalachian Plateau whose northern edges overlook the Mohawk Valley and the Hudson Valley and whose southern end merges gradually into the Gulf slope in the cotton belt of Alabama. This region of horizontal rocks has been cut by numberless streams into a labyrinth of sharp valleys — a dissected plateau.

The eastern boundary of the region is formed by the Allegheny Front, which extends from Tennessee to Pennsylvania, and includes the steep eastern wall of the Catskills in New York. The western boundary is less definite because the plateau slopes gently westward and finally merges into the lake plain and the hills of the Ohio Valley.

To one crossing it by rail this plateau appears to be a series of mountains. This is because the railroads follow the deeper valleys which the larger streams have cut through the plateau. The steep valley walls look like mountains. The tops of these many mountains usually have the same level in the same locality — the level of the ancient plateau. The tops of the many hills are often sharp, and again sometimes extensive stretches of the old plateau remain, bits of land very hard to reach with a vehicle — dissected remnants of an old plateau.

### The Northern Part of the Plateau

That part of the plateau which is in New York State and the northeastern part of Pennsylvania is more extensively eroded and lower in elevation than the southern part. Therefore, the surface is composed of rolling hills which are no steeper than parts of the Northern Piedmont and, like it, are used for general farming and dairying. This area has been glaciated; it has many small lakes and certain places have been visited by the glacial curse of stone, though not so extensively as in New England. This section has the best agriculture of all the plateau. Like New England its chief dependence is in the pasture field, the hay field, silo and dairy cow.[1]

Express trains, carrying milk only, run from the New York part of the plateau to the great city markets. The map of creameries and cheese factories shows a surprising number of these plants. A rough country which has much pasture but little tilled land is admirably suited to the cheese industry. Milk and butter dealers require a regular supply throughout the year, but cheese, because it keeps well, can be made in the summer season while the cows are at pasture, and stored for future use. It is interesting to find this development of the plateau industry here; it is a response to environment like the extensive cheese industries of certain mountain districts of Europe, as in Switzerland, France and Italy.

About two-thirds of the nation's supply of buckwheat is grown in this part of the plateau. This crop is peculiarly suited to cool climate and rough or poor land. It has great ability to feed, which means that it can make a crop on poor soil. Buckwheat grows so quickly that it can be planted and still mature after a late May or June frost has killed the corn of an earlier planting.

This Northern Plateau is crossed by two New York to Buffalo trunk-line railroads — the Lehigh Valley and the Delaware, Lackawanna and Western. These roads carry anthracite coal and the commerce of the two leading cities, Elmira (pop. 45,000) and Binghamton. With adjacent communities Binghamton has 110,000 people whose chief industrial occupation is making shoes. A Binghamton shoe factory is the largest in the world, and it seems to be a model of good management and efficiency. The plant employs almost half of the industrial workers of the community, and turns out a dozen pairs of shoes per day per worker. If all the shoe operatives of the United States did as much, only one-fourth of the present number would be required to make all our shoes. The shoe factory at Binghamton is an example of the amazing possibilities of machine manufacture when controlled by good management. The amazing inefficiency of many American factories is not generally known.

### The Central and Southern Section

In north central Pennsylvania one sees the sharp valley and pointed ridge type of landscape. The rough land has remained uncleared. On one forty-four-mile trail between the Pennsylvania towns of Bradford and Kane there were but two houses in 1920.

---

[1] We see a resemblance to New England in eighteen contiguous abandoned farms in northeastern Pennsylvania in 1921. This fact helps to bear out New York State's reported loss of 4% of the farming population in one year, 1920, of exceptionally prosperous city wages.

FIG. 89 — What should be your notions if you had been born, had lived, and had made your living upstream from here at a place that could only be reached by riding ten or fifteen miles on horseback, often along creek bottoms — when not in flood? Typical Allegheny Plateau, where streams have cut almost the whole land into steep slopes, leaving sharp hilltops of almost uniform level. Little Savage River, W. Va. (Courtesy Baltimore & Ohio R. R.)

This dissected plateau of sharp valleys and steep hills extends south-ward through West Virginia, Kentucky and Tennessee. In Tennessee the streams have not eaten their way into all of the plateau and part, therefore, remains as a table-land, although it is flanked and shut off by many miles of sharp valleys. This steep land of Southern Appalachia is heavily peopled considering its resources and life conditions. South of central West Virginia isolation is the great dominating factor of much of the mountain country. It has given the people a distinctive character.

As everyone knows, the Southern Highlanders are an interesting people. It is not easy to establish definitely the lines of their ancestry, but the following opinion of Mr. Cecil J. Sharp is quoted by Mr. Campbell.[2]

" Perhaps Mr. Sharp's designation ' Anglo-Celtic ' may be a name under which can unite the contending forces that have arrayed themselves as supporters on the one hand of the claim to Scotch-Irish blood, and on the other to Anglo-Saxon lineage — meaning thereby pure English, Without doubt these two elements are the strongest in the mountain population, though the Highland people are not different from the Low-land Southerners in this respect. The Scotch-Irish strain is strongest in some mountain sections; the English in others."

When these people emigrated to this continent, many of them landed at Philadelphia to join Penn's more tolerant colony. Gradually they pushed their way up the Cumberland Valley into Maryland, then up the valley of the Shenandoah and the narrow valleys of southwestern Virginia. Then they pressed beyond the Cumberland Gap and gradually took possession of the great region of the Southern Appalachians. As Bishop Burleson well puts it:

" Most of them broke through the barrier of the mountains and founded new commonwealths in Kentucky and Tennessee. But some stopped in the mountains. A horse died, a cart broke down, a young couple could not leave the little grave of their only child; fatigue, illness, the lure of the mountains — now it was one thing and now another; but when the host had passed, there were scattered dwellings being reared among the great hills, and a few hundreds — progenitors of many thousands — had begun a course of life which was to continue unchanged for genera-tions. They came in poor, . . . and they are today the poorest people in America. As in all races, there are different grades among them, ranging from the fairly well-to-do farmers along the river valleys to the squatters in the cabins on the high mountains, where the cultivated land is often so steep that the harvested crops can only be brought down in sleds."

This condition makes trade, in the modern sense, impossible.[3] There-

[2] Campbell, J. C., *The Southern Highlander and His Homeland*.
[3] The following direction for a journey shows the importance of streams in travel and transport. "From the ' college ' go down Greasy six miles to the mouth of Rockhouse; go up Rockhouse and take the right fork over the mountain; across

fore the mountaineer has remained in the primitive stage where farming yields a bare subsistence and condemns the people to a life of poverty. The poorer mountain farmer usually has woodland, a steep field or two, fenced with rails, a cabin to live in, a gun, an axe, a home-made plow, a rude wagon, or, if the ground is too steep for wheels, a sled. The usual farm animals consist of one or two oxen, a cow, some pigs and

FIG. 90 — "Our contemporary ancestors" in the Appalachians still turn out to build their neighbor a house in the course of the day, quite independent of architects, contractors, labor unions, cement plants, brick manufacturers, hardware trusts, and electricians. (Courtesy Olive D. Campbell.)

sheep that run in the forest. If the family is more prosperous it may have a horse or two.

In this environment there is no chance to sell a few bushels of corn, but corn made into whisky is a source of income. Therefore, the United States Internal Revenue Tax on whisky threw the mountaineers of western Pennsylvania into armed rebellion in George Washington's first administration. They fled from the United States army, but they kept on distilling and have waged ceaseless guerrilla warfare against the Revenue officers. The mountaineer receives a great ovation from the neighbors

Wolf and Coon to the headwaters of Cutshin; down Cutshin, forking three times; up Flacky, across a right rough little hill to the head of Owl's Nest; down Owl's Nest to Middle Fork, and up Middle Fork a piece to a deep ford; ford the river, and you are at the place you are aiming at." *The Southern Highlander and His Homeland*, by John C. Campbell, p. 36.

The fact that roads are so often in or along the streams is a great bar to travel. Any rain may keep the children home from school by flooding the roads.

when he returns from the penitentiary after serving time for shooting a " revenooer."

The mountaineer woman often has pitifully few household utensils, perhaps no stove; she may even yet be using the spinning-wheel, for if you have nothing to sell you cannot buy and therefore you must make what you have or else you must do without.[4]

This is a land of fried pork, fried squirrel and corn cakes or corn pone and beans. Corn is the mainstay. It is the chief crop, almost the only crop, of thousands of these mountain farms.

For the most part, pre-Revolutionary ideas remain where the mode of

FIG. 91 — If you live in a one-crop country, and that crop is corn, and you must grow it on hillsides like this, poverty is explained — and also " corn licker," and a century of strife with the revenue officer. (Courtesy Olive D. Campbell.)

life is pre-Revolutionary. In most places books and newspapers have killed out the age-old practice of singing ballads, but the collectors of this form of folklore have made in Southern Appalachia a rich collection of Elizabethan song. Shakespearean language long in disuse in England and in the Atlantic Coast Plain where these people once lived survives in Appalachia.

The private rifle is still used to settle personal difficulties, and family feuds, with plenty of killing, still survive.[5]

[4] For vivid and accurate pictures of geography and people of the mountains, see the novels of John Fox, Jr.: *Blue Grass and Rhodendron, Courtin' on Cutshin* and others. *Our Southern Highlanders,* Horace Kephart; *The Southern Highlander and His Homeland,* 403 pp., by John C. Campbell, 1921, the work of a sane and sympathetic missionary. *The Kentucky Mountains, Transportation and Commerce 1750–1911,* Mary Verhoeff — a mine of information. "The Anglo-Saxons of the Kentucky Mountains: A Study in Authropogeography," by E. C. Semple, *Geog. Jour.,* Vol. 17, 1901, 35 pp.; excellent.

[5] To get the spirit of the feudist re-read Scott's " Lady of the Lake " and remember that many of the Allegheny Plateau people are Scotch. The following story shows the feudist — at his best and worst:

In the first few years of this century one of the many old feuds of the Kentucky

As a supreme example of the influence of isolation on ideas I cite the following: In the fall of 1922 a school teacher was dismissed in the heart of this region for teaching that the world was round. It was proved to be "agin Scripture." The school board upheld the teacher but some of the mountain families took their children from school. The young man had to go.

Illiteracy is high in the Southern Highlands, but illiteracy does not prove anything about one's brain capacity. We were all recently illiterate, and furthermore, gentlemen are born, not made with print. Friends of the mountaineer state it thus:

"It is the fatal fallacy of a public-schooled world that literacy is counted the earmark of civilization. The keenest intelligence, the sweetest behavior, the most high-born distinction of manner are gifts of the gods to those who can neither read nor write. A dear friend once said: 'We-uns that cain't read or write have a heap of time to think, and that's the reason we know more than you-all.'" [6]

"If the time ever comes when the requirements for citizenship are based on intelligence rather than information, perhaps these people will make a better showing than the multitude in cities

FIG. 92 — If this road is your outlet to the world market it is not hard to understand why little is sold and little is bought. Mountains of western North Carolina. (Courtesy O. W. Price, U. S. Dept. Agr.)

---

mountains broke out afresh more than forty miles from the nearest railroad station. Within a year a hundred men had been shot. About this time one of the young men, named Burns, had managed to go away and get six months of schooling and then, despite lack of preparation, a year in Dennison University. He went back home, called together at an appointed place twenty men of his clan and twenty men of the other clan. They met armed to the teeth, young Burns standing between them. A wrong gesture or tone might have caused the death of a dozen men on the spot. But there was no shooting — instead Burns persuaded them to start a school. Twenty years later the school had 1200 acres of land and was in a prosperous community. Feud fighting has stayed down because education has put it down and all because of the enthusiasm and energy of one man working with a neighborhood of high-spirited people — honorable after their own code. It is a great and inspiring story as Burns now tells it on the lecture platform. (Information from Paul M. Pearson.)

[6] An article in the *Survey*, March 13, 1917, page 267.

who have just enough education to read the sporting pages of the newspapers." [7]

The missionary spirit of other parts of the United States (chiefly the North) is sending nearly a million dollars a year to the Southern Highlands in the attempt to give the people an opportunity for education.[8]

Some of the schools, particularly the older schools, and those of the type called church schools, have adhered too closely to the classical course. One such school, in forty years, sent not one graduate back to the mountains. The concept of fitting a man to live in his environment guides some of the more recent schools.

For example a school at Madison, Tennessee (near Nashville), teaches

Fig. 93 — The mountain home must be nearly independent or very uncomfortable. Wild berries, game, home-grown meat, and dairy products reduce cash outlay. (Courtesy Wisconsin Dept. Agr.)

mountain girls elementary education and cooking, dietetics, and the elements of home nursing. In connection with the school is a sanitarium. The boys run the farm, learn farming, the care of milk goats, and cheese and butter making. These young people often take goats back to the mountain and start local schools similar to the school at Madison.

[7] From *Distribution of Illiteracy in Alabama in 1920*, by Roland M. Harper.

[8] In 1917 I met Cecil J. Sharp, Director of the Stratford-upon-Avon School of Folk Lore and Folk Dancing. He was at Knoxville, Tennessee, just back from the mountains, joyful over a book full of new ballads, copied down as people had sung them to him. " These missionaries with their schools! " he exclaimed indignantly. " I'd like to build a wall about these mountains and let the mountain people alone. The only *distinctive culture in America is here*. These people *live*. They sustain themselves on the *meanest* food. They are not interested in eating but they have time to sing ballads."

At Pine Mountain Settlement School in Harlan County, Kentucky, the fireside industry of weaving has recently been revived. " Every blanket copied from some old pattern is a hand-made product. The wool is sheared, washed, carded and spun by hand, and colored by our children according to ancient recipes, from bark and roots which our forestry boys have gathered by forestry regulations. Our brown from walnut, our hickory yellow, the soft pink of ' spruce pine ' and many others have come out with a fair degree of success. The story of the search for the famous blue of the Kentucky Mountain coverlet is a complete one in itself, and must wait for more space in another issue of the Notes." [9]

## Fuel and Power

The Allegheny Plateau should have been called the Plateau of Vulcan. In no other place has nature made such variety and wealth of fuel. On the hills are pine forests; on the hillside are outcrops of coal; the rocks when pierced release natural gas and petroleum. Here indeed is the basis for a rich materialism; here is the power-house of the richest nation in the world.

Coal underlies most of the plateau from Alabama almost to the northern edge of Pennsylvania. Pennsylvania alone has nearly 20,000 square miles of bituminous coal land, and that is less than half of this Appalachian coal field. The oil field extends diagonally down the Allegheny Valley and on past Pittsburgh into West Virginia and Kentucky. Oil was found in the Allegheny Valley in 1859, and that was the beginning of the world's petroleum industry. Unfortunately, an oil deposit is only a temporary resource; Pennsylvania, once the leader of the oil-producing states, has long since been surpassed. Oil fields where men feverishly made their millions are now scenes of desolation and decay. Gas wells that once discharged their millions of cubic feet per day have breathed their last [10] and no longer deliver that most usable of all fuels.

At present the southwestern extension of the field in West Virginia is productive of both oil and gas both of which are piped to near-by cities and to points as far away as Baltimore. The combination of oil, gas and cheap coal gave western Pennsylvania an era of cheap fuel, an era

[9] Quoted from " Notes from the Pine Mountain Settlement School " — a leaflet containing many interesting facts of contemporary life, which can be secured by addressing the school at Pine Mountain, Harlan County, Kentucky.

[10] " The discovery of gas in and about McKeesport in September, 1919, started one of the largest gas booms in the country; some wells totaling as high as fifty million cubic feet per day. Nearly a thousand wells were sunk; so many, in fact, that the valuable gas pool, underlying this city and environs, was drained in a year's time, there being but a few paying producers at the present time." Letter, McKeesport Chamber of Commerce, Nov. 16, 1920. We can appreciate this gift of the gods better after figuring on these facts — 1000 cubic feet of natural gas equals 2000 cubic feet of manufactured gas, or 8½ gallons kerosene, or 9 gallons gasoline, or 322 kw. hrs. of electricity.

FIG. 94 — In western Pennsylvania and West Virginia and other parts of the plateau, coal often outcrops near the hilltop. The mine car runs by gravity to the coal tipple over the railroad beside the river. The miners, whose houses are perched on the hillside, have village life or town life in the wilderness. Kanawha River, W. Va. (Courtesy U. S. Geol. Surv.)

that will neither return nor be duplicated elsewhere. The Americans have indeed been a fortunate people, if natural riches be the measure of good fortune.

The coal in this Appalachian field is very easy to mine [11] because the seams are nearly horizontal, and over much of the area they are above the stream levels and therefore outcrop in the hillsides. In many places the mine car runs horizontally into the side of a hill, and when loaded it runs out and down to the railroad or even to a boat at the foot of the hill. The famous Pittsburgh coal-seam is reached by going up-grade by railroad in any direction from Pittsburgh.

Mining has had the earliest and greatest development adjacent to the headwaters of the Ohio River for two reasons: nearness to the great centers of population and accessibility. The Ohio River and its tributaries in carving the valleys have made the best of natural highways to the coal fields, and they also provide a means of transportation for many miles within the coal field. The Ohio River, which gave early access and early development to this coal field, still carries important amounts of coal to ports on the river as distant as New Orleans. It may be expected to carry increasing quanti-

[11] DAILY PRODUCTION OF COAL PER MAN UNDERGROUND — TONS

| Year | U. S. | Nova Scotia | U. K. | Prussia | Belgium | Japan |
|------|-------|-------------|-------|---------|---------|-------|
| 1901 ........ | 3.37 | 2.74 | 1.50 | 1.22 | 0.84 | 0.73 |
| 1918 ........ | 4.40 | 2.50 | 1.19 | 1.26* | 0.72 | 0.83 |
| * 1913. | | | | | | |

ties of coal as we improve our waterways, and especially if the congestion of our railways continues.[12]

## Iron

Not far from Pittsburgh there is a layer of coal that is known as Connellsville coal. It is the best coking coal in America, perhaps in the world, and especially when used under the old-fashioned beehive oven which was the only device used in this country before 1900. The unusual excellence of this coke for making iron gave Pittsburgh an advantage at that time over all other iron centers, and since there were limestone and iron ores near by it is easy to see why this city became the greatest iron-manufacturing city in the world.

Pittsburgh is now losing its advantage over other places. A new method of making coke in by-product ovens will make good coke out of many kinds of coal. As a result Johnstown (67,000 pop.), in the plateau east of Pittsburgh, now makes good coke and good iron, and the town is rising in importance. Pittsburgh's exclusive advantage also waned when it was found (1884) that it was cheaper, even in Pittsburgh, to make iron from the very rich iron ores from the western end of Lake Superior than it was to use the poorer local ores. These Lake Superior ores are now almost exclusively used for making iron in western Pennsylvania and eastern Ohio. Any place between Pittsburgh, Buffalo and Chicago where the coke of Appalachia or Illinois and the ore of Lake Superior can be brought together is now about as good for making iron as is Pittsburgh itself. The Lake Shore points are better because one less handling of the ore is required. As early as 1907 the town of Ashtabula on the shores of Lake Erie, halfway between Erie and Cleveland, received 7,500,000 tons of iron ore and shipped back 2,500,000 tons of coke to the upper Lakes. The iron industry in the Ohio towns on or near Lake Erie has grown much faster since 1904 than that of Pittsburgh. Within fifteen years, 1904 to 1919, the iron of Pittsburgh increased 50%, while that of eastern Ohio doubled. Blast furnaces are increasing in importance in Newcastle, McKeesport and Sharon, Pa., Youngstown, Ohio, as well as in the cities on the shore of Lake Erie. The iron industry in various forms is also to be found in the Ohio River towns of Wheeling, West Va. (pop. 56,000), Ironton (14,000) and Portsmouth, Ohio (33,000).

[12] The heavy industries of this plateau produce an amount of freight which is almost inconceivable. A maximum cotton crop of 15,000,000 bales, 500 lbs. to the bale, weighs less than 4,000,000 tons, a figure that is less than half of the coal and iron-ore trade of the small lake-port of Ashtabula in the year 1907. The greatest wheat crop ever grown in the United States was less than 35,000,000 tons, while six times that much bituminous coal is mined in the Allegheny Plateau each year, and the total railroad tonnage of the Pittsburgh district alone amounts to more than 130,000,000 tons per year. In this we see a reason why there is a demand for the improvement of our rivers and waterways, including one from the Upper Ohio to Lake Erie. In 1922 the river tonnage at Pittsburgh was 20 million tons. Some of the steel companies have gone back to the river to move their materials.

The traffic conditions of the Pittsburgh district furnish a modern example of a permanent geographic fact. The plateau is a barrier. From central Pennsylvania southward all natural routes of travel, all railroad lines are in the bottoms of sharp valleys. Here then must be the assembling points for materials and the natural locations for towns, and they are very cramped locations.

Pittsburgh, like almost every other plateau town, is in a gulch or rather in the junction of gulches. Where the Pennsylvania Railroad enters the city, a blank retaining wall as high as a six-story building keeps the shale rock from falling on the tracks. At the top of this wall is a street and beyond the street is another retaining wall. At the top is the upper

FIG. 95 — Pittsburgh skyscrapers crowd the point of land at the junction of the two rivers. Railroads crowd the river bank. In the distance is one of the steep inclines up which passengers are carried to the higher levels of the land. (Photo John C. Bragdon.)

city to which elevators and inclined planes carry people from the lower city. This is typical of plateau town-sites.

Now look at the freight situation. The railroads *must* follow streams. Since all stream-bank locations were already pre-empted by tracks and buildings, a newcomer, the Wabash Railroad, tried to get into Pittsburgh without coming in along the stream. The attempt cost thirty-five million dollars and failed because cost prohibited its completion.

The map shows that the north and south branches of the Ohio River bring all railroad routes in western Pennsylvania through Pittsburgh, and Pittsburgh has been choked with freight since before the World War. In 1924 the Pennsylvania Railroad was considering two ways of creating an outlet for freight. One way was to spend forty or fifty million dollars and make a new freight-line that avoided Pittsburgh, and the other way was to lease the Norfolk and Western Railroad, send freight over that line from Columbus and Cincinnati, Ohio, to Norfolk, Virginia, and to the Pennsylvania Lines at Hagerstown, Maryland. Thus do the sharp valleys of the plateau harass alike the cabin mountaineer and the master of millions and machinery.

### Pittsburgh [13]

Pittsburgh and the mill-towns in the various valleys within thirty miles contain 1,200,000 people. Industrially it is a land of fire. Study the Pittsburgh district and you will have a mental picture of miles of coal-cars, of burning coke-ovens, smoke, dust, sweat, black hillsides, collieries, mine conveyors, railroad tracks, blackened steel plants, flaming furnaces, white-hot metal pouring, red-hot metal cooling, heavy rolls, pressing red-hot plates with roaring noise, shears cutting the plates into pieces, giant cranes lifting and dropping them with a clang. Highly perfected machinery replacing man's labor adds to the impression that here is a kind of mechanical volcano, if not indeed an inferno. As one rides through Connellsville at night the fires from countless coke-ovens seem to line the track for miles — a land of fire.

Pittsburgh is an important center for the manufacture of electrical and other machinery. This was a very natural next step in the development of a city which must use so much heavy machinery in her industrial plants and furnish it also for many near-by mines. The riches of fuel in this district have made Pittsburgh the leading center for the manufacture of glass. To make glass, sand is melted by fuel, preferably gas, of which, for a time, there is an unlimited supply.[14]

The textile industry, chiefly silk manufacture, is coming into a number of plateau cities where the men are busy working in iron, steel, and coal. Many women are engaged in textile industries.

### The Mine and the Miner

Mines can be opened with ease anywhere along hundreds of miles of railroad. This has made great competition among soft-coal producers. There are more mines than we need. Thus the distributors of cars for the railroads can decide which company shall get the cars. Here is a great temptation to favoritism, perhaps to graft. The charge has often

[13] Pittsburgh, the key to the Ohio and Allegheny Basins, was the trans-shipping point for goods that were hauled by wagon to Pittsburgh, then transferred to boats to go on West. The Erie Canal, opened in 1825, favored Buffalo. For a long while Pittsburgh grew slowly, but eventually it made up the loss of commercial advantages by utilizing industrial advantages.

[14] In the golden age of gushing gas people often let their gas-grates as well as house and street-lights burn night and day because it was cheaper than turning the gas off.

been made that railroad officials have made great fortunes by this means. One of the simplest ways to get rich quickly was to buy distant coal-lands cheaply, build a railroad to them, open a mine in the absolute certainty of getting cars to carry coal.

The coal industry has worked southward from Pittsburgh through West Virginia, Kentucky and Tennessee. Its development in the Cumberland Plateau has been rapid.[15]

The date of the coming of the railroad and the opening of the coal mine is the date of greatest possible change in these mountain communities. When a community changes from a land of cabins to a mining town, the change is sudden and violent.

Digging coal and making iron in the Appalachian Plateau often results in making communities that are far from the American ideal. This combination of resources and environment forces us to see the raw edge of our industrial system. The opportunity for acquiring wealth often tests ideals. I know of a case where a far-seeing man of great intelligence bought 60,000 acres of hilly, inaccessible, most unarable land, in the central part of the Allegheny Plateau. It was all underlaid with coal, but as there was no railroad near, and almost no population, he got it for $1.00 an acre. In a short time the railroad came and the land was then worth $50.00 an acre. But if he holds it until the coal is mined at a low royalty of ten cents a ton, the 450,000,000 tons of coal will yield $45,000,000.00.

If this coal is mined it will probably be done by a corporation, as with most of the other coal-mining enterprises. The absentee and invisible corporation sends its men into the green and peaceful wilderness where they build little houses for two or three hundred workers; put up a power-house to pump and ventilate the mine and to run the electric cars; erect a barn for the mine mules, and get everything ready for the arrival of the superintendents and mine bosses, the time-keepers and foremen.

The typical mining community, therefore, usually consists of a few superintendents who have some education and several hundred employees who are able to dig coal but who do not need any education at all. In many cases these miners know little of the English language and practically nothing at all of American customs and ideals. They live in the company's houses, buy at the company's store, and have a little city of their own in the wilderness. One coal-mining district has negro labor. Most of the mining towns in the Allegheny Plateau are peopled by newly arrived immigrants from Europe (15–25% in western Pennsylvania). Towns in the Cumberland Plateau are often filled with mountaineers who have come from the isolation of their mountain farms to experience the

[15] The Ford Enterprises own 125,000 acres of coal-lands in Kentucky — said to be the largest land-holdings of any kind in the South.

crowded conditions of a mining town where the valley is so narrow that the houses must be perched up on the side of the hill like bleacher seats around an athletic field. It is not difficult to see why the individualistic, independent, feudist mountaineer with the point of view of the mountain cannot become at once a public-spirited townsman.[16]

A community composed of mining towns planted in the wilderness where there are a few farms and no other industries lacks the variety needed for a good community. It also lacks that middle class of independent property-owning citizens which has long been the pride and hope of Anglo-Saxon democracy in both Britain and America. Lacking the conditions of democracy, it shows the result in undemocratic government. In Pennsylvania, where this condition is oldest, we find that the maintenance of peace is not left in the control of township or county. There is, instead, the State Constabulary.

## The Future of the Plateau

Plainly the future here is primarily coal. Despite the enormous production of the present, there is every reason to think the output will be greater in the future.[17] The Connellsville coking coal-seam is relatively exhausted, but it may be said that we have scarcely begun to use the great resources in the Appalachian Plateau.[18] New districts are being opened up and more coal-mining towns are being built. As the public conscience improves, each decade should make the mining town a better place in which to live. Some of the newer ones show great improvement in physical excellence.

In the age of super-power and transmission from mine-mouth plants, this coal-field seems destined to be the power-house for nearly half of the American people. But this does not mean the development of the plateau. The mine-mouth power-plant will tend to prevent city building in the plateau because it will be so easy to wire the power out to better town locations — Atlantic Coast, Lake Shore or the banks of the Ohio.

Coal mining can occupy but a small acreage at a time. All of the plateau was forest, much of it is now forest, and most of it should remain forest. So much lumber has been taken from the northern part that localities which in 1890 or 1900 shipped trainloads of lumber now buy

[16] In a typical coal-mining town of this sort an intelligent mining engineer of my acquaintance finds great difficulty in educating his children, because no one cares much about schools, and public schools, unfortunately, have to reflect public sentiment. When a typhoid epidemic breaks out, it results in needless deaths, because the enforcement of the rules of public sanitation by a board of health again demands public sentiment and knowledge of sanitation. When a mountaineer shoots some one, only the immediate family of the victim follows his coffin to the grave. Others stay away lest their presence might offend the one who did the shooting.

[17] Our per capita coal consumption increased as follows: 1829–1879 from 0–1 ton, 1879–1899 from 1–3 tons, 1899–1919 from 3–6 tons.

[18] We waste 50% of our coal in mining. England and Germany waste about one-third as much.

lumber by the carload.  After the lumberman came the fire, and one-third of the State of Pennsylvania may be classed as huckleberry desert (see preceding chapter).  The state is taking for taxes such burned-over lands as have been abandoned by their owners.  Occasionally some tracts are bought and the state is making vigorous efforts to protect them from fire.  Some have to be replanted, so complete has been the tree destruction.  The West Virginia, Kentucky and Tennessee parts of the plateau,

Fig. 96 — Model of a coal mine with the part above the coal seam removed. We can see how pillars of coal are left to support the roof while the men work.  Steel cables running over the wheels at top lift the coal to the big building (tipple) for screening and weighing.  (Courtesy Smithsonian Institution.)

being less accessible by rail and farther from markets, have not been lumbered so extensively and are now the seat of a great hard-wood lumber industry.  The National Government is steadily acquiring forests in Appalachia.[19]  No wiser thing can be done for future economic welfare, for the timber famine approaches.

Forest studies in Tennessee show that chestnut, one of our most rapid-growing trees, adds seven cords of wood per acre in the second decade, and twenty-five in the fifth.  Meanwhile it is necessary that fire should be kept out during this half century — a convincing proof that eternal vigilance (against fire) is the price of timber.

[19] It had acquired four thousand square miles by November 1923.

## Blue Ridge and Carolina Mountains

Between the Great Valley and the Piedmont is a long, narrow strip of the Blue Ridge which, except for a short distance in Pennsylvania, is continuous from the Hudson to southern Virginia, where it widens into an upland mountainous country, embracing several thousand square miles of western Carolina, eastern Tennessee, and small corners of South Carolina and Georgia.

The Blue Ridge is much like the other parts of the Appalachian Ridge already described. The Carolina Mountains, often called the Unakas, resemble the Appalachian Plateau more than they resemble the ridges, except that instead of being flat strata they are just a mass of rounded mountains with some rather wide valleys between.

The soils are better here than the soils either in the Appalachian Ridges or the Appalachian Plateaus. The rainfall is heavy and nature has,

FIG. 97 — If another field is needed it is sometimes even today made, Indian-fashion, by girdling trees. These are left standing, because there is no use for the wood after worm fences and log houses are built, and open fireplaces are supplied. Summit of Blue Ridge, Mitchell County, N. C., eight years after girdling. (Courtesy U. S. Forest Service.)

therefore, covered the south with fine forests and much grass, especially with Kentucky blue grass.

Although the valleys are not quite so narrow and sharp as in the Cumberland Plateau, travel has been difficult.

The elevation of these Southern Appalachians up to four thousand feet on the plateaus and higher valleys, and five and six thousand feet on the higher peaks, produces a country of great beauty, of surprisingly low temperature in winter,[20] and delightful coolness in summer — a com-

[20] This elevation really extends the climate of New York into North Carolina. It also extends the forest of hemlock and spruce. The influence of small elevation

bination of advantages which make it a natural pleasure-ground and summer resort for the people of the hot south-land, by which it is surrounded
on three sides.   Asheville is the best-known resort center.

All the settled parts of the Blue Ridge Country, as well as Cumberland
and Allegheny Plateaus, have suffered terribly from soil erosion, [21] because
man has attempted to use level-land agriculture upon its steep hills.
When plowed for corn the earth upon the steep slopes is soon eroded
and then abandoned for a fresh field.

in Appalachia on winter weather is surprising.   On the 11th of March, 1924, I saw
twenty-five inches of snow (temperature 31) fall on the Blue Ridge, altitude 1300
feet, fifty miles from Washington.   Washington got about five inches of slush.   Two
days later the White House grounds were green and the Blue Ridge was still knee-
deep with snow, and horseback the only means of travel.   Almost every winter
storm that comes up the Atlantic coast deluges Appalachia with snow.

[21] *Denudation and Erosion in the Southern Appalachian Region,* L. C. Glenn,
U. S. Geol. Surv. Professional Paper No. 72.

FIG. 98 — This Blue Ridge slope, six miles from a railroad, in Nelson County,
  Va., has the earth skin held upon its rock body by the roots of blue grass
  and Albemarle Pippin apple trees.   These pippins are prized in the British
  market.   (Courtesy W. M. Scott.)

# CHAPTER XII

## THE OZARK–OUACHITA UPLANDS

THE center of North America is an extensive plain, low and open from the Gulf of Mexico to the Arctic Ocean. In the center of the plain, between the Cotton Belt and the Corn Belt, are 60,000 square miles of upland — the Ouachita Mountains and the Ozark Plateau. These uplands are a kind of miniature Appalachia, divided in two parts by the Arkansas Valley.

The Ouachita Mountains, which constitute the southern part of the region, reach two hundred miles westward from Little Rock, Arkansas, and are a mass of ridges somewhat like the Allegheny Ridges. These ridges are composed of sandstone and miles of it are fine enough, and sufficiently uniform in quality to be made into whetstone. This industry, however, has been injured by the more abrasive product of the electric furnace.

The Ozark Uplands were caused by a slight bulge in the generally horizontal rocks of the Mississippi Valley. This bulge or very low dome raised a limestone formation in which streams have been able to cut valleys, until they have worn away the limestone entirely over most of its extent. This has not happened in the western part of the Ozarks where the limestone layer still makes up the level upland surface into which valleys have been cut. In the center and toward the east the upland is worn away until only long shreds of limestone remain with valleys between.

This shredded plateau of the west is surrounded on the north, east and south by a rough, hilly country very difficult of access and merging off in all directions in low hills that sink gradually into the surrounding plains.

The parts of the Ozark Uplands from which the limestone surface has been worn is covered with many small flint stones called chert. Originally the chert, or flint, was embedded in the limestone, and when the limestone dissolved the hard chert remained.

### Another Surviving Frontier

The whole region was originally forested and its outer hills were the site of the first permanent white settlement west of the Mississippi River. The open prairie grew better crops of grain, but the wooded hilly country

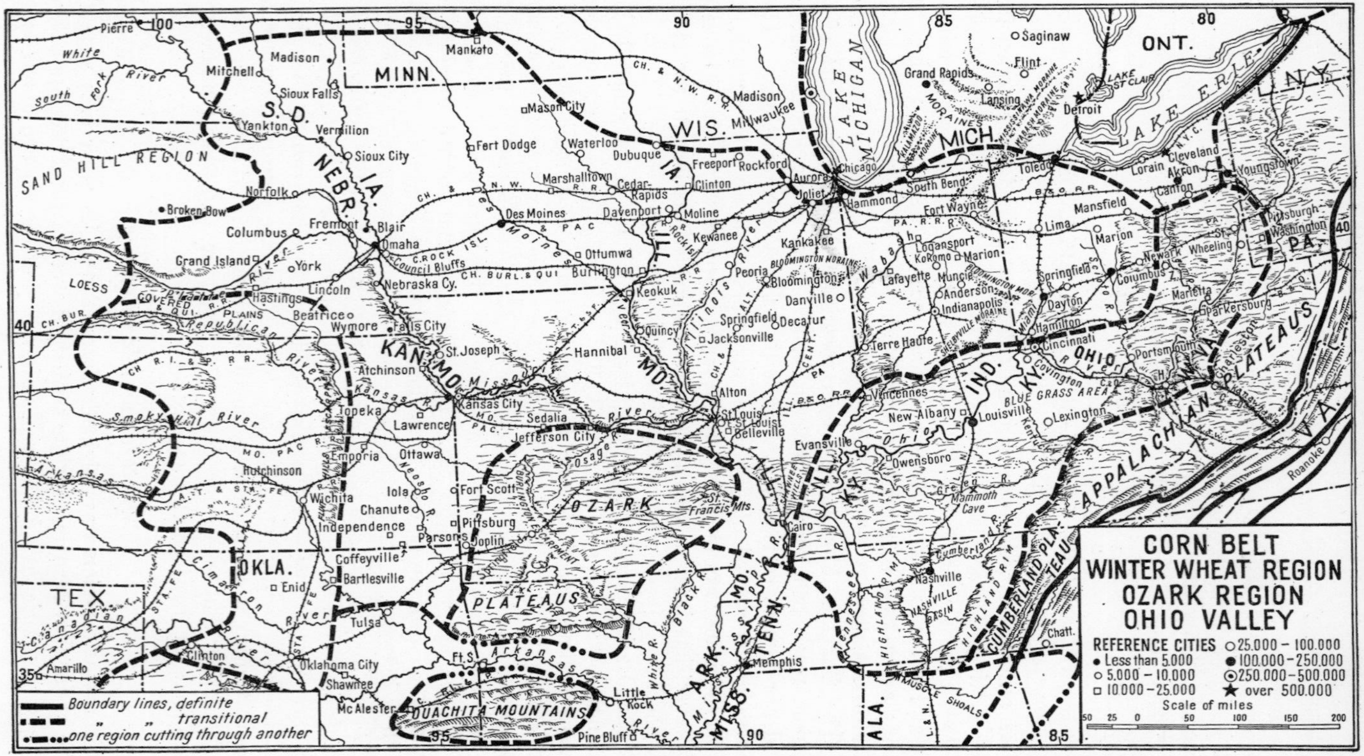

CORN BELT
WINTER WHEAT REGION
OZARK REGION
OHIO VALLEY

REFERENCE CITIES
• Less than 5,000    ⊙ 25,000 – 100,000
• 5,000 – 10,000     ⊙ 100,000 – 250,000
□ 10,000 – 25,000    ⊙ 250,000 – 500,000
                     ★ over 500,000

Scale of miles
50  25  0    50    100    150    200

Boundary lines, definite
      transitional
one region cutting through another

FIG. 99.

furnished logs for house, wood for fire, mast for pig, small areas of lowlands for field, opportunity for hunting and fishing. For several generations the westward-moving American could take his choice: move to the open prairies and become rich at hard labor, move to the Ozark woods and live more easily and simply by occasional labor. The frontiersman likes freedom. He prefers occasional labor to a steady job. He prefers joy to property. Therefore, he is not so capitalistic as the builders of cities and the owners of big, painted barns.[1] Great wealth and degrading poverty are seldom found here. The farther the frontiersman of 1790 or 1820 got into the Ozarks the more difficult it became for him to get away, so here as in Appalachia we have a kind of surviving frontier.

Corn is the chief crop, grown alike on rich lowland, level upland and steep hillside. No other grain yields so much or is so suitable as food for man, horse, cow, pig. Unfenced land is public range where anyone may turn out his horses, cattle or pigs to pick their living. The man of the Ozarks is primarily a farmer whose small farm is unspecialized and whose income is derived chiefly from corn and range-fed cattle, and mast-fed pigs.[2] In the odd season he hunts for the roots of ginseng and golden seal, and furs. Coon-skins have been accepted for taxes even in the twentieth century.

In the winter the cash crop of lumber has been cut, chiefly oak railroad ties and mine props. The lumber has been hauled out over frozen ground often to be floated down streams in flood.

[1] C. L. Edson, in *These United States,* p. 361, says of these people: "They have not, in all their philosophy, any complaint against anything. They are the only white tribe among us that habitually fiddles and sings." A humorous book called *The Arkansas Traveler,* once much read in parts of the United States, tells a not uncharacteristic episode. In passing a miserable shanty one day the author looking through the open door saw the owner sitting in the midst of streams of water that poured through a leaky roof. "Why don't you fix your roof?" called the stranger. "Can't. It's rainin'," came the answer. The next day as the traveler returned the philosophic native still sat, although the sun was shining. "Why don't you fix your roof?" he asked again. "No use," came the answer, "'tain't a-rainin'." This non-capitalistic attitude is perhaps well characterized by the experience of a traveler whom I know to be veracious. After spending many days in this country the monotonous diet of corn bread and fried pork palled on his taste, and one day he inquired of the woman who was serving him his dinner why they did not keep some chickens and have eggs and chickens to eat. "Wall," said the woman, " he (meaning her husband) did bring some hens home once, and we cooked one of 'em, and, stranger, don't you know, they was sech pow'ful good cookin' we jes' fell to and cooked 'em all up."

[2] "In many cases these hogs are turned into the woods and run there in large numbers. They are earmarked in order to be able to identify the hogs of the different owners. Usually no feed is given these hogs except a small amount of corn which is fed them when the owner or man in charge goes into the woods and calls them up in order to check up on the number which he has. Usually the practice of calling the hogs up and feeding them some grain is followed, this being done about once a week in order that the hogs may not become too wild so that they may be caught when ready for market." Letter, March 1923, from T. Ray Reid, Sec'y Agriculture Extension Service for State of Arkansas.

## The Breakdown of Exploitation

This exploitive system of the frontier still goes on, but production has reached its peak and begun to decline under it. The timber is about all gone, although two-thirds of the land is still uncleared. The grass of the forest range is declining through over-grazing and the scrub cattle and razorback hogs are of poor quality. The timber is not reproducing well because too many animals are allowed to graze in the woods. Fortu-

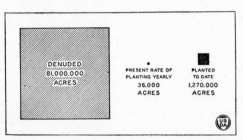

FIG. 100 — This graphic presentation of a national problem shows that the Ozarker as well as any and all others will soon get a higher price for his timber.

nately, the forests have been burned but little, chiefly because pasturing has kept down undergrowth so that nothing would burn. The yield of much of the land is declining through unscientific methods of farming. All of the land that is fit for the plow has been cleared. The population increased until the beginning of this century. The people lived a self-sufficient kind of life, knowing little of the outward world and caring less. Then came three revolutionary things. Rural free delivery brought knowledge of the outside world and its opportunities; the draft took the young men from every valley and every ridge and by putting them into the army showed them the world; the placards of the United States Government searching for the war workers appeared in every post office and offered wages undreamed of in a land of nominal wages. The decline of rural population has begun through the migration of the more ambitious.

## The Need of Reconstruction

The region is therefore one having great need of social reconstruction. Fortunately, it has good economic possibilities. The climate is excellent. The short winter and good rainfall give nine months of pasturage. The valleys are surprisingly wide, with lowlands good for corn, alfalfa, and other crops necessary to support live stock.

Roads are a problem — the greatest physical problem. The railroad map of the United States shows how the hills have kept the railroads out. Several branch-line railroads in the Ozarks have recently been abandoned. For many years the zinc-mining town of Yellville, Arkansas, was reached by sixty-five miles of stage, and numerous communities are from ten to thirty miles from a railroad. The best sites for roads are the tops of the plateau, two or three hundred feet above the valleys, and where the best farm-land is. The valley road is muddy; it must continually cross unbridged streams and suffer from washouts and flood. Live animals, butter and cheese can stand such transportation, and the resources of the country for dairying are excellent. But the traditions, habits and inclinations of the people are as yet foreign to scientific live-stock husbandry. To make over the Ozarks is one of the many problems in constructive sociology which face the American people in the attempt to adjust life to its surroundings. I state this Ozark problem in the words of Professor Carl Sauer, who has written an excellent book [3] about the region:

" Even more significant than the exclusion of the outside world is the detached manner of living of the people. Valley is separated from valley; valley settlement is out of touch with ridge settlement; often family is isolated from family.

" The simple result is that the isolation has kept social and economic progress at snail's pace. The people were primitive in their condition when they came, they are nearly as primitive now. Without strong social instincts and training to begin with, how were they to achieve common interests, common opinion, and common effort? For the economic problem of the Ozark Highland is after all social in its fundamentals. The difficulty that the people experience in getting to market is less serious than their failure to get together. There has been no substantial economic development because topographical isolation has maintained successfully the social anarchy of the frontier. It is the solitary position of the individual, rather than the poverty of the soil, that at the bottom is at fault with the Ozarks. The so-called political conservatism of the Ozarks is well known. It has its full social and economic equivalents.[4] The individualism is almost static. The individual produced under this system is bound down by it. . . .

" Unless the region is to become decadent, the isolation and its resultant excessive individualism must be broken down, and this must be done by the governments among which the highland is divided. The first corrective measure must be improved means of communication. . . .

" Roads, live stock and a forest policy point the solution to the stagnation of Ozark life. . . .

" Help is needed for the Ozarks. The condition of the people is such that they cannot well help themselves. They are standing singly, uninstructed in their larger possibilities. It is a numerous population that needs to be made more effective, before degenerative selection destroys its best capacities. . . .

" If the states involved have the patience and the wit to plant the com-

[3] *The Geography of the Ozark Highland of Missouri.* Geographical Society of Chicago, 1920.
[4] Economic *causes* would perhaps have been a better term.

munity spirit in the valleys and on the ridges of the Ozarks, the native will find in himself and in his constructive environment the resources with which to develop a permanent constructive economy in place of the present self-destructive system handed down from frontier ancestors." [5]

### Fruit

Small areas in northwestern Arkansas, near Fayetteville and Bentonville and adjacent parts of Missouri, have an extensive apple industry. It is located on the level upland remnants of the plateau and is not at all typical of the Ozark country in general. As in Appalachia there is much more fruit land than market demand. The particular fruit sections have excellent frost drainage and are developing efficient production and marketing organizations.

### Lead and Zinc

Joplin, in the southwestern corner of Missouri (pop. 29,902), calls itself the gateway of the Ozarks and has long been the center of an important zinc-mining region. Ozar zinc-mining has been carried on very wastefully.[6] The passing of Missouri from first place in zinc-production to fifth place is again suggestive of exploitation. The northeastern Ozarks have large quantities of low-grade lead-ore which caused Missouri to produce about two-fifths of the American supply of that metal in 1922.

At best these mineral deposits will occupy but a small proportion of the people and a small proportion of the area for a short period of time. The main Ozark problem is one of rural organization and the establishment of a permanent agriculture, for this land has no prospect of becoming a land of cities. Springfield, Mo. (pop. 39,631), a distributing center in the best part of the limestone upland, is the largest city, but it is not growing so rapidly as many manufacturing cities of the northeastern states.

The present practice of fattening pigs on acorns combines with factors of surface, soil and climate to show that it is a land *par excellence* for the tree-crop agriculture.

[5] " The Economic Problem of the Ozark Highland," *The Scientific Monthly,* September 1920.

[6] The deposits are often leased to small operators who must pay 20% or 25% royalty. Since they must make a profit, they can take only the best and leave the rest. From one-third to two-thirds is wasted. See Van Hise, C. R., *Conservation in the United States,* pp. 84–5.

# CHAPTER XIII

## THE COTTON BELT

" Cotton is King " was truly said of politics a century ago when the Cotton Bloc in the Senate at Washington governed the United States for decades. Cotton was king of Southern agriculture and of the foreign trade of the United States. In a sense this is still true of our foreign trade, for our exports of unmanufactured cotton far exceed in value that of any other single commodity.[1]

### Bounds and Climate of the Cotton Belt

The cotton plant is not very particular as to soils, but it requires a long growing season with summer rain. Therefore, in most places climate sets the bounds of the Cotton Belt. Its eastern boundary is the Atlantic. The northern boundary is set by length of season.[2] Cotton can succeed only where there are two hundred frostless days in the growing season. The western boundary is also fixed by climate, the line of twenty-three inches of rainfall. At the south again it is a climate line, this time a wet one. The Gulf Coast is so thoroughly drenched with summer rain that tillage is almost impossible, and in Florida the autumn rains beat off the cotton before it can all be picked. A dry autumn for harvest is part of the ideal cotton climate — less than ten inches of autumn rain.

The eastern part of the Cotton Belt has a humid summer. The western part, the part that is north of Mexico, rather than north of the Gulf, has at times hot southwest winds, dry and very hot.

### Slavery and the Plantation System

The agricultural start of the Cotton Belt was quite the opposite of that of New England. Instead of the small general farm, supporting the family by a group of complementary crops, as was the rule in New England, the South started on the plantation system of selling one or two things and buying many others. In the Colonial time, rice, indigo

---

[1] U. S. Exports, million dollars: Wheat (grain and flour), 1921 — 550, 1922 — 291; Machinery, 1921 — 411, 1922 — 239; Refined mineral oils, 1921 — 363, 1922 — 312; Cotton, 1921 — 534, 1922 — 673.

[2] Little cotton is grown north of the line of 77° F. for average summer temperature. The cotton boundary tends to move north, owing to the improvements of early-maturing varieties of cotton.

Fig. 101 — Many tenants dump their few bales of cotton at the factory's receiving
Belt town.  Cotton is not spoiled by getting wet — one of the

and tobacco were the money crops.  There was no extensive settlement
far from the seacoast until cotton became commercially important.  Then
the supreme commercial importance of cotton enabled it to support a
brilliant civilization by the plantation system — slavery, and the sale
of cotton.  Some corn was produced for food for mule and slave.

In this period of slavery the abundant land of the South permitted cotton prosperity to be based upon a most wasteful system of land exploitation.  In the winter the slaves chopped down forests and burned the trees
to clear fresh fields for cotton.  In summer they tilled the crop, men
plowing, women hoeing.  In the autumn, men, women and children picked
it.  When continuous cropping of cotton and corn impoverished the soil
and made the yields low the field was abandoned to grow up again in
woods, and fresh clearings gave new land for the soil-robbing system.[3]
Thus settlement rolled westward from the Atlantic to Central Texas.

> " Men of mark from old Virginia,
>   Men of daring from Kentucky,
>   Tennessee, Louisiana,
>   Men of many states and races,
>   Bringing wives and children with them,
>   Followed up the wooded valleys,
>   Spread across the rolling prairie,
>   Raising homes and reaping harvests."
>                     *Ode to Texas*.  HENRY VAN DYKE.

This plantation system of the white manager, the colored worker and
the ruthless exploitation of land, has received two shocks — one from
the Civil War, one from the boll weevil.  The boll weevil shock was

[3] From the top of the State University buildings at Athens in the hilly country
of North Georgia, one sees varied landscape of field and woods spread out in all
directions.  But professors at the University tell me that every bit of the woods
covers land that has at some time been cotton field.

yard. Will the credit slips pay the mortgage? Eight thousand bales in a Cotton
reasons why it is *king*. (Courtesy *The Country Gentleman*.)

the greater, furnishing strong evidence of the power of the insect as man's
rival for the dominance of the earth.[4]

### The Civil War and the Tenant System

Those who think that revolution comes by legislation should compare
the Southern agricultural system before the Civil War and after to see
how much easier it is to change names and statutes than to change economic fact. Before the war the plantation of a thousand acres had its
owner, a white foreman or two, and many families of negroes, who lived
in cabins near the mansion. The negroes worked the master's fields,
drove his mules and picked his cotton. After the Civil War they were
free negroes, but most of them did not move away. They usually lived
in the same cabin, drove the same mule which belonged to the same
white man, grew cotton in the same fields. In the autumn the men,
women and children picked cotton as before the War, but this time as
tenants receiving a share of the crop, thereby being, in a certain sense,
their own bosses.

[4] " Man imagines himself to be the dominant power on the earth. He is nothing
of the sort. The true lords of the universe are the insects. While it is true that
man has invented and perfected so many destructive agencies that he has attained
to a predominance over the most fierce and powerful mammals and the most deadly
reptiles, it is also true that in face of an attack of insects he and all his works are set
at naught." " Value of Birds to Man," by James Buckland. (Smithsonian Report,
1913, p. 439.) If Mr. Buckland had been illustrating his point from the Cotton
Belt he might have pointed to the following: (1) Mosquito, bearer of misery and
malaria, which has done so much to keep the white man out of important sections
and to keep down his numbers in others. (2) Cattle tick, which held the cattle
industry at bay and almost reduced it to naught until this generation discovered
the potency of cattle dipping. (3) Hookworm, the extent of whose ravages in
keeping man down is only now being discovered. (4) Boll weevil. Before the
World War it was estimated that insects did $700,000,000 worth of damage each
year in the United States. The figure would be much larger now. Therefore, in a
zoölogic sense, the Bureau of Entomology (for the study of insects) in the Department of Agriculture might be considered our real war department, and it is
probable that larger appropriations for it would be highly profitable.

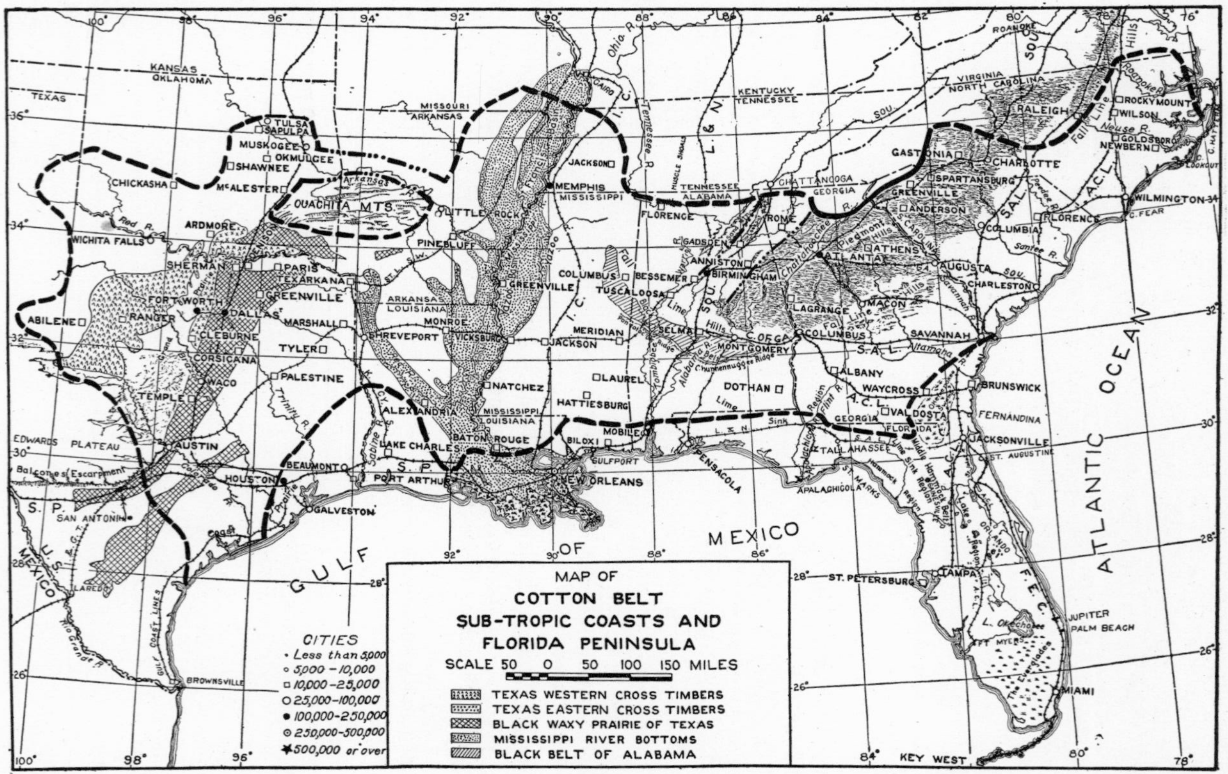

FIG. 102.

The independence of the new freedom was more nominal than real. It was greatly limited by the financial situation. The ex-slave was not used to saving money. After the Christmas celebration, the great holiday of slavery, the negro was usually penniless. He lived through the winter and spring and early summer on what he borrowed from the owner of the plantation or a local storekeeper or other capitalist. If he did not keep on working he could not keep on buying corn meal, overalls, tobacco, bacon and molasses. The white man, of course, advanced as little as he could, and in turn the negro worked as little as he could. If the cotton sold for enough to pay back what the negroes had borrowed all concerned

FIG. 103 — For a hundred years the negro of the cotton plantation has spent his winter slaughtering forests to make new fields for cotton. (Courtesy Southern Alluvial Land Association, Memphis.)

felt that they had completed a lucky episode, and were ready to start all over again for the winter of borrowing and the summer of work.

Cotton is still king of the countryside. If the price is good the negro has a joyous winter, or at least a big Christmas, and the planter's daughter goes to college with a trunk full of new clothes. If cotton slumps the girl often has to leave college.

The common tenant's unit is one mule and the land that he can cultivate with a one-horse plow, hence the term " one-horse farm." This system has naturally tended to make a race of supervisors of the white population, especially as the unskilled and uneducated negro needs a great deal of supervision.

The attitude of the two races toward each other is shown by the following stories: (1) A Northerner from the two-horse-plow or three-horse-plow country, seeing the negroes on a Southern plantation creeping across the field with a one-mule plow, asked the white man why he did not give the man a two-mule team. " What! " he exclaimed. " Let that lazy nigger waste *two* mules' time? " (2) " Marse Jeems," asked an old negro of a leading citizen, " what wuz you-all white folks havin' dat meetin' about terday up thaiah at de coht house? " " We're gettin' up a plan, Jim, to try and get some more white people to come and settle in this country." " Good Lordy, Marse Jeems, don't you do it! Please don't do it. Why,

FIG. 104 — In thousands of Southern fields the rows of cotton and corn wind about at right angles to the slope. Thus do men try to prevent the soil from washing away. At intervals the field is divided by banks which lead the water gently across the face of the hill — but I never saw a field where *all* the water was controlled. (Courtesy H. H. Bennett, U. S. Bureau of Soils.)

Marse Jeems, don't you know that us poh niggahs has got jest all we kin do now ter suppoht de white folks dat's heah already? "

This one-crop and mortgage system led to a great commerce. The Northern farm furnished the mule and often the hay that it ate and the bacon and lard for the negro's frying-pan. Mills and factories in the North and in Europe furnished thousands of commodities sold in the stores throughout the broad Cotton Belt.

The razorback hog was part of this system. Here, as in Appalachia (see Chapter X), unfenced land was public property. The hog was turned out to root for himself, and generations of self-support made him long of leg, flat of side, sharp of back (razorback) and very long of snout — the implement by which he rooted up much of his living.

A New Jersey pork breeder who years ago showed beautiful, round, well-bred porkers in a cotton state fair saw with amazement the premium put upon the razorback. He could not understand it at first. " You see, Mistah, them hawgs of yourn may be all right fer up Nawth where you come from, but they ain't wuth five cents apiece heah. Youah hawgs ain't got no speed. Hawgs must have *speed*. Down heah, if a hawg

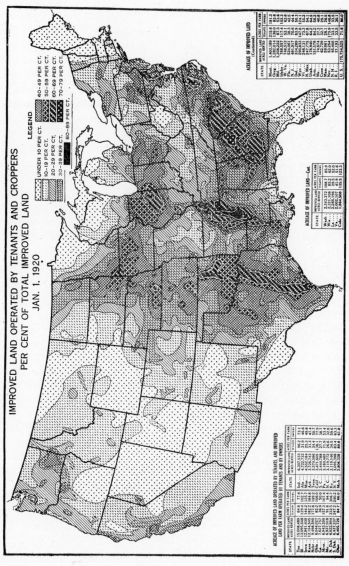

Fig. 105 — The map of tenancy always shows rich land, but not necessarily *all* of the rich land (California for example). (Courtesy U. S. Dept. Agr.)

can't beat a niggah to the swamp he ain't wuth havin', for you won't have him long."

Mast, acorns, hickory nuts, pecans and roots are still an important element of hog feeding in many sections of the Cotton Belt.

The period following the Civil War saw less clearing of Cotton Belt forest for fresh fields than before the War, although the process still continues to this day. There are two reasons why less land is being cleared for cotton: the declining supply of fresh land, and the use of commercial fertilizer, which permits land naturally exhausted to continue production for a time. The South, with its robber agriculture, is the part of the country which requires the greatest amount of fertilizer.

The one-crop system was destructive of land through lack of proper rotation and great soil erosion, but it continued because of the commercial superiority of cotton and the ease with which it could be mortgaged. But finally from Washington, from the State Agricultural College and from other sources, came eulogies on the excellence of the country for diversified agriculture. The whole South rang with the din of sermons exhorting the farmers to grow many crops. When it came to a consideration of the negro tenant, no one wanted to mortgage his prospective crop of pigs. It was too easy for them to "run away." If his crop were hay or beans or oats the rain might ruin it. Indeed, nothing was so easy to mortgage as cotton because it was easy to grow,[5] easy to keep, nothing could eat it (a point of very great importance), and it had to be taken to the ginnery before it could be sold.

### Cotton Belt Soils

The plantation system is not the only reason for the extensive use of commercial fertilizer in the Cotton Belt. Its soils, on the average, are naturally less fertile than those of the Corn Belt, or the Wheat Belts to the north of it. This misfortune is due to two reasons: first, the Coastal Plain origin, explained in Chapter VIII, and leaching. Iowa has thirty inches of rain and her soil is frozen all winter so that no water can get into it. It is evident that the soil of the Cotton Belt, because it receives an annual rainfall of fifty to sixty inches, and because there is no frost,[6] suffers much more from leaching than does Iowa. This climatic factor, which tends to reduce fertility in all lands of warm climate and heavy rainfall, explains the distinctly lower fertility content shown by many soil analyses made by the United States Bureau of Soils. It also explains the necessity for the rapid shifting of cotton from field to field in the exploitive system.

[5] A leading citizen of North Carolina used to declare: "I wish it was harder to grow cotton. Then there would be some money in it. As it is now, any fool nigger with a bull yearlin' can make cotton." The bull yearling was a one-year-old ox, often used in place of the mule to draw the plow and cultivator.

[6] See Bowman, Isaiah, *Forest Physiography*.

An area as large as the Cotton Belt has a great variety of soils. Nearly everywhere along the coast there is the barrier beach and behind it the enclosed lagoon with often large areas of sandy lowlands, called flat woods, near the coast. Much of it is so poor that it is called " pine barrens," and so flat as to be swampy after heavy rains.

Farther inland are better areas of sandy loams, good for cotton. Back in the Carolinas and Georgia, the sandy loams are flanked by a row of sand hills, five to thirty miles wide, and of low fertility. They appear on the cotton map as an area of small production.

Beyond the sand hills are the clay hills of the Piedmont, here, as in the North, more fertile than the Coast Plain. The commercial excellence of cotton caused the subsistence farmer on the Piedmont to turn to cotton early in the nineteenth century, or else to migrate over the Alleghenies to the Ohio Valley.

In eastern Texas and other parts of the infertile sand pine country so few farmers arrived after lumbermen had cut down the forests that there were not enough to support railroads and they were abandoned.

In this relatively undeveloped region of varied soils, cotton has been grown chiefly

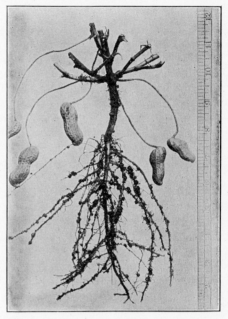

FIG. 106 — Nitrogen comes on the farm very expensively by way of bought fertilizer or very inexpensively by way of the nodules on the roots of peanuts and of all the other legumes. (Courtesy U. S. Dept. Agr.)

on the best soils. The Cotton Belt has three soil areas of especial fertility which are famed for their rich agriculture. These are the Black Belt of Alabama, the Black Prairie of Texas and the Mississippi Bottoms.

### The Black Belt of Alabama

The Black Belt of Alabama is a layer of soft chalky limestone, which outcrops in a great curve through central Alabama (Fig. 102). This limestone is one of the rich soil areas of the world. For many years it yielded crops of corn and cotton without the necessity of rest. This is ideal for the tenant system. The natural result was a large production of cotton before the boll weevil and of livestock since. Eighty per cent of the population on this good renting land is black.

### The Black Prairie of Texas

As one goes westward through the sandy forested plain of eastern Texas, he passes suddenly out of forests into a treeless plain, whose fine-textured black soil is made from weathered limestone. It is the " Black Land Prairie " of Texas, formed by the same geologic formation as the Black Belt of Alabama. This area of fine farm-land, often spoken of as " Black Waxy," because it is so sticky when wet, lies in a long belt northeast to southwest from the Ouachita Mountains to Austin and beyond.

The great fertility of the Black Waxy causes it to be extensively used for cotton. As is usually the case with rich lands where good salable crops can grow, it is high-priced and most of it has passed into the hands of tenants and supports a landlord class. It has been too much devoted to one-crop, land-robbing cotton farming, though it is entirely suitable for many other crops.

Central Texas has five clear-cut belts of vegetation due to soil: 1st, the eastern sand and pine forest; 2nd, Black Waxy grassland; 3rd, west of the Black Land Prairie is a long narrow strip of sandy soil bearing forest, the " Eastern Cross Timbers "; 4th, west of that is another limestone prairie, the " Grand Prairie "; and 5th, west of that another sand-formation bearing forest — the " Western Cross Timbers."

The lime formations (Fig. 102) were naturally grass-covered because they make a close-textured soil, good for grass, which is the great enemy of trees. The sand does not make such good grass and absorbs more water and hence is forest-covered.

The same general conditions prevail on the Grand Prairie as on the Black Waxy, but the former is hillier and dryer, and not so extensively cultivated. The northern part of the Grand Prairie is called the Fort Worth Prairie; the southern part is known as the Lampasas Cut Plain. In this part the nearly horizontal strata of limestone have been eroded into a series of valleys and divided, the divide in many cases being composed of perfectly bare limestone rock flanked by shallow soils which tend to restrict cultivation to the small valleys between.

These two prairies, 30,000 square miles in extent, and divided up into a number of smaller areas with local names, are the center of cotton-growing in Texas. They are the center of her densest rural population, of her highest land-values, of her greatest prosperity. To surrounding territories they are as the Blue Grass of Kentucky, the Valley of Virginia, or the " Black Belt " of Alabama are to their surrounding districts.

This prairie region of agricultural riches has naturally become the

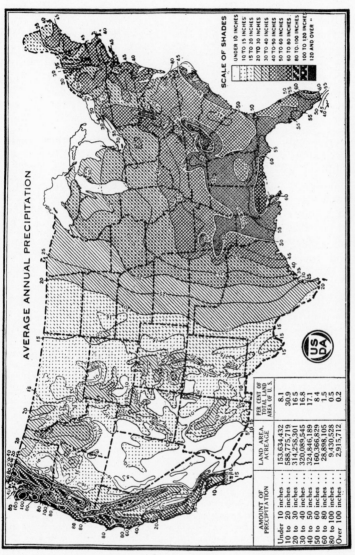

AVERAGE ANNUAL PRECIPITATION

| AMOUNT OF PRECIPITATION | LAND AREA. ACREAGE | PER CENT OF TOTAL LAND AREA OF U.S. |
|---|---|---|
| Under 10 inches .... | 153,634,432 | 8.1 |
| 10 to 20 inches .... | 588,775,719 | 30.9 |
| 20 to 30 inches .... | 314,258,301 | 16.5 |
| 30 to 40 inches .... | 320,089,545 | 16.8 |
| 40 to 50 inches .... | 324,846,189 | 17.1 |
| 50 to 60 inches .... | 160,366,829 | 8.4 |
| 60 to 80 inches .... | 28,898,105 | 1.5 |
| 80 to 100 inches ... | 9,430,528 | 0.5 |
| Over 100 inches ... | 2,915,712 | 0.2 |

SCALE OF SHADES

UNDER 10 INCHES
10 TO 15 INCHES
15 TO 20 INCHES
20 TO 30 INCHES
30 TO 40 INCHES
40 TO 50 INCHES
50 TO 60 INCHES
60 TO 80 INCHES
80 TO 100 INCHES
100 TO 120 INCHES
120 AND OVER "

Fig. 107 — The low rainfall of western Texas limits the Cotton Belt.

seat of most of the cities of the interior of Texas — Dallas, Fort Worth, Austin, Waco, Paris, the natural trade centers of the fertile plains.[7]

The Black Prairie of Texas was not settled much until after the Civil War. Therefore, it differs from the Black Belt of Alabama in having fewer negroes. They comprise less than one-fourth of the population and one-sixth of the tenants, but the total proportion of tenants is very high. Tenant and landlord questions arising from this prairie have often dominated the politics of Texas.

## The Mississippi Delta

The Mississippi, carrying mud at the estimated rate of thirty-three carloads per minute, has built up thousands of square miles of land between the mouth of the Ohio and the Gulf of Mexico. About twenty-nine thousand square miles is still so low that the river has in recent years overflowed it. When the river in flood rises above its banks, the whole lowland becomes a lake, and as the current flows from the deep, swift channel into the quiet back waters of the lake, the velocity of the water is checked. This has caused the stream to drop much of its burden of mud and sand. This builds the bank (natural levee) higher near the stream than at any other part of the flood plain. The immediate banks of the Mississippi are usually built up ten or fifteen feet higher than the swamp two or three miles back. This is naturally the most valuable land for plantations. The soil is often drained by ditches which run at right angles to the river. The ditches carry water back to the edge of the swamp, which to this day covers most of the area of the Mississippi flood plain. The marvelous richness of its alluvial soil has not yet tempted man to undertake the necessary drainage. They have a saying in Arkansas that the little frogs in the swamps pipe in their shrill voices, " Quinine, quinine, quinine," while the big bull-frog with his deep bass voice chimes in, " Double the dose! Double the dose! "

The value of the plantations on the Mississippi flood plain led, many years ago, to the building of artificial banks or levees to hold the river within its banks. There are now fifteen hundred miles of these structures.

[7] From Austin southward the boundary of the Black Waxy is a cliff of limestone rocks, the Balcones Escarpment, a great fault that stands up almost like a mountain front, and runs for a long distance through Texas. It is the front of the Edwards Plateau. This escarpment divides Travis County, Texas, with Austin in the center, into two parts, one Black Waxy, which looks like the prairies of Illinois — all cultivated, having good farm buildings and worth from fifty to three hundred dollars an acre. The other half of the country is dissected plateau. The people have little patches of cleared land in the valleys. Their cattle run in the woods. They make their money by hauling wood to Austin if they are near by; or charcoal if the distance is greater. Many of these people are from Southern Appalachia and they live and think much as the more isolated Appalachian mountaineers live — another of the innumerable examples the world affords of the influences of environment upon life, society and thought.

They have cost one hundred million dollars, and are sometimes spoken of as " twenty-five dollars a yard protection."

In times of flood the water rises twenty-five feet above the level of the plain outside the levee. The river steamboat is then the highest thing in the landscape. Sometimes floods break through this artificial levee, and water flows out through the ever-widening gap, until often it covers hundreds, even thousands of square miles. At these tragic times boat service has to be organized to rescue the dwellers on the flood plain. The War Department often loans tents and the people camp for

Fig. 108 — Noah is a popular hero in the 25,000 square miles that are all too often flooded by the Mississippi. Beulah, Miss. Refugees from the flooded cottages in the background living on the levee in Government tents. The levee at the right was made a little higher with sandbags in the hope of restraining the flood. This picture shows well the appalling fact that the river is the highest part of the landscape. (Courtesy Illinois Central R. R. Co.)

weeks on the levee, which is the only land visible in miles of muddy water.

The most extensive reclamation of the bottom lands has occurred north of the Red River in northeastern Louisiana, northwestern Mississippi and eastern Arkansas. These lands are richer even than the Black Belt, and can stand much continuous cropping of cotton or corn. From 75% to 90% of the population is negro. The organization of the plantation is much like that of a coal-mine. The absentee owner is represented by a superintendent, foreman, book-keeper and store-keeper. The labor is done by dozens or scores of negro tenants — poor basis for a democracy.

Early in this century the rising price of land in the Middle West caused the beginning of a more ambitious plan of swamp reclamation, which closely resembles that of Holland. A steam dredge floating on a barge cuts a canal, and then, floating along in the canal it has cut, lifts the earth up and with it builds a levee beside the canal. The dredge goes around the bounds of a several-thousand-acre tract, leaving the canal on the inside of the dike to serve as a master drainage canal. Since the elevation of this land is less than five feet above the far distant Gulf, the drainage of the enclosed land can only be accomplished by pumping, for which the fuel cost is usually less than a dollar per acre per year.

FIG. 109 — Mississippi Delta reclamation work. The steam shovel uproots the forest and digs the canal along which its barge floats. At the same time it builds a levee to protect reclaimed land from flood. (Courtesy Southern Alluvial Land Association, Memphis.)

Several of these reclaimed units were built before the World War by Northern capitalists, who sold the land at comparatively low prices to people from the North Central states. On at least one of the reclaimed units there was not a single Northerner left in a few years. The possibilities of rich production were there in the black soil, but man does not live by crops alone. The constant humidity, the steady, wilting heat of summer, the mosquitoes, the monotony of life in a little frame house set on posts and without a cellar — all this lacked the charm of the old home in the land of frosty winters, in a place where you could get into an automobile and ride in any direction.

The coming of the boll weevil, which injured the cotton crop, has caused much land along the Mississippi to go out of cultivation, because

wet lands make the cotton late in blooming and therefore more exposed
to the hordes of weevils which increase through the summer.

This Mississippi Delta offers an interesting dare to man. Can we
use all of its wonderful soil to the best advantage? To do so will require a more wholesale attack than has yet been attempted. There are
three enemies — the mosquitoes, the flood and soil exhaustion. We need
to go after them in the same way that an army goes after an intrenched
enemy — with a solid battle-line and an unbroken front. This is especially necessary in order to get rid of the malaria, which can only be
controlled if constructive imagination is applied to hard work.[8]

FIG. 110 — Licensed to kill under the law! That is what land ownership often
means in America — license to kill the home sites of the future. Winter
rain and summer rain, falling on bare, unprotected corn fields and cotton
fields has washed away land enough to support millions of men. (Courtesy H. H. Bennett, U. S. Bureau of Soils.)

The flood has not yet been conquered. It has only been brought to
a truce, and even that is occasionally violated. It is the habit of
meandering streams to cut the outside of their curves. Thus, the river
is always eating at its levees. Sometimes the river is one hundred feet
deep ten feet from the bank — a good illustration of levee difficulties.
The United States Government has been sued for the value of a thou-
sand-acre plantation which was swallowed by the Mississippi as one part
after another caved in. Government engineers were trying to control
the river, and in so doing they caused the stream to change its course,
which resulted in the caving.

The method of dividing the flood plain into a number of individual

[8] See *A Plea and Plan for Redemption of Malaria Throughout the Western
Hemisphere,* Hoffman, Frederick L., Prudential Co. of America.

diked areas and pumping out the water is most promising for ultimate success. To maintain soil fertility some provision is needed for the introduction of river water which brings the blessing of an annual coating of mud. It is river-borne mud which has for so long maintained fertility on the flood plain of the Nile.[9] Arthur E. Morgan, a very expert drainage engineer, says this is technically feasible. It requires large-scale organization to make it effective.

If the twenty-five thousand square miles of Mississippi flood plain were brought into permanent cultivation and annually fertilized by the stream, it could easily support one thousand people to the square mile,[10] or about one-seventh of the present population of the United States.

### Soil Erosion

The Cotton Belt has suffered more from soil erosion than any other part of the United States. The heavy rain and frostless winter conspire to this end and man has assisted almost miraculously with his grassless, humusless agriculture, the two chief crops of which are cotton and corn. Both of these crops require that all other vegetation shall be killed, and earth loosened by the cultivator is in 100% readiness for removal by the next rain. The commercial value of cotton in the past has cursed the

#### SEASONAL DISTRIBUTION OF MAN LABOR ON CROPS
#### 5 COUNTIES IN CENTRAL ALABAMA

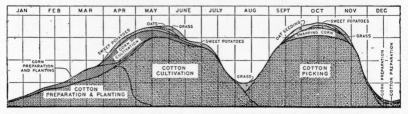

FIG. 111 — If you can grow nothing but cotton, there is leisure time — for joy or for more labor according to the point of view. (Courtesy U. S. Dept. Agr.)

future. It made the bare field. It made the one-crop system. It made the mortgage system. It made the tenant system, and the tenant, being human like the rest of us, let the fields wash away and let the homelands of the future wash down with every shower to choke the rivers and spoil the navigation of the future.

[9] Parts of the Miami Basin in Ohio, subject to an almost regular winter flooding, have maintained a record of seventy-five bushels of corn to the acre for fifty-six consecutive years.

The building of the Nile Dam at Assuan promptly caused a reduction of productivity in the land below it because it held the flood which previously covered the land, fertilized it and kept it fertile from the days of Pharaoh to those of Edward VII.

[10] King, F. H., in *Farmers of Forty Centuries*, reports similar land at the mouth of the Yangtze-kiang to be supporting three thousand people per square mile, without the aid of much machinery.

For decades reports of ruin have come out of the hill section — thousands of square miles of ruin. Some counties were reported one-third worn out before 1850. Worst of all is the plight of the loess lands east of the Mississippi. This layer of rich, wind-blown soil,[11] half as wide as the State of Mississippi, reaching nearly all the way from the Ohio to the Gulf, is a kind of thin veneer lying on top of coastal plain sands. It is extremely rich, and erodes very easily.

" The washing away of the surface soil . . . diminished the production of the higher lands, which were then (at the time of the Civil War) commonly ' turned out ' and left without cultivation or care of any kind.

Fig. 112 — In a few decades erosion has destroyed an area of Cotton Belt farm land equal to populous European kingdoms, Belgium, for instance. This fact makes the mangum terrace one of the great inventions. The older terrace, shown in Fig. 104 divided a field into many little inefficient bits. This ridge of earth, quickly heaped up with the plow, before planting, leads the water harmlessly away and yet permits cultivation of rows in any direction across it, permitting maximum efficiency of machinery. Effective with care on slopes of 10°. (Photo J. S. Kates, U. S. Dept. Agr.)

The crusted surface shed the rain water into the old furrows, and the latter were quickly deepened and widened into gullies — ' red washes.' . . .

" As the evil progressed, large areas of uplands were denuded completely of their loam or culture stratum, leaving nothing but bare, arid sand, wholly useless for cultivation; while the valleys were little better, the native vegetation having been destroyed and only hardy weeds finding nourishment on the sandy surface.

" In this manner whole sections, and in some portions of the state (Mississippi) whole townships of the best class of uplands, have been transformed into sandy wastes, hardly reclaimable by ordinary means,

[11] For origin see Bennett, H. H., *Agriculture in the Southern States.*

and wholly changing the industrial conditions of entire counties, whose county-seats even in some instances had to be changed, the old town and site having, by the same destructive agencies, literally ' gone downhill.'

" Specific names have been given to the erosional features of this district; a ' break ' is the head of a small retrogressive ravine; a ' gulf ' is a large break with precipitous walls of great depth and breadth, commonly being one hundred or one hundred and fifty feet deep; a ' gut ' is merely a road-cut deepened by storm-wash and the effects of passing travel." [12]   In this way we have already destroyed the homelands fit for the sustenance of millions.  We need an enlarged definition for treason.  Some people should not be allowed to sing " My Country." They are destroying it too rapidly.

The above-quoted passage makes clear the statement of an intelligent Southerner that it would be a boon to the nation if this land could become worth one hundred dollars an acre, so that people could not afford to destroy it and then move on and buy more for ten or twenty or thirty dollars per acre, to be in its turn destroyed.

### The Boll Weevil and His Revolution

In 1892 a few strange insects, quite unobserved, made their way across the Rio Grande into the southern tip of Texas.  They were the first arrivals of the boll weevil, destined to upset the one-crop system of agriculture, upon whose ruin diversified farming came into the Cotton Belt.  Thus the boll weevil made a greater agricultural revolution in the South than had resulted from all the teaching and preaching of the previous half-century.  It was more potent economically than the Civil War.

The infant larvae of the boll weevil eat their way into the bolls or unripe pods of cotton and spoil it.  They then come out to fly away, lay their eggs, and take part in that rapid geometric increase of organisms which lets two boll weevils, in theory at least, start in the spring and have twelve million offspring before the summer is over.

It was two or three years before the United States knew what was spoiling the cotton crops in the corner of Texas, and a few people actually died of starvation in the early years of the boll weevil.  The adult insects fly a few miles in early autumn and have thus, in thirty-two years, spread across the Cotton Belt like concentric waves.

Varieties of cotton that ripen early escape better than late-ripening varieties, but there is no known cure for the ravages of the weevil.  Dusting with arsenate of lime, a poison, is now being tried.  The chief means of escape has been to plant less cotton and grow other crops instead.

[12] From *Forest Physiography*, by Isaiah Bowman, p. 524, referring to E. W. Hilgard, *Soils*, 1906, pp. 218–219.

Fortunately, the Cotton Belt is well suited for the success of this diversification and the necessity for it came at a fortunate time.

It was in the decade of rising land-values in the Central West (see Chapter II) and the accompanying increase in the cost of meat and grain supplies from the North. This gave increased costs to the Southern buyer of Northern supplies and increased income to the Southern grower of supply crops. The movement for agricultural education and county demonstration-service was also organized at this time. In 1915 it was estimated that the South was still buying from the North six hundred million dollars' worth of farm supplies that might have been grown at home. Then came the World War which greatly enhanced all farm prices, so between 1913 and 1920 ten Southern States increased their production of corn 18%, oats 50%, rice 72%, white potatoes 60%, sweet potatoes 111%, hay 150%, milk cows 16%, hogs 23%. There was also a substantial increase in the shipment of truck-crops to Northern markets. Georgia watermelons and peaches supply half the United States during the early part of the season.

In 1918 a traveler taking a 15-mile ride east of Montgomery, Alabama, in the Black Belt, saw almost no cotton, but much corn and many cattle at pasture, and fields of alfalfa. In March 1919, the State of Mississippi alone shipped sixty-five thousand hogs to St. Louis.[13] Then came the slump in farm prices which depressed agriculture in all parts of the country, both North and South.

## Science, Mechanism and the Agricultural Future

The agricultural possibilities of the Cotton Belt are astonishing. If they can be utilized as fully as are those of Denmark or Prussia, the Cotton Belt will make those countries, originally poor like the Cotton Belt, seem like poverty-flats in comparison. I have said that much Cotton Belt soil is poor. But the climate is wonderfully productive, about twice as productive potentially as that of Denmark or Prussia. We have discovered technique, supplies of commercial fertilizer, of lime, and the lore of legumes. If all these things are well used in the productive climate of the Cotton Belt, poor sandy soil can be made very productive. The method is to stuff the soil with humus by plowing under legumes. In some cases this is being done by growing a succession of crops[14] the

---

[13] In 1919 the people of Enterprise, in Southern Alabama, flush with pig money, peanut money and cattle money, erected a monument to the boll weevil, whose advent had caused their prosperity — they were " rolling in prosperity," the mayor said.

[14] Oats, rye, vetch, crimson clover, red clover, alfalfa, Sudan grass, Bermuda grass, sorghum, Japanese cane, cow peas, soy beans, velvet beans, sweet potatoes, peanuts, corn — and still the list of possibilities is not exhausted. The western part of the Cotton Belt in Texas and Oklahoma has less rainfall than the rest. Here the possible crop-list is smaller and the possible production per square mile is less. In this area, the drought-resisting kafir corn often replaces maize.

tops of which the pigs eat, leaving nearly all the organic matter on the field (Fig. 144).

Schools, colleges, county demonstration agents and the United States Department of Agriculture and the agricultural press all join in one chorus urging the people to diversify — grow a variety of crops — become independent by the " cow-sow-hen " method.

It is difficult to appreciate the significance of our recent and yet undeveloped conquests by agricultural machinery. The cotton gin is an

FIG. 113 — Corn harvesters in the Cotton Belt — the cheapest possible labor. (Courtesy U. S. Dept. Agr.)

old story, but it made a revolution and created states, policies and wars. The reaper is another old story, but it made a revolution in the North Central States. Recently machine processes long used on wheat have been applied to rice. Since colonial days a few thousand acres of rice had been grown by negroes who waded about the swamps along the Atlantic coast of Carolina and Georgia, after the age-old fashion of the Orient. Suddenly we apply tractors, road graders, steam pumps, reapers and threshers. Between 1909 and 1922 the rice acreage of South Carolina shrunk from 18,000 acres to 8,000, and that of Louisiana increased from 375,000 to 555,000; that of Arkansas from 28,000 to 154,000.

The ability of the tractor to double the amount that the farmer can plow is well known, but its significance is rarely appreciated. The principle is applicable to all cultivated crops.

The South has applied machinery to the culture of the soy bean, long the chief source of protein and cooking fat for millions in China, Japan and Manchuria. On the sandy loams of eastern North Carolina, near Newbern, they make corn rows five or six feet apart, with a row of soy beans between. There seems to be enough moisture and light to make almost a full crop of each — twenty to thirty bushels of beans. The beans are threshed by driving a machine astride the row. With one journey through the field the machine shakes the beans into a sack and delivers them harvested and threshed at the end of the row. Mechanical production of nearly a full crop of corn and soy beans on the same ground the same year is indeed a triumph, and the resulting possibilities rival those of the reaper itself.

The peanut, which grows on the underground stems of a clover-like plant, was originally picked from the plants by hand. Seven people might pick twenty-five bushels in a day. Now three people will operate a peanut-thresher, four others will haul to it, and together they will thresh three or four hundred bushels in a day. The peanut has come out of the garden into the broad field, and become a staple of agriculture in the Cotton Belt. It has gone from the peanut roaster on the sidewalk into the eight-story factory, and is rapidly becoming a staple article of diet, and a staple cooking fat as a substitute for butter and olive oil.

FIG. 114 — Two crops of Cotton Belt cow-feed. When these half-developed velvet beans have finished their growth the corn will be almost hidden. Cattle are often turned in to eat the crop as it stands. The beans and bean vines are rich in protein, the corn stalks are rich in fat. The ears are sometimes snapped off by hand before the cattle are turned in. (Courtesy U. S. Dept. Agr.)

The harvesting of a tangled mass of corn and velvet beans by cattle, and of fields of peanuts and sweet potatoes by pigs, might be called super-mechanical agriculture.

The Cotton Belt is too humid to permit hay to be satisfactorily cured, but the invention of the silo permits almost any kind of forage to be kept perfectly. This method of utilization of crops is a great aid to the cattle industry. It is also possible in much of the Cotton Belt to pasture animals nearly all of the year, if a proper succession of crops is planted.

The cattle industry of the Cotton Belt, which for decades languished because of the ravages of a fever spread by the cattle tick, is now in a position to compete on more than even terms with the North, because the cattle tick has been conquered. The process is simple now that we have found that the tick is to blame. Keep the cattle out of a field for a period and the ticks left in the field starve to death. Drive the cattle through vats of disinfecting liquid and every tick on them is killed.

FIG. 115 — Long lines of cattle swim through deep concrete tanks full of disinfecting liquid. When their heads are pushed under the last disease-bearing tick is killed. Thus Texas fever is eliminated and the South is rapidly changing from a meat-importing to a meat-exporting area. But eternal vigilance is needed. (Courtesy U. S. Dept. Agr.)

The cattle are clean; the field is clean. By this method the whole State of Mississippi has become clear of tick fever and can produce as good cattle as any state, and many sections are doing it.

If swamp lands are needed for farm purposes, steam dredges and ditching machines of many designs enable us to cut ditches a hundred times as fast as could be done with the spade in grandfather's time.

The ability to drain land and the knowledge of the life-history of the malaria germ will enable us to wipe out malaria in the Southern States whenever we take the matter as seriously as we do war, or even automobiles.

By learning how to bud and graft the pecan tree, and by planting it in orchards, the South has made the most important addition of a native plant to Caucasian agriculture since the Indian gave us potatoes, tobacco and corn. The best specimens of native pecan trees have been selected as parents, propagated by the thousand and set out in large orchards, a few of which have begun to bear, giving promise of a substantial addition to our food supply in a short time. These lordly trees permit the growth of many crops between and beneath them, thus permitting a two-story agriculture, important in itself, and suggestive of the future of intensive agriculture if we ever need it.

The above-mentioned list of things that have come to pass in the Cotton Belt, many of which are revolutionary if carried to a logical conclusion, is not meant to be complete, but merely suggestive. In the long growing season, the possible crop-list is so rich that there might be developed many kinds of farms, each best in its place.[15] The important thing is that every Southern farmer shall promptly adopt some rational system.

[15] A rotation followed successfully in some localities, particularly in Texas, is most suggestive: first year, corn with cow peas sown in it at last cultivation;

The long growing season, with abundant rain, the possibility of growing several crops of vegetables per year, would enable the Cotton Belt to keep on growing present supplies of cotton, and enlarge them, and to produce almost incalculable quantities of food if we should make large use of dehydration, a method of food preservation now thoroughly established and awaiting the spread of knowledge and a slight change in

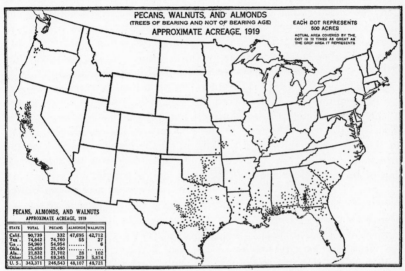

PECANS, WALNUTS, AND ALMONDS
(TREES OF BEARING AND NOT OF BEARING AGE)
APPROXIMATE ACREAGE, 1919

EACH DOT REPRESENTS 500 ACRES
ACTUAL AREA COVERED BY THE DOT IS 10 TIMES AS GREAT AS THE CROP AREA IT REPRESENTS

PECANS, ALMONDS, AND WALNUTS
APPROXIMATE ACREAGE, 1919

| STATE | TOTAL | PECANS | ALMONDS | WALNUTS |
|---|---|---|---|---|
| Calif. | 90,739 | 332 | 47,695 | 42,712 |
| Tex.. | 74,842 | 74,760 | 55 | 27 |
| Ga... | 54,960 | 54,954 | ........ | 6 |
| Okla. | 25,450 | 25,450 | ........ | ... |
| Ala.. | 21,832 | 21,702 | 28 | 102 |
| Other | 75,548 | 69,345 | 329 | 5,874 |
| U.S. | 343,371 | 246,543 | 48,107 | 48,721 |

FIG. 116 — The pecan, a giant native nut tree, grows throughout the limit of the Cotton Belt and beyond — significant of a possible rich agriculture.

culinary and dietetic habits. Sandy land produces sweet potatoes to perfection, and the Cotton Belt has large areas of sandy land. With dehydration [16] this or some other starchy root might easily be grown in quantities that rival our present supply of wheat, along with almost limit-

second year, winter oats, followed by peanuts; third year, cotton followed by bur clover, sown in it at last cultivation; fourth year, same as first.

This rotation permits the farmer to grow the old staples of cotton with two of the world staples, corn and oats, and each year the field also produces a leguminous crop to leave nitrogen and humus in the soil. The cow peas may be harvested and sold as grain, eaten by pigs, or plowed under to fertilize the earth. The peanut, which can be grown after the harvesting of winter oats in May or June, can yield a ton of hay to the acre and then a rich crop of food for men, or for the pigs to root up and eat at their leisure. The bur clover that follows the cotton, like the other legumes leaves nitrate in the ground and can be used to some extent as winter forage for pasturing animals. The oat plant is a grain, which, fortunately for the South, will mature in more moisture than wheat, and having an extra husk will keep in climates where wheat will spoil.

[16] Ordinary dehydration is not the only method of preserving the sweet potato, which is a nutritious but very perishable root. A process of making sweet-potato flour by flaking, the process used for white potatoes, is described in *Chemical Age*, April 1921.

less amounts of dehydrated spinach, cabbage, beans, carrots, tomatoes and other vegetables. It is true, of course, that changes in diet come slowly. Canning as a process was invented in 1786. The United States Civil War established the use of canned food.

The experience of an old negro (ex-slave), Sam McCall, was made the subject of a bulletin by the United States Department of Agriculture. This old man owned many acres, but he preferred to get much income from few acres rather than little income from many. Accordingly, he limited himself to two acres, but for many years he got $200.00 to $350.00 from the two acres, an amount more than that which his negro tenant neighbor got from twenty or thirty acres. In a typical year one of these acres yielded seventy-five bushels of winter oats and three bales (1520 pounds) of cotton. The other acre yielded three crops as follows: one bale cotton, fifty bushels corn, fifty bushels oats.

The negro farmer planted the cotton in pre-weevil days in the same rows with the corn. As soon as the ear of corn was established, he cut off the tops above the ear to let light in on the cotton. As soon as the corn stalk was ripe,[17] he removed it, thus giving the cotton the full possession of the ground during the latter part of the summer.

When we notice that the average yield of cotton per acre in the United States was then about three hundred pounds, the production of the old negro's farm is astonishing, but it is much less than the yet more careful farmers of China produce. McCall had a better income than the average farm hand or city worker of the same territory and time, and his work left him in better condition and with more leisure than the average factory worker. This story is exceedingly suggestive of the possibilities of the South if population should press heavily upon resources.

The long growing season of the Cotton Belt has a handicap — the cold wave. A warm week in winter, green with growing things, may end with hard freezing. New Orleans has had a winter temperature of 5° F. These occasional winter freezes almost limit winter crops to hardy forage, and point the way to the animal industry.

### The Population of the Cotton Belt

It is one thing to point out the great possibilities of agricultural production, as in the above paragraphs, and quite a different thing to produce the millions of days of hard work necessary to bring the possibilities to pass. The people of the South admit a difference between themselves and the people of the Northern States. They confess that they have a desire not to duplicate the "Yankee" rate of speed and hustle and Yankee thrift. A delightful friend of mine in the South said: "The Yankees eat what they can't sell. We sell what we can't eat." There is a savor of truth in this. It is an admirable description of two points

[17] See the account of the tropic garden in this book.

of view, and it is true that Southern fried chicken and hot corn pone
have a better reputation as delicacies than the fried potatoes and cold
wheat bread of the North.

Perhaps this difference in attitude toward thrift and expenditure is a
legacy of the society based upon the old aristocratic concept of slavery.
Perhaps the lesser keenness for work is a natural result of the climate.
Certainly, many people of the South think so, and frankly tell a newcomer from the North: " If you stay down heah six months you won't
rush about like that. Take your time," they say. Also I remember
the sense of wilt in the summer weather of Louisiana and Carolina.[18]

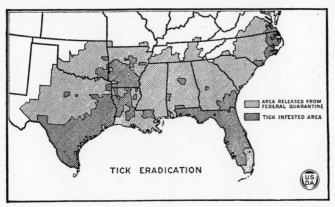

Fig. 117 — The line of battle between man and the tick which kills
the cow.

Certain it is that the Cotton Belt is a land where resources are relatively undeveloped, even for the United States. This may be partly due
to the Civil War, which the South fought to the finish. Since nearly half
her population was black and all the fighting was done by the white
population, the relative losses were several times as great as those of
the North. It is impossible to speculate what might have happened had
the hundreds of thousands of young men been preserved to live their

[18] I was spending a little time one July on an island off the Carolina coast.
A physician, a native of the state, but Northern-trained, came. "Well, Mr. Smith,"
said he on the third day, "has the climate down here got you yet?" Then he
stated how yesterday morning he got fixed on the porch after breakfast and just
couldn't move for two hours. Whereupon our hostess, who had spent some time
in Oklahoma, chimed in: "I just hate to *move* down here. When I am standing
up I just want to keep on standing. If I am sitting down I want to keep right
on sitting. It's just an effort to move, and you know that's no way for folks like
us to be." Personally I should not be inclined to blame the climate quite so much
as these people did. They were too highly fed on fried meat, fried fish, fried
hominy and other frying-pan products with a dearth of vitamines, milk and greens.
It is a fact that hundreds of thousands, if not millions, of people in the Cotton
Belt suffer from malnutrition, in a land carrying every possibility of riotous plenty
— if the people only knew — and *did*.

normal lives and to influence the region through the half-century just passed. Another retarding influence has been the loss of 5,000,000 white people by emigration from the Southern States east of the Mississippi River, between 1865 and 1900. There are hosts of Southern men in positions of influence in Northern cities from New York to San Francisco and Seattle.

The undeveloped condition of the South might also be attributed to the large proportion of negroes in the population. In the Coast Plain the proportion is often more than half, and South Carolina, being largely a Coast Plain state, has for many censuses shown a majority of negroes. The negro, with his low standard of living, his low rate of daily wage, has effectively kept the nineteenth and twentieth century European immigration out of the South. While the negro has done the bulk of the

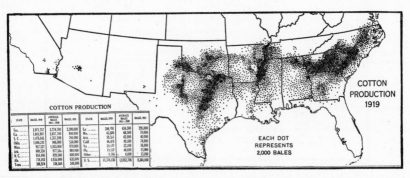

FIG. 118 — Cotton has been chiefly grown on the richer soil belts — mining the land where the mining was good. (Courtesy U. S. Dept. Agr.)

manual labor, his race is without experience in organizing industry or government or participating in democracy. Nearly all the burden of carrying civilization has been upon the white faction of the population. The large proportion of negroes has often caused social isolation for the white people as well as rural neglect, because whenever possible in many localities the whites have moved to town even if moving has resulted in financial loss and in the decline of the rented land.[19]

Whatever the differences between the white and the black may be, the dark skin, geography's greatest curse to man, marks off the man of color and keeps him and his seed forever classified, and keeps him from receiving the treatment accorded to a white. This is true even if the negro chances to be similar in all cultural, intellectual and economic respects.[20]

[19] "If the negro is in the minority he tends to move to town." *Geographical Review*, October 1919, p. 275.

[20] The Indians of Oklahoma (late Indian Territory) have the advantage of being received by the whites more nearly as social equals. The home training of the Indian woman makes her a good wife and intermarriage in not uncommon.

Some tribes still holding their lands in common have become enormously rich

We hear much about negro shiftlessness and laziness, but, taking a long view, one of the most startling things about the negro is the amount of property he has managed to amass since his emancipation and the progress he has made. Perhaps this is a result of climate. The negro, coming from the tropics, is in a climate that is more stimulating and invigorating than that from which he came. It is also a fact that the whites from northwest Europe are in a less invigorating climate than the one from which they came. What happened in one of the Cotton Belt states in a recent summer school is suggestive of the racial com-

Fig. 119 — Weighing and loading in the cotton field. Hundreds of thousands of negroes have left the cotton fields for Northern towns since we shut down on European immigration. (Courtesy U. S. Dept. Agr.)

petition. All the teachers, both white and colored, were urged to come to summer schools and similar inducements were offered to both races. There was a school for white teachers and one for colored teachers, and both were addressed, in some cases at least, by the same men. Thirty per cent of the whites came and 60% of the colored came. This is perhaps ominous for a region where the population is almost evenly divided and where the whites feel that it is a duty of life and death to dominate society in every respect and where they expect to maintain dominance or die in the attempt.

### Negro Migration to the North

A sudden change has taken place in the negro question in the United States. The negroes have begun to go North in vast numbers. Since

through oil royalties. This new wealth in such hands has made many ludicrous incidents. For example, one chief fancied only a white automobile hearse, so he bought one and used it for his private conveyance.

the middle of the nineteenth century periods of industrial prosperity in the Northern States have drawn hundreds of thousands of unskilled workers per year from Europe. These people have stayed in the North, while the negro stayed in the South. The World War shut off European immigration. The Northern mills demanded labor. The negro moved North to supply it. Then Congress checked immigration and the Northern mills again demanded labor. The negro moved North to supply it. By hundreds of thousands he went. Unofficial estimates have it that 500,000 went North in the twelve months ending September 1, 1922 — 120,000 from Georgia alone. The 1923 census showed that in the decade 1910–1920 the number of negroes had actually declined in Mississippi, Louisiana and Alabama, while the percentage loss had been as follows: Mississippi, from 56% to 52%; Georgia, from 45% to 41.7%; Louisiana, 43% to 38.9%; South Carolina, 55.2% to 51.4%; Alabama, 42.5% to 38.4%.

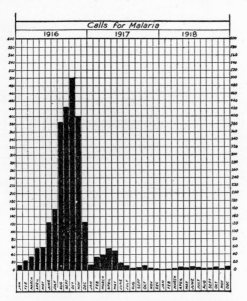

FIG. 120 — Physicians' calls for malaria in a Cotton Belt town before and after the beginning of active control measures by the Rockefeller Foundation. This one thing is enough to settle the fate of empires. (Courtesy The Rockefeller Foundation.)

South Carolina claimed (1924) for the first time in generations that she had a majority of white population. It appears that by checking European immigration we have elected that the Northern states shall be filled with Southern negroes rather than with Europeans.

The transfer has thrown Southern agriculture into a turmoil. Wages are rising to heights before unknown. The farmers cannot pay them, land is going out of cultivation and is often for sale at nominal prices, $10.00 to $20.00 per acre. The Cotton Belt used to be a little low-wage world of its own. It promises soon to be on a price level with the rest of the United States.

### Future of the Whites

The prospect of the white race in the Cotton Belt is distinctly better for the future than it has been for the past. The continued vigor of the

Acadian French after two centuries [21] in the swamps of Louisiana is very encouraging for the possibilities of good stock in the Cotton Belt.[22]

The better prospects for the future seem very clear when we consider the sciences of sanitation, preventive medicine, and nutrition. The puzzle of malaria has been solved and its eradication is easier than was the defeat of the Central Powers.[23]

The science of nutrition is young. Industrial education, health education, rural organization [24] are all young yet, and the earnestness of the educational reconstruction in the South promises the rapid utilization of

FIG. 121 — Arrival of Boys' Club members at a country railroad station for a county short course. (Courtesy U. S. Dept. Agr.)

all these things for the improvement of the mental and physical welfare of the white man in this land of great possibilities. In some Southern States faith in education amounts almost to a superstition. Between 1910 and 1920 illiteracy among people over ten years of age declined in Alabama from 40% to 31.3% among negroes; and from 9.9% to 6.4% among whites.

Tomato clubs, pig clubs, chicken clubs, corn clubs and canned food week are very practical and effective kinds of education for the improve-

[21] The case of a Norwegian colony in Texas reported by Dr. Austin O'Malley (*Literary Digest,* September 6, 1919), seems to show that perhaps some races cannot survive. In fifty years there was no surviving Norwegian descendant.

[22] These people have maintained such complete isolation that the companies of recruits in the draft army during the World War had to be drilled by French-speaking officers.

[23] Between 1900 and 1914 the death-rate from malaria declined 80% in twenty Southern cities. Between 1918 and 1922 the establishment of milk inspection in Birmingham was accompanied by a decline of 75% in the death-rate from typhoid fever, and of 73% for colitis.

[24] In 1923 Alabama sent a commission to Kansas to study Corn Belt efficiency.

ment of the people in a region where malnutrition stalks and land is still almost free.

In June 1923, the North Carolina Agricultural College put out a leaflet (No. 31) comparing the acre yields of high-school agriculture students with the state average for the years 1919–20, as follows: Corn, 52 to 17.7 bu.; Cotton, 512 lbs. to 278; Tobacco, 814.8 lbs. to 610 lbs.; Sweet potatoes, 178 bu. to 106.6. These figures promise better economic conditions for the next generation, especially when the progress in agricultural education is taken into account.

### Lumber and Forestry

The Cotton Belt was originally all forested, with the exception of certain Coast Prairies and flood lands that were too wet, and with the further exception of the Black and Grand Prairies of Texas and the country beyond them where the Cotton Belt has been extending westward in the attempt to escape from the boll weevil. The prairies inland from the coast in Texas and Louisiana are so flat that the trees drown out after periods of rain, although an elevation as much as a foot or two makes an island of pine forest in a sea of grass. Similar prairies of much smaller extent are found along the coast of Carolina and Georgia where the savannah type of landscape, grass with occasional clumps of trees, gave the name to the city of Savannah, Georgia.

In the Cotton Belt as a whole, pine trees grew on the sandy soils; oaks, hickories, pecans, gum and some other broad-leaved trees grew on the clay hills or flood plains; while the moisture-enduring cypress produced its valuable timber in many areas of swamp. In the wetter parts of the Cotton Belt the branches of the trees are draped with the long hanging moss (an epiphyte or air-plant) which nearly always produces a depressing effect upon the stranger because of its resemblance to crape and mourning veils in the somber shade of the draped forest.

In no other part of the United States has lumbering been easier than in the Cotton Belt. Wagons and temporary railroads can run in almost any direction over most of its surface. Hither came the lumberman who had migrated first from New England to the Lake States, then from the Lake States to the South. For a time these states led the United States in lumber production, but the lumberman, after his usual orgy of appalling waste, has gone on to the Pacific Coast [25] and with him the leadership in lumber production.

Mississippi, which took the leadership after Minnesota, Wisconsin and Michigan had had it in turn, has now been surpassed by Washington.

The cheap pine of the South is shifting the paper industry to that sec-

---

[25] On the banks of the Columbia River in Washington State, a Southern lumber company was building in 1923 and 1924 a lumber city, probably the greatest lumbering enterprise in the world. (See Chap. XXXIII.)

tion. The eleven Southern mills produced 65% more in 1920 than the same region produced in 1916.

In the decade 1910 to 1920, 250,000,000 acres of Cotton Belt pine were being logged to the sawmill at the rate of five to ten million acres per year. Destruction in the Southern forest proves again the oft-proven charge that we regard timber as a mine, rather than as a crop. In this region fire often ran through the forests ahead of the lumberman. It was set to clear out the brush so that grass would grow for the roving cattle. The razorback hog finds a good morsel in the thick root of the young longleafed pine when it is a few inches high, so he roots it out as he does sweet potatoes or peanuts in the fields of the more progressive farmers. Turpentine and rosin, so called " naval stores," have long been made from the sap of pine trees that were killed in the process of turpentining. This industry began in eastern North Carolina in 1810. In 1849 this locality led with 91% of the national output. In 1879 South Carolina led. In 1889 and 1899 Georgia led. In 1909 and 1919 Florida led, while North Carolina, the original home of rosin, produced less than half of one per cent of the crop, so thorough had been the annihilation of the Carolina forest.

FIG. 122 — A death dealer and his victim. The life blood of tens of millions of pine trees has been carried to the turpentine still. Long-leaf pine tree, Florida. The landscape would be thick with pine-tree children but for fire and pasturing animals. (Courtesy *American Forestry Magazine*.)

Fire and the razorback keep most of the cut-over land from reproduction, although the long, warm, moist summer makes this the region of greatest possibility for quick timber growth. The United States Forest Service reports measurements of red spruce in Maine, at the age of seventy years, showing an average diameter of 1.8 inches. Hemlock in Otsego County, N. Y., at seventy years averaged 3.3 inches, while loblolly pine in eastern Texas at the same age was twenty-four inches in diameter. A lumber company in East Texas finds that it can cut the lumber on a tract every five years if it keeps the fire out and takes no trees smaller than fifteen inches in diameter. The removal of these larger trees leaves light and fertility for the smaller trees, which add a half-inch ring (an increase of one inch in diameter) each year. Thus, fifteen-inch trees become twenty-inch trees and good saw-logs in five years.

There have been enough experiments in scientific forestry in the Cotton Belt to show its great possibilities if fire and pig can be kept in check.

### Cities, Manufacture, and Trade

The Cotton Belt has resources for manufacture almost as great as its resources for agriculture. Everywhere there is cotton, wood, material for power, and possibilities of rich and varied food production.

In the western part the power resources are the coal-fields of Oklahoma (the lignites of Texas being a poorer reserve), while the present generation uses and wastes the fleeting stores of oil and natural gas which Texas and Oklahoma are now producing in such quantity. The eastern part of the Cotton Belt has the coal of Alabama, of the near-by Cumberland

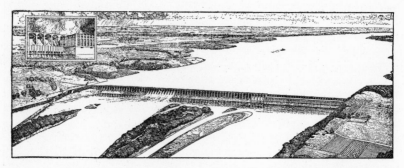

FIG. 123 — Drawing of completed dam at Muscle Shoals, with locks. This is one of the many things made possible by cement. (Courtesy Hugh L. Cooper & Co., New York.)

Plateau and hundreds of thousands of horse-power now being developed and yet to be developed from streams flowing from mountains where the rainfall is seventy inches. The iron and steel of the Birmingham district are one more asset of the eastern Cotton Belt.

The central part, that is to say, the banks of the Mississippi, including New Orleans, has the possibilities of a cheap coal and iron supply by barge from Pittsburgh. Barges also carry coal cheaply from the Birmingham, Ala., district down the Warrior River across Mobile Bay, Mississippi Sound and Lake Borgene to New Orleans.

In the coast section of eastern Texas and western Louisiana is the world's cheapest and greatest sulphur-producing region. By the simple device of driving superheated steam down a pipe a few hundred feet into the earth the sulphur is melted. Then it flows up another pipe, solidifies, and is ready to be sent to market.

Despite these almost fabulous resources for transport and manufacture, little use was made of them until about the beginning of this century.[26]

The Georgia orator, Henry W. Grady, described a Georgia funeral in 1899 as follows:

" The grave was dug through solid marble, but the marble headstone came from Vermont. It was in a pine wilderness, but the pine coffin came from Cincinnati. An iron mountain overshadowed it, but the coffin nails and screws and shovels came from Pittsburgh. With hardwoods and metals abounding, the corpse was hauled on a wagon that came from South Bend, Indiana. A hickory grove grew near by, but the pick and shovel handles came from New York. The cotton shirt on the dead man came from Cincinnati; the coat and breeches from Chicago; the shoes from Boston, the folded hands were incased in white gloves from New York, and round the poor neck, that had borne all its living days the bondage of lost opportunity, was twisted a cheap cravat from Philadelphia."

In considering manufacturing we may divide this region into sections, the Coast towns, Texas and Oklahoma towns, and the Piedmont towns.

The Coast towns [27] have been primarily occupied with foreign trade, chiefly in exporting the raw materials of the region — lumber, cotton, cottonseed cake, rosin and turpentine, and with importing fertilizer materials, petroleum and sugar. Because of the long, hot, humid summers and the proximity of swamps Coast towns are limited to such commercial enterprises rather than to the extensive development of manufacturing. Manufacturing has been limited largely to sugar refineries for home supply, wood products, for which the locality afforded such abundant raw material, and to fertilizer factories, for which the cotton fields afford the market. Even New Orleans is growing much more slowly than many Northern cities and like the other Coast towns is primarily commercial. New Orleans is setting out to create ideal physical conditions for manufacturing plants. Tens of thousands of cisterns were destroyed to get rid of yellow fever mosquitoes. The fear of bubonic plague was removed by building rat-proof warehouses on the water-front. Building sites with ideal transport possibilities are being provided. They may be reached by belt-line railway and also by a ship canal that connects the river with the Gulf by a short cut to Lake Ponchartrain.

[26] In January 1924, one towboat left Cairo, Ill., for New Orleans with a tow of 16,000 tons of grain, steel and merchandise — the equivalent of 450 carloads. *Philadelphia Ledger,* January 9, 1924.

[27] The map shows that some of the Southern ports are not in this region, but they are treated here because their commercial life depends upon this region.

The city water-front on the canal is as great as that of Manhattan Island on the Hudson River. There is limitless opportunity for more water-front.

Galveston has huge exports of cotton and wheat and imports of jute bagging for grain sack and cotton bale and of sisal for binder twine. The commercial future of Galveston is menaced by the building of a twenty-million-dollar ship canal to Houston, the inland railroad center through which nearly all of Galveston's trade passes. If the ships all go to Houston, there will be small service for Galveston to perform.

FIG. 124 — Bananas at New Orleans. The unloading machine (see bunches at the right) delivers them to the horizontal conveyor, thence to the trains (see left). (Courtesy P. K. Reynolds, United Fruit Co., Photo H. J. Harvey.)

In some years Galveston, with fifty-nine steamship lines, is the second port of the United States.

In addition to Cotton Belt produce, New Orleans exports machinery and other Northern manufactures, and has heavy imports of coffee, sugar and bananas.

The cities of interior Texas — Dallas, Fort Worth and Waco — are commercial centers of a rich region. The skyscraper section of Dallas looks truly metropolitan. Manufacture in these cities is mainly concerned with the use of local raw materials as in meat-packing, oil refining and machine shops to supply local demand. As yet few Texas manufactures are sent out of the state.

The cities of Oklahoma are the newest of all, for Oklahoma was long reserved for the Indians and called Indian Territory. In 1892 the white man entered it on the run. At the firing of a signal gun, announced months in advance, thousands of homesteaders, waiting at the boundary line, surged into Oklahoma in the great race for a quarter section of land. This land was immediately valuable because the lands of Kansas and Texas were already occupied. Then oil was found. Oil, the greatest goad to speculation known to man. In rushed other thousands. As a result of newness and oil the Oklahoma cities are chiefly local commercial centers and oil-field centers where the fortunes of people, and the people themselves, come and go with the ups and downs of oil. (Fig. 78.)

Cotton Belt manufacturing is chiefly centered in a ring of cities spread out around the southern end of the Appalachian Mountains. Here are advantages not shared by other parts of the Cotton Belt. The elevation of the Piedmont hills affords a cooler climate than any other part of the Cotton Belt and it is essentially free from the mosquito, and therefore from malaria. For the present there is an abundance of water-power. The Appalachian mountaineer, with his large family, gravitating down the sharp valleys, has been attracted by the opportunity for work which mills afford for men, women and children. For a man with a large family this was a multiple lure. It is these mountain people, accustomed to little at home, who are furnishing New England cotton-manufacturing such fierce competition. This is because they are willing to work longer hours and for lower wages than prevail in Massachusetts. It is persistently claimed that Southern child labor is a factor in this competition. The problem of child labor illustrates the development of social processes. First, the problem develops by gradual and unseen steps; its existence is discovered; agitation for amelioration begins; education is continued until a solution is found. The cycle takes years. Most of the Northern States have legislated against child labor. The Southern States have not yet had sufficient time fully to realize the necessity, but they have made a start. Perhaps the advantage due to young workers and long hours which Southern manufacturers have had over the manufacturers of the North is only temporary. Whether permanent or temporary, the advantages favoring the South have certainly produced conspicuous results. Once the spindles in the South were one-twentieth as numerous as those in the North. By 1920 the South had 14.5 million and the North 19 million. South Carolina was the second cotton-spinning state in the Union. North Carolina was third, Massachusetts first. Most of these Southern mills were built by Northern capital, and many of them are owned by companies having large mills in New England.

The North Carolina towns close to the Appalachian hardwood forests have developed a furniture industry which in the decade from 1910 to 1920 grew several times as fast as that of the whole United States.

The advantages of Birmingham for the manufacture of cheap iron previously discussed (chapter on Appalachian Ridges and Valleys) are supplemented by barge-transportation to Mobile. This port counts upon having a greater export of steel to South America, the Pacific Coast and the Orient than it now possesses.

Atlanta is the largest city of this area because it is a railroad center with a large distributing trade [28] and a very metropolitan appearance, with many steel skyscrapers in the business section.

Manufacturing in this region is young. Its exports are steel rails, beams, girders, the coarser, not the finer cottons, furniture made of

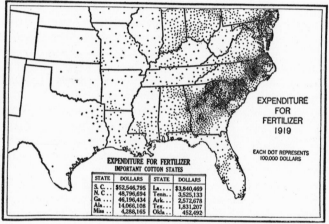

FIG. 125 — The location of our fertilizer market shows why this industry belongs to the South Atlantic ports. (Courtesy U. S. Dept. Agr.)

local wood, and the furniture not of the highest quality. Will the time come when this region competes with Michigan in automobiles, and New England in the finer manufactures of metal and cotton? This question is for future decades and generations to answer, but at present the progress of Southern manufactures is rapid. In the meantime it already has excellent power resources and service. A super-power system of interconnecting power wires serves the whole area from southern Virginia to Alabama. The power is derived from water-power plants and steam plants with large water-power resources, including those of Muscle Shoals yet to be utilized. Charlotte, N. C., calls itself the electric city.

[28] Atlanta is a railroad basing point. All freight rates from distant points to places near Atlanta are made up of the rate from distant point to Atlanta plus local rate *from* Atlanta. Therefore it is more convenient to deal with Atlanta, and over 400 cars of package freight leave the city daily.

Within fifty miles are four water-power plants developing 250,000 horse-power, and extensive enlargements were in progress in 1924.

This widespread distribution of power gives any village the same power advantages as a larger city. There seems to be a tendency for manufacturing to be scattered in many small cities. This is good. It affords opportunity for better living conditions than can be afforded in larger rival places such as Detroit, Pittsburgh, New York and Philadelphia.

F<small>IG</small>. 126 — The swampy forest is the best type of landscape of all this region. Good prospective truck land near Tampa, Fla. (Courtesy Tampa Board of Trade.)

## CHAPTER XIV

## SUBTROPIC COASTS AND THE FLORIDA PENINSULA

### A. T<small>HE</small> G<small>ULF</small> C<small>OAST</small> S<small>ECTION</small>

T<small>HE</small> north coast of the Gulf of Mexico is a hot, moist lowland which consists of barrier beach, lagoons, tide marshes, flat forests, wet prairies too flat to grow trees, Mississippi flood plain. East of the Mississippi are sandy forests. Most of this land or semi-land is the natural home of waterfowl and of the mosquito, which has a long breeding season in a land where frost never lasts more than a day or two at a time (Figs. 19 and 20).

### *Rice*

Large areas of the flat prairies west of the Mississippi delta have water-tight subsoil. This is necessary for impounding water in rice fields. Rice is a native of the swamp and thrives best under swamp conditions which are here more or less guaranteed by the heavy rain of this sub-tropic coast. The practice of flooding the rice is here greatly aided by the extreme flatness of the land. This makes it easy to enclose large areas with one embankment. Supplies of artesian water, fed in from sand outcrops west of the Black Prairie, supply the rest of the necessary water. This combination of factors aids in the wholesale production of rice, which is produced here with less labor than in any of the old rice-growing countries of Asia (Fig. 72).

## Sugar

On the delta lands of the Mississippi south of New Orleans is a long-established sugar-cane district. For a long time there was no other in the United States. Sugar-cane needs several years without frost. There-fore this is a perilous and costly place in which to grow sugar. Cool, wet autumns sometimes give the cane low sugar content. Because of frost one planting produces only one good crop and one poor one.[1] The

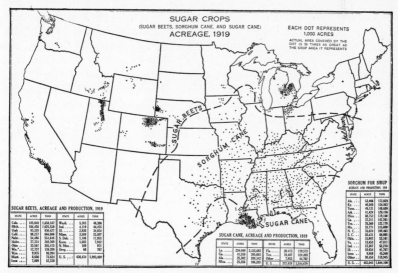

FIG. 127 — The Louisiana sugar is for the factory. The scattered cane and sorghum is mostly for syrup, a simple manufacture. (Courtesy U. S. Dept. Agr.)

nearness of this section to the northern limit of cane-growing is well shown by the influence of small lakes a few miles wide, which often serve to temper a " norther " so that cane-fields along the south shore escape a freeze which destroys cane on the north shore of the lake.

Sugar would not be grown in Louisiana at all except for the fact that the tariff permits the American sugar-grower to receive about twice as much for sugar as it costs to grow it in the West Indies.

Rice and sugar cover but a small percentage of this area of heavy

[1] For a full discussion of this disadvantage see cane sugar section in chapter on the West Indies.

soils. A considerable proportion of it is flooded at times by high tide, heavy rain or Mississippi overflow. Large tracts of this unused land have been set aside [2] as a national bird refuge, where hunter or gun cannot enter, and where birds and wild animals can live undisturbed in their native haunts.

This section contains some sulphur deposits like those previously described in the chapter on the Cotton Belt. There are also some valuable and puzzling deposits of salt, valuable because they are more than 99% pure and exist in solid layers hundreds of feet thick. One of the layers comes to within twelve feet of the surface of an island on the south shore of Louisiana. The puzzle is, how did salt, a product of desert conditions, come to be produced in this place?

The sandy lands of southern Mississippi, southern Alabama, and western Florida, the home of the long-leaf pine, the turpentine-still and the sawmill, are but little used for cultivation. The greatest culture in this section is found east of Mobile Bay, where there is considerable trucking, and about 20,000 acres of a hardy variety of orange, the satsuma.

This whole coast is subject at times to the visitation of stray West Indian hurricanes. These storms, a hundred miles wide and whirling with destructive fury, normally pass east of Florida and proceed northward at a safe distance from the coast. Once in a while one is pushed westward and crosses the Gulf, whence it turns northward into the United States. Such was the storm that destroyed Galveston in 1900. From time to time New Orleans or Mobile receives the deluges of rain and fierce winds that accompany one of these storms. In 1909 and again in 1915 a storm was strong enough to blow down the iron bridges of the Louisville and Nashville Railroad east of New Orleans. A special type of bridge had to be designed to resist them. Fortunately, these storms rarely visit any one particular place, and their fury abates when they reach the land.

## B. The Florida Peninsula: An Economic Frontier

The Florida peninsula is about 140 by 400 miles, as long as the distance from Washington to Albany. It was recently raised from the bottom of the sea. The surface is low, flat, or rolling sandy plains dotted with swamps, lakes, lagoons and old beaches. During the seventeenth and eighteenth centuries, when the North Atlantic states were developing populations, industries and institutions, Florida was an almost unsettled claim, a small pawn, passed back and forth across the treaty tables by England, France and Spain, in their rather frequent settlements of wars. Bought by the United States from Spain in 1819, it had no feverish period of ante-bellum settlement and exploitation,

[2] A result of diligent effort of Theodore Roosevelt and many other nature-loving, far-seeing citizens. Such is the technique of social progress.

because it had no areas of rich land suitable for cotton or any other exploitive agriculture.[3] Therefore, Florida has been a late arrival in settlement. Progress began about 1870 and received a great impetus after the completion of the first railroad line from the North. Indeed, Florida may still be called a frontier in the economic sense — the last frontier east of the Mississippi River. She shows her frontier character by the rapid increase of population, which was 42% in the decade ending 1910 and 28% in the decade ending 1920. In no other Eastern state, not even in metropolitan New York, have numbers increased so rapidly.

This is striking in comparison with static Mississippi or with almost static Iowa. To duplicate such increase we must look to the Far West. Florida also shows her frontier character by the small amount of cultivated land. Of her total area of 35,000,000 acres, but 6,000,000 are in farms, 2.3 million in improved land, and in 1920 less than 2,000,000 acres, or 5.2%, were actually in crop. Parts of the south are mangrove swamp, but little explored, and coral reef (Fig. 64).

Still further proof of the frontier stage is to be seen in the land speculation which accompanied the rapid arrival of Northern people between 1920 and 1924.

## Population

Florida is the only Southern state with a large Northern element in her population. She calls herself the melting-pot of the states. The percentage of negroes has declined sharply from 43.7% in 1900 to 34% in 1920. It is a strange and appalling fact that in Miami, largely Northern, the suppression of the negro is perhaps more complete and merciless than in any other Southern city.

## The Climate and the Tourist

The most distinctive thing about Florida is her climate. It has been called the "most marketable climate in the world." Florida is marketing her climate in three ways — through her fruits, her vegetables, and her tourists. She sells climate to tourists either by the day or by the building lot.

Florida's climate is chiefly made by warm water. The equatorial drift in the Atlantic flows through the Caribbean into the Gulf, out through the Florida Straits as the Gulf Stream, which is like a mighty river of warm water carrying in a northeasterly direction toward Europe 1800 times as much volume as the Mississippi pours into the Gulf. Thus the Florida peninsula has warm water on three sides and on the north is exposed to the land influence which means an occasional dash of cold, carrying frost to the very tip of the peninsula. Then all Florida shivers,

---

[3] A few clay hills in the north long marked the end of cultivation as well as the bounds of the Cotton Belt.

the houses being built for comfort for the average warm days. The visitor from the North is naturally most chagrined by frost in Florida.

The summer from May to November is showery without the extremes of heat (especially in South Florida [4]) that occasionally visit Washington or Chicago. The winter is bright and sunshiny with occasional showers which are soon over. This winter climate is attractive to the denizens of the North. For an unknown time hundreds of thousands of water-fowl in search of food have winged their way from the Northern United States and Canada to spend the winter on the lakes and swamps of Florida and have flown back again in the spring to rear their families in the North. And now Northern man, the sun-hunter, with new-found powers of flight, is following the water-fowl to Florida. The tourist is the people's greatest source of income. The Jacksonville Chamber of Commerce estimated that 900,000 Floridians had 700,000 travelers in their state in January 1923. Express trains brought fifty sleepers a day from New York, fifty sleepers a day from Chicago, and they came from other Northern cities. Two million came by automobile, and the improvement of roads in that direction is making the number increase yearly. Some come down the coast in private yachts and on the line steamers. By the middle of January the migration is at its height. By the end of February the rush homeward is at its height. The last to go, as well as the first to arrive, is the horde of hotel-keepers, waiters and others who take care of vacationists in Florida in winter and in the North in summer.

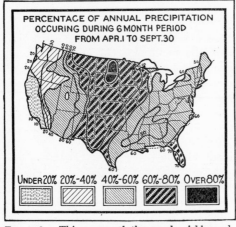

| PERIOD WITHIN WHICH 50% OF THE ANNUAL PRECIPITATION OCCURS | | | | | | | | | | | | |
|---|---|---|---|---|---|---|---|---|---|---|---|---|
| REGIONS | JAN | FEB | MAR | APR | MAY | JUNE | JULY | AUG | SEPT | OCT | NOV | DEC |
| NEW YORK LAKE R. | | | | | | ▓ | ▓ | ▓ | | | | |
| CENTRAL VIRGINIA | | | | | ▓ | ▓ | ▓ | ▓ | | | | |
| NORTHERN FLORIDA | | | | | ▓ | ▓ | ▓ | ▓ | | | | |
| OHIO | | | ▓ | ▓ | ▓ | | | | | | | |
| MISSOURI | | | | | ▓ | ▓ | ▓ | ▓ | | | | |
| GULF COAST | ▓ | ▓ | ▓ | | | | | | | ▓ | ▓ | ▓ |
| NORTHERN GREAT PLAINS | | | | ▓ | ▓ | ▓ | | | | | | |
| SOUTHERN GREAT PLAINS | | | | | ▓ | ▓ | ▓ | ▓ | | | | |
| SNAKE RIVER REGION | ▓ | ▓ | ▓ | | | | | | | | | |
| ARIZONA | | | | | | | ▓ | ▓ | ▓ | | | |
| WILLAMETTE VALLEY | ▓ | ▓ | | | | | | | | | | |
| CENTRAL CALIFORNIA | ▓ | ▓ | | | | | | | | | | |

PERCENTAGE OF ANNUAL PRECIPITATION OCCURING DURING 6 MONTH PERIOD FROM APR.1 TO SEPT.30

UNDER 20%   20%-40%   40%-60%   60%-80%   OVER 80%

FIG. 128 — This map and the graph yield much information if studied.

[4] In twenty-one years the extreme of heat recorded at Jupiter was 96°. A million square miles of the North had higher temperatures.

The millionaire goes to Palm Beach, Miami, Jacksonville, where he can stay in some of the most luxurious hotels in the world at a charge of $20.00 to $100.00 per day. This tourist enjoys the beach and the bathing. He goes golfing or tarpon-fishing and gets his picture in the Sunday supplements of metropolitan dailies.

The farmer of the Middle West, New England, even of Canada, gets an equal amount of vacation in a very different way. He ties his tent and

FIG. 129 — Florida's crop of surest profit — tourists. Winter on a Miami golf course. (Courtesy Miami Chamber of Commerce.)

cooking outfit on the running-board of his Ford and camps by the wayside — "tin-can tourist," the hotel-keepers contemptuously call him. Many spend the winter in one tourist camp after another, at an expense of a dollar a day per person or even a little less. Others take rooms, which are to be had at very reasonable prices away from the few fashionable and very expensive resorts.

The "tin-can tourist" has free access to the pines, the sun and the seashore. He has the gentle excitements of a strange land, and of moving from place to place, and pitching horseshoes. The enthusiasm for this simple sport is amazing. Its contestants compete for a national championship. To the slightly rheumatic of advancing years it is refreshing to see the Florida sun and read about blizzards back home. The Florida papers give him plenty of chance to read about the blizzards because it is a part of the stock in trade for the Florida paper to cheer up its guests with news of freezing weather in the North and especially of misfortune in California. According to the Florida papers this great rival winter-tourist region is a terrible place, going rapidly to the bad with frost, storms, earthquakes and other calamities. California and other resort places reciprocate.

It is estimated that the tourists spend $300,000,000.00 [5] in Florida, and that in the season 1923–24 they paid an additional $25,000,000.00 for

[5] This is convincing proof of the soundness of the answer that a little Florida colored boy gave my uncle years ago: "We lives on wattermillions in summah and sick Yankees in wintah."

Florida land. It seems to the traveler that there is a lot staked out for every inhabitant of the United States and people from the North have probably done more of it than the natives of Florida. There are daily auction sales of lots in many towns and sometimes in country places which seem puzzlingly remote.[6] An Illinois man of my acquaintance who had bought a " Miami " lot by mail went to hunt it up. He did not succeed in seeing it but he got it located — twelve miles from Miami. It was in the Everglades, two miles from the nearest passable road.

The chief objective of this lot-buying is not to produce crops, nor to build, but to sell again, a process that is very profitable while it lasts and is characteristic of land-booms everywhere. In 1924 tourist and native alike had caught the universal fever to hold a lot or two, perhaps half a dozen, as a speculation. Meanwhile, of course, each year brings tens of thousands more winter tourists and many thousands who buy lots on which to build bungalows where they hope to pass the winters of their later years.

The development of Florida as a place of residence and resort has been greatly promoted by the enthusiasm of New York multimillionaires who have been charmed by the state and have thrown money into it without thought of adequate return. One of these men built a railroad into the unsettled wilderness, and actually carried it ninety miles at sea, flinging the railroad from islet to islet with concrete arches at fabulous cost that could only have been a profitable investment in such a place as the English Channel or New York Bay.

## Climate and the Money Crops

Climate makes Florida's first money-crop, tourists, and also the second and third, fruits, chiefly oranges and grapefruit, and vegetables for the Northern markets in winter. Both industries are cursed by a double dread — the glutted market and the freeze. From time to time a cold wave brings stark frost into the green and palm-embowered winter. Tampa has had temperatures below 20° F. Once she has had also in succession four winters out of five without frost, and the one frost came on November 21.

### Fruits

Citrus culture is one of the oldest industries in America, for the orange and grapefruit were grown in Florida by the Spaniards more than three centuries ago. Through-railroad transportation made it an export industry. Most of the first commercial groves were located along the St. Johns and other rivers, as the early growers had been dependent on the

---

6 " Hence an endless, vociferous campaign of real-estate enterprise, of building and boosting, of speculations and bonuses and invitations to free trips with luncheons and eloquence thrown in." From " Florida," Clara G. Stillman in *The Nation,* Oct. 31, 1923.

river-boats. In the early nineties both banks of the river were lined solidly with prosperous groves, each grower with his own wharf and small packing-house.

Then came what the old residents of Florida still call the " Big Freeze." Previous freezes had often destroyed a crop without damaging the trees

FIG. 130 — Florida's crop of second surest profit — wide-reaching orange groves near Tampa. Note the Spanish moss which gives a funereal note to the Gulf Coast forests. (Courtesy Tampa Board of Trade. Copyright by Burgert Bros.)

greatly. The two severe cold waves in the winter of 1894–95 ruined the orchards of the entire state by killing the trees down to the ground. A period of warm, moist weather in which the trees had been growing was followed by a quick drop in temperature, a factor which very much increases the destructiveness of frost. Thousands of groves were so completely ruined that the owners did not even try to restore them.[7]  The industry started up again in central and southern Florida. Even this move did not bring with it frost immunity, for other freezes have killed young orchards until, from experience, the margin of safety from ordinary frost is now fairly well defined. It is the practice in Florida to protect the lower trunk and bud union of young trees by piling up eighteen inches of earth around them. Systematic frost-protection has not become as well recognized a practice as in California, but some of the growers keep oil-heaters in their groves or piles of wood ready to be ignited at the approach of a cold wave. In the central lake region of Florida the numerous lakes reduce the frost hazard: during the freeze of 1917 groves on the south shore of Lake Apopka suffered little damage, while others two miles farther south were severely set back. Air drainage is also

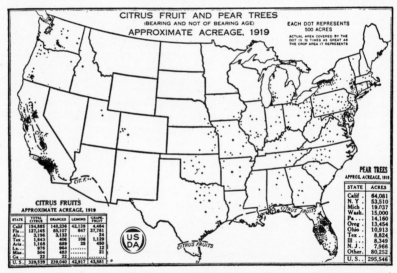

**CITRUS FRUIT AND PEAR TREES**
(BEARING AND NOT OF BEARING AGE)
**APPROXIMATE ACREAGE, 1919**

EACH DOT REPRESENTS 500 ACRES
ACTUAL AREA COVERED BY THE DOT IS 70 TIMES AS GREAT AS THE CROP AREA IT REPRESENTS

**CITRUS FRUITS**
APPROXIMATE ACREAGE, 1919

| STATE | TOTAL CITRUS | ORANGES | LEMONS | GRAPE-FRUIT |
|---|---|---|---|---|
| Calif | 194,885 | 148,236 | 42,139 | 4,464 |
| Fla.. | 127,145 | 85,107 | 647 | 37,781 |
| Ala.. | 3,196 | 3,133 | .... | 24 |
| Tex. | 1,643 | 406 | 106 | 1,129 |
| Ariz. | 1,168 | 689 | 25 | 450 |
| La. | 976 | 964 | .... | 12 |
| Miss. | 504 | 483 | .... | 21 |
| Ga.. | 22 | 22 | .... | .... |
| U.S. | 329,539 | 239,040 | 42,917 | 43,881 |

**PEAR TREES**
APPROX. ACREAGE, 1919

| STATE | ACRES |
|---|---|
| Calif . | 64,081 |
| N.Y. | 53,510 |
| Mich. | 19,037 |
| Wash. | 15,000 |
| Pa.... | 14,160 |
| Oreg . | 13,454 |
| Ohio . | 10,913 |
| Tex .. | 8,824 |
| Ill ... | 8,349 |
| N.J ... | 7,966 |
| Other. | 80,252 |
| U.S.. | 295,546 |

FIG. 131 — The table at left shows state specialties. The tender lemon is a good frost index.

better understood, the groves which were even slightly elevated above the surrounding country having fared better in 1917 (with five degrees difference in temperature) than groves in the flat lands.

While oranges are grown to some extent in every county in Florida, the heart of the citrus belt at present is the central lake region, the so-called " Backbone of Florida," famous for its timbered hills and innu-

[7] The extent of the catastrophe is best realized by a glance at the production figures: the Florida orange crop of 1893–94 was 6,000,000 boxes; there was no crop at all in 1894–95, and in 1895–96 it was only 75,000 boxes.

merable clear lakes. There are extensive plantings of young orchards here because of the good air and water drainage and the sandy soil underlaid with a clay subsoil at a depth of about six feet. There is also still plenty of unused land.

Florida has developed almost a monopoly in the production of the pomelo, better known as the grapefruit, which it seems to be able to produce in better quality than any other part of the country. Although the grapefruit has been known and grown for a long time it only attained to popularity in the last few years — a striking example of the possibilities

FIG. 132 — Interior of orange packing-house showing efficient mechanical methods of handling fruit and boxes. (Courtesy Tampa Board of Trade. Copyright by Burgert Bros.)

of developing the public taste for many other now unknown fruits. The tangerine and other kid-glove varieties are also grown all through the citrus belt. Lemons and limes do not meet with as much favor in Florida, being delicate and easily frosted. The lemon can be commercially grown only in the warmest sections of the peninsula, as the trees are subject to great injury when the temperature falls below twenty-eight degrees.

One cannot take a trip through the citrus area with its young groves springing up on every side without wondering who will buy all this fruit and what the price will be. In 1923 many growers did not meet the cost of production. Glutted markets or a marketing clash with California, which is also extending citrus plantings, seems inevitable within a few years unless the demand for citrus products is miraculously increased.

### Truck and Vegetable Growing

As the boll weevil changed the planters of the cotton belt from one-crop farming to diversified agriculture, so the freeze of 1894 gave Florida a widespread trucking industry in place of the single crop, oranges.

Much of the soil of central and south Florida is a fine sandy loam, an excellent garden soil like that of the North Atlantic Coast Plain. Express-train service to the Northern cities gave a winter market to the Florida truck-grower. Green beans, lettuce, tomatoes and other vegetables are now seen in an ever-increasing number of markets every week in the year. The vegetable business has become so important to the coast-line railroads that it has been said, partly in jest but actually in fact, that a trainload of millionaires en route to Palm Beach will be run off to a siding to wait for a trainload of cabbages to pass.

Although the trucking industry is general throughout the Peninsula, the process of centralization has worked its normal result (see chapter on North Atlantic Coast Plains). Sanford, near the central interior of the state is, by actual records, the greatest celery-producing and shipping point in the world. The Sanford " Celery Delta " comprises some thirty thousand acres lying in a rough triangle between Lakes Monroe and Jessup and the connecting St. Johns River. Part of the soil is a sandy loam underlaid with clay at a depth of eighteen inches to two and a half feet, while the rest is muck, black as any prairie of Illinois or Texas. The celery fields have all been carefully tile-drained, irrigated by means of flowing artesian wells, made productive by heavy applications of commercial fertilizer, and given a very intensive cultivation. Although only one-tenth of the Delta is in use, this section shipped 6299 cars during the season 1922–23, as follows:

| | | | |
|---|---|---|---|
| Celery | 4812 cars | Peppers | 498 cars |
| Lettuce | 670 cars | Miscellaneous Vegetables | 319 cars |

Although Sanford produces five-sixths of Florida's celery crop there is nothing to indicate that its soil or climate has any celery superiority to dozens of other localities in the state or elsewhere.

Just as a reference to Sanford means celery, the name of Hastings, near the mouth of the St. Johns River in northern Florida, means Irish potatoes. Potatoes often bring fifteen cents a pound at Northern stores during the latter part of March. Three-fourths of the Hastings crop is dug and shipped before the end of May, which is the usual planting month for the great potato-producing sections of the North.

Plant City near Tampa is a strawberry center. It shipped more than 653,000 quarts of strawberries to the North between January and May 1924.

While individual truck-crops may be localized, as in the above-mentioned cases, the truck business itself is not limited to any one section of the state. Dozens of towns are centers of districts where vegetables are grown wholesale — islands of agriculture in a sea of pines. Many of these centers have growers' associations that sell produce, buy supplies and run packing-houses and icing plants. When it is remembered that it takes five tons of ice for the first refrigeration of each carload of perishable stuff sent out and several re-icings en route, and that Florida shipped 85,000 cars of fruit and vegetables during the season of 1921–22, some idea may gained of the importance of ice in this business.

In supplying the Northern markets with vegetables the Florida grower has high transportation costs which limit the amount that can be sold and the markets are easily glutted. The Florida grower is shut out from the market as soon as the market gardens farther North can get

FIG. 133 —Tourist's winter bungalow on a water-front. Vegetable garden in rear supplies the family's needs. Note the white sandy soil. (Courtesy Tampa Board of Trade. Copyright by Burgert Bros.)

into the swing of production. South Florida has the shipping season first. Then it shifts to central Florida, then to Savannah, Georgia, Charleston, S. C., Newbern and Wilmington, N. C., and on to the North Atlantic Coast Plain. The Florida grower who netted just seven cents for a whole car of fine cabbage (March 1922) when it was retailing at eight cents a pound in Atlantic City, was merely experiencing one of the common hazards of his business which has been well described as one having a six-weeks season and a gamble at that. In a land of limitless resource something must limit an industry.

While Florida has about 30,000,000 acres of land suitable for truck-crops, a study of the small acreages [8] needed to produce the vegetables used by the nation will show the futility of the belief that any large part of Florida can be used for market gardens or citrus fruit for generations or even centuries.

### The Future of Florida Lands

What then is to become of these millions of acres of sandy loams and mucky swamp soils? It is a land reserve. First it should be put to growing pine, all of it — immediately. The long-leaf pine forest was the only thing in Florida to exploit, and it has been exploited as ruthlessly as any other American forest. It passed its peak of lumber production in 1916, and is now leading in the production of naval stores. In traveling through the state one becomes increasingly impressed and depressed by the seemingly endless stretches of cut-over and burned-over forest, all of which is public open range for stock, mostly undersized victims of the tick.

Florida's lands are relatively infertile; all save a very few muck soils need to be fertilized from the beginning of cultivation. This low fertility is not so great a drawback to producers' cost as at first appears. For corn and meat it differs but little perhaps from that of the richest lands of Illinois. Land worth three hundred dollars an acre (Illinois) has an interest charge of $18.00 per acre per year. Put $18.00 worth of fertilizer on cheap Florida sandy loam each year, and it can be built up quickly by stuffing it with legumes, especially the giant velvet beans.[9] It is simpler of course to mine the rich land than to make the infertile land productive. Therefore we used Illinois and neglected Florida.

Here and there in the Florida peninsula are dairy-farms and hog-farms of the most modern type where animals of the finest breeds are pastured twelve months in the year, on a variety of forage plants similar to that discussed in the chapter on the Cotton Belt. These are suggestive examples and it should be remembered that corn, the great Southern supply crop, covers more acres than all of Florida's truck and fruits combined. The level surface and sandy soil invite intensive and continuous agriculture, as erosion will not be a problem here and machinery can be used to the maximum.

[8] 

| Commodity | Area Cultivated, Thousand Acres, 1919 | |
|---|---|---|
| | U. S. | Fla. |
| Citrus fruits | 329 | 127 |
| Vegetables grown for sale | 1,475 | 60 |
| Peanuts, velvet beans, cow peas | 2,921 | 217 |
| White potatoes | 3,251 | 17 |
| Sweet potatoes | 803 | 26 |
| Corn | 87,771 | 790 |

[9] It is more nearly true than was once believed that " the sterility of the Florida soil is compensated by the fertility of the air."

It is probable that the first extensive agricultural development will be in the Everglades, where there are five thousand square miles of treeless swamp. It looks like a vast wheat-field, being covered with a crop of saw grass six or eight feet tall. Experiments with saw grass indicate that it may become the basis of an important paper industry, while experimental sugar plantations on newly drained land suggest great possibilities that this area of relative frost immunity may be better than Louisiana for growing sugar.

The development of the Everglades will advance only as the result of extensive enterprise. Florida now leads all other states in swamp land,[10] having twenty-eight thousand square miles — almost half her total area — so afflicted.

Because of porous sand and undergound channels in the soft limestone, much of Florida has no surface streams.

The possibilities of new subtropic or foreign crops are indicated by the fact that 250 acres of trees have been planted for producing tung oil, a valuable Chinese paint material. As the result of an experiment which lasted for thirty-six years, 12,000 acres of camphor trees have been planted, and mangoes, avocados, papayas and other tropic fruits have been planted experimentally.

Granted the continuous growth of population in the United States, the greatest question concerning the full development of Florida is probably the climate. The winter sojourner takes the best of it and flies away, leaving the permanent resident to face the long season of steady, humid heat without the bracing effect of cooler dry spells.[11] The temperature is less extreme and therefore less unpleasant than Washington or Philadelphia.

Mr. R. DeC. Ward, of Harvard, one of the most diligent students of hygiene and climate in America, says: " Too long a sojourn in such a climate, may, however, lead to a marked toning down of the system, to loss of appetite, and to digestive and nervous difficulties." Mr. Howard Martin, of Illinois, says: " In plain English, you get lazy. I noticed it. The first two weeks I was there I ate oranges with enthusiasm. Then I got too tired to peel an orange and always bought tangerines; the skins pull off with about two motions. Then I got too lazy to handle the tangerines and ate kumquats [12] the rest of my stay."

[10] Many of Florida's swamps are due to sheer flatness and many are due to the lime sinks. Soft limestones underlie much of the state. Limestone dissolves and the material above caves in. This may dam up an underground water-course and make both a lake and a swamp.

[11] According to Huntington (Ellsworth), *Civilization and Climate,* man is most energetic in a temperature of 60 to 70 degrees with frequent small changes of temperature. For the production of ideal climate inside of community houses, see last chapter.

[12] Kumquats, the smallest of the orange family, about the size of the last section of a man's thumb, are eaten as one eats a cherry.

### Florida Phosphate

Florida phosphate beds contain great store of phosphorus preserved in fossil bones — jaws of rhinoceros and crocodile, teeth of mastodon and shark, ribs of whale and myriads of small crustaceans whose remains give us the most important element in commercial fertilizers. The de-

Fig. 134 — Solid black shows location of phosphate deposits. Heavy line is fall line.

posits are scattered over a hundred miles along the west side of the peninsula where two-fifths of the world's phosphate is mined. The phosphate, usually in small pieces of hard rock, scattered through much earth, is obtained by open-pit dredging. Improved machinery permits the poorer deposits to be worked.

As the use of phosphatic fertilizers must steadily increase with soil exhaustion, the future growth of the Florida phosphate industry seems assured. At present most of the two million tons output is consumed at home, although before the World War the amount was about equally divided between the United States and Europe. Without available phosphorus the Coastal Plain sands would remain in scattered pine. Huge elevators at Port Tampa provide the fastest and most efficient phosphate-loading facilities to be found in the world and give the port a heavy shipping business.

### Manufacturing

The Florida Peninsula has many thriving small cities and towns. Its metropolis, Jacksonville, locally known as " Jax," had a population of

91,000 in 1920.  Coasting steamers help to make it a distributing point for the northern part of the State, and it is an ocean port of considerable importance.  Jacksonville claims to be the second largest lumber-shipping point in the world.

Tampa (51,000), the distributing center for the west coast, shares with Key West (19,000) the cigar-manufacturing industry of Florida.  Cigar-making started at Key West because an American duty on Havana cigars gave a decided advantage to cigars made inside this country.  Tampa has over two hundred cigar factories at the present time, most of which employ Cuban and Spanish labor.  The cigar industry is growing.

There is as yet no sign of any important manufacturing in Florida aside from lumber, fertilizers and cigars.  The most probable addition is that of fruit and vegetable canning and sugar refining.  Some progress has been made in the successful canning of grapefruit, and development along this line is probable.  The amount of vegetables that might be produced for canning or dehydration is beyond computation — witness the practice of a truck farmer who marketed, from the same ground, lettuce in January, tomatoes in March, potatoes in May and then grew a huge crop of velvet beans to feed the mules and enrich the land with their nitrogenous nodules, which are about as large as the end of your thumb.

FIG. 135 — Maud Muller on a summer's day, in the meadow sweet with hay, used a hand rake. She did less than one-fiftieth as much work as one of these men, who are using horse muscle, and who might use tractor power. Without ever touching or lifting it they transfer the standing, living grass to the finished load of hay. When machines replace men, rural population declines. (Courtesy International Harvester Co.)

# CHAPTER XV

## THE CORN BELT

THE Corn Belt is a gift of the gods — the rain god, the sun god, the ice god and the gods of geology. In the middle of the North American continent the gods of geology made a wide expanse of land where the rock layers are nearly horizontal. The ice gods leveled the surface with their glaciers, making it ready for the plow, and also making it rich. The rain god gives summer showers. The sun god gives summer heat. All this is nature's conspiracy to make man grow corn. Having corn, man feeds it to cattle and hogs, and thereby becomes a producer of meat. (Fig. 149.)

This Corn Belt, a quarter of a million square miles in extent, is one of the finest blocks of farm-land in the world. It enabled the United States to export wheat through the troubled years of our Civil War, to the astonishment of Europe and the support of our foreign credit. Again its products sustained the Allied armies during the World War.

### Glacial Benefits

Repeatedly did the continental glacier advance and retreat across the Corn Belt. The glacier moved across a rolling and hilly land, much like the Northern Piedmont. The pushing ice sheet, like a giant gardener, scraped off the tops of little hills and with the materials filled up the little valleys. Wells and excavations show the story piece by piece, and the record is now plain.

Because rain leaches the rich qualities from the earth and plants extract food from it, surface soil is poorer than subsoil. The glacier mixed subsoil with surface soil, thereby putting greater soil riches within reach of the farmer's crops. One measure of this enrichment is seen in the high lime content of the recently glaciated areas as compared to the low lime content of the unglaciated areas which have been exposed to continuous leaching by rain.[1]

By some freak of surface form, none of the six glaciers overrode an area several thousand square miles in extent which is situated in the southwestern corner of Wisconsin, and includes parts of Minnesota, Iowa and Illinois. This region is known as the " driftless area." Here is an admirable chance to compare the land before and after glaciation. Careful studies [2] on both limestone and sandstone formations show conclusively that the glaciated land is richer and more level. Consequently, glaciated land has a larger percentage fit for the plow and gives larger yields per acre.

Geologists are fairly well agreed that the glaciers, scooping out the beds of the Great Lakes, spread earth to a depth of about one hundred feet over the surface in northern Ohio, and to a depth of about three hundred feet on the southern part of Wisconsin. These glaciers, because they crossed no mountains, found but few stones to spread upon the land. New Englanders, familiar with millions of glacial boulders, would be amused at the labors of the students of Cornell College, at Mt. Vernon, Iowa. They went several miles into the country, and with hard work and the help of many horses managed to drag a large glacial boulder to the campus, to be its crowning ornament and curiosity. The campus of the University of Nebraska at Lincoln and other Corn Belt institutions have similar curiosities.

## Surface and Arability

The stoneless surface of the Corn Belt is either level or gently rolling and wonderfully fitted for the plow. Save for a few steep hills near the streams, and for structures made by man, a plow could run almost without interruption from Columbus, Ohio, to the western bounds of the Corn Belt in Dakota or Nebraska or indeed much farther. In this level or gently rolling country hills are so rare that the United States Government, in parceling out this empire for the homesteader, laid off the roads at right angles, one mile apart and running due east and west, and due north and south. The square mile contained between the roads was

[1] The differing lime content of soils placed by different glacial advances serves as one means whereby age may be estimated. Great age makes great leaching. Therefore little lime remains.

[2] Whitbeck, R. H., *Annals of the Association of American Geographers*, 1915 — a most excellent and convincing study. Similar results were obtained by Edgar W. Owen, on the south edge of glaciation in Ohio. See *Bulletin of Scientific Laboratory*, Dennison University, Vol. 17.

divided into four quarter-sections, each of which, therefore, faced a mile of road. This plan gives so great a total mileage of roads that a neighborhood is burdened to maintain its roads in good condition.[3]

During the glacial era Lakes Erie and Michigan were larger than they now are. As the waters receded the old lake bottoms appeared as very flat lands. These old lake beds along with river bottoms and tens of thousands of square miles of flat uplands in many parts of the Corn Belt, are so wet in rainy years as to spoil the crop because it is impossible to

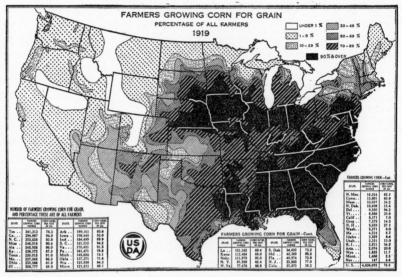

FIG. 136 — This map shows interesting comparisons with Fig. 137. (Courtesy U. S. Dept. Agr.)

cultivate. Most of these lands have been ditched and underdrained with tile, of which there are literally hundreds of thousands of miles.

This is a laborious and costly process, but it means that the land is so level that erosion is impossible and the moisture supply for crops is good. Upon the whole it is difficult to conceive of better or more enduring agricultural lands.[4]

[3] Many parts of Europe have an entirely different rural organization, more favorable to sociability and transport, but less favorable to farm operation. Twenty or a hundred farm families live in a village and go out to till the lands within a radius of several miles. *Lanes* reach the fields. Roads connect the villages. The roads are good.

[4] In many localities the land is so flat that it has been necessary to dig main ditches which were virtually canals or artificial creeks miles in length, in order to give run-off for the drains from the individual farms.

This necessity of the environment has produced an interesting response in the organization of a new governmental unit; namely, the drainage district, whereby the people of a given territory vote for or against a bond issue to pay for digging

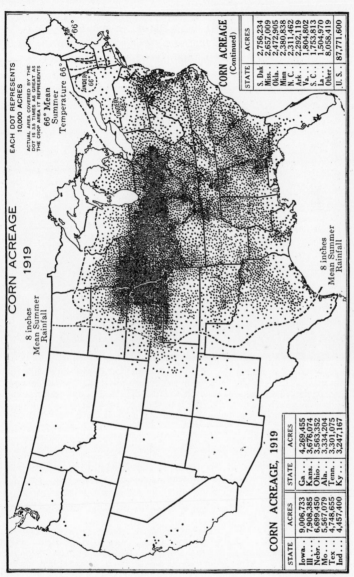

CORN ACREAGE
1919

EACH DOT REPRESENTS
10,000 ACRES

ACTUAL AREA COVERED BY THE
DOT IS 3.5 TIMES AS GREAT AS
THE CROP AREA IT REPRESENTS

66° Mean
Summer
Temperature 66°

8 inches
Mean Summer
Rainfall

8 inches
Mean Summer
Rainfall

CORN ACREAGE, 1919

| STATE | ACRES | STATE | ACRES |
|-------|-------|-------|-------|
| Iowa. | 9,006,733 | Ga... | 4,269,455 |
| Ill... | 7,908,385 | Kans. | 3,676,074 |
| Nebr. | 6,699,450 | Ohio. | 3,563,352 |
| Mo... | 5,567,079 | Ala... | 3,334,204 |
| Tex.. | 4,748,655 | Tenn. | 3,301,075 |
| Ind... | 4,457,400 | Ky... | 3,247,167 |

CORN ACREAGE
(Continued)

| STATE | ACRES |
|-------|-------|
| S. Dak | 2,756,234 |
| Miss. | 2,657,009 |
| Okla. | 2,472,905 |
| Minn. | 2,380,838 |
| N. C. | 2,311,462 |
| Ark. | 2,292,119 |
| Va... | 1,804,802 |
| S. C. | 1,753,813 |
| La... | 1,504,970 |
| Other. | 8,058,419 |
| U. S. | 87,771,600 |

FIG. 137 — This map shows many contrasts. (Courtesy U. S. Dept. Agr.)

## Climate

The climate of the Corn Belt rivals its soil in suitability for corn production.  Corn needs heat and sunshine.  The summer is hot, with bright sunshine.  Corn needs moisture, but the ground should not be so wet

FIG. 138 — In the afternoon the white-capped cumulus clouds, with their rumbling thunder, approach and send the farmer to shelter, where he waits and rejoices while nature waters his crops.  The heavy downpour, accompanied by much noise of thunder and flash of lightning, may last for an hour or two; and then the sun is again shining, and the farmer is at work. (Courtesy U. S. Weather Bureau.)

as to interfere with weekly cultivation.  The moderate rain of the Corn Belt comes nearly always in the form of thunder-showers which last but an hour or two and are promptly followed by the return of sunshine.

---

main canals.  This method is, of course, exactly analogous to school and road districts in many parts of the country.

The disastrous flood of 1913, when as much as eleven inches of rain fell on already saturated soil in central Ohio and caused over $100,000,000.00 worth of damage to Dayton and vicinity, has had a similar and more extensive social result. It was found that the streams subjected to this unusual demand had choked up partly because of the encroachments of the abutments to highways and railroad bridges.  To control this matter the state, within a few months after the floods, created a new piece of government; namely, the conservancy district.  This is a territory having drainage or a flood problem as its basis of unity.  Thus the Miami Valley becomes a conservancy district which runs across the boundaries of county, township, congressional district, and any or all other political divisions except the state.  It is authorized to take such action as seems best to cope with the one

This gives the corn the combined benefit of heat and light and lets man get back to his fields after the shortest possible interruption of labor.

The summer weather cycle consists of some bright, sunshiny days, increasing in heat and sultriness, which culminate in a series of showers lasting a day or two. The rain is usually followed by clearing weather with northwest breezes and cooler dry air that is distinctly more bracing than the air in the Cotton Belt.

The summer is, to be sure, too warm for the comfort of man, but Corn Belts are not summer resorts. In the hot nights which we dislike corn grows so fast that you can literally hear it grow. But it is a wholesome climate. It makes for a vigorous, energetic type of man, one who is able to produce great quantities of crops in the summer season, when the longer period of sunshine sometimes produces greater heat than that of many tropic places (Fig. 19).

The rainfall declines from east to west (Fig. 107) and the winter is cold with little precipitation, mostly in the form of snow. The western boundary of the Corn Belt is at the place where the rainfall is so slight that corn is no longer the main crop dependence. The northern boundary is set by the line of shorter growing season which again limits corn from being the main crop dependence.

## Natural Vegetation

When the white man found the Corn Belt, its eastern part, which was in Ohio and Indiana, was a magnificent forest of oak, hickory, maple, ash, elm and other hardwoods. Here and there were open, grassy glades, where buffalo, deer and elk fattened. The western part was as completely treeless as the eastern part was completely forested. The lessened rain made it possible for the grass fire [5] to kill out the tree growth and have wide stretches of grass where now tall shade trees grow. Only along the streams of Kansas, Nebraska and Iowa was there forest. Illinois was transition ground with forest along the streams and large

---

problem of water control. The conservancy district controls the character and location of roads, bridges and structures near the streams.

The conservancy district bought a whole village and the adjacent farms and made it a dry reservoir. A dam was built with an opening of such a size that the water flows out of it no faster than the stream can carry it away. Thus, at times of flood, the reservoirs may be full of water three days or a week. At other times the dry reservoir, enriched by flood mud, is ready for maximum and continuous corn production.

This flood prevention was very different from the outcome of the Pittsburgh Flood Commission survey following the disastrous flood of 1907. Deforestation was found to be increasing the height and frequency of floods at Pittsburgh. The recommended cure was reservoirs in mountain sites which were in four states, and would benefit the entire river to the Gulf. Therefore, Pittsburgh waits for help to proceed with this great enterprise, whose benefit may be considered almost national in scope.

[5] It was the Indians' custom to burn last season's dead areas so that buffalo and other game could eat the tender young grass.

FIG. 139 — Hot, dry winds, which burn the corn as it stands, help to make the
for windbreaks.  (From Minnesota

stretches of open prairie [6] between.  There were even large tracts of open
prairie in northern Indiana and southern Michigan.

## Settlement and People

Two streams of colonists flowed into this Eden.  The Yankees from
New England and New York came by way of the Erie Canal into north-
ern Ohio.  Some went on westward through Indiana, Illinois and Iowa to
Nebraska and down through northern Missouri to Kansas.[7]

The southern stream of colonists, having passed through the Cumberland Gap into Kentucky, went down the Ohio River.  Groups of the
people would find a place where they wanted to live and there they
would stay and settle together in a neighborhood.  The others went on
down the river and even up the Missouri River, carrying with them from
Virginia, Carolina and Tennessee their slaves and their politics.

The prairie land offered no wood.  The Easterner, accustomed to forest
land, thought there was something the matter with land that did not
grow trees.  The first settlers, therefore, took land along streams where
there were woods and with painful labor and with axe and fire cut themselves clearings and fought stumps and roots as their fathers and grand-
fathers had done in the Atlantic Coast, Piedmont and Appalachia.

Sometimes these clearings were right beside the open prairie.  The
tough sod of the prairie was a substantial discouragement to the poor

[6] A prairie is an extensive tract of land, level to gently rolling, without a timber
cover and having grassy vegetation — a sod.  It may or may not be dotted with
trees.
[7] " . . . the State was invaded by immigrants from New England or sons and
daughters of New Englanders, who came to Kansas to make this a Free State.  A
fair fight in an open field ensued; the abolitionists crowded out the proslavery
people, outvoted them, and captured Kansas.  The first Kansans, therefore, were
crusaders, intellectual and social pioneers, covenanters of various sorts; which, if you
like to live comfortably upon your soft yesterdays, means that Kansas was full
of cranks.  Slavery being abolished your Kansan had to begin abolishing something
else.  Abolitionism was more than a conviction; it was a temperamental habit."
Willian Allen White of Kansas, in *These United States* (New York, Boni and Liveright, 1923), p. 2.

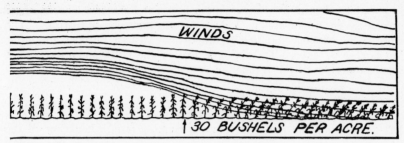

WINDS

↑ 30 BUSHELS PER ACRE.

western bounds of the Corn Belt. This Minnesota drawing is a cogent argument
Forestry Board F. S. Bulletin No. 1.)

plow of that day, and the prairie was settled only when good timber
lands along streams were no longer available. Professor H. H. Barrows
tells the story of a man in southern Illinois who lost an election because
his neighbors knew that anybody who was fool enough to go into the
prairie and settle, as he did, was lacking in the necessary good judg-

FIG. 140 — Corn Belt farm lanes usually produce only shade trees and poor
wood. This lane in France, with less than twenty grafted English walnut
trees, yielded $150 gold per year before the World War, and was also
growing wood of great value; a suggestive lesson for the Corn Belt, where
there are several species of fruitful but unused wild nut trees, with here
and there a rare specimen waiting to be propagated. (Photo J. Russell
Smith.)

ment required by persons in office. The first arrivals, being from the
South, got the woods and voted Democratic. Those who came later,
being from the North, got the prairie and voted Whig or Republican —
a line of difference that was visible for decades.

The third element in the population is recent European. Those whose occupation is farming are chiefly German, Scandinavian and British. The more recent immigration from southern and eastern Europe came after the land was taken. These people live in the cities and make but a small proportion of the population.

### The Corn Belt Farm

This Corn Belt, with its great uniformity of climate, surface and soil, has a corresponding uniformity in the type of farm. Look out of the car window in western Ohio; you see about the same thing that you will see in Indiana, and again in Illinois, Missouri, Iowa, South Dakota, Nebraska and Kansas — a seemingly endless expanse of black, flat or gently rolling land upon

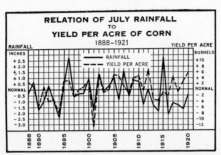

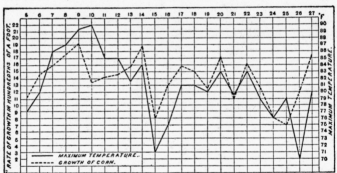

Fig. 141 — These two graphs show the intimate dependence of plants (and prosperity) upon the weather — man's dependence upon his environment. (Courtesy U. S. Weather Bureau.)

which is a seemingly endless succession of farms with rich fields of corn, oats, hay or wheat, herds of big, cubical cattle or fat, cylindrical hogs. The good homes and big fat barns are sheltered behind a wind-break of trees and surrounded by yard, garden, orchard and perhaps feed-lots, the whole comprising from two to four acres. There is commonly a hog pasture, of from one to ten acres; a cattle and horse pasture of ten to thirty acres; a hay field of uncertain size, and the rest of the farm is given over to growing grain. More than half of the grain acreage is in corn, and the rest in small grains — oats, wheat, barley, sometimes even rye.

This is not a land to thrill one who loves hills, wild landscape, mountain panorama, waterfalls, babbling brooks and nature undisturbed.  In this flat land of food crops and murky streams, rich with silt, man must find thrills in other things, perhaps in travel, print, radio or movie.

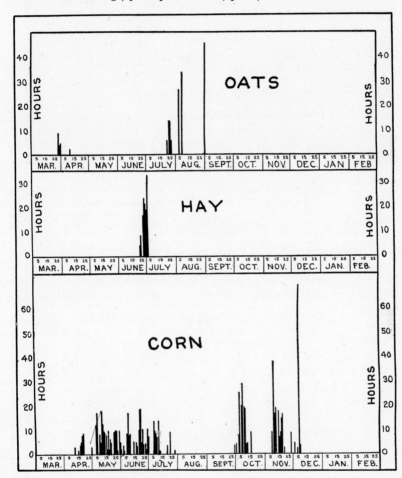

Fig. 142 — The amounts and times of labor show the non-competitive character of corn and oats.  (H. C. Taylor, U. S. Dept. Agr.)

The Corn Belt farmer cannot grow one crop only and keep himself, his teams and his hired man busy.  Therefore, he has a crop series, which divides his time to good advantage.  If his small grain is oats it can be planted while frost is still in the ground, and before corn can be planted.  Afterward come corn planting, corn cultivation, hay harvest and oat harvest.  Then comes August, when the weeds are cut, the

FIG. 143 — The bang of the ears of corn in the empty wagon-bed on crisp autumn mornings is a characteristic sound. The Corn Belt farmer starts across the long field, husking the ears from the standing stalks and clucking to his horses, who follow the rows with well trained obedience. If need be, the corn will stand throughout the frosty winter waiting for the harvester. (Courtesy U. S. Dept. Agr.)

fences are mended and other repair work is done. Now is the time for a little rest and vacation, for soon it will be autumn and corn harvest. The winter is a dull season of idleness save for feeding the stock and tinkering with the machinery. If the children are grown and times are

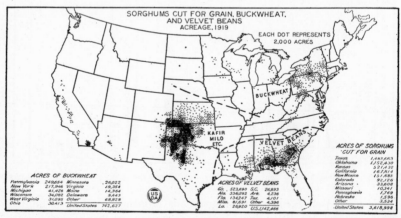

FIG. 144 — The concentration of the sorghums results from their ability to resist hot dry winds.

good the farmer may leave his animals in the care of a neighbor and spend the winter in Florida or California.

Corn Belt agriculture is not the hoe or garden type of agriculture, not

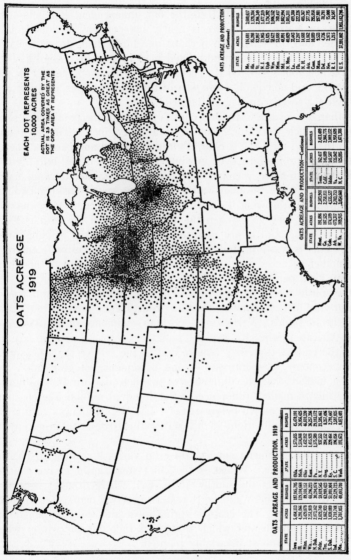

Fig. 145 — Comparing this map with the Wheat maps (Figs. 172 and 178) shows that oats fit in between spring and winter wheat. (Courtesy U. S. Dept. Agr.)

saddle-supervision of a bunch of cowboys raising cattle, or a bunch of
negroes raising cotton.   Neither is it the foreman-bossing-a-gang-of-
dagoes-weeding-onions type.   It is the old, independent kingdom-of-my-
own type, in which the farmer is nearly independent of outside labor.
The farmer and his sons, with perhaps one hired man, do all the work,
except at harvest time, when additional help is secured.   The hired man
is often a neighbor's son and the social equal of his employer.   Few parts
of the world, and no equally large part of the United States, can match the
Corn Belt for social equality of the people.

Less than 2% of the Corn Belt corn is put up in the poetic corn shock.
This is too much work for broad acres and few men.   The corn stalks
stand in the field until the ears are thoroughly dried and cured.   Then, in
the autumn and sometimes even in winter, the farmer drives into the corn-
field with a two-horse wagon.   The horses are trained to walk astride
a row of corn, while the man walks beside the wagon husking two rows
as he walks and throwing the ears into the wagon-bed.   Back and forth
across the field they go.   When the wagon is loaded the corn is hauled
to the corn-crib.   Cattle are now turned in to pick the leavings of the
fodder.   This is wasteful, but it permits one man to cultivate the maximum number of acres and get maximum output per man, although not
maximum yield per acre.

In the southwestern part of the Corn Belt, in Oklahoma and Kansas,
the drier and hotter summer weather injures corn more often than it
injures the sorghums.   Varieties of sorghum commonly called Kafir corn,
of dry African origin, are rapidly replacing corn.   Sorghums are like
corn in the culture that they require and in the service that they render
in farm economy.   So intimate is the dependence of corn upon rain,
July rain indeed, that the difference of an inch of Corn Belt rainfall in
that one month made a difference of five hundred million bushels in the
crop on the acreage grown before 1914.[8]   The Hopi Indian, a corn-grower
in a dry land, is quite right in his elaborate attempts to propitiate the
rain god.

The Corn Belt farmer's small-grain crop varies according to location,
soil and circumstance.   Wheat is the chief small grain in the southern
part and especially in the southwestern part, where drought becomes a
menace.   In the northern and northwestern part the maps show that oats
take the preference.   The crop is spring-sown and therefore misses the
rigors of the colder winter which sometimes kills out the winter wheat,
which is the kind almost invariably planted.

### Alfalfa

West of the Missouri River the Corn Belt farmer grows much alfalfa
because of a nice adjustment of soil and climate to this most valuable

    [8] Smith, J. Warren, " Effect of Weather on the Yield of Corn," *Monthly Weather
Review,* February 1914.   One of many remarkable studies by the same author.

hay plant. Alfalfa does best on a deep, limy soil. Soils such as those of western Kansas are limy because of lack of leaching, but they do not have enough water without irrigation for alfalfa. Eastern Kansas and eastern Nebraska are arid enough to be limy and wet enough to suit

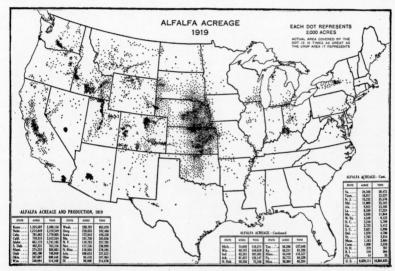

FIG. 146 — West of Kansas the Alfalfa map almost serves to locate the irrigated agriculture. (Courtesy U. S. Dept. Agr.)

alfalfa, and they have much loess soil well suited to deep-rooted plants. Here is the greatest alfalfa section of the United States. With corn alfalfa makes a splendid cattle-fattening ration.

### The Meat Industry

What does the Corn Belt farmer do with his crops? He sells the wheat for human breadstuff. Most of the oats and corn are fed to stock in the states where grown. Selling grains is generally conceded to be a bad agricultural policy because of the large loss in soil fertility, and the high cost of freight to market. The grain-shipping practice is therefore greater in central Illinois (see maps of animal production) because this locality is near the city markets and the freight-rate is low. Also, it is the levelest and richest part of the whole region. Between 1912 and 1922 it took 11.25 bushels of corn (630 lbs.) to pay for 100 lbs. of pork in Ohio, according to the Ohio experiment station.

This shows that the freight problem is less if the produce of the farm is condensed into meat. So the Corn Belt farmer usually takes his choice between fattening cattle, growing hogs, or less frequently growing horses and mules. If the price of grain goes up he may be losing money to feed pigs, so he stops as soon as he can and sells some corn. At other times the price ratio may send him hunting around among his neighbors to buy additional corn to fatten more animals for the meat market.[9] The influence of distance in this process gives the largest number of hogs per farm to the most distant parts of the Corn Belt;

Fig. 147 — The cattle pens, unsightly and unsavory, are nevertheless the economic heart of hundreds of Corn Belt small towns. (Courtesy John Clay & Co., Chicago.)

Iowa, forty-five hogs per farm, Nebraska, thirty-four, and South Dakota, thirty.

The hog industry has been greatly benefited in recent years by the discovery of serums which, by a process akin to vaccination, permit the farmer greatly to reduce loss of animals by hog cholera. This disease is highly contagious, fatal to nine-tenths of its victims and was for decades the bane of the hog-grower. He rather expected his herd to be wiped out every third or fourth year. Even in 1922 cholera killed 4% of American swine, numbering more than 100,000 victims in each of nine states.

Fattening cattle is more speculative than growing pigs. It costs $40.00 to produce a calf in the Corn Belt. Therefore most of the young

[9] A change of $.02 to $.04 per bushel for corn, granted static hog prices, decides whether a man wishes to ship or feed his corn. The great fecundity of swine permits their numbers to rise and fall quickly in response to demand. The female will give birth to two litters a year of from four to ten each, and pigs are commonly marketed at the age of six months.

cattle are produced on the ranges in the arid country to the west and southwest and pastured there until they are ready to be fattened. Tall and lanky — called "feeders" — they are then sent to Kansas City, Omaha, Minneapolis, Sioux City or Chicago for distribution over the

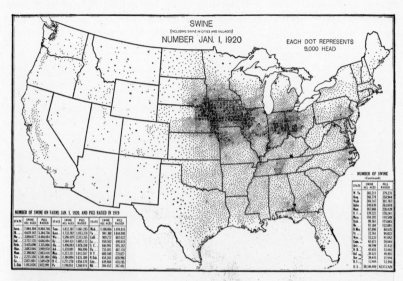

SWINE
(INCLUDING SWINE IN CITIES AND VILLAGES)
NUMBER JAN. 1, 1920

EACH DOT REPRESENTS 5,000 HEAD

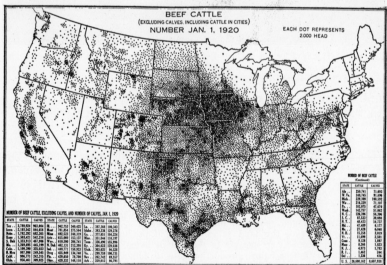

BEEF CATTLE
(EXCLUDING CALVES, INCLUDING CATTLE IN CITIES)
NUMBER JAN. 1, 1920

EACH DOT REPRESENTS 2,000 HEAD

FIG. 148 — Cattle are located by corn, alfalfa, or good grass, but swine depend more exclusively on grain. (Courtesy U. S. Dept. Agr.)

Corn Belt farms for what the farmers call the "corn-crib cross"—
fattening for a few months before going to the slaughtering-house. Sometimes the cattle market is such that the farmer buys stockers low and
increases their weight and sells them at a distinct advance per pound.
This is profitable. But it frequently runs the other way, making loss.
This speculative element of buying and selling does not occur with hogs
because they are nearly always born on the farm where they are fat-

FIG. 149 — The feed-lot on a Corn Belt farm. The cattle eat all they desire and
the hogs get the leavings. Note the form of the beef animals. (Courtesy
U. S. Dept. Agr.)

tened. They also make more pounds of meat per hundred pounds of
feed [10] and are therefore increasing in popularity in Corn Belt agriculture.

### Land Values and Migration

The jump in land-values since 1900 has been the most dynamic thing
that has happened to the Corn Belt in this century. This phenomenon,
mentioned in Chapter II, so full of social results [11] occurred in the

[10] About six pounds of grain and six pounds of hay produce one pound of lamb
live weight; ten pounds of grain and ten pounds of hay, one pound of beef, and
5.6 pounds of corn, one pound of pork.

[11] The influence of this land value on cost of production was promptly passed
on to distant peoples as an increase in the cost of living. With land at $260.00 per
acre, Iowa State College figures production costs as follows:

|  | Per acre | |
|---|---|---|
|  | *Wheat* | *Oats* |
| Seed | $3.41 | $3.23 |
| Labor, man and horse | 9.18 | 6.01 |

*Continued on page 307*

Corn Belt with almost unbelievable speed. A particular farmer bought unbroken prairie in central Iowa in 1877 for $7.00 an acre from a railroad company. He gradually increased his holdings at $25.00 an acre, $46.00, $70.00, $84.00, and finally in 1914 at $195.00 an acre. At that time fully improved farms in his neighborhood were bringing from $200.00 to $225.00 an acre. This was only one generation (thirty-seven years) from the time when the land was just raw prairie.

The first white woman born in Nebraska, died in 1922. During her life whole counties of land had risen from free homesteads to a value of $200.00 an acre.[12] Then came the World War, trebling the prices of corn and meat. As a result the Corn Belt, after two decades of profitable land-buying, had one of the wildest orgies of land speculation on record. Farmers would drive up to the court-house and sell or buy a farm without getting out of their automobiles. Prices went to $400.00, even $500.00 an acre. The same farm often changed hands several times in the course of a few months. This increase of land values added billions to Corn Belt valuations. Then came the post-war decline in meat, and the farms went back to $300.00 or $200.00 an acre. Billions of supposed valuation were gone and thousands of men who had bought by making partial payments at the high value were ruined.[13] This shows us that life in the Corn Belt is not so simple after all. This place was recently a free Eden, but it is no Utopia. Mr. Henry Seidel Canby, editor of the *Saturday Review of Literature,* startled me by saying that the Middle West had produced the literature of despair.[14] In explanation he pointed to the fact that this Eden was settled, particularly in Indiana, by many groups of people who entertained Utopian ideas for the revolution of the world by improved social organization. Others

| | | |
|---|---|---|
| Machinery | 1.24 | .79 |
| Threshing, including fuel | 1.83 | 1.62 |
| Twine | .35 | .39 |
| Manure | 1.49 | 1.66 |
| Storage | .44 | .91 |
| Miscellaneous | 1.04 | .48 |
| Total, exclusive of land charges | $18.98 | $15.09 |
| Land charges | 16.80 | 15.53 |
| Total | $35.78 | $30.62 |

[12] The men who owned this land while its mounting value made them rich instinctively felt virtuous about it, as little Jack Horner felt virtuous when he found a plum that he had neither made nor earned. This unearned land value enabled tens of thousands of farmers to retire, especially to California.

[13] As a measurement of this sad settlement, the *Literary Digest,* January 26, 1924, cites the case of 8½% of 69,000 farm-owning farmers who had lost their farms, while 15% more, actually insolvent, held on through leniency of creditors. Similarly, of 26,000 tenants, 14% lost their farms and 21% more held on only through leniency of creditors.

[14] He cites as examples, *Main Street* and *Babbitt* by Sinclair Lewis, *The Spoon River Anthology* by Edgar Lee Masters, *Miss Lulu Bett* by Zona Gale.

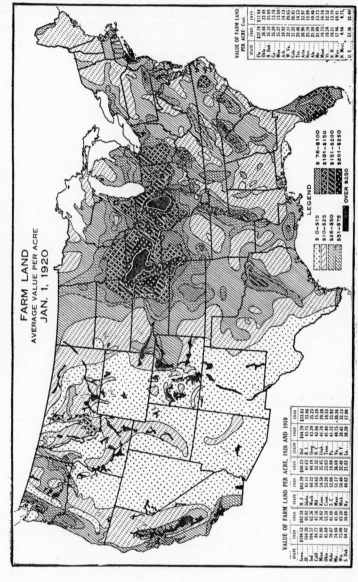

Fig. 150 — It should be noted that this is for *farm land*. Compare Florida and Iowa. (Courtesy U. S. Dept. Agr.)

believed that mankind would receive enormous benefit by the practice and spread of their own particular religion, their own new kind of education, their own diet reform, etc. Two generations later their grandchildren found themselves in a world still unregenerate, and tortured by a terrible World War in which the grandsons of the Utopians had to take part.

As another cause for despair I would add that they settled in an Eden that was given away to the homesteader and now find themselves in a region of high-priced land. A farm such as grandfather got free, the grandson must buy for $40,000. To equip the farm he needs $5000

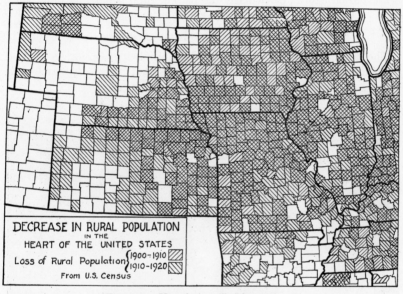

DECREASE IN RURAL POPULATION
IN THE
HEART OF THE UNITED STATES
Loss of Rural Population {1900-1910
1910-1920
From U.S. Census

FIG. 151 — How long will this continue?

more. To make interest on such a valuation the farmer may have to face the extreme of deadening drudgery by being always in attendance upon the dairy cow, the most exacting of mistresses. If he cannot pay for land and wishes to farm he must bear a great burden of debt, become a tenant on a farm that he rents, or migrate.[15] Thousands have migrated to the Pacific Coast, to Canada, some even to the Atlantic slope, where farm land is cheaper and the young farmer's opportunities for independence are much better. Tenancy, the sign of good land, is increasing rapidly, alarmingly I should say.

[15] The relation of men to land in the Corn Belt is shown by the following: In 1840 we had per capita in the United States 1.44 hogs. In 1900 we had 0.82, in 1920, 0.56. In 1861 dressed pork cost $2.50 per hundred pounds in southeastern Iowa, corn was $.15 a bushel, wheat $.43. Common labor was $.75 per day. That seeming low wage bought forty pounds of pork and five bushels of corn. What will a day's wage at common labor buy now?

With high schools almost everywhere, with excellent state universities whose buildings are of imperial magnificence, the splendid educational opportunities of the Corn Belt States have trained thousands of young people for whom the farms offer no opening. They must go to town or to the East, and their own region has few towns. A cursory examination of lists of Eastern educators, professional and business men, shows that astonishing numbers were born west of the Alleghenies.

Like New England the Corn Belt has become a region which exports its men — a sad thing indeed for any region that is compelled to do so.

Population figures, particularly the map of rural population (Fig. 151), show in a startling manner this movement of men.

### Machines, Population and Tenancy

The declining rural population of the Corn Belt does not, as in New England, mean abandoned farms. It means that machinery enables the

Fig. 152 — This gully in Mason County, central Illinois, started less than forty years ago, is now from 100 to 1250 feet wide and from 25 to 65 feet deep. (From Illinois Argicultural Experiment Station Bulletin 207.)

farmer to cultivate more acres of land and that he therefore needs less help.[16]

The influence of machinery on the decline in rural population is proved

[16] The Research Department of the National Association of Farm Implement Manufacturers announced in 1924 that American farmers had saved 1,382,000,000 days' work in a year on leading crops by using modern machinery. That amounts to fifty days' work for twenty-seven million men who would probably have been needed to grow the crop. This helps to explain why the nation is so rich and why it can feed itself with only one-fourth of its workers on the farms.

in an interesting way by comparing the hilly and less valuable sections of southern Indiana and Illinois below the Corn Belt with the level, productive and more valuable machine-using lands of the Corn Belt. The decline was less in the hilly, non-machine-using section because there men had to do the work.

The tractor, the most revolutionary farm invention since the reaper, enables the farmer to seize a spell of good weather, plow with great speed night and day and greatly enlarge the acreage that he can plant. Everywhere except in market-garden localities, farms throughout the Corn Belt are getting steadily larger.[17] In twenty years, 1900 to 1920, the average size of all farms in Illinois increased from 124.2 acres to 134.8; in Nebraska from 246.1 to 339.4. The high value per acre of the enlarging farms makes ownership more and more difficult and increases the tendency to rent. A man who operates a farm as a tenant may not have the hope of being able sometime to buy the farm. But the larger farm, because of its great productivity, can support both landlord and tenant.

The Corn Belt rivals the Cotton Belt as one of the two great areas of tenancy in the United States, and presents one of the many social problems facing the American people. The writer of the allegory of the Garden of Eden has Jehovah tell Adam, " In the sweat of thy face shalt thou eat bread." Today he might tell the man of the Corn Belt, as of almost any other region, " In the sweat of thy mind shalt thou have a good society." Can we organize rural production on the basis of tenantry and have a good society? [18]

### Future of Agriculture in the Corn Belt

" Skimming the cream " off a farm has long been a common saying and a common practice in the Corn Belt. Some of the first settlers made a practice of moving farther west every ten years to get new land to skim. The inhabitants of the black and fertile lands have been outspoken this last half-century in their contempt for what they called the poor, red-looking soils of the East, and for the Eastern practices of saving manure and buying fertilizer. Their soils, deep with fertility, and black with the myriad roots of prairie grass, had no such needs.[19] But soon even those rich black lands will need fertilizer. Already soil erosion has become a problem. Bulletins of Indiana and Illinois agriculture experi-

---

[17] U. S. Dept. Agr. Bulletin No. 963 gives the explanation.

[18] Paul E. Vogt, in *The Land Problem and Rural Welfare*, American Economic Association, 1916, advanced arguments showing that the advance of Corn Belt tenancy is disastrous to education, standards of living, and above all, to the co-operative movement which is regarded as so highly necessary for rural advance. A socially satisfactory tenancy system has not yet been achieved in America.

[19] Tree roots are larger than grass roots. They do not incorporate themselves so intimately with the soil, and they do not make soil black.

ment stations show pictures of desolate destruction [20] and abandoned lands; Illinois gullies, sixty-five feet deep in extreme cases, are rapidly removing the leveling benefits of the glaciers. By 1910 [21] it was reported that " it is safe to say that at least two-thirds and probably three-fourths of all the cultivated soils of Illinois are already in need of phosphorus and organic manures, and most of this vast area is also deficient in limestone." Equally significant was the experience of the Ohio Experiment Station at Wooster which took a four-year rotation of corn, oats, wheat and clover and fertilized the fields with commercial phosphate,

FIG. 153 — Roadside posters put up by the Peoria County Farm Bureau so that he who runs may read. Only the hermetically sealed mind (very common) can escape this.

lime and stable manure. This treatment cost (Circular No. 138) for the four-year period $14.50 an acre, and was paid for by the increased yield of each of three of the four following crops: corn, twenty-seven bushels per acre (increase); wheat, fourteen bushels per acre; hay, one and one-half tons to the acre; oats, ten bushels per acre.[22]

Since the Corn Belt is now primarily producing meat, the next steps

[20] University of Missouri Bulletin No. 211 and Research Bulletin 63 give definite and alarming results of erosion measurements. We must mend our ways or few will be our generations in the land.

[21] Illinois Soil Survey Circular No. 167, p. 9.

[22] This is a suggestive parallel to the achievements in Belgium where similar improvements were inaugurated with the aid of agricultural demonstration service among the people, very much like that which we later established in the United States. The following were obtained:

| Crop (bu.) | Belgium Yield Per A. 1880–1885 | 1907–1910 | Bu. per acre Increase | Per acre Ohio Inc. | U. S. Yield |
|---|---|---|---|---|---|
| Wheat | 24 | 38 | 14 | 14 | 14 |
| Rye | 23 | 36 | 13 | .. | 15 |
| Oats | 49 | 81 | 32 | 10 | 29 |
| Barley (winter) | 38 | 57 | 57 | .. | 26 |
| Corn | .. | .. | .. | 27 | 28 |

in development are to increase the intensity of the type of agriculture, and to use methods that are more scientific.

Dairying is the most natural step toward intensification of agriculture in a meat-producing region. Dairy products are of increasing importance in the Corn Belt, particularly around its margins where corn production is less easy. The silo, with its great efficiency in the use of fodder, is increasing rapidly in numbers. Some cattle men use silage in the summer instead of pasture, thus letting corn, the greatest yielder, replace pastures, the smallest yielder.

The application of more scientific methods is aided mightily by the very efficient agricultural experiment stations and agricultural colleges with their highly specialized staffs of well-trained men. It is estimated that their work has increased the average yield of corn in Illinois by six bushels per acre.[23] Their lines of work and the possibilities of the results are indicated by the following:

1. Introduction of the soy bean. The Iowa station began experiments in 1910. Soy beans covered 230,000 acres in Iowa in 1922. The acreage had been doubling every year for several years. Experiment proved that these beans can be grown along with corn. This makes a slight reduction in the yield of corn but leaves a profit through the increased value of the beans. The beans are hogged down with the corn, and furnish protein to the pig to balance the starch of the corn — the " cafeteria system of pig-feeding," as it is called. This, the cheapest way to make meat, is spreading rapidly in the Corn Belt. Soy-bean oil-mills are also appearing.

2. Plant breeding and the use of the best strains of seed hold great possibilities of increased output without much increase of farm effort. Six years of experiment in Illinois changed the oil content of Indian corn from 4.7% to 7%, and during the same period other experiments reduced the oil content from 4.7% to 3%. Since corn oil is edible and is a substitute for lard, olive oil, cottonseed oil and butter, the significance of this experiment is at once evident. Other Illinois experiments with corn changed its protein content from 6.6% to 16%, which is more than the average protein content of wheat. If the population of the United States should double, treble, or even quadruple, the Corn Belt, with the assistance of the Cotton Belt, could easily feed all the people, provided they made a heavy reduction in the consumption of meat and ate instead grain and vegetable products.[24] At the present time the animals eat the produce of more than three-fourths of all our agriculture.

[23] The European corn borer, a pest already introduced into Ohio and a possible analogue to the boll weevil, may make terrible havoc with the major crop of this region. The U. S. Dept. Agr. will probably keep us informed of its activities.

[24] While meat is good, the heavy consumption of it has no defense whatever in the science of nutrition. See *Blood Pressure, What Affects It,* by Hunter, Arthur, Chief Actuary, New York Life Insurance Co., N. Y.; McCollum, E. V., *The Newer Knowledge of Nutrition;* the works of Chittenden, R. H., also Smith, J. Russell, *The World's Food Resources.*

## Cities and Manufacturing

The Corn Belt is not a great manufacturing region, though it is rich in material and human resources. In addition to being rich in food, the Corn Belt is also rich in power and it is close to raw materials. There is coal in Ohio, Indiana, Illinois, Iowa, Missouri, Kansas and Oklahoma. Nearly half the area is underlaid with coal, of which there is more than in all Europe. Right through the center of the region, in Ohio, Indiana, Illinois and also in Kansas and Oklahoma, there are or have been [25] oil

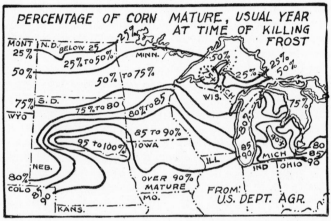

FIG. 154 — This map shows one of the climatic boundaries of the Corn Belt, and explains the statement of October 5, 1924 (Philadelphia *Public Ledger*) that "each day without frost means millions to South Dakota." The season was late. (Courtesy U. S. Dept. Agr.)

fields, and oil pipe-lines (Fig. 78) traverse the region in a great arc from Oklahoma to Ohio.

Along with the oil was natural gas, which gave the cheapest and best of all fuel to many Ohio and Indiana towns. Much of this gas was wasted, as was the case in most other places that possessed it; but while it lasted its excellence made Indiana the leader in the production of glass, which is so easily melted by the gas-flame. Gas was also used in cement mills. Many of these gas-using plants have since been compelled to put in equipment that uses coal.

The Corn Belt has not become a great manufacturing region because it has no great waterways to give it the advantages of location.

The levelness of the Corn Belt, which permitted railroads and highways to pass freely in all directions across its surface, gives no paramount superiority of location to any point within the Corn Belt such as prevails

[25] In 1916 five hundred and sixteen oil-wells were abandoned in Indiana.

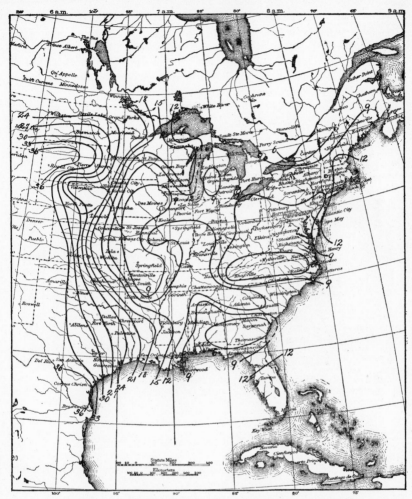

FIG. 155 — Another boundary of the Corn Belt. Map showing the number of times in twenty years that there was a 30-day period without a rainfall of 0.25 inch in any 24-hour period. (Courtesy U. S. Weather Bureau.)

at New York or Chicago. Most of the Corn Belt small towns are completely dependent upon the farms around them for their livelihood, their chief activities being the collection of grain and farm produce, the distribution of merchandise, or the marketing of small amounts of home manufactures that have a local demand.

Agricultural implements are the manufactured product for which there is the greatest advantage of production in the Corn Belt. There is a distinct advantage in making a bulky product in the locality in which it

is to be used.  Nevertheless, the decline in the number of agricultural
implement works shows the fate of the small plant in the small town when
competing with the great organizations of a big city.

Chicago is, in reality, the economic capital of the Corn Belt, but it
is also a product of the lake, and will be discussed with other lake cities
in the chapter on the Lower Lakes.

The Mississippi waterway cutting through the Corn Belt gives the
most commanding city locations in its area.  We see its fruit in the two

Fig. 156 — The Mississippi — a wasted waterway.  It will probably be used
    much more than it now is as freight costs rise and we develop a national,
    organized system of transportation.  Looking south from Alma, Wiscon-
    sin.  Railroad tracks, water tank, Mississippi stern wheeler, log raft, tug.
    Wing dams — a device much used in Europe to narrow the current, deepen
    the water and also make the water dig the channel deeper.  (Courtesy
    H. Burgess, Corps of Engineers, U. S. Army.)

largest cities, St. Louis (772,000 pop.) and Kansas City, Missouri
(324,000; Kansas City, Kansas, 101,000).

St. Louis started as Astor's fur post, and became an outfitting point
for Western trade.  Its location near the junction of the Mississippi and
Missouri rivers on the first high ground [26] south of the mouth of the
Missouri made it a river emporium in the days before the railroads.
When railroads came, they naturally sought St. Louis as an established
city, and this made it a railroad center.  The city has a great distributing trade in the Southwest, even into Mexico; it has a square mile of
stock-yards, the largest horse and mule market in the country, and important manufactures of boots, shoes, tobacco and agricultural implements.

[26] East St. Louis suffered continually from flooding and malaria until its street
level was raised, in some places as much as fifteen feet, and levees were built to
keep out flood waters.

Kansas City, located at the bend of the Missouri River nearest to Santa Fe, was for a time a terminus of boat traffic [27] on the Missouri and an outfitting point for wagon trains for Santa Fe and for Southwestern trade and settlement. This soon made it the focus for railroads and it now has thirty-nine lines and a new fifty-million-dollar terminus for handling freight-cars. Kansas City is a great grain and live-stock market, the greatest goat market in the world,[28] and also the greatest market for stock cattle. In 1922, 1,150,000 of these animals passed through its yards en route to Corn Belt farms. A slightly greater number passed in from the land of grass to the land of corn through Omaha, Sioux City and Minneapolis. Three-fourths of Kansas City manufacturing employees are engaged in the slaughtering industry, in which the city is second only to Chicago.

Kansas City is one of a ring of cities located just far enough within the Corn Belt to have an advantage of location as grain markets and for the meat-packing industry. These cities, Kansas City, St. Joseph, Mo., Omaha, Neb., Sioux City, Iowa, have a hundred miles or so of corn-fields beyond them, so that range cattle can be fattened and never break their eastward movement from the range to the corn-field, to the packing-plant, to the Eastern market. Before the invention of cold storage and the refrigerator car it was necessary to send live animals to Eastern cities to be slaughtered near the point of consumption. But now, since it is cheaper to ship meat than live animals, the packing-plants are in the western edge of the Corn Belt, not in the Eastern cities. Grass grew for some years, literally, in the stock-yards of Philadelphia before they were abandoned in 1923. Meanwhile, directly across the street carloads of chilled beef had been unloaded every day for years.

Des Moines, Iowa, a state capital, shares some of the industry of Omaha and Kansas City, but it has only recently passed the 100,000 population mark.

Cedar Rapids, Iowa, in the midst of the oats belt, has the largest cereal mills in the world, and is the home of Quaker Oats.

The Corn Belt small town may be termed inert. Except for the grain dealer, the coal dealer, the storekeeper and the garage man its population consists chiefly of retired farmers and their families, most of whom live on fixed incomes, and are much more desirous of economy than keen about enterprise. Now in the age of the automobile, the main highways

[27] After completely dying out, this boat traffic revived after the World War, owing in part to the congestion of the railways. A towing-boat with a thirty-six-inch draft draws seven barges 200 x 36 x 8 feet, with a draft of only eighteen inches. The boat rate to New Orleans was but 80% of the railroad rate, a fact which has always caused the Mississippi to have a lowering influence on the railroad rates in the whole area from Chicago and Kansas City to the Gulf, very much as the Erie Canal has controlled rates from the Lakes to New York.

[28] These animals come from the arid Southwest, especially the Edwards Plateau, where they browse on the coarse bushes of the cropless range.

are being built from county seat to county seat, leaving the hamlet out
in the mud.  And sticky mud it is that the Corn Belt soil makes when wet.

The Corn Belt small city, ambitious like all small cities to become
a metropolis, has often tried its fortune in manufacturing, but rarely has
it developed beyond what might be called the subsistence type of manufacture whereby things are made to be sold near home.  As an example
I cite the case of a certain small Illinois city of 10,000 people.  It has
two farm-implement factories, a pottery and stoneware plant, a brick
plant, a tile-drain plant, a soap plant, a cigar plant, a mitten factory
(corn huskers use a pair of cheap mittens per day), and a boiler plant
for making culverts to use in roads.  Most of these small industries are
purely local in scope and several of them are not prosperous.

The eastern end of the Corn Belt, with the lake cities to the north
of it, plateau cities to the east of it, Ohio River cities to the south of it,
and coal, oil and gas under it, has fared better in manufactures than the
western part.  Indianapolis, population 314,000, said to be the world's
largest railroad center (and also largest city) away from water transportation, has caught the overflow of the automobile industry to the north,
and, like Hamilton, Dayton and Springfield, has many manufactures of
machinery.  Dayton, the birthplace of the airplane, makes most of the
cash registers of the United States and has extremely varied manufactures.
Many towns in the eastern Corn Belt make wire fencing and other iron
manufactures, especially agricultural implements.  The list of workers of
Feoria is instructive — 4000 making agricultural implements; 3000 wire,
steel and stoves; 2000 in cereal mills; 800 in textile mills.

The absence of most Corn Belt towns from water transportation is
a financial disadvantage.  In 1924 Robert Hula, of the Chicago Association of Commerce, asserted before the Interstate Commerce Commission
that because freight rates by rail across the continent were higher than
by water by the Panama Canal, " investment capital was keeping away
from the Middle West and that every manufacturer who could abandon
his Western properties and move to the Atlantic Coast was doing so." [29]

An opposite force, perhaps also the sign of an opposite tendency, was
the fact that Mr. Henry Ford had announced three years before this his
intention of scattering manufacturing plants throughout the Middle West
so that farmers could have a job working in his plants in the winter
when their farms did not need them.  How these forces will work out
remains to be seen.

[29] The comparison of population on both coasts with lake and inland states
seems to back up Mr. Hula.

PER CENT INCREASE OF POPULATION

|           | U. S. | N. Y. | Calif. | Iowa | Mich. | Kans. | Mass. |
|-----------|-------|-------|--------|------|-------|-------|-------|
| 1890–1900 | 20.7  | 21.1  | 22.4   | 16.7 | 15.6  | 3.    | 25.3  |
| 1900–1910 | 21.   | 25.4  | 60.1   | −0.3 | 16.1  | 15.   | 20.   |
| 1910–1920 | 14.9  | 14.   | 44.1   | 8.1  | 30.5  | 4.6   | 14.4  |

There is much to be said in favor of an industrial organization which gives to the farmer a winter job with modern machinery and under modern efficiency management. This merely restores the yearly round of labor that he had in the old days of home industry and the domestic system described in the chapter on New England. The winter-work factory would tend, however, to be limited to the full employment a part of the year of all those whom agriculture needed there. This is the choice: shall men or machines loaf half the year. The growth of population in Iowa (8%) between 1910 and 1920, after remaining static for a decade, is a thing to watch with much interest. The early prospect of the universal distribution of electric power to every hamlet makes possible this development of small-town manufacture. A good start in power supply has been made by the carriage of current from the power plant (200,000 horse-power) at Keokuk, Iowa, two hundred miles to St. Louis and considerable distances across the prairies both east and west.

FIG. 157 — A hundred thousand rounded hills make up most of the Ohio Valley.

## CHAPTER XVI

### OHIO VALLEY

THE Ohio Valley is wedged between the Corn Belt, the Cotton Belt and the Appalachian Plateau and it partakes somewhat of the character of each of its three neighbors. Its climate is a thorough mixture of Corn Belt and Cotton Belt climate. Every week all winter the wind blows from every point of the compass. Wind from the northeast may bring snow; from the northwest may blow the snow into drifts; north wind is sure to bring cold; south wind is sure to bring thaw, slush, mud or warm rain, or all of them. So it is from November to March; first, two or three days of Corn Belt weather, then two or three days of Cotton Belt weather. This kind of climate is not to be recommended for human comfort, but it is wholesome and far better for man than is the continuous heat of the West Indies.

The chief difference between the Corn Belt and the Ohio Valley is found in the surface of the land. The Corn Belt is nearly level. Most of the Ohio Valley is hilly. Its northern boundary in Ohio and Indiana is the beginning of the more level glaciated land of the Corn Belt — a transition zone ten to twenty miles wide. Its southern boundary is at the line where the season is too short for cotton. If the Ohio Valley were as level as the Corn Belt it would be a part of the Corn Belt. Corn is grown on almost every Ohio Valley farm, but it is not the crop king that it is in the Corn Belt. Kentucky and Tennessee together produce only half as much as Illinois. In 1920 the parts of Kentucky and Tennessee that are in the Ohio Valley had about one-tenth as many tractors as Illinois, and the decline in rural population was not quite so universal.

The Ohio Valley has a longer summer than the Corn Belt, but not so long as the Cotton Belt. While Ohio Valley agriculture resembles that of the Corn Belt, the people of the Kentucky and Tennessee part of the Ohio Valley partake more of the Southern than of the Northern point of view. They also have a considerable proportion of negro population. The North may be said to begin at Cincinnati, which has a large German element in its population, and people on the Ohio River above Cincinnati

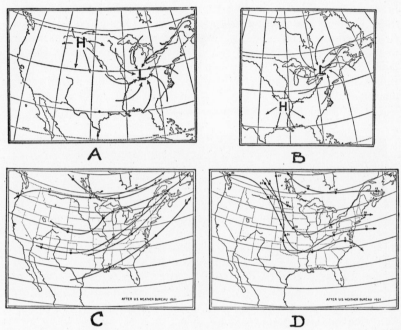

FIG. 158 — The essentials of American weather. (A) *L* is center of an area of low barometer, a center toward which winds blow spirally inward. See arrows. Ascending they condense and make rain. This area of rotation and precipitation, cyclone, moves forward. The paths of U. S. cyclones for a month are shown in (C). It can be seen that the cyclone in (A) gives to Ohio Valley places winds from all points of the compass as it passes. It is a matter of profound difference if the cyclone passes north or south of the point of observation. *H* is a center of high barometer, a center from which winds blow outward — clear, cold and dry, a cold wave. Cold waves also move. The paths of U. S. highs for the same month as the lows are shown in (D). It can be seen that the high, sweeping down behind the low, brings cool or cold clear weather to the Mississippi Valley. These units with variations make up most of the American weather. In summer the low may produce scores or hundreds of thunder-storms in a day.

and on the hills of West Virginia and Ohio belong socially to the North rather than to the South. They came originally by way of Pittsburgh, not by way of Cumberland Gap.

Most of the Ohio Valley is composed of the same rock strata that appear in the Appalachians, but they are of lower elevation, with lower hills. Geologists sometimes call it the "Inland Low Plateau" (Fig. 82).

## The Low Sections and the Highland Rim

Three sections differ from the rolling hills of the usual Ohio Valley type of land. One of these is the alluvial lands along the Ohio and its branches, the Wabash, Cumberland, Green and Tennessee. Many of these lowlands are continuously planted in corn, and occasionally the river overflows them, to the great enrichment of a crop, but sometimes to its destruction. There are several truck-growing centers on this lowland. The two other tracts of smoother land are the limestone plains, called the Kentucky Blue Grass, and Nashville Basin. These areas of limestone plain are much like the Great Valley in their origin (Fig. 82) and therefore in fertility and use. Between these limestone plains and

FIG. 159 — Race horses at home in the Kentucky Blue Grass section. Pasture and crop trees (which these are not but might be) are one of the ideal combinations for hill lands. (Courtesy *North and South Magazine,* Louisville, Ky.)

the Appalachian Plateau is an area of rugged hills of sandstone and shale, the outer fringe of Appalachia, known locally as the Barrens, the Knobs and the Highland Rim (Fig. 82).

One day I crossed from the plateau down into the Blue Grass — a journey of contrasts. The transition hills reminded me of some of the more isolated parts of the Appalachian Ridges and Valleys or of some of the rougher sections of the Virginia-North Carolina Tobacco Belt. The hills were often gullied but sometimes covered with blue grass sod, which held the earth. The proportion of land under the plow was small. The barns were poor; the houses, usually of one story, were poor; paint was rare and most fields were without fences. There were many unused tracts of land and they were mostly covered with oak and other bushes. I traveled miles without seeing a farm that was systematically laid out, fenced and cleaned up. Instead there were little patches of corn and occasionally of wheat stuck around here and there in what seemed to be almost wilderness. Trees were everywhere, up the gullies,

along the fences, along the roads, in the fields, but saw-logs were rare.
Many of the fields were so worn by erosion that the corn was small
and the hillsides were often uncultivated, with little corn patches in the
moister places at the foot of the hills.  In the midst of it all, a beautiful
farm with tile silo, good buildings and good crops showed what the
region might become, and what I think it will become in the next fifty
years — granted world peace.

Suddenly I passed out upon the limestone.  It seemed to be another
world instead of a part of the same country.  The white surface of a
limestone pike shone in the sun.
Farmhouses were of two stories and
painted.  The barns were good, the
fields were fenced, the sod was thick
and heavy, like that of the Valley
of Virginia.  A Jersey cow was the
first pure-bred animal I had seen in
fifty miles.  Near by were herds of
fat beeves, flocks of sheep and a
big steam thresher at work.  The
land here was worth three hundred
dollars an acre, but most of it was
not for sale.  Twenty miles back on
the shale, land was worth only
twenty-five dollars and most of it
was for sale.

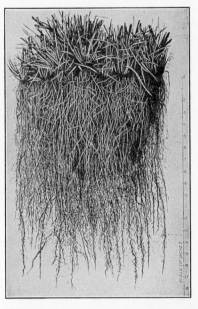

FIG. 160 — This mass of roots, 18
inches long, produced by the short
blue grass sod shows how it stops
erosion, and feeds a fine crop when
plowed under.  (Courtesy U. S.
Dept. Agr.)

## Tobacco

Tobacco is the most distinctive
thing in the agriculture of the Ohio
Valley.  In the days of isolation at
the beginning of the nineteenth
century, the only means of exporting
heavy produce from this region was
by flatboat to New Orleans.  The
high value of tobacco gave it an es-
pecial fitness for export.  Then, as now, the farmer on the fertile soils
of the Blue Grass found tobacco to be his best money crop.

It is common for the Blue Grass farm-owner to have much of his land
in sod and a small proportion of corn, wheat and tobacco.  The tobacco
field, usually not more than six or eight acres in extent, is made by plowing up old blue grass sod.  The soil is so rich in phosphate that fertilizer
is not commonly used.  To grow tobacco requires much labor,[1] and because

[1] Cost-of-production studies by the U. S. Department of Agriculture found
ninety-four hours of horse-labor and 318 hours of man-labor per acre where the

much of the work can be done by women and children, tobacco is largely
grown by tenants — " croppers " they are often called — who work a
field on shares.  In 1920 the rental of Kentucky Blue Grass on this basis
amounted to more than $100.00 an acre, but it is usually several years
before the same field is again in tobacco.

West of the Kentucky Blue Grass area is the section locally known as
the " Pennyrile " because of the pennyroyal plant which grows so thickly

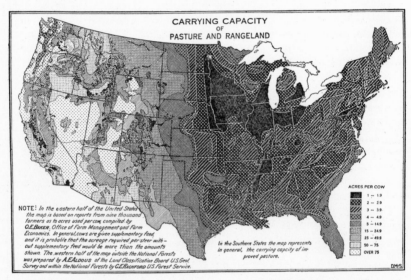

FIG. 161 — It is interesting to compare this map with the rainfall map (Fig. 107).
    If the limestone areas of the Great Appalachian Valley could have been sepa-
    rated from the shale they would have been in the highest class.

on neglected fields.  This is the same formation as the shale hills of the
Highland Rim [2] (on the eastern side of the Blue Grass), but it is less
steep and much of it is in general farms with tobacco as a money crop.
Here more fertilizer must be used and the tobacco is dark, in contrast
to the light Burley tobacco of Blue Grass.

Farther westward yet, dark tobacco is grown on alluvial lands near
the junction of the Ohio and Mississippi.  In some places the tobacco
area has crossed the Ohio into Indiana and Illinois and also southward
into Tennessee, but it is chiefly in Kentucky, where one-third of the

yield of Burley tobacco was six hundred to a thousand pounds per acre.  The cost
was $237.00 per acre and $.30 per pound.  Where the yield was over 1500 pounds
per acre, the cost was $330.00 per acre and $.24 per pound, an argument in favor
of large yield.  Agriculture affords many examples of this.

[2] Farther south in Tennessee the western Highland Rim is higher, steeper, poorer,
and shows its small production on many of the U. S. Department of Agriculture
production maps.

tobacco in the United States (1919) was grown upon 143,000 farms. The market-towns of the Tobacco Belt have large warehouses where the leaves are sorted and piled in classified heaps for the inspection of buyers. Louisville is the greatest tobacco market of the world. Tobacco mostly comes to this place in hogsheads, which often cover the sidewalks and can be seen dimly in great vault-like warehouses as one passes along the streets.

### The Blue Grass

The Kentucky Blue Grass pastures have been famous for a century as the food of fast horses. The pastures are probably no better than are similar pastures of many Corn Belt localities, but to the first settler, as to the present traveler, the impression of richness is most vivid after

FIG. 162 — Comparative harvest from two adjacent rows of unplowed apple trees. Difference, 150 lbs. of nitrate of soda per acre on Ohio River hills, run down to non-productivity by corn-field erosion. (Courtesy F. H. Ballou, Ohio Agricultural Experiment Station.)

long journeys through rough Appalachia,[3] with its poor, sandy hills, and shaly ridges. Because of this contrast, the blue grass has perhaps received a fame greater than its excellence merits.

Once this was the center where were bred the carriage horse, driving-horse and race-horse of the United States. Horses are still raised, but the rich man of Chicago and Boston drives through the park in an automobile now, instead of behind a pair of $1000.00 or $5000.00 horses, and the Kentucky horsemen of Lexington and Frankfort talk mournfully of the golden age which is past. The practical mule, destined for the cot-

[3] The first fifty villages of Kentucky were on the blue grass.

ton fields of the South, often nibbles the grass that his more romantic and pedigreed half-brothers trod in the opening years of the twentieth century.

The Nashville Basin, with little tobacco, is more like the Corn Belt in producing larger quantities of corn and hogs.

### The Sheep and Apple Hills

Ohio is surpassed in the number of her sheep by only three states — Texas, California and Idaho; and these do not surpass her much. Most of the Ohio sheep are on the Ohio Valley hills. This area, including near-by parts of West Virginia and Pennsylvania, has more sheep to the square mile than any other part of the United States. Most of the sheep are merinos, specialists for wool production. Even in the Pennsylvania part of this area the snowfall of winter is so light that many farmers keep their sheep at pasture the year round, with a haystack or two handy to carry them through periods of deepest snow.

They will dig through moderate snows to get their winter grass, as is the case in many of the sheep sections of Scotland and England.

The hills of southern Ohio and adjacent West Virginia support a considerable apple industry. Experiments conducted by the Ohio Experiment Station showed that old orchards so starved by corn and erosion that trees would not grow an inch in a year or bear any crops would respond with luxuriant growth and good crops to the application of a few pounds of nitrate of soda per tree. Most of these orchards are unplowed and therefore an excellent adaptation of crop to resources

FIG. 163 — Roots hold soil — one of the arguments for tree crops on hilly land. (Courtesy Charles C. Deam, State Forester, Indiana.)

### Agricultural Future

The forward movement in agriculture described at some length in the Cotton Belt and the Corn Belt includes this region also. Tennessee affords an interesting example of the revival. It was not until 1909 that the per capita wealth in this state equaled the figure it had attained at the opening of the Civil War. It doubled between 1909 and 1917. In 1903 Tennessee had one rural high school.

In 1917 there were seventy, and a state law made at least one high school compulsory in every county. The county farm-agent has become general here as elsewhere. In many locations in both Kentucky and Tennessee the bankers are selling calves, and eggs for hatching, to schoolboys and girls, to be paid for at the end of the season. The thoroughbred stock movement, characterized by the slogan " Better sires, better stock," is making such progress that Kentucky is now the third state in the union in pure-bred stock. Crimson clover, a soil-building legume which is used for a hay crop, is being increasingly grown. Thirty creameries in the Nashville Basin and a few in the Kentucky Blue Grass perhaps indicate the coming of the better agriculture to the Ohio Valley.

FIG. 164 — A wild pecan tree in northern Kentucky. One of millions on the overflow lands of the Mississippi system. (Photo J. Russell Smith.)

If one takes a long look ahead the greatest problem of this region of hills is to keep the land from washing away. With its summer rain and winter rain [4] the toll of erosion is one of the most difficult problems that agriculture must face. Thousands of acres in each of the five states have been ruined and abandoned. Nature's invitation to develop a tree-crop agriculture is particularly strong. Wild pecan trees of excellent fruiting habits reach the height of more than a hundred feet along the Ohio lowlands west of Cincinnati, the walnut attains its most majestic proportions and the fruitful persimmon grows wild in what they call " throwed-out land," so that in the autumn pigs and sheep make paths from tree to tree as they gather the fruit. The Highland Rim has been described as being fairly alive with food in the autumn — butternuts, hickory nuts, walnuts, chestnuts, pawpaws and persimmons lying on the ground in great abundance.

### Cities and Manufacture

The Ohio Valley seems to be quite the equal, possibly the superior of the Corn Belt in materials of manufacture and possibility of access. The element of superiority comes from the Ohio River, a navigable water-

[4] " Even on the fairly level lands of central Kentucky, soil washing is a serious problem. Every summer witnesses one or more torrential rains, which carry many thousands of tons of rich soil into the creeks and rivers; and an equally serious loss occurs in the winter time. Unlike the soils of northern latitudes, which freeze up during the winter and remain frozen until late winter and early spring, Kentucky soils wash badly during the winter. This is due to the frequent thaws followed by hard rains, which result in the sloughing off and washing away of land which is at

way running through the center of the region, connecting with the coal [5] and iron centers around Pittsburgh at one end and with the great Mississippi at the other. In 1824 our first national river and harbor bill was passed to improve the Ohio-Mississippi. At the end of a hundred years we have not made a very good demonstration of our efficiency in this form of social activity. Log-rolling, the curse of Congressional legislation, has caused us to spend millions improving one section of the Tennessee River, but no large boat could reach this section or get out of it because of unimproved reaches both above and below. We have spent enough money on the rivers of the Ohio Valley to make what we will probably have before much longer, good navigation from Pittsburgh

FIG. 165 — A tow of steel barges approaching a lock on the Ohio River, which should be a great thoroughfare. (Courtesy Cincinnati Chamber of Commerce.)

to Cairo, up the Tennessee to Chattanooga, with navigation for lighter boats on the Cumberland, Green and Kanawha.[6] These waterways should be a much greater boon to cities along their banks than they now are.

The Ohio River made Cincinnati the first metropolis of the West. It is now a city with 400,000 people, but in 1860 it was the largest city west of the Alleghenies and north of New Orleans. The Civil War shut

all sloping, unless this land is covered by a heavy sod." (W. D. Nicholls, *Country Gentleman*, Feb. 2, 1918, " Two Thousand Acres of Grass.")

[5] During the first twenty years of this century, many towns in the upper Ohio Valley had natural gas at $.15 per 1000 cubic feet for houses, and $.05 per 1000 for factories.

[6] The low water in the Ohio in seasons of drought embarrasses boats. In combating this, Federal engineers have dredged out many rocks and built many slack-water dams. These are dams hinged in sections to masonry foundations. In periods of high water they lie flat upon the river bottom. In low water they are propped up to impede the flow. Sometimes the water from a number of these dams is released to make a " wave " upon which a collection of coal barges and boats is floated downstream to break a coal famine at Cincinnati or some other river city.

off and devastated its trade area in the South [7] and it has long since been surpassed by Chicago, Cleveland and St. Louis, but it still has a great distributing trade and important manufactures of great variety. Its leading manufacture is meat-packing, drawing supplies from the Corn Belt and the Ohio Valley. Other industries are clothing, boots, shoes, machinery, especially machine tools, and leather. The city is sometimes spoken of as the most Northern of Southern cities and the most Southern of Northern cities.

The up-river cities, Portsmouth, Huntington, Wheeling, Steubenville, close to the coal of West Virginia, Pennsylvania and Ohio, have industries of iron and steel, glass, pottery and wood. Cincinnati and Louisville seem to be the southwestern outposts of the northeastern manufacturing region, which may be said to go from southern Maine to Chicago. Other cities of the Ohio Valley, Nashville (pop. 118,000), capital of Tennessee, Evansville, Indiana (pop. 85,000), an important lumber market and furniture center, Lexington, the horse market and capital of the Blue Grass, do not seem to show signs of becoming large cities, although they have excellent access to the sources of power and raw materials. It may or may not be a temporary incident that the cities of the Great Lakes and the Atlantic Plain have grown more rapidly than the cities of the Ohio Valley. Perhaps in the course of time it will be found that summer temperature makes the factory worker on the shores of the Great Lakes slightly more efficient than his brother on the banks of the Ohio. This is a matter which only time can tell.

The study of this region in comparison with some of those previously described shows what needless curses some American states have received from the accidents of history combined with the facts of geography, facts quite unknown to statesmen of the past. Kentucky, for example, has in its legislature men from two worlds — the Blue Grass and the " mountain " (Cumberland Plateau). Which shall rule? Sometimes it has taken rifles to decide. Someone has said that Tennessee has no state consciousness, no *state* ideals. How could it be otherwise? Look at the *different states* within her borders: from east to west — a part of the Great Smoky Mountains, a part of the Great Valley, a part of the Cumberland Plateau, the Nashville Basin, the Western Highland Rim and finally a part of the Coastal Plain, with a climate that makes it Cotton Belt. Tennessee is a most amazing cross-section of many good things, but it is too much to put their representatives into one legislature and ask them to make good *state* laws. It is more difficult than making general dietary regulations for Mr. and Mrs. Jack Spratt. Many of our states share Tennessee's perplexity. The efficiency of government in America would be considerably enhanced if existing state boundaries were wiped out and new states created upon the basis of human use regions. This would simplify and unify the problems of government.

[7] In the attempt to regain Southern trade, the city built a railroad to Chattanooga, the longest municipally owned railroad in the world.

FIG. 166 — Wisconsin farmstead. The silos at extreme right bespeak live-stock, the cows tell what kind. At left, house, automobile and ice pond. (Courtesy College of Agriculture, University of Wisconsin.)

## CHAPTER XVII

### NORTH CENTRAL DAIRY REGION

THE Corn Belt has a relative and near neighbor — the North Central Dairy Region. Like the Corn Belt it has corn, small grain, hay and pasture; nevertheless, there are differences. In this region earth, air and history join to make the silo and the dairy barn the most conspicuous parts of the farm equipment: the herd of cows in the pasture replaces the fat beef cattle of the Corn Belt, and the creamery and the cheese factory at the station replace the stock-yards and the grain elevator.

Earth helps to make these changes, chiefly through what the glacier did and left undone. Here the glacier dealt more roughly with the land. There are many long or roundish hills called drumlins, which the glaciers made, and there are moraines piled up marking the ends of glaciers. The landscape is dotted with glacial lakes, wet with glacial swamps, interspersed with gravel banks and sand stretches; and in other places it is littered with stone.

This region also includes the non-glaciated area, which is more hilly and less fertile than the Corn Belt. Unlike the Corn Belt, too, this region was fully forested, and farming therefore started with a long fight against the stumps. In comparison with the Corn Belt farm, the grain area must be smaller. More land must be in pasture — hill pasture, wet pasture, rough pasture.

As this territory is farther north than the Corn Belt, it has a slightly longer winter and a shorter and slightly cooler summer which is less suitable for corn. The problem of escape from frost sometimes arises. Dr. O. E. Baker gives the experience [1] of a section in the driftless area

[1] 1915 meeting, Association of American Geographers.

330

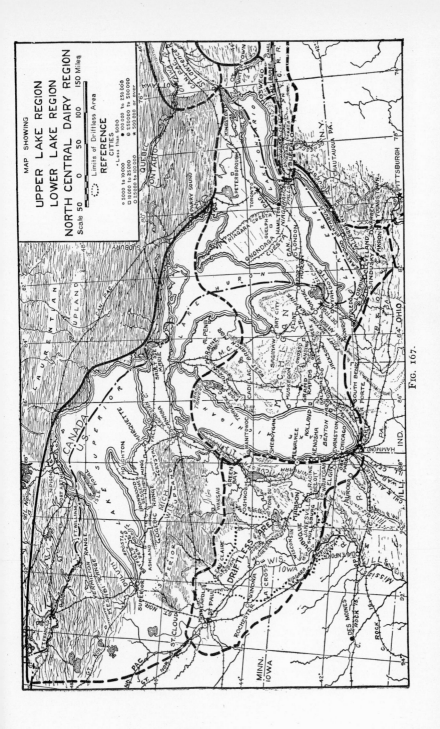

FIG. 167.

near Madison where the hills were much better than the valleys for growing corn because air drainage made the valleys cooler at night. Sometimes this difference amounted to 15° F. in 100 to 150 feet of elevation,
and because of it different varieties of corn were grown on the hills and
in the valleys. Corn was planted in the valleys a week or ten days later
than on the hills. These facts indicate the necessity for a very careful
utilization of the crop land. The conditions favor the silo for the more
careful preservation of forage and the cow for more efficient utilization of
forage. Two hundred and thirty-four million dollars' worth of milk was
produced in Wisconsin in 1920; and in 1919, 300 million pounds of
cheese and 180 million pounds of butter. The rapid increase of dairying
here and not in the Corn Belt is striking.[2]

Most of this region is in Wisconsin, and Wisconsin had been through
two periods of exploitation before it entered the epoch of the cow. The
need for lumber was responsible for the first period of exploitation. The
treeless Corn Belt called for lumber with which to build houses, barns
and fences; lake boats gave easy access to the Eastern markets; the
rafts on the Mississippi reached the Southern markets, so the trees of
Wisconsin floated away and that state was of the first importance as a
producer of lumber.

Following the lumberman came the stump-fighting farmer. He grew
wheat — wheat by exploitation: again and again he planted wheat in the
same place and then the wheat business was bowled over by soil exhaustion, chinch bugs and cheaper wheat from the Northwestern Plains.
Wisconsin then heard the call of diversified farming. The long season of
frost gave the cow the queen's position in the new régime.

### The Historical Factor

History has furnished its contribution to the changes in this region
because the land was settled by the Yankees, who were accustomed to
strenuous labor; by Danes, Swedes, Norwegians, Swiss and Germans, also
accustomed to strenuous labor and to dairying.

Then came Governor Hoard and the University. As a practical dairy-

[2] Number of Milk Cows on Farms, January 1 (Thousands)

| | 1913 | 1923 | Per cent increase |
|---|---|---|---|
| Wisconsin | 1,504 | 2,195 | 46 |
| New York | 1,465 | 1,678 | 14 |
| Minnesota | 1,129 | 1,641 | 45 |
| Iowa | 1,337 | 1,160 | —13 * |
| Illinois | 1,007 | 1,148 | 13 |
| Pennsylvania | 943 | 1,071 | 13 |
| Ohio | 869 | 1,069 | 23 |
| Texas | 1,034 | 1,052 | 1.7 |
| United States | 20,497 | 24,429 | 19 |

\* Decrease. — Yearbooks, U. S. Dept. Agr.

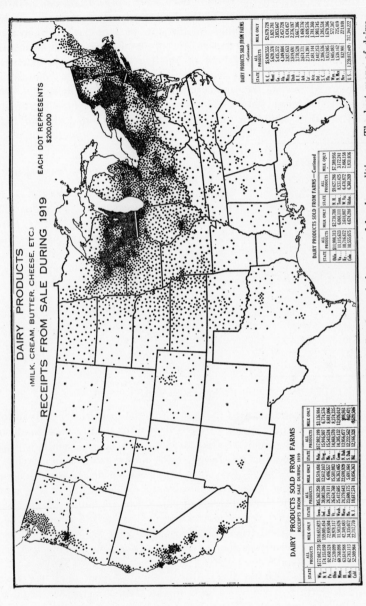

Fig. 168 — An industry located by the call of the city and the urge of hard conditions. The best maps of dairy resources are the corn map (Fig. 136) and the pasture map (Fig. 161).

man Hoard established the periodical called *Hoard's Dairyman*. It became the leading dairy journal of the United States. Hoard was elected Governor. He put the machinery of the state back of the state's greatest industry. The agricultural department of the University of Wisconsin became the leading dairy school of the United States. Its extension service carried dairy lore to every hamlet and farm; in its laboratories were produced five of the six tests used everywhere in dairying. One of its staff, Professor Babcock, invented in 1890 a machine for testing milk. Instead of making a million out of his invention, Professor Bab-

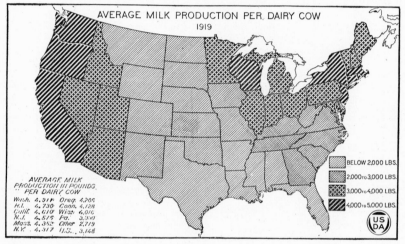

FIG. 169 — A map showing large areas of unused intellect.

cock patented it, and gave to the world the Babcock Tester. By using this machine in his own barn a farmer can test the quality of the milk of every cow. The machine records the cow's history and her horoscope — it tells of her past and her future. The farmer reads that this cow's milk has 3.1% butter fat — away with her to the hot-dog factory! She is not worth milking, nor is she fit to become the mother of the next generation of cows. By the simple process of eliminating the unfit and breeding from the best sire, the average annual output of a herd of cows can, in a decade or two, be raised from 3000 to 6000 or 7000 pounds of milk per cow. Good cows occupy no more space than poor cows, nor do they eat very much more food.

When one notes that an average of a pound of milk more per week per cow is worth $20,000,000 a year to the United States, we begin to see how millions and even billions of new wealth are arising and may arise from the application of science to production. In giving this boost to farming, these agricultural colleges and their extension service (" Univer-

sity on Wheels ") are among the great creative factors in national enrichment. Wisconsin was a leader in this, but every state in the United
States and Canada is also working at it.

Wisconsin was fortunate in her human material. She started with the
Yankees who emigrated. Then she received a lot of German Liberals
who were driven out in 1848. These people attracted other North European Liberals. Her young State University had a president named John
Bascom who taught C. R. Van Hise, who in turn became president and
was able, perhaps more than any other, to make a university a part of a
state and to make the state feel it. " Wherever spirit grows by mysterious contact with spirit, in the passion to make knowledge serve human
needs, there is the essence of the University Idea," says Major Edward
Fitzpatrick, of the Wisconsin Board of Education.

Out of all this came the ability to co-operate, so necessary in agriculture,
especially in dairying. Wisconsin has co-operative creameries, cheese factories, milk-selling associations, breeding associations, telephone companies, insurance companies, live-stock shipping associations, etc., to the
number altogether of more than two thousand, the majority being creameries and cheese factories. Thus geographic, historic, racial and cultural
factors have worked together to make a dairy industry.

### The Dairy Farm

The typical farm in the Dairy Belt has a corn-field and a silo into
which a substantial part of the corn is put. Fields of corn are not left
standing, while the fodder wastes, as is expedient in the Corn Belt. Instead, most of the corn is cut and put in the shock or in the silo and the
fodder is carefully saved for winter feed. The hay field is more important
than on the Corn Belt farm. Pasture fields cover a larger area of the
surface. A small grain-crop is not so universal. Pigs are fed, in part, on
the skimmed milk that remains after the cream has gone to the churn
and are an important side crop.

The successful dairyman, unlike the successful Corn Belt farmer, is
not in a position to spend the winter in California. His twenty, thirty
or forty cows must be milked morning and evening. Their stables must
be cleaned. The milk must be cared for every day, including Sunday,
the Fourth of July, Christmas and all other holidays. The cow is terrible in the regularity of her production, especially the butter cow. The
cheese cow is not so terrible. She takes some time off.

In the more hilly sections the cheese industry predominates. Cheese is
a good summer industry, because the cow, supported by the pasture of
the farms where it is difficult to raise winter forage, spends her winter
on scanty maintenance ration. For the continuous production of milk —
the practice on farms which sell milk to the butter factory — it is necessary to provide expensive milk-producing winter ration for cows.

European cheese-makers who emigrated to Wisconsin brought their art with them, so Wisconsin turns out American Swiss, American Camembert, American Roquefort, American Limburger, and many other brands, each with its hosts of appreciators in many Eastern cities.

In comparison to the Corn Belt, the North Central Dairy Region bears other marks of a land that is less fat, farther north and in need of more intensive utilization. In some places, barley, the great European substitute for corn, is grown instead of corn and used as food for cattle and swine. Rye is grown instead of wheat. On the sandy loam-lands of central Wisconsin, potatoes are an important money crop. The heart of the Corn Belt is too hot for a good crop of potatoes. Not so the heart of the Dairy Belt. Its summer coolness permits green peas to thrive so well that they are grown in the fields as a money crop. Peas are planted broadcast like wheat, cut with a mowing-machine like hay, and raked up with a horse rake, thrown upon a wagon to be forked off into a threshing-machine that hulls them out as peanuts, wheat or rice are threshed. The pea-vines are put into the silo and thus finally get into human consumption as milk.

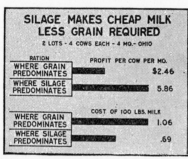

Fig. 170 — This graph from an Ohio bulletin explains the vogue of the silo in dairy and live-stock sections. (Courtesy Ohio Bulletin 159.)

In considering this agriculture, it should be remembered that the Corn Belt has more possible productivity per square mile and that the Cotton Belt has more than either — granted similar expenditures of capital, labor and intelligence.

The southern corner of the Dairy Belt owes its existence to market conditions — the demand for fresh milk by the millions who live in Chicago and other cities near the southern end of Lake Michigan. Further growth of Lake Shore cities will increase the Dairy Region at the expense of the Corn Belt, but its more rapid extension is toward the northwest. The boundaries between the Dairy Belt, the Corn Belt and the Wheat Belt are transition lines that tend to move. The movement will come as the needs for more intensive utilization of the land and for greater supplies of food cause the milk, butter and cheese industry to invade the lands of meat and wheat.

### Agricultural Future

The agricultural future of this region has already begun. Increasing population in North America, causing an increased demand for food, can also cause an increase of output through the use of better animals, better varieties of crop plants, better tillage, reduced acreage of pasture and other forms of intensification such as prevail in Denmark, Holland or Switzerland. Filled milk, a cooking material in which vegetable oil of tropic origin replaces the fat of skimmed milk, is a suggestive way, of increasing regional efficiency. Class legislation killed this perfectly good food.

## Cities and Manufacture

Milwaukee is on the edge of this district, but like Chicago it is primarily a creation of the lake and is presented in another chapter. The northwestward extension of dairying places St. Paul and Minneapolis within the dairy district, but the economic function of these cities is as the metropolis of the Spring Wheat Region, and they are presented in that chapter.

The other Dairy Belt cities have no particular advantage as cities, as is attested by their small size and slow growth. Most of them, espe-

| City | 1900 | 1910 | 1920 | City | 1900 | 1910 | 1920 |
|------|------|------|------|------|------|------|------|
| | (pop. in thousands) | | | | (pop. in thousands) | | |
| Minneapolis....... | 202 | 301 | 380 | Madison.......... | 19 | 25 | 38 |
| St. Paul.......... | 163 | 214 | 234 | Elgin............. | 22 | 25 | 27 |
| Oshkosh.......... | 28 | 33 | 33 | Aurora........... | 24 | 29 | 36 |
| Fond du Lac...... | 15 | 18 | 23 | Dubuque.......... | 36 | 38 | 39 |
| Winona.......... | 19 | 18 | 19 | Eau Claire........ | 17 | 18 | 20 |
| La Crosse........ | 28 | 30 | 30 | | | | |

cially those in the North, began with the riotous, exploitive prosperity of the sawmill town, which has since matured into various manufactures of wood, and in some cases paper-mills for which glacial streams furnish a moderate amount of power. Some of these towns have developed textile mills and small manufactures of various kinds, including machinery, especially dairy machinery. But their slow growth serves to emphasize the primary importance of agriculture, a conserving agriculture that in this region is well-established, scientific and prosperous. Because the cities are small and situated in the midst of agricultural plenty, they are good places in which to live. In comparison to the Corn Belt cities, the longer, colder winter is a disadvantage, and the cooler summer in the vicinity of many beautiful lakes is a distinct advantage, especially with regard to the joy of living.

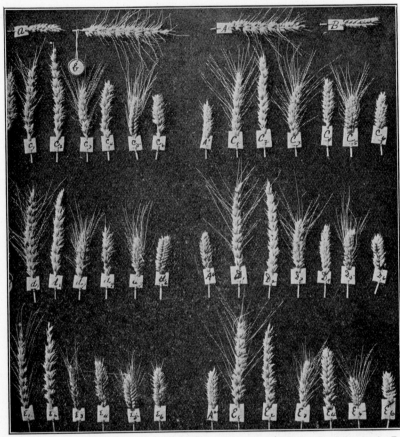

Fig. 171 — An exhibit in plant breeding. At the top, parent wheat heads A, B. They were artificially crossed, producing the heads A', A", A'''. The natural offspring of *A'*, *A"*, *A'''* are beside them. Note the difference in size and character. At the left are three other families similarly descended from the same stock (parents reversed) shown at the top. (Courtesy W. J. Spillman, U. S. Dept. Agr.)

# CHAPTER XVIII

## THE WINTER WHEAT BELT

In the middle part of Kansas and the neighboring parts of Nebraska is the Winter Wheat Belt, 50,000 square miles more or less, in that sea of treeless prairie that stretches from the Missouri River to the Rocky Mountains and from Texas far into Canada. In so vast a stretch of surface uniformity, climate sets the limits of producing regions. This region is a wheat region because of a series of neat adjustments of the requirements of the wheat plant to the climates of Central North America.

Wheat is a native of some Mediterranean land where the rainfall is slight and occurs chiefly in winter. The wheat plant is adjusted to those conditions. It sprouts in the fall and survives the frost of a moderate winter, and in the warmth of spring the little plant makes a big bunch of grass-like leaves. (It is a grass.) In the sunny weeks at the beginning of the dry summer it throws up tall stalks that bear the heads into which the plant finally sends its vitality in the form of rich kernels of grain that fill and mature best during weeks of unbroken sunshine.

### Bounds of the Winter Wheat Belt

The western boundary is set by drought at the place where wheat fails so often that the farmer leaves most of his land in ranch. The eastern boundary is set where the rain increases to an amount necessary for corn. There is not enough to hurt wheat much, but corn is a more profitable crop and therefore becomes the farmer's chief dependence (Figs. 99, 214).

To the south the increasing humidity and heat permit cotton and at the same time injure wheat. At the north the cold winter, in a land of little snow, kills the plants too often. Spring-sown oats takes its place.

### The Wheat Farm

Since 1890 the farmers here have had a fairly steady practice of putting about three-fourths of their crop area in wheat. Although this belt is not the best place in the world for wheat,[1] wheat happens to be the best

[1] Kansas grain yields show very clearly why a part of the state is corn belt and how much better the climate in central Kansas is for wheat than it is for corn.

Continued on page 340

crop for it, although the yield is uncertain, as must be the case in a region which has calamity for three of its boundaries.

In 1901, an unusually good year, twenty-eight contiguous counties in Kansas earned the title "million-bushel counties." Sometimes wheat spreads over the level or gently rolling plain almost as far as one can see. With the aid of tractors, gang-plows and wide-reaching seeders, farms

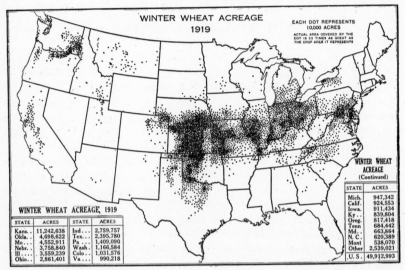

FIG. 172 — Compare this with the Oats map (Fig. 145) and see how the two grains share the Corn Belt. (Courtesy U. S. Dept. Agr.)

here are growing more rapidly than they are in the Corn Belt, and consequently the crop acreage is growing and population is shrinking.

| Kansas corn av. yield | 1911–1920 16.2 1918–1923 18.6 | Kansas wheat av. yield | 1911–1920 13.9 1918–1923 13 |
| U. S. corn av. yield | 1911–1920 26.5 1918–1923 28.9 | U. S. wheat av. yield | 1911–1920 14.5 1918–1923 13.7 |

| Kansas | Wheat | Corn | Kansas | Wheat | Corn |
|---|---|---|---|---|---|
| 1912........... | 15.5 | 23.0 | 1918........... | 14.1 | 7.1 |
| 1913........... | 13. | 3.2 | 1919........... | 13.8 | 15.2 |
| 1914........... | 20.5 | 18.5 | 1920........... | 15.4 | 26.5 |
| 1915........... | 12.5 | 31. | 1921........... | 12.2 | 22.2 |
| 1916........... | 12. | 10. | 1922........... | 12.6 | 19.3 |
| 1917........... | 11.2 | 3. | 1923........... | 10.1 | 21.7 |

The average yield of five counties around lat. 39°, long. 99°, in the heart of this belt, was as follows: 1874–80, 14.1; 1881–90, 14.4; 1891–1900, 9.6; 1901–10, 10.4; 1911–20, 10.8. Source, *U. S. Department of Agriculture Bulletin 1094,* "Winter Wheat Production at the Fort Hays Branch Station." The lower yields of later years show that exploitation is going on — "mining" the land.

The great crisis of the year is the wheat harvest which comes in June and early July. Can the farmers get enough labor? A campaign of advertising through half a nation brings thousands of floating laborers. Some are bums, some are only temporarily unemployed, some are seekers after adventure, and others are college students who are interested in storing up tuition money — "locusts," the farmer sometimes calls them all, locusts who eat up the crop. This indispensable floating help starts in Texas and Oklahoma, and when the wheat of one locality is harvested the laborers move farther north to the next place where wheat is ripe. Thus labor follows the northward march of the season.

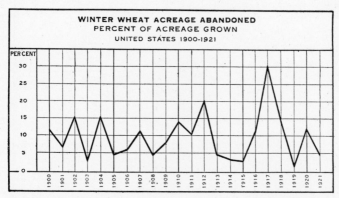

FIG. 173 — This graph shows how nature continually raps the knuckles of the men who try to extend the wheat areas un- wisely. (Courtesy U. S. Dept. Agr.)

The life of a farmer in the Wheat Belt is a double gamble. Will he get a crop? Climate answers mostly in the affirmative. Will he get a good price? The answer comes from other continents. When Euro- pean business went bad after the World War, hard times hit the Wheat Belt with especial severity.

So great is wheat specialization that only one-quarter of the Winter Wheat Belt farm-crop acreage is corn, alfalfa, barley, milo maize and sorghum. All the crops other than wheat are forage crops, and fattening cattle is the other occupation of the Wheat Belt farmer. Newer drought-resisting crops are increasing. The limiting influence of light rain is shown by the fact that after a crop of the deep-rooting, water-searching sorghum or alfalfa, the wheat crop is poor because alfalfa and sorghum have taken the water out of the subsoil.

Life on the big farms is lonely at best, but the almost universal tele- phone, automobile and radio have done much to enrich living. The small rainfall and snowfall give a short season of bad roads — a social asset.

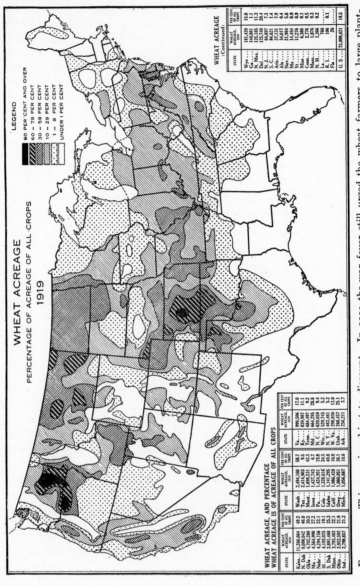

## WHEAT ACREAGE

### PERCENTAGE OF ACREAGE OF ALL CROPS

#### 1919

**LEGEND**

| | |
|---|---|
| ■ | 80 PER CENT AND OVER |
| | 60 - 79 PER CENT |
| | 30 - 59 PER CENT |
| | 10 - 29 PER CENT |
| | 1 - 9 PER CENT |
| | UNDER 1 PER CENT |

WHEAT ACREAGE, AND PERCENTAGE
WHEAT ACREAGE IS OF ACREAGE OF ALL CROPS

| STATE | WHEAT ACREAGE 1919 | PER CENT OF ALL CROPS | STATE | WHEAT ACREAGE 1919 | PER CENT OF ALL CROPS |
|---|---|---|---|---|---|
| Kans. | 11,266,664 | 49.3 | Va. | 990,596 | 17.0 |
| N. Dak. | 9,098,042 | 46.0 | Ky. | 839,987 | 11.1 |
| Okla. | 6,702,280 | 36.5 | Tenn. | 684,497 | 9.2 |
| Mo. | 1,564,990 | 27.2 | Md. | 664,295 | 28.8 |
| Nebr. | 4,234,156 | 22.1 | N. C. | 620,659 | 9.4 |
| Ill. | 4,103,035 | 19.5 | Wis. | 528,745 | 5.2 |
| S. Dak | 3,691,468 | 25.3 | N. Y. | 463,461 | 5.2 |
| Minn. | 3,783,402 | 22.1 | W. Va. | 298,036 | 13.0 |
| Ohio. | 2,922,592 | 21.9 | Utah. | 266,657 | 25.1 |
| Ind. | 2,798,857 | 21.2 | Ark. | 256,231 | 3.7 |

WHEAT ACREAGE
(Continued)

| STATE | WHEAT ACREAGE 1919 | PER CENT OF ALL CROPS |
|---|---|---|
| Wyo. | 181,020 | 15.0 |
| Ga. | 140,861 | 1.1 |
| N. Mex. | 135,185 | 11.3 |
| Del. | 125,740 | 20.1 |
| N. J. | 84,887 | 7.3 |
| S. C. | 84,621 | 1.4 |
| Ariz. | 37,131 | 7.9 |
| Ala. | 34,017 | 0.4 |
| Me. | 21,984 | 5.4 |
| Nev. | 14,464 | 0.9 |
| Vt. | 11,226 | 0.9 |
| Miss. | 6,336 | 0.1 |
| Conn. | 2,776 | 0.5 |
| Mass. | 1,876 | 0.3 |
| N. H. | 1,266 | 0.2 |
| La. | 166 | |
| R. I. | 106 | 0.1 |
| Fla. | 26 | |
| U.S. | 73,099,421 | 19.5 |

FIG. 174 — This map is subject to discount. In 1919 the war fever still urged the wheat farmers to large plantings. (Courtesy U. S. Dept. Agr.)

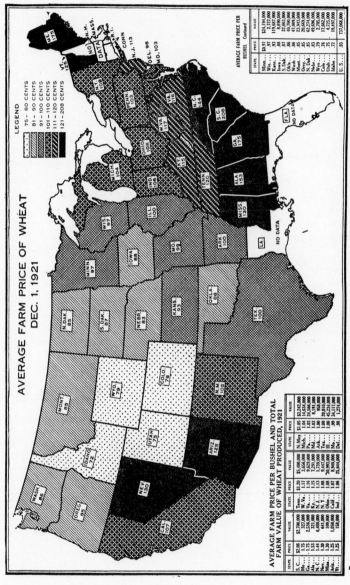

Fig. 175 — The influences of surplus, deficit, and distance from market are clearly visible. (Courtesy U. S. Dept. Agr.)

Fig. 176 — Kafir corn. A drought-enduring immigrant toward which there is no race prejudice. (Courtesy C. R. Ball and A. B. Conner, U. S. Dept. Agr.)

The future of this land will not differ greatly from what it now is. Any permanent system of agriculture will probably have a reduced acreage of wheat. Some kind of crop rotation will be worked out which will provide wheat for the mill and cattle for the packing-plant. The silo is coming in but the farm will remain large. The dryness and levelness of the land compel it. Because it is dry, the yield per acre is small, and because the land is level great areas may be tilled. Lack of abundant moisture also limits the number of crops that may be grown. This place has no choice among dozens of crops as the Cotton Belt has. Sixty-four thousand apple trees in a single orchard were pulled up about 1910 in the middle of this belt because frequent frosts in the level country injured fruit so often that it was more profitable to grow grain.

The largest city is Wichita, with 72,000 people, whose chief occupations pertain to the stores which distribute produce over a wide area and to the railroads with their train-crews and repair-shops. There is no reason to expect any extensive manufacturing (save that pertaining to meat and grain) to develop in Winter Wheat Belt towns, in competition with more favored locations both East and West.

Fig. 177 — Typical landscape and typical harvest equipment in the world's greatest export wheat region. (Courtesy Great Northern Railroad.)

## CHAPTER XIX

### THE SPRING WHEAT REGION

THIS region reaches from central Minnesota, one might say from Minneapolis, to Winnipeg, northwestward to Edmonton and the Rockies, a wide, windswept, level, or slightly swelling, or gently rolling land of dark fertile soil. Here the rain falls chiefly in summer. The average amount of rainfall suits spring wheat. The seed is sown in spring, the crop grows well through the summer rains, and ripens in the fall after the rains decline (Figs. 19, 128).

Only in the age of the railway, the reaper and the other devices of the machine epoch have white farmers and townsmen attempted to transplant their sedentary civilization to the land of the Tatar of Central Asia and the Sioux of Central North America. When the Corn Belt was full they settled the Wheat Belt of Kansas. They went northwestward beyond the Corn Belt into the Red River Valley of Minnesota and the Dakotas, where bonanza wheat-farming was in the height of its boom in 1885. On the rich, level, treeless plains, railroad-building and farm-making were at their absolute maximum of ease. Railroads went first and the settlers followed quickly. On through Manitoba they went, and through Alberta and Saskatchewan, to the foot of the Rockies.

Most of this region is not yet under cultivation; nevertheless it is the world's greatest wheat-exporting region. New settlers arrive and produce wheat and more wheat. This land, and other country much like it in Kansas and Nebraska, has been the seat of political unrest. In the '70's this grain-growing frontier with its financial difficulties produced the Greenback Movement. Populism came out of it in the '90's. In the '20's of this century, it produced the Non-Partisan League of North Dakota [1] and the Farm Bloc in the American Congress. In the Canadian

---

[1] This was an attempt of the North Dakota farmer to solve most of his business troubles by having the state run banks, elevators and other business enterprises. It failed. It had the difficulty of business decision plus political selection.

345

Parliament, too, the conservative East wrestles with the radical West. The shore-land men of New York and Boston sometimes seem to think that Kansas, Nebraska, the Dakotas and Minnesota, with their fads and "isms," are places where men's brains are inherently cracked. But such is not the case. For explanation examine the environment.

### The Center of Troubles

Man is a land animal. The earth is his mother, but the sea seems to be his nurse, and the farther he is from Sea, his nurse, the worse he gets along with Earth, his mother. The sea, with its even-tempered water, tends to evenness of climate. The land, now hot, now cold, tends to extremes of climate. The greater the distance from the sea, the greater the extremes. Extremes make trouble. The Spring Wheat Belt is a land of climatic extremes, hot summer and cold winter, and of swift change. In the same year you may see $-50°$ F. and $100°$ F. Devil's Lake, North Dakota, has zero one-fifth of the days of the year. One wonders why the Devil got the honor of the name.

The similar area in the Old World, the wide, flat, black, hot-cold plain of Central Asia, has for ages been a seat of trouble for that continent. There, as in America, the changeable climate was too much for the primitive farmer. Only the nomad, with his flocks, could survive. It was these nomads on their horses, taking flocks, wives and children with them, who battered at West Europe and Rome under the name of Scythian, Goth, Vandal, Hun, and, turning the other way, battered at China under the name of Tatar, Mongol, Manchu.

The region which we are now considering is a natural seat of troubles for the farmer — troubles of a kind that do not stay bottled up at home. At this point we must consider the troubles. It is true that the averages of temperature and rainfall are good. But crops are not grown in average weather. They grow in the weather of the moment, and because of the continental climate of the Spring Wheat Region, the crops of particular localities have often proved to be uncertain. One year, in large sections of South Dakota, the early summer rains did not come until September, and wheat sown in April or May sprouted in September, making, of course, not a money crop, but only a little late pasture. The drought over much of the Wheat Belt is occasionally desolating. So is frost. If the season happens to be damp, rust may annihilate crops almost like fire. In the year 1916 it is estimated that the black rust did $200,-000,000.00 worth of damage to the wheat crop in the United States part of this region alone. Hail comes with a frequency unknown in the East and in five minutes beats a promising crop into the dirt. Unexpected grasshoppers rise up in countless millions and devastate whole counties. If the crop comes through to a full, fair harvest, the grower often finds himself competing with a bumper crop from Russia, or Australia, or Kansas, or West Europe, or with all of them. That makes a low price. If we compare these new settlers with the early settlers of Massachusetts and Pennsylvania, we find a great contrast in economics and psychology. Instead of a self-sufficient little farm, supplying all its own needs, we find the Western settler depending upon a money-crop or two, selling wheat or oats or flaxseed to markets thousands of miles away, and buying everything from the store supplied largely from factories also thousands of miles away. The grower is absolutely dependent upon the railway, which at best must haul a crop hundreds or thousands of miles, and the freight must be paid. If his business is bad it is not unnatural for the farmer to think that he has been imposed upon by the grain-dealer, or the unseen Chamber of Commerce man who graded his wheat as No. 2 or No. 3 or worse, or the banker who loaned money at high rates, or the railroad with its freight-rate. In addition to these man-made troubles, nature staggers him with visitations of frost and drought and rust and hail and grasshoppers. A farmer is no match for all these enemies, but (sometimes) he does not run away, or migrate as the hordes of Central Asia did. He fights. He organizes and turns to government. Hence we find here the most active governments in North America (Fig. 78).

## Government Activity

I select as a type Saskatchewan, the middle province of the Canadian Plains and the greatest wheat-producer. It has an excellent and aggressive university, whose buildings are of stone, solid, ornate, standing above almost raw prairie where shade-trees have not yet had time to grow. In addition to the ordinary branches one would expect in such an institution, special and very practical courses are offered — short courses in rural telephony, agricultural extension after the style of Wisconsin, running " better-farming trains " with poultry-cars, tree-planting cars, dairy-cars, etc. Live-stock conferences are held at the University, which owns a Clydesdale stallion which is said to be the finest in the province.

Since wheat-growing is so often a gamble, all students of agriculture at once take up the Cotton Belt refrain, " Diversify." Escape from the banker, the store-keeper and the railroad by the " cow-sow-hen " route. The " better bull " campaigns amount almost to rivalry. The live-stock branch of the Provincial Department of Agriculture sells pure-bred bulls at cost to farmers. Meanwhile the live-stock branch of the Dominion Government loans them free. The Provincial Government takes charge of testing dairy cows and grading for improving the breed, and avails itself of the advice of a Better Farming Commission composed of wise men not *elected* to office.

The Provincial Government aids in marketing in many ways. It sees that egg-dealers are licensed and that they candle eggs before selling them. The provincial grader grades cream to guarantee the quality of butter. There is an annual inter-colonial butter contest, won in 1922 and 1923 by Manitoba creameries. The state government aids co-operation [2] all it can. The Premier addressed a meeting called to establish a wheat pool to sell provincial wheat in one block, and assured the meeting of the moral support of himself and his government.

The government labor bureau seeks farm-hands at harvest and issues a call to townspeople to close their places of business early and help the farmer with the harvest. The Weed and Seed Commissioner advises farmers to have seeds tested and send them to the Dominion seed-analyst

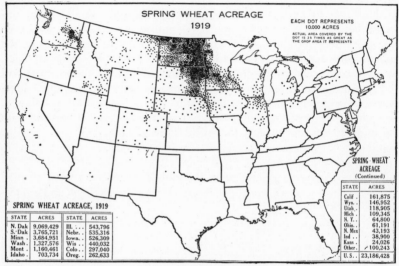

SPRING WHEAT ACREAGE
1919

EACH DOT REPRESENTS
10,000 ACRES

ACTUAL AREA COVERED BY THE
DOT IS 25 TIMES AS GREAT AS
THE CROP AREA IT REPRESENTS

SPRING·WHEAT
ACREAGE
(Continued)

| STATE | ACRES |
|---|---|
| Calif . | 161,875 |
| Wyo. . | 146,952 |
| Utah . | 118,905 |
| Mich . | 109,345 |
| N. Y. | 64,800 |
| Ohio. . | 61,191 |
| N. Mex | 43,193 |
| Ind . . | 38,900 |
| Kans . | 24,026 |
| Other. . | 100,243 |
| U. S. | 23,186,428 |

SPRING WHEAT ACREAGE, 1919

| STATE | ACRES | STATE | ACRES |
|---|---|---|---|
| N. Dak | 9,069,429 | Ill. . . . | 543,796 |
| S. Dak | 3,765,721 | Nebr. . | 535,316 |
| Minn . | 3,684,951 | Iowa. . | 526,309 |
| Wash . | 1,327,576 | Wis . . | 440,032 |
| Mont . | 1,160,461 | Colo . . | 297,040 |
| Idaho . | 703,734 | Oreg. . | 262,633 |

FIG. 178 — Compare this map with Winter Wheat (Fig. 172) and Oats (Fig. 145).
(Courtesy U. S. Dept. Agr.)

at Winnipeg. " Municipalities " (townships) have laws providing for weed-cutting so that the wheat may be free from tares.

Swampy lands are drained for settlers at cost by the government, which also runs a soil survey.[3]

The Provincial ornithologist introduces foreign birds, and figures that one pair of birds per two acres would in the course of a season eat 100,000 insects, to the great relief of agriculture. The state government

[2] For reasons never explained, the United States Government has stimulated production but has strangely neglected marketing, especially co-operative marketing.

[3] The *Public Service Monthly*, Regina, Sask., June 1923, says: " A preliminary report on the soil-survey work carried on last year again emphasizes the importance of diversifying farming, more especially in areas of light rainfall, the report declaring about one locality in particular that ' steady wheat farming, even under ideal conditions, will fail ultimately, and that under conditions in this district it cannot even carry the farmer through until better methods are established.' "

carries war into the land of the grasshopper. In May 1919, upon telegraphic appeal, the state officials accompanied the Dominion entomologist on a field-survey. They found forty-six municipalities affected by grasshoppers, which were sweeping across the country in a strip fifty miles wide. Poison is the cure. In 1922, materials used for this purpose in Saskatchewan were as follows: 2668 tons of bran, 1671 tons of sawdust, 260 tons of molasses, 220 tons of arsenic, 120 tons of salt, 810 tons of amylacetate. All these cost the Provincial Government $150,000.00, and very few grasshoppers were to be found there the next year.[4]

The Saskatchewan Government and also that of Alberta render the farmer a service that is sinister in what it implies about a part of their area. It is the debt-adjustment bureau, which by special legislation protects debtors from the legal enforcement of collections by creditors. This, however, is done only in certain sections of the country, the drier parts, where nature has been so hard on man that the provincial legislatures thought it fair to protect him for a time from his creditors.

Municipal hail-insurance is another government aid, resembling the debt-adjustment in its implications.

The fury with which the problems of the Spring Wheat Belt are being attacked by states, nations and private organizations promises speedy solutions. In a short time we may expect knowledge and organized effort to reduce uncertainty.

## Bounds

The ranch country of the Great Plains which makes the western boundary of the Winter Wheat Belt and the Corn Belt is also the southern and southwestern boundary of the Spring Wheat Belt. Fortunately for Western Canada, fifteen inches of rainfall produce a crop, while twenty inches are inadequate in Kansas or Nebraska.[5] This difference permits the wheat belt to cross the whole plain, from Lake Winnipeg to the Rockies. It has two perilous boundaries of climatic transition. The southwestern boundary is a drought boundary. The northern boundary is a frost boundary. These boundary lines fluctuate from year to year and will be finally settled by experience, the improvement of crops and the adjustment of farm practices. (See general map.)

The western boundary is the clear-cut wall of the Rocky Mountains.[6]

[4] Mr. C. L. Corkins reported to the American Red Cross in 1920 concerning its donation of $15,000.00 to fight the grasshopper in a North Dakota county. He reported 240,000 acres of wheat in that county yielding eight bushels of wheat to the acre, or 1,920,000 bushels, of which one-third was saved by the grasshopper campaign — an excellent illustration of the need of organization and quick action in this land of uncertainty, where there are at times twenty to fifty bushels of grasshoppers to the acre.

[5] U. S. Dept. Agr. *Farm Bulletin 690*, "The Field Pea."

[6] An area at the foot of the Rockies in southwestern Alberta gives promise of having a winter-wheat crop rather than a spring-wheat crop, for the following reasons. The mountains shelter it from the full force of prairie winds. It is also

The eastern boundary is almost equally definite, the edge of the old, hard-rock formations we have previously seen north of the St. Lawrence lowlands. The Canadian Pacific Railway train rushes out of 800 miles of rock cuts into the smooth plain around Winnipeg, an old lake bed.

### Surface and Soils

The continental glacier, as it retreated, blocked the Red River of the North so that no water could flow to the Hudson Bay. Therefore it filled all the land in front of the glacier until it overflowed at the source

FIG. 179 — Red River Valley. The earth affords few better places for machine agriculture. (Courtesy Great Northern Railway.)

of the Red River into the Minnesota River (branch of the Mississippi), as a wide channel still shows. At its height this glacial lake, called Lake Agassiz, had an area of 110,000 square miles, more than the present combined area of the Great Lakes. It was 700 miles long. Parts remain — Lake Winnipeg, Lake Manitoba, Lake Winnipegosis, Lake of the Woods. Several deltas built in this lake still remain. One covers 400 square miles, another 100 square miles. Some have steep fronts 100 feet high. Some are fine farm-land. Some are assorted sand and gravel. One has yielded tens of thousands of carloads of gravel for railroad ballast and road-making.

The main floor of the old lake is made of material that settled from

warmer in winter than localities farther east. This is usual with lands to leeward of high mountains. It has more snow, more rain and more spring rain than the open plains farther east, so that the Canadian Wheat Belt is likely to include a little corner of winter wheat. Unfortunately, this area seems to be strictly limited; beyond a brief stretch from the foot of the Rockies it is too dry for the farm, and the land is good only for ranching. (Information from Charles F. Brooks and A. C. Stine.) This temperature influence of the mountain foot is very pronounced.

muddy water, making a fine soil, almost as sticky as taffy when wet, but fertile and most easily cultivated by machinery. The old lake-bed, about 800 feet above the sea-level, ends in a series of hills that rise to another plain about 1600 feet high, which in turn ends at another step up called the Missouri Couteau (Fig. 214). The plain west of this Couteau is about 3000 feet high.

West Canada is very fortunate in her elevations. Near the Alberta-Montana boundary it is about 4500 feet. Streams drain away toward the Arctic so that declining elevations combine with the longer day of increasing latitude to maintain great temperature uniformity. Thus, Fort Chipewyan on Lake Athabasca, latitude 59 degrees, has a summer temperature only 1.8 degrees cooler than Edmonton, latitude 54 degrees, elevation 2200 feet, and 1.6 degrees cooler than Calgary, latitude 51 degrees, elevation 3400 feet. We appreciate these facts better by noting

FIG. 180 — Ditch dug to drain glacial swales. (Courtesy Great Northern Railway.)

that the distance between Calgary and Fort Chipewyan would take one from Norfolk (Virginia) to Albany (New York), from Memphis (Tennessee) cotton to Madison (Wisconsin) potatoes and milk.

In the northern part of the wheat region the transition to northern forest is shown by the growth of small aspens and willows, which grow larger as one goes north and finally merge into a kind of park landscape where there is enough wood to aid the settler. The glacier leveled much of this land, made some change in the direction of streams, created numberless lakes and ponds and left in some sections just about enough stones for building purposes.

These glacial ponds and swamps give the settler clouds of mosquitoes, water-fowl by thousands, and a considerable problem of draining swampy lands. There are large areas of swamp that cannot be drained, for when an acre or two of swamp is in a little round hole in the middle of a farm there is no place into which its water can be drained save at an expenditure beyond any possibility of profit.[7]

## Settlement and Agriculture

In 1870 Alberta and Saskatchewan were the range of the buffalo and the Indian, occasionally traversed by fur-traders. In Manitoba there were 12,000 white people. By 1900 there were 420,000 white people in the three provinces. The free lands of the United States were about gone. Then Canada's opportunity came. She began to build railways across her plains, and to advertise. Figures of population show the result.

| Population | 1901 | 1911 | 1921 |
|---|---|---|---|
| Manitoba | 255,000 | 461,000 | 610,000 |
| Alberta | 73,000 | 374,000 | 588,000 |
| Saskatchewan | 91,000 | 492,000 | 757,000 |
| | 419,000 | 1,327,000 | 1,955,000 |

In addition to the many aids previously mentioned, the Canadian government ran a regular sales campaign to attract settlers. In the years 1914 and 1915 alone, nearly $2,000,000.00 was spent in advertising. For twenty years free homesteads were advertised in many American farm papers; Canada maintained immigration offices in Syracuse, N. Y., Harrisburg, Pa., Omaha, Neb., and in many other American cities — a regular real estate business with land being given away.[8] The young men of the Corn Belt sought escape from high-priced land. The station at Omaha, Neb., forwarded nearly 50,000 emigrants in twenty years. The good homesteads are now about gone,[9] but 669 homesteaders took up land in the three provinces in the first quarter of 1923.

It was found that a homesteader could haul his wheat about twenty to thirty miles as a maximum, so if railroads were forty or fifty miles apart settlers could cover the whole territory.

In the treeless areas some sod houses were built, but the railroads, in the attempt to encourage settlers, carried lumber back from Eastern forests as return freight at low rates. The later settlers in the park country to the north have often built a house called a mudhouse. Posts are set vertically in the ground, and laths of willow branches nailed across them. Mud or tenacious clay is next plastered upon this, with bare

[7] Near Indian Head, on the main line of the Canadian Pacific, I passed sixteen miles where not a single field was as large as forty acres. This was a section where all good land was in use, but nearly all the area was swamp and wet thicket — the wild duck's idea of heaven.

[8] Canada's migration problem has had two sides. Between 1901 and 1910 she received 1½ million immigrants but increased her population by only 1,835,000, or 5% more than the immigrants. Canada has for a long time sent many immigrants to the United States, especially from the Eastern provinces.

[9] Much of the land is in the hands of the absentee owners, land companies and railroad companies and still waits for users.

hands, greased or frequently wet to keep the mud from sticking to them.
Pieces of sod, one foot by two, resting upon poles and laid on after the
fashion of shingles, make a roof that is warm in winter and cool in
summer. With a dirt floor this makes an inexpensive house, very warm
and comfortable, in which flowers can bloom all winter.

The winter is the bane of this wheat region. As a Canadian settler
told me: " We have a great country, we have good soil, and can grow
great crops. We mostly have a good summer, but the winter gets your
goat." In the five months of cold, with frozen ground, mostly covered
with snow, there is not a thing for the wheat-grower to do in the little

Fig. 181 — The substantial stations of the Canadian Pacific Railway indicate faith
in the future of the country. (Courtesy Canadian Pacific Railway.)

one-story house of hope or in the straw-covered shed where he hopes to
have a barn. In the spring he plows and plants. In summer he watches
it grow. He watches the sky and the crop with anxiety. Will the next
few weeks bring hot, wet weather that will rust his crop, or hot, dry
weather to wither it? Will grasshoppers come, or will there be devastating
hail? Or will good fortune bring a rich harvest of stiff upstanding straw
supporting heavy heads of No. 1 hard? Must he go back to his people
or to his wife's people, or will he strike it rich? In the late summer or
autumn, if the season has been good, he has a fury of labor, with harvesting, threshing and hauling to the station. Then five months of leisure
by the fire.[10] The short work-season is an incentive to grow oats, which
happen to ripen before wheat and lengthen the work season, but all grains
grown are planted in the spring and harvested in the fall. The winter
is too cold for winter grain, but hardy strains are being tried.

The evils of the labor situation of this business appear plainly in Cal-

[10] Sometimes the farmer who is in luck turns the horses out, watches them
for a couple of days to see that they have established themselves by the pile
of oat-straw left from threshing, and goes away to Vancouver or California for the
winter. In spring he returns, finds the horses in good order and starts another crop.

gary, in western Alberta. To help harvest, thousands of harvest hands are brought in, in summer. Forty thousand came in 1923. In the winter some of them go to town, along with some of the settlers whose crops have failed. There is not enough work for them to do in town, so Calgary often takes up contributions for soup kitchens and advertises in the papers advising people without money to stay away. This is a strange cry for a new country, a relatively empty land, where one would expect papers to say, " Come and grow up with the country."

This winter idleness, combined with the midsummer idleness of untilled small grains, is one of the reasons for keeping cows. I should think the homesteader who stays home would want a few cows merely for the sake of their company through the long days of whistling wind, when a basket set down by the kitchen door will go skating away across the prairie until it disappears in the distance. On the other hand, there are many persons just suited by a spasm of work and a long period of loafing.

Fortunately the occasional crop-failures previously mentioned make the income of the grain-grower so uncertain that preaching diversified farming to Spring Wheat Region farmers brings about a change more speedily than in the Cotton Belt.

We should naturally expect this diversification to begin in the older settled parts. The statistics [11] for Minnesota prove the point beautifully. In that state, which, by the way, has part of the Corn Belt and part of the Dairy Belt, the wheat acreage was half the total crop land in 1899,

[11] Note especially the figures of yield per acre. These fluctuating figures of state and province yields do not cover the situation of individual farms. They are an average of many successes and failures. Small-area records would be worse.

WHEAT A = ACREAGE, THOUSANDS. P = PRODUCTION, MILLION BU.
Y = YIELD PER ACRE, BUSHELS

The facts of yield, acreage and production in different parts of the Northern Wheat Regions are very suggestive.

| | Minnesota | | | S. Dakota | | | N. Dakota | | | Manitoba | | |
|---|---|---|---|---|---|---|---|---|---|---|---|---|
| | A. | P. | Y. | A. | P. | Y. | A. | P. | Y. | A. | P. | Y. |
| 1910 | 4000 | 64. | 16. | 3650 | 46.7 | 12.8 | 7700 | 38.5 | 5. | 3014 | 41.1 | 12.3 |
| 1911 | 4350 | 43.9 | 10.1 | 3700 | 14.8 | 4. | 9150 | 73.2 | 8. | 3095 | 62.6 | 22.5 |
| 1912 | 4325 | 67. | 15.5 | 3675 | 52.1 | 14.2 | 7990 | 143.8 | 18. | 2839 | 63. | 22.2 |
| 1913 | 4200 | 68. | 16.2 | 3775 | 33.9 | 9. | 7510 | 78.8 | 10.5 | 2804 | 53.3 | 19. |
| 1914 | 4050 | 42.9 | 10.6 | 3469 | 31.5 | 9.1 | 7285 | 81.5 | 11.2 | 2616 | 38.6 | 14.8 |
| 1915 | 4160 | 70.8 | 17. | 3725 | 63.7 | 17.1 | 8350 | 151.9 | 18.2 | 2800 | 69.3 | 24.7 |
| 1916 | 3465 | 26.4 | 7.6 | 3650 | 24.8 | 6.8 | 7150 | 39.3 | 5.5 | 2726 | 29.6 | 10.8 |
| 1917 | 2947 | 51.6 | 17.5 | 3200 | 44.8 | 14. | 7000 | 56. | 8.0 | 2449 | 41. | 16.7 |
| 1918 | 3619 | 75.7 | 20.9 | 3280 | 62.1 | 19.0 | 7770 | 105.6 | 13.6 | 2984 | 48.1 | 16.3 |
| 1919 | 3793 | 35.7 | 9.4 | 3896 | 31.7 | 8.2 | 9098 | 62.7 | 6.9 | 2880 | 40.9 | 14.2 |
| 1920 | 2880 | 28.1 | 9.8 | 2930 | 26.9 | 9.2 | 8916 | 80.2 | 9. | 2706 | 37.5 | 13.9 |
| 1921 | 2371 | 22.9 | 9.7 | 2845 | 25.9 | 9.1 | 9500 | 80.7 | 8.5 | 3501 | 39. | 11.1 |
| 1922 | 1939 | 27.0 | 13.9 | 2989 | 40. | 13.4 | 8740 | 123.2 | 14.1 | 3125 | 60. | 19.2 |
| 1923 | 1728 | 20.7 | 12. | 2812 | 26.9 | 9.6 | 8262 | 58.6 | 7.1 | 2915 | 32.8 | 11.2 |

Table continued on page 355

one-fourth in 1909, one-sixth in 1920. Between 1910 and 1922 the oats-area increased one-third and the corn-area doubled. The experiment stations have striven [12] to create improved, quick-growing varieties of corn. For example, Minnesota No. 13, which ripens in thirteen weeks after it is up, was perfected in one of the Minnesota stations, and with other varieties is steadily permitting corn to grow farther north. The silo, which so materially shortens the period necessary for corn to grow to a useful stage, permits a great advance northward. Occasional fields of silage corn are to be seen in the latitude of Winnipeg and Regina.

The strife to adjust corn may wane because of the greater promise held out by the sunflower. Numerous experiments have shown that silage made by chopping up the whole sunflower plant, just as the whole corn plant is chopped up, has feeding value nearly or quite equal to that of corn silage.[13] The sunflower will stand more drought, more coolness and much more frost than corn. For example, the agricultural experiment station at Fort Vermilion, latitude $58\frac{1}{2}°$, nearly 700 miles north of the American boundary, about 300 miles north of Edmonton, in 1921 had corn seriously injured by frost. At the same time sunflowers were un-harmed and yielded thirty tons of silage to the acre, a yield that would make an Illinois corn-grower think he was a silage king.

The Canadians have found that they can keep silage in a hole in the ground. They dig a pit eight feet deep, sixteen feet wide, and as long as desired. The silage is packed in tight, and covered with two or three feet of straw. This is a very inexpensive kind of barn and a great boon

| | Saskatchewan | | | Alberta | | | Ohio | | | United Kingdom |
|---|---|---|---|---|---|---|---|---|---|---|
| | A. | P. | Y. | A. | P. | Y. | A. | P. | Y. | Y. |
| 1910 | 4848 | 81.1 | 15.8 | 533 | 6.5 | 10.3 | 2125 | 34.4 | 16.2 | 31.4 |
| 1911 | 5256 | 109. | 20.7 | 1640 | 36.6 | 22.3 | 2265 | 36.2 | 16. | 32.5 |
| 1912 | 5582 | 106.9 | 19.1 | 1590 | 34.3 | 21.5 | 1220 | 9.7 | 8. | 30. |
| 1913 | 5720 | 121.5 | 21.2 | 1512 | 34.3 | 22.7 | 1950 | 35. | 18. | 32.7 |
| 1914 | 5348 | 73.4 | 13.7 | 1371 | 28.8 | 21. | 1975 | 36.5 | 18.5 | 33.8 |
| 1915 | 8929 | 224.3 | 25.1 | 2138 | 66.5 | 31.1 | 1980 | 40.1 | 20.3 | 32.7 |
| 1916 | 9032 | 147.5 | 16.3 | 2605 | 65. | 24.9 | 1600 | 21.6 | 13.5 | 30. |
| 1917 | 8273 | 117.9 | 14.2 | 2897 | 52.9 | 18.2 | 1870 | 41.1 | 22. | 31.6 |
| 1918 | 9249 | 92.4 | 10. | 3892 | 23.7 | 6. | 2290 | 43.5 | 19. | 34.4 |
| 1919 | 10587 | 89.9 | 8.5 | 4283 | 34.5 | 8. | 2922 | 58.1 | 19.9 | 29.2 |
| 1920 | 10061 | 113.1 | 11.2 | 4074 | 83.4 | 20.5 | 2395 | 30.4 | 12.7 | 28.7 |
| 1921 | 13557 | 188. | 13.7 | 5123 | 53. | 10.3 | 2434 | 30.1 | 12.4 | 35.4 |
| 1922 | 12332 | 250.1 | 20.2 | 5765 | 64.9 | 11.2 | 2526 | 35.3 | 14. | 31.4 |
| 1923 | 12791 | 252.6 | 19.7 | 5958 | 166.8 | 28. | 2350 | 42.7 | 18.2 | |

[12] Mr. M. R. Gilmore (Heye Foundation, New York), authority on Indian agri-culture, bewails the stupidity of the white man who has brought to the West and Northwest the strains of corn he secured from the first Indians he met, namely, those of the Atlantic Coast. Centuries ago, meanwhile, the Indians had adjusted corn to the particular climates and were growing corn far beyond our Corn Belt and well up into the present wheat region of Canada — varieties which have not thus far been made the basis of agriculture.

[13] The Canadian Pacific Experiment Farm near Calgary reports it quite the equal of corn. See also bulletins from Illinois Station.

to the man who is earnestly tackling the long, hard job of building up
a farm home on the treeless plain.

This pair, the sunflower and the pit silo, may help greatly to emanci-
pate the stock-farmer from dependence on root crops, which the European
farmer produces by much labor as a substitute for our corn silage. Already the dairy industry is making rapid strides in the Spring Wheat
Belt, especially in the longer settled southeastern part.[14] At the same
time that the Corn Belt farm grew in size so rapidly that the rural
population is declining, the farm population increased (1910–1920) in
nearly all counties in the Red River Valley because the dairy farm is
replacing the bonanza wheat farm.

In the Corn Belt and the Winter Wheat Belt of the United States we
find a kind of normal farm evolution: (1) the grain-growing stage; (2)
the meat-making stage; and then gradually, after decades and the pressure of land-values, (3) the introduction of the dairy-stage. In the Spring
Wheat Region the long, cold winter, the shorter pasture season, the risk
of grain crops and greater expense of winter feeding are causing a swift
jump from the grain-stage to the dairy-stage, with much less of the intervening meat-stage. Dairying here has an advantage over that in the
Eastern United States and Canada. Modern sanitary methods do not
have to compete with old established notions of the " way Father did."

## The Agricultural Future

As a basic fact, it should be remembered that the soil of this region
is rich. It is frozen all winter and leached but little in summer. Erosion
is much less of a problem here than in the Corn Belt. It is therefore
reasonable to assume that the heroic, almost frantic efforts of governments,
railroads, civic organizations and individuals will result in the working
out of crop rotations that fit the various parts of this Wheat Belt. For
a long time to come this region promises to export vast quantities of
bread-stuffs and butter and cheese, and probably some meat and potatoes
if they are wanted.

It is a good land for grain. Market conditions and farm plans decide
which of the small grains — wheat, barley, rye and oats — shall be grown.
It is a good place also for flaxseed, but flax is a soil-robber grown chiefly
in the first years after breaking the new prairie. Its acreage is declining
both in the United States and in Canada, and Argentina is growing it
for us.

The quality of grain grown in the Spring Wheat Region is usually
good.[15] The oats are heavier per bushel than in the United States.

---

[14] During the first three months of 1924 Saskatchewan increased her butter
produce 32% over that of this same period in the previous year.

[15] The prize wheat at the Philadelphia Centennial Exposition in 1876 came from
Alberta. In 1922, at the Chicago International Grain and Hay Show, Saskatchewan
took eleven out of twenty-six wheat prizes. It had taken the best prize nine out
of the eleven previous years.

Spring wheat is harder than winter wheat, makes better flour and commands higher prices. Some of it is imported from Canada by the Minneapolis millers to mix with the American wheat. It makes what is called a " strong " flour.

We may expect much improvement in varieties of wheat and other grains suited to the climate of this region. Unsuitable varieties of wheat from farther south were a handicap in the days of early settlement. In the deliberate search for drought-resisting varieties, the United States Department of Agriculture sent Mr. Mark Carleton, cerealist, to the dry country of southeastern Russia. There in a transition zone of scanty

FIG. 182 — North Dakota Agricultural Experiment Station. An outdoor laboratory where man's battles with nature can be fought out in miniature. (Courtesy Agricultural College, North Dakota.)

rainfall between good farm-land and the dry pastures of the cowboy Cossacks, he found the seed of Durum wheat. It proved to be hardier than any we then had, earlier ripening, and so much more drought-resistant that in some seasons it produced 40% to 50% more than any other variety. In 1901 there were 70,000 bushels of Durum wheat grown in the United States; in 1903, 6,000,000; in 1906, 50,000,000. Thousands of farmers were successful in the dry western part of the Spring Wheat Region of the Dakotas. Without this wheat they must have failed (Fig. 209).

Equally swift has been the rise of other wheats. By 1918, 90% of the wheat grown in western Canada was of the variety called Marquis,[16] much superior to Red Fife which had been the standard variety. The history of Marquis wheat is suggestive of the new agriculture. Dr. Charles E. Saunders, the Dominion cerealist, found one head of superior

[16] Buller, *Essays on Wheat.*

wheat growing in test plots. It was a fine-looking head with unusually choice grains. Chewing tests showed it to be highly elastic, therefore glutinous. This was in 1903. Careful planting had produced twenty-three pounds by 1907. By 1909 it was tested on many farms, and in nine years it had swept most of the spring-wheat-growing section of this continent. Its origin is due to a cross between Red Fife and an Indian wheat, made in 1892, and it was one of thousands of strains produced by deliberate hybridization in search of new strains.[17]

The resources for the home garden are better than one would expect. Raspberries, currants, strawberries and gooseberries find a natural home in most localities. At the North blueberries also thrive. Watermelons will ripen over much of the area. A wind-break of trees and irrigation will permit the growth of surprising gardens. After much search and thousands of tests, a few varieties of hardy Russian apples have been found. The scientific creation of fruits for this area has only begun. Similarly, almost nothing has been done toward domesticating and improving many promising wild plants. Why should agriculture be so deferential to the grains domesticated by our primitive ancestress!

## The Potato

Many parts of the spring wheat country are as good for the potato as they are for wheat, and the potato looms large in any consideration of this region as a part of a future North America with 200 or 300 million people. Possibilities of production are enormous. A tractor can draw across the level plain two potato-diggers, each laying out behind it a row of potatoes. In part, at least, the potato has also joined the machine-grown crops. In 1916 it was estimated that potatoes could be grown in rotation with wheat in the Red River Valley of Minnesota for $.25 a bushel. Potatoes can survive more frost than grain and they do particularly well in the greater coolness and the humidity along the northern edge of this whole wheat region. They also thrive in a large area along the foot of the Rocky Mountains, where there is more rain than in the middle of the plain.

The fact that 50,000,000 bushels of potatoes rotted or were fed to the pigs in the United States in the winter of 1922–1923 is one of several good reasons why potatoes are not more extensively grown in the Spring

[17] " Crossing two kinds of wheat is a relatively simple operation, the technique of which it is not difficult to acquire. However, new varieties are not obtained in one generation only; for a cross-bred kernel in succeeding generations always gives rise to a large number of plant types which differ from one another in one or more characters — such as length and strength of straw, length, compactness and upright-ness of the heads, the color and hairiness of the chaff, presence or absence of awns, color, shape, size and milling qualities of the grains, liability of the grains to shell, earliness in maturing, resistance to diseases, baking qualities of the flour, and so forth — and most careful selection through a series of years is necessary in order to isolate the best of its progeny." (P. 150, *Essays on Wheat,* Buller.)

Wheat Belt at present. When we develop an intensified agriculture like that of Germany,[18] Spring Wheat Belt farms will have various rotations, including wheat, other small grains, corn, the sunflower, hay and potatoes. If exhaustion of resources should shift motor fuel to alcohol, this whole area would quickly have a great money-crop of potatoes for the distillery.

### Population

The population of this region is good. It may easily be said to be the best. Sociologists are generally of the opinion that mixed races are

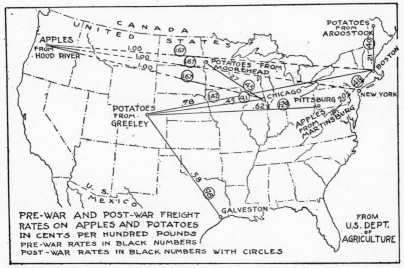

FIG. 183 — This map shows the dependence of inland producing-centers on freight rates which tend to shut them out of many distant markets.

the best, especially if the mixture is of North European stock. On both counts, the wheat region ranks high. In the Canadian part of the wheat region the matrix is East Canadian, largely British, but partly French. Mixed with this is the recent immigration. About one-third were from the American Middle West, one-third from the United Kingdom, one-third from widely scattered (chiefly northern and central) European countries. Winnipeg bookstores have on sale forty-eight translations of the Bible.

The American part of this region has in most sections a Yankee matrix, but more Scandinavian and Teutonic blood than the Canadian section. A survey of a township in south central Minnesota at the very

[18] In Germany the pre-war price-levels gave the potato an indefinite outlet as stock food and distillery material. (See Smith, J. Russell, *Industrial and Commercial Geography*.)

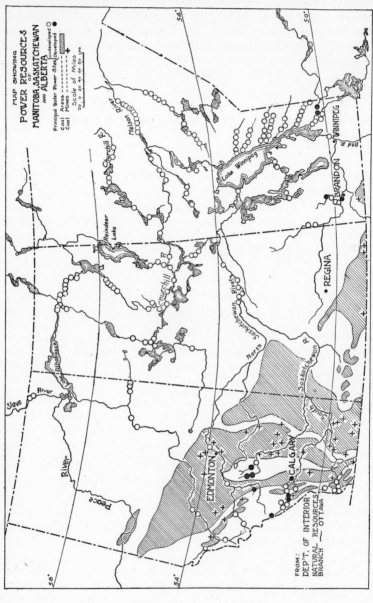

FIG. 184 — A quarter of this coal would change the fate of any European country if the next century is to be like the last.

southern edge of the region showed in 1910: 30.8% German; 24.2% Norwegian; 21.3% mixed; 11% American; 5.8% English; 3.7% Irish; 2.9% Swedish. This particular township had far less Swedish than many other parts of North Dakota, South Dakota and Minnesota. Witness the Iowa College yell at football games with Minnesota in the '90's — " Ole, Ole, Ole, Ah', Better go back to Minnesotah'." Ole is the best known, almost the type Swedish name.

If the verdict of history is worth anything, the people of the Spring Wheat Country will achieve. If they do not, we should consider climate, resources and location carefully for the explanation.

## Cities and Manufacturing

The Northern Wheat Region is not a land of cities, save those needed for its own trade. It is too new. Perhaps it is not destined to be a land of cities. Such cities as it has show well the influence of the small, local advantage in a wide area where every place has about the same possibility as every other of becoming a city.

Minneapolis and St. Paul [19] are the largest cities anywhere near this region, because Minneapolis, at the falls of the Mississippi, has the advantage of water-power; and St. Paul, a few miles below, was at the head of navigation and had steamboat service in the pre-railroad days. Sioux Falls, with about 25,000 people, is South Dakota's largest city. It was started by water-power advantage, as its name indicates. Fargo, the largest city of North Dakota, is like Omaha in being on the west side of a river that naturally stopped travel in the early days. It was the natural place for a road center and later a railroad center. Bismarck, North Dakota, was a railroad terminal point long enough to get an advantage over neighboring bits of prairie. Grand Forks, North Dakota, was for a time head of the steamboat service which once worked on the Red River.

Minneapolis and St. Paul have an enormous mercantile business with the whole territory lying between Lake Superior and the Rocky Mountains and reaching well into northern Iowa — the " Bread Basket of the World," they call it. These cities, but seven miles apart, had a period of delightful and bombastic rivalry in the boom decade of the '80's. Streets were being laid out rapidly across the prairies, new houses were going up, newcomers arriving by every train, and each town had the great pleasure of boasting of its growth and telling how it was beating the other town. So earnest was the desire for the winning record of numbers that in the United States Census of 1890 the enumerators, being residents of their respective towns, gave way to the boom fever and padded

[19] It is but a short time ago that the advance of dairying pushed the boundary of the North Central Dairy Region north of Minneapolis and St. Paul. These cities had their origin and have their life as trading center, grain market and milling center for the Spring Wheat Region. Therefore I present them in this chapter.

the returns to such an extent that the United States Government had to send in outside enumerators to retake the census. The rivalry of this period is well indicated by an oft-told story to the effect that one Sunday evening a Minneapolis minister started his sermon by saying, " I take my text this evening from St. Paul," whereupon the congregation rose en masse and filed out of the church, refusing to listen to any such doctrine.

The rivalry is now over. The leadership is settled by the greater growth of Minneapolis and the cities now speak of themselves as the " Twin Cities." [20] St. Paul has the state capitol, but Minneapolis has the splendid state university and has become the head of navigation because of a government dam and locks. Minneapolis also has the waterfalls of St. Anthony, which make power. This has given the city a wonderful sky-line of flour mills [21] and made it the greatest flour-milling center of the world. In 1919 flour and grist-mill products furnished nearly half of $491,000,000.00 worth of manufactures. The industries next in importance were foundry and machine-shops, $34,000,000.00; printing and publishing, $13,000,000.00; car-shops and repairs, $12,-000,000.00; bread and bakery products, $12,000,000.00, showing that the city has not yet attained the stage of extensive manufacture for export beyond the limits of its region. Diversified manufactures are, however, on the increase. It is a natural center for making agricultural machinery and has an important knit-goods production.

The absence of other cities in the American part of the Spring Wheat Region is shown by a combined population of less than 50,000 in Grand Forks and Fargo, metropolises of the Red River Valley. The Canadian

[20] Flashes of the old fighting spirit sometimes disturb even the calm of " Twin-City " existence. Outsiders still chuckle at the pass made by the Minneapolis business man, when the Chambers of Commerce met at a Twin-City banquet to bury the hatchet once for all. He rehearsed the essential unity of Minneapolis and St. Paul and concluded: " Even the names of these cities might to advantage be combined. I would suggest Minnehaha: ' Minne ' for Minneapolis and ' Ha! Ha! ' for St. Paul."

[21] W. L. George, the British novelist, says of these mills: " It was at Minneapolis, at the Washburn-Crosby Mills, that I rediscovered the magnificence of the Middle West. Here again is the immense swiftness of modern industry, not bloody this time, but dainty. The flour-mills are like drawing-rooms, lightly powdered as befits. For the first time in my life, I saw a factory with parquet floors. There is a fascination in these things, the fascination of uniform movement. You watch the grain from the elevator on to the belt, then to the grinder, to the shaking-sieves, to the tests which exhibit purity, to the hoppers, which humanly discharge just as much as the sack will hold. The sack falls into a truck, and it is gone. There is something lovely in these great works. They are deserts, void of men. Nothing is handled that can possibly be seized by fingers of steel. There is solitude and activity; there is nothing there save iron and lumber, in the midst of which sits some secret invisible soul. Somehow I feel that in these great plants I see before me the future of the world, a world where the machine will be a servant shepherded by new men and women, in raiment which they no longer need to soil, and who will with polished finger-nails touch buttons that convey intelligent messages. The great plants of the Middle West seem to me to sublimate human intelligence and to promise a time when mankind will be free from sweat." He forgets that sweat is essential to health.

cities other than Winnipeg are provincial capitals (made by politics), local distributing centers and centers for the collection of grain and live-stock, with here and there a little subsistence manufacturing.

Winnipeg is properly called the Chicago of Canada. It started at the junction of canoe-routes on the Red River and Assiniboine. With the coming of railroads it was found to have an advantage not unlike that of Chicago. It is situated virtually at the south end of Lake Winnipeg, which is almost as long as Lake Michigan, and to the north reaches into the rough woods beyond the limits of agriculture. Any railroad going to the West must pass around Lake Winnipeg as rail-

FIG. 185 — Freight yards in Winnipeg, the world's greatest primary grain market. (Courtesy Natural Resources Intelligence Service, Ottawa.)

roads do around Lake Michigan. Winnipeg (pop. 179,000) is the center of twenty-seven converging railroad lines. (The Twin Cities have twenty-three.) Winnipeg long since surpassed Chicago as the world's greatest grain market. The freight-yards, full of box-cars in the rush season, cover an astounding expanse of flat land. She has the largest stock-yards in Canada and like Chicago has many mail-order houses sending packages to the isolated farm-houses.

The populations of the largest cities in the Canadian section other than Winnipeg (Calgary, 63,000; Edmonton, 58,000; Regina, 34,000) rank them in population with the minor manufacturing cities of Massachusetts.

What will be the future of manufacturing in this region, which is yet so young? To the east and the northeast there is much water-power (Fig. 184). Winnipeg, with a municipally operated water-power plant selling power at cost, claims to have the cheapest power in the world, and 5000 families cooking with electricity. The coal-field underlying the western part of this region is one of the richest in the world. If it had been possessed this past hundred years by Italy, France or Japan, the course of world history might have been changed. Near the town of Macoun, Sask., on the east side of Souris River, longitude $103\frac{1}{2}°$ W., and between 49° and 50° north latitude, there is perhaps a world's record for coal. Here a drill found a hundred feet of coal in the first thousand feet of depth.

It is impossible to predict the result of these power resources in the

FIG. 186 — A street in Winnipeg, the Chicago of Canada, which resembles its name-sake. (Courtesy Dept. Immigration & Colonization, Ottawa.)

middle of the continent. The distance to other well-established centers of manufacturing is great and the freight-rate must be high. Therefore it is difficult to see why this region should import after a few decades, shoes, stockings, underwear, plows, or many other standard manufactures. Mr. Ford's idea, mentioned in the chapter on the Corn Belt, of establishing factories for the part-time employment of farmers, finds even a greater function in this land of longer winter.

Whether the inland location can support extensive populations manufacturing goods for export is a question that can only be answered by the coming decades. It has resources of food and fuel, but it has the disadvantages of a winter that is too cold and a location that is far removed from the advantages of the ship. The ship question has been in all Canadian minds for years. It is still unsettled. The Hudson Bay Route is a ray of hope on the commercial horizon. Because of the narrowing longitude of high latitudes, the distance from Port Churchill on Hudson Bay to Liverpool is less than the distance from New York to Liverpool. The distance by rail from Edmonton to Port Churchill will be 400 miles less than to Port Arthur on Lake Superior. It is estimated

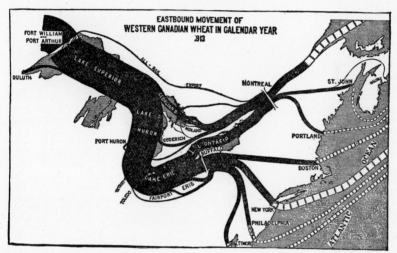

EASTBOUND MOVEMENT OF
WESTERN CANADIAN WHEAT IN CALENDAR YEAR
.913

FIG. 187 — There has not been much change in proportions since this map was made. From *The Story of Wheat,* Butler.

that the rail and ship route via Hudson Bay will save the West Canada grain-grower six or seven cents per bushel on his wheat — quite a tidy sum if half the crop went that way.

Every Canadian administration and every Canadian opposition party since 1908 has promised to build that railway to Port Churchill. Instead of setting to work they have a new investigation and hear testimony every little while. There is quite a library of it by now, all proving that the route can work and that it cannot work. The factor of uncertainty is the ice.

There seem to be two certainties: one that its rivalry will almost or quite bankrupt the great Canadian Pacific Railway by diverting half its freight, and the other that the Canadian plainsman is bound to have it. In 1924 it was reported to be complete to within 220 miles of Port Churchill, but it has been a work on which vacation periods exceed those of the bonanza wheat-grower.

Fig. 188 — The lake freighter with many hatches to receive ore from many chutes. Note the freight train. (Courtesy United States Steel Corporation.)

## CHAPTER XX

### THE UPPER LAKE REGION — A LAND OF EXPLOITATION AND RAW MATERIAL

#### Glaciation, Soil and Surface

SUPPOSE that some one should cut down a big tree six inches below the surface of the earth and fill the hole with dirt and take away every vestige of the tree. Suppose that afterwards a forester should come and excavate the roots. It would be a simple matter for him to tell how much earth had been filled in where the tree had been. By examining its roots the forester could tell the age and size of the tree, and what kind of tree had been there.

By a similar process of interpreting the signs, the geologist can tell us that the region of the Upper Lakes, that is, eastern Minnesota, northern Wisconsin, the upper peninsula of Michigan and the northern part of the lower peninsula of Michigan, has been through the following processes in its making. Long ago mountains were there, mountains as high as the Alps and Rockies, perhaps even higher. These were worn down to an almost level plain where hills of harder rock were left sticking up here and there.[1] These mountain roots of old, hard, twisted, bent and broken rocks were loded, here and there, with rich deposits of iron and copper. Then the whole area was submerged for a long time beneath

[1] Only a little of the land is more than 1600 feet above sea level now.

366

the sea. Sandstones and limestones were spread over it. Then, millions of years ago, it was raised up and these newer rocks were partly worn away. One particular layer of stone, the one over which the Niagara River pours, hence called the Niagara Cuesta, has been traced by geologists from New York, through the Lake Region and on to Iowa. It lies on top of the old sawed-off mountain roots above mentioned.

Next came the continental glacier, benefactor in the Corn Belt, destroyer in the Upper Lake Region. In some places it scraped bare the old hard rocks of the ancient mountain roots. On far too many acres they are still bare of that few feet of earth that permits the land surface to be the home of plants and the sustainer of man. The digging glacier gouged out the softer rocks, leaving holes, often now filled with water — lakes. Most unfortunately, iron deposits were softer than the rocks in which they lay, and billions of tons of good iron ore were scooped up, scattered uselessly over a hundred counties to the southward. In scattering its scrapings the glacier left rock piles, piles of gravel, stretches of sand,[2] stretches of sandy loam and of clay. Hence even in a small area the soils sometimes exist in greatest variety.

Glacial dumpings dammed up stream valleys, making lakes. Nowhere in the world are lakes so numerous. Minnesota has 11,000; Wisconsin, 2000; Michigan, 4000; most of them being in this region which we call the Upper Lake Region. Many depressions were not quite deep enough to become lakes, and remained swamps — hummocky swamps with cedar trees in them; flat swamps with tamarack trees; weedy-looking swamps with cranberries; and many other kinds of swamps, besides partly filled lakes, called "muskegs," where the newly made muck is covered with bushes and grass. Some of the muskegs are filled with peat, in which trees do not grow.

Much of the northern peninsula of Michigan was covered to a depth of more than three hundred feet with scrapings from farther north, and its surface is often an outwash plain, suitable for pine, but poor for farming.

The Upper Lake Region is bounded on the west and south by transition to three regions where farming can occupy most of the land. Its northern boundary as shown is an arbitrary line in a vast area of rock, wood and water (see Chapter XXII), which ends in cliff along the shore of Lakes Superior and Huron (Fig. 167).

It would be hard to find a greater contrast between two regions than that between this Upper Lake Region and its neighbor, the Spring Wheat Country, or its next neighbor but one, the Corn Belt. It is no wonder that the waves of migrating farmers drove past it to the prairies of Illinois, Iowa, Kansas, Nebraska, Minnesota and Dakota. It is also no

[2] A locality on the Wisconsin-Michigan boundary has the suggestive name, "Lac Vieux Desert" — Old Lake Desert.

wonder that even yet the maps of agricultural production show it to be a land that figures little in agriculture.

## Lumber — The First Exploitation

This region has more rain than the Spring Wheat territory. The lakes and swamps put moisture in the air, so that the whole of it was forested, save for areas of muskeg and bare rock. The varying soils gave a forest of great variety —chiefly white p i n e, spruce, hemlock and maple. The fall of snow is heavy. Snow piles up from November to March as it does in the Northeastern Highlands, and it was easy to move the logs. The lumber industry moved hither from New England, New York, and Pennsylvania — lumbermen, chopping - camp, logging methods, log-drive

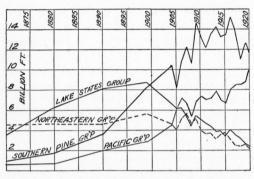

FIG. 189 — The handwriting on the wall. These figures of lumber cut are in *quantity*.

and all. Statistics show us that exploitation has marked our short possession of this continent. First Michigan led in lumber production. Then Wisconsin led. Then Minnesota led. Then the lumbermen flitted to the South. In 1904 Michigan cut only half as much lumber as was cut in 1890. In 1910 she cut half as much as in 1900 and in 1920 half as much as in 1910; and the state is now a heavy lumber importer, having dropped from first place in 1890 to sixteenth place in 1920. Wisconsin's decline has been almost as rapid, and Minnesota has followed suit.

In 1920 Michigan began a popular movement to save Isle Royal in Lake Superior, an island which was forty miles long and ten miles wide. Isle Royal was said to contain the only piece of virgin wilderness in the North Central States. Moose and caribou still roamed there, but a lumber company was about to begin on it.

It would not be bad if the lumbermen had left what they could not use, but the fire followed them and kept on coming. It seems that in humid climates, forests can, in the course of centuries, make a soil and extend themselves over bare rock. When a dead tree falls outward on bare rock surface a mass of wind-blown leaves and trash catches in its reclining top. In time the trash decays and short-lived weeds take root from wind-blown seed. They add to the accumulation. Little trees take root and die. Later they live and grow to bush size. Meanwhile more trash collects around them and an extension of earth and a crop of trees spreads across the erstwhile bare stones.[3] In the course of thousands of years this has happened over large areas of otherwise bare stone. A thousand years of building are as but a day — a day of destruction by fire.

Professor Frank Williams, of the University of Pennsylvania, tells me that he has done much geological " cruising " for lumber companies in northern Minnesota. He traversed the section lines, advising the companies as to the possible mineral content of their lands, whether it was worth keeping or should be abandoned to save paying taxes. For hours at at time he walked over smooth, bare, gently rounded knolls of granite smoothed off by the continental glaciers. Swamps often filled the depressions between them. But here and there, sitting on the smooth granite, was a telltale stump left by the lumberman. Repeated fires had killed the small growth and all new growth and burned up most of the sponge-like vegetable soil. The digging rain-drops and wind had done the rest. The lumberman had found a fine stand of timber and a producing forest — the ten or twenty years of fire had made it bald knobs of granite, more sterile than Sahara.

Professor Carl Sauer, late of the University of Michigan, speaking of the sand-pine lands of the upper part of the lower peninsula, reports that repeated fires have so eaten the humus out of the soil that nothing but the jack-pine, the poorest of timber trees, will grow. He estimates that it will take five hundred undisturbed years for nature to restore the soil, and produce a pine forest like that which was so recklessly lumbered in the '80's and '90's.

The slow process of restoration had begun when the states got possession of some land through default of taxes. There are also some small national forests, but the fire still runs over most of the area and reconstruction is far below destruction. The forest fire here is sometimes a sweep of death; scores of villages and hundreds of people have been burned. In 1908 one Wisconsin fire burned two thousand square miles and destroyed young trees that would have been worth scores of millions in a few score years.

### Mining — The Second Exploitation

In the chance shufflings of geology nature seems to have handed her highest cards to the Upper Lake Region. On the south shore of Lake Superior were large deposits of copper, pure copper, not merely ore. The deposits were worked before the white man came and they made Michigan the leading copper-producing state for many years before it was surpassed by Montana in 1887. Inasmuch as this was the greatest mining industry for a time, almost the only mining industry of the state, the Michigan School of Mines was located near by at Houghton. Some of these mines

---

[3] Observation in humid forests will show many small examples of this process on the flat tops of large stones.

have now reached such a depth that the miners actually travel more than a mile in going from the outlet to their work in the mines. This fact indicates the approach of the end. Meanwhile, Montana has passed Michigan in copper production, and in turn has been surpassed by Arizona.

The stores of iron were much more extensive than the copper, and, like the copper, the richest in the world. Both to the north and to the south of the western end of Lake Superior, there are ranges of hills containing great solid masses of iron ore. It is not only the richest in the world,

FIG. 190 — Duluth harbor. Ore dock with lake steamer loading at left dock. Grain elevator in distance. (Courtesy United States Steel Corporation.)

but the most easily mined. The solid masses are near the surface, and so soft that a steam-shovel can scoop up the ore, which it drops into a freight car to be whisked away to the lake steamer beside the wharf at Duluth, Superior, Ashland or Marquette. It is no wonder that the iron mines of the Pittsburgh District and the Champlain District and many less important locations in the United States have shut down for a time, while the furnaces of Buffalo, Pittsburgh and Chicago and all the region between are fed exclusively by the mines of Lake Superior. Even the furnaces of the Schuylkill Valley and Harrisburg are sometimes supplied in part from this source, although most of the ore used east of the Alleghenies and north of the Potomac is imported.

The chief population [4] of the region is found in the series of towns

[4] " A school principal in New Duluth, near Duluth, analyzed his three hundred and thirty children as Slovene, 49; Italian, 47; Serbian, 39; American, 37; Polish, 30; Austrian, 22; Swedish, 22; Croatian, 20; colored, 9 (it is instructive to note that he did not include these among the ' Americans '); Finnish, 7; Scotch, 6; Slav unspecified, 5; German, French, Bohemian and Jewish, 4 each; Rumanian, Norwegian, Irish, Ukrainian and Greek, 2 each; Russian and English, 1 each — 60% of them from Southern and Eastern Europe." (From *The Nation*, May 30, 1923.)

clustered around the iron mines. Since the iron mines are owned by great absentee corporations and embrace most of the property of the locality, the people of these counties succeed in saddling most of the taxes upon the foreign corporation. One sees sometimes very odd contrasts — there will be a big, magnificent high school and a beautifully kept highway, with uniformed workmen caring for the road, and then, at the next moment, as you make a little turn, a deer may dash across the road and vanish in the scrubby wilderness, which should be a forest but is not.

### Cities

The chief cities of this region are the ports on Lake Superior — Duluth (pop. 98,000), Superior (39,000), Ashland (11,000), Marquette

FIG. 191 — Grain elevators and flour mills, Fort William. (Courtesy Natural Resources Intelligence Service, Ottawa.)

(12,000), and Sault Ste. Marie (12,000), and on the Canadian side, Port Arthur (14,000), and Fort William (20,000). Duluth and Superior, economically one city like New York and Brooklyn, are the first port of the world for iron ore export and coal import.

Port Arthur and Fort William have been the chief outlets for wheat from Western Canada. A small portion sent from time to time by way of Duluth has been sold to American millers. Duluth is the chief outlet for the wheat of the American part of the region. Duluth and its smaller neighbors also handle the export of iron and such lumber as still goes eastward.

In theory these cities should be large because they handle the trade of an extensive territory. One thinks of Chicago and San Francisco. Instead, these cities remain small because primarily, they have been points of *transfer* rather than centers of *distribution*. The centers of distribution are on the edge of a productive plain. Hundreds of thousands of shipments of goods are sent into this plain over the many railroads which meet at distributing centers such as the Twin Cities and Winnipeg.

Through shipments of goods between these distributing centers and the East are transferred from boat to rail, or rail to boat, at Port Arthur, Fort William, Duluth, but the actual distribution takes place at the big city nearer to the people. There is no reason for the twenty railroad lines of Winnipeg to run their lines on through the unproductive woods to Port Arthur, or for the twenty railroad lines of Minneapolis and St. Paul to run their twenty lines through the unproductive woods to Duluth, so these ports have remained but little more than ports for distributing centers. They hold records for handling vast quantities of material and records for speed. Grain is poured from elevator to ship.

FIG. 192 — Potatoes in bloom, clover, oats and evergreens on the rolling glaciated land. A northern landscape. Cass Lake, Minn. (Courtesy Great Northern Railway.)

Ore is dumped from the freight-car to the ore-pocket on the dock, and from the ore-pocket to the ship below. There is a basis for the statement that these cities are funnels through which great quantities of traffic pour. The urge to speed is great because a year's work must be done in the seven months during which ice does not lock the harbors.

These Upper Lake ports tend to be storage places for grain. Only about 20% of the crop can get down to Montreal before frost. The rest must be carried down the next spring and summer, a point in which the Great Lakes route is not so much better than the Hudson Bay route. The operator of a grain-ship tries to get his vessel at the Upper Lake port the last thing in the autumn so that she may be loaded with grain and thus through the winter earn a little as a storage warehouse and be ready to sail away in the spring at the first hour that the harbor ice-breaker can let her get through the ice cakes to the open lake. The lake traffic opens in the spring with a great rush. Sixty vessels, some of them holding 14,000 tons of grain, sail from Fort William and Port Arthur at the opening of navigation. Two abreast, they go in regular procession, as though on parade, every captain doing his utmost to make a quick journey to the lower lake and to get to the dock ahead of his rival.

Duluth has an iron industry. It is the natural site for the production of iron destined for points west. The returning ore-boat carries coal very cheaply, and I can see no reason why the west end of Lake Superior should not have a large iron industry in the course of a few decades.

### The Farmer — The Third Exploitation

Some counties in this region have twenty, forty, even sixty per cent of their area covered with bare rock, swamp and lake. Scattered around among these are patches of arable soil, that is to say, arable after the

FIG. 193 — The light that failed. The land would not support the family.
(Courtesy Wisconsin Dept. Agr.)

stumps and perhaps some stones have been removed and perhaps some ditches have been put in to drain it. These tracts of arable land are of all shapes and sizes. As previously explained, the soils are of great variety. Some of them look good, and are. Some of them look good and are not. Thereby hangs the tale of many a bankrupt settler who tried to make a home where a living could not be made. Parts of the sand plain of the upper peninsula of Michigan have been called " a fire-blasted wilderness that sends the settler's wife to the insane asylum."

In the enthusiasm for development which is so strong in America the states having parts of their area in this territory have created immigration bureaus whose task it was to get settlers. A state bulletin showing nice pictures of barns, homesteads, cattle and crops looked good to the land-hungry man of Norway, England or New York, or even of Illinois, especially when the low price of the land was considered. Land companies, getting cut-over tracts, have sold forty-acre units to settlers for a small cash payment, and required no further payments and no interest for three or five years. This was fine for the man who succeeded, but it tempted the man destined to failure to hang on for a heartbreaking length of time and then be forced to abandon his house and improvements to the land company. The company then had an " improved farm " to sell.

Settlement here required exact knowledge of the locality and considerable capital — two things that the frontiersman usually lacks. Here is one case in America where it was the man who got exploited more than the land. Upon the average it is probably true that most of the farmers who have gone into this territory would have gained more material possessions for the same effort if they had bought the cheap lands of the North Atlantic Coast Plain, some parts of the Northern Piedmont, of the more wholesome sections of the Cotton Belt. But thousands of them have gone in and have succeeded, and as demand for agricultural produce increases more will follow. In this climate men are hardy and vigorous.

The season is short. In some places it does not exceed one hundred growing days, and summer frosts are much too common, especially on flat ground. The summers are especially cool in the peninsula lying between cold Lake Superior, the tip of cold Lake Huron and the tip of cool Lake Michigan. Perhaps it earned the name of " Michigan's Ice Box." Snow on the ground and ice on stream and lake get two or three feet thick every winter. Strawberries do not ripen here until August, and along the eastern shore of Lake Superior the July temperature of 60° F. is as cool as southern Norway — a very proper place for Scandinavians.

Upon the whole, the agriculture of this region has a clearly marked tendency toward live-stock, especially the dairy farm, and above all, the potato, for which its cool, moist summer gives conditions that are almost ideal. As in Maine, many of the farmers have a second job for winter — in mine, woods or town.

### The Future

In value and weight the most conspicuous thing about this region in the ensuing decades will be the millions of tons of iron-ore from the hustling mining-towns. In a few generations most of the mines will be empty holes, unvisited save by the curious. In that day the mining-towns may shift over to manufacturing, using electric power for which the lakes of this upland region are so helpful. There is also much Canadian water-power within present transmission distance.

Most of this region should be at once protected from fire. This will make it automatically a forest in most places. In others, replanting is necessary. The agriculture here can be increased by intensification and by reclaiming land from water, stump and stone.

The efficient utilization of this region must make it a sea of forest, scattered with islands of farms and islands of water — its thousands of lakes. These are already a favored summer pleasure and vacation ground. Fishing, canoeing, sailing, swimming, sitting on the cool veranda in the presence of a beautiful landscape of lake, hill and forest is a beneficial way for any industrious·person to spend a part of the year, if one happens to like it. In a continent of increasing population this region should have steadily increasing use as a vacation land.

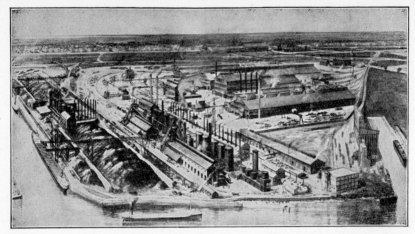

Fig. 194 — A Lake Shore steel works. From left to right, artificial harbor and ore boat, ore storage, blast furnaces, rolling mills, railroad carrying product away. (Courtesy International Harvester Co.)

## CHAPTER XXI

### LOWER LAKE REGION

FACTORIES — factories with boats and trains bringing crude raw materials — of such is the Lower Lake Region. Iron ore, pig-iron, steel, coal, coke, cement, sand, gravel, lumber, rubber, cotton, wheat, corn, oats, flaxseed, cattle and hogs — these are the things that glide and dump, bellow and squeal, make dust, smoke, tonnage, jobs and profits in this region of cities; cities which the lakes have created.

On the shores of the lakes are focus points of traffic. Water freight-rates of lake steamers are cheaper than land freight-rates of railroads.[1] Therefore, traffic seeks the lakes where it can flow more cheaply in boats. Cities — cities with great advantage of location — have risen at lake-shore points which command the trade of interior areas. These areas are rich. They have made lake cities prosperous. At the ends of Lake Erie, Buffalo commands the east and Toledo the west. At Cleveland the rich and heavy tonnage of the Appalachian coal and iron region connects with Lake Erie, the most used of inland waterways. Where Lake Superior reaches out its ports toward the rolling grain-fields of the Spring Wheat Region, we find Duluth, Port Arthur, Fort William. Greatest of all,

[1] In July 1924, the railroad rate on grain from Chicago to Buffalo was $.19½ per hundredweight. By boat it had ranged since May from $.0225 to $.02575. The year before the boat rate had been $.06, because of competition for space. The lake boats would be used much more than they are but for the determined and skillful opposition of the railroads by their refusal to co-operate, and in other ways.

376

Chicago stands where Lake Michigan carries the lake steamer farthest into the rich central region of farms — the region of corn, oats, wheat, hay, hogs, cattle, and the need for manufactured goods (Fig. 167).

The Great Lakes favor traffic in a wonderful manner. Four of them are now one navigation unit. Only Lake Ontario is cut off by Niagara Falls from the others. The low falls at Sault Ste. Marie once isolated Lake Superior, but now the United States Government and the Canadian Government are friendly rivals in offering free passage to ships through the canals, which have been built at an expense of more than $30,000,000. Michigan and Huron are on the same level, with a wide channel between them. Dredging and blasting have enabled the passage of steamers from Lake Huron through the ledges into Lake St. Clair and on to Lake Erie without canals or locks.

Canals, locks and artificial channels of these four lakes are limited to a depth of twenty feet. But the standard freight-boat of the lakes is 600 feet long and will carry over this rather shallow depth 475,000 bushels of wheat, 760,000 bushels of oats, 10,000 tons of ore and sometimes even greater quantities.

These lake steamers [2] are the most industrious of boats. Quick loading and unloading makes them without rivals in the percentage of time during which they actually transport cargoes. At Lake Superior ports 10,000 tons of ore thud and rumble into a boat in less than two hours. At the other end of the journey the ore has been unloaded in five hours. Such speed is possible because the boat has thirty-five continuous hatches. When they are all opened the boat is little more than an open barge with boxes perched fore and aft, the one for the crew, the other for the machinery. Clam-shell buckets enfolding ten tons at a scoop work along almost the whole length of the vessel. Hence the great speed of ore unloading.

Coal for the return cargo is loaded into the ore-boat at the rate of a thousand tons an hour by a great machine which picks up freight-cars, one after another, and dumps their contents into the ship. It makes one think of the grocer with scoop and funnel transferring sugar from bin to bag.

Aided by these most efficient freighters the heavy industries of the surrounding regions have sent over the Great Lakes so much traffic that the St. Clair River has well been called the greatest commercial artery in the world. It carries several times as much traffic as the Suez Canal, by weight.[3] Freight traffic figures show the speed of manufacturing development not only in this region but also in the United States, for

---

[2] On June 30, 1923, there were 2,286,000 gross tons of American shipping on the Great Lakes. Of this the Standard Oil Group owned 586,000 tons and the United States Steel Corporation 237,000 tons.

[3] By *values* the comparison of ore and coal of the Lakes with tea, rubber, silk, seeds and spices of Suez tells a different story.

the Lakes serve a national trade.   In 1889 the total traffic of the lakes [4]
was estimated at 25,000,000 tons.   In 1916 it was 125,000,000 tons.
In 1920 it was 111,000,000 tons.   Lake traffic fluctuates greatly.   This
is because iron ore is by far the greatest single factor in lake freights.
The iron industry lives continuously in chills and fever, the fever of boom
and the chill of depression.   For example, the Lake Superior district
mined sixty-four million tons of ore in 1916, fifty-eight million in 1920,
and twenty-two million in 1921.   Accordingly, the Soo Canal carried

FIG. 195 — Dumping carloads of coal into a lake steamer in Cuyahoga River,
Cleveland.   (Courtesy Cleveland Chamber of Commerce.)

92,000,000 tons of freight in 1916 when munitions for the World War
called for steel without limit, and only 49,000,000 tons in 1921 when
industry slackened.   Then the traffic of the Soo Canal rose to 66,000,000
tons in 1922.

The passenger traffic of the lakes is carried in the finest fresh-water
boats in the world.   They rival ocean steamers in excellence.   The lake
shores also furnish recreation in many beaches and summer resorts.

[4] Department of Commerce, Miscellaneous Series 119, *Inland Water Transportation in the United States.*

## The Automobile Industry

The age of machinery which began about the time of the American Declaration of Independence maintains its revolutionary influence in the industrial world by a process of continuous mechanical improvement. This progress has been marked by a few machines of especial importance, each of which has made or made over man's affairs in a particular section of the earth's surface. Thus, cotton-spinning and weaving machinery made England a manufacturing nation. Because of the cotton gin the South re-embraced slavery and produced cotton. In the first quarter of this century, the automobile, like an industrial rocket, made Detroit increase its population four-fold; [5] Lansing, four-fold; Flint, eight-fold; and scores of Michigan towns have shared this growth and prosperity. The automobile area also includes Toledo, Cleveland, and Akron, the tire center. The speed of the automobile conquest is evidenced by the manufacture of 2,000,000 horse-drawn carriages in 1909 and 10,000 in 1923; 80,000 automobiles in 1909 and 4,000,000 in 1923.

The Lower Lake Region, with its cheap lake transportation and its supplies of heavy metal and wood, is a natural place for this industry. In addition to its cheap lake transportation to bring raw materials, it also has the best of railway transportation, for it is threaded by the various railways connecting Chicago with Philadelphia, New York, Boston, Montreal and other population centers. This region is also close to the center of population on the American continent. For these reasons it was the center of the carriage manufacturing before the automobile came. It was very natural that the carriage center should take over the successor of the carriage, the automobile.

It is probably an accident that made Detroit the center rather than Toledo or Cleveland or another city. Detroit happened to have the factory of Mr. Henry Ford, who most effectively applied cheap mass production to the automobile. He secured cheapness and efficiency to an

---

[5] Detroit alone does not tell the tale. In ten years' time the two suburbs of Highland Park and Hamtramck increased their population from 7000 to 92,000. Most of the cities of the southern peninsula of Michigan were sharing in the prosperity by making some of the many things that are assembled in the process of making the completed automobile.

Between 1910 and 1920 the urban population of Michigan increased from 47% to 61.1%. In the same period the urban population of Nebraska increased from 29% to 31.3%.

MICHIGAN

| Year | Total rural population (thousands) | Per cent of population urban |
|------|------------------------------------|------------------------------|
| 1900 | 1,468 | 39.3% |
| 1910 | 1,483 | 47.2% |
| 1920 | 1,426 | 61.1% |

The lure of high wages in automobile factories caused many thousand farms to be abandoned in Michigan alone in a short time after the slump in farm prices in 1921.

almost unimagined degree by the use of specialization and the inter-
changeable part. Time was when machines were individuals, as individual
as men, each part made to fit its particular fellows. Then by standardization we began to make wheels, axles, bolts, nuts, bodies, engines all
alike so each one would fit any machine of the same model. Specialization permitted machines to turn out these standardized parts in indefinite
quantities at low cost. This made a world market for machinery. Because of the advent of the cheap standardized part the reaper-owner or

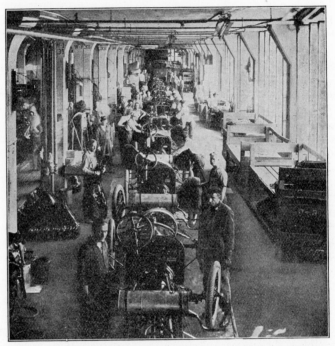

FIG. 196 — That endless procession of Ford cars, growing piece by
piece as they go. (Courtesy Ford Motor Co.)

the plow-owner or the automobile-owner can rush to the agency in
Argentina, Australia, Arizona, or Alaska, call for part number so and
so, and get it. He takes out the old part, sticks in the new one, cranks
up the machine or clucks to his horses and away he goes. The art of
repairing machinery has almost disappeared through the simplicity of
sticking in a new part. The cheap, standardized machine is not a particularly good machine but it is a wonder for the money. This can easily
be proved by comparing cost and possibility of performance by a Ford
car and by old Dobbin. It has been well said that there are about ten

million farmers in the United States who cannot afford to be without automobiles, now that standardization has made them so cheap.

The wonder of speedy production in the Ford plant is one of the oft-told tales. The axles and running gear of the machine are placed on a belt conveyor. Another skeleton car follows, and many others in endless succession. The conveyor carries them forward between two rows of workmen each standing in his place and each repeating continually his small part of the speedy and endless performance. Piece after piece appears from the sides or from above, is grabbed by the appropriate man and bolted into place. An engine swings out on a little crane and drops upon the moving frame. It is bolted on. A gasoline tank follows, then a seat, and this and that and the other piece, until in very few minutes indeed a car — a Ford — rolls off on its own wheels. You look back at the long belt, full of other cars each going through the various stages of completion. So rapid is this process and so cheap the product that the plant turns out 6000 cars a day.

The Ford plant has had an output as follows: 1903–04, 1700 cars; 1908–09, 106,000; 1912–13, 181,000; 1915–16, 534,000; 1920, 1,074,000. In 1923, the Ford enterprises produced 2,200,000 automobiles, trucks, and tractors — 775,000 more than in any previous year.[6] There is basis for the joke about the man who applied for a position as an experienced mechanic, because he had worked in a Ford plant for four years. "What did you do?" he was asked. "I put on bolt No. 47."

The result of standardization and specialization on cost of product is well known. What its monotony will do to man by reducing his ingenuity and leaving his capacities unused is not yet known. This universal correlative of manufacturing is one of the problems of our age. Experiments seem to show that a chimpanzee or an ourang-outang could learn to do many of the jobs of a modern factory, but spiritually he would not stand for it.

Detroit grew like a mining town after a rich lode is struck and it shared many of the signs of the frontier town, both physical and psychological. Physically there was house shortage and extreme congestion.

Detroit got rich quick. This is a psychological as well as a financial fact. The mechanic who has suddenly become a millionaire and the workman whose wages have been doubled and trebled have an interest-

---

[6] The Ford Company with its unprecedented surpluses has built up a gigantic example of vertical consolidation of industries. It makes most of the things it needs, even down to glass and paint. At River Rouge, a short distance from Detroit, is an iron plant smelting ore dug from Ford's own mines, using coal brought from Ford's own coal-lands in Kentucky and carried from Toledo to River Rouge in Ford's own boats. Ford's steamers carry lumber to Detroit from Mr. Ford's large timber holdings in the Upper Lake Region. Forestry is being applied to the 125,000 acres of coal-lands in Kentucky and also to Ford's other timber-lands. Mr. Ford's railroad, the Detroit, Toledo and Ironton, renders great service by connecting Ford enterprises with each other and with various markets.

ing and a conspicuous psychology.  Publishers say that Detroit is a poor book market.

Detroit also has the mixed and foreign population of the boom-town. Its analysis [7] shows the wide human pull of its prosperity and explains the need of the great efforts that have been made to teach English and to Americanize the population.

The statistics of manufactures show that the growth of Detroit has been chiefly dependent upon the automobile industry and its allies.[8]

Booms swell and swell until something stops them.  This is as true of manufacturing as of orange-growing or vegetable-growing.  The automobile boom grew almost without ceasing until the year 1924.  Then it was found that the United States had automobile plants capable of turning out more cars than the people of the country could buy.  Many factories ran on short time or partly closed and the demand for covering more farms with rows of apartment houses had temporarily ceased. Detroit had apparently caught up with the United States demand and her boom era had closed — unless some other new industry should open for her another gold-mine.

The automobile industry, however, is not a gold-mine.  It is better. It is a permanent industry, promising on the average an enduring prosperity to the automobile workers.  It is probably true that no other industry has a national field for its distribution that is quite so extensive or uniform as that of the automobile industry.  California, Florida,

[7] Detroit population (1919 census) 993,678.  Native white of native parents, 314,000 (less than one-third of total); native white of foreign parentage, 247,000; native white of mixed parentage, 101,000; foreign-born white, 289,000; negro, 41,000. Country of birth of the foreign-born: Canada, 20.4%; Poland, 19.6%; Germany, 10.5%; Russia, 9.4%; England, 5.6%; Italy, 5.6%; Hungary, 4.7%; Austria, 3.7%; Ireland, 2.4%; Scotland, 2.4%.

[8] MANUFACTURES, 1919, VALUE OF PRODUCTS (In Millions)

| | |
|---|---|
| All industries........................ | 1,234 |
| Automobiles, bodies, and parts........ | 550 |
| Foundry and machine-shop........... | 123 |
| Brass, bronze, copper, tin and sheet metal products.......................... | 58 |
| Other metal-working industries....... | 21 |
| Slaughtering and meat-packing........ | 59 |
| Printing and publishing.............. | 27 |
| Bread and bakery.................... | 22 |

Metals 752 (Automobiles 550; Foundry 123; Brass 58; Other 21)

| | Automobile Industry (Million Dollars) | | Value of All Products, (Census) (Autos, Bodies and Parts) | | |
|---|---|---|---|---|---|
| | 1919 | 1914 | 1909 | 1904 | 1899 |
| Detroit............. | 550 | 164 | 59 | 6 | .... |
| Cleveland........... | 154 | 27 | 21 | 4 | .... |
| United States........ | 3,080 | 632 | 249 | 30 | 4 |
| Michigan............ | 1,610 | 398 | 96 | 8 | .... |
| Ohio............... | 379 | 85 | 38 | 6 | .... |

Iowa, Alabama and New England are alike in their dependence upon Detroit. If they can buy, Detroit is prosperous. Conversely, if Detroit buys, they can prosper — witness the complaint of the secretary of a Washington State Apple Growers' Association that hard times in Detroit dropped the purchase of Washington apples (largely used in lunch-boxes) from five cars a day to one car a week.

As sharers in automobile prosperity there is close rivalry for second place between Flint, Michigan, Toledo, Ohio, and Cleveland, Ohio — cities that differ but little in commercial advantages. The automobile business did not happen to develop in these cities as it did in Detroit. However, Cleveland and other automobile cities have grown [9] rapidly enough — much faster than the United States or Ohio. Too much speed does not accord with the social good of any group.

Cleveland and other cities on the south shore of Lake Erie are on the thoroughfare from New York to Chicago and are the natural meeting-place of iron-ore and coal. They have a great variety of manufactures of iron, steel and machinery. Before the automobile absorbed Michigan her cities (especially Grand Rapids and Saginaw) were famed for their furniture mills. This was a second stage of industry that grew up in places that started as sawmill towns. Many of these furniture mills, long established, now operate under the handicap of imported lumber. Others are following the example of the Cadillac Table Company, which is fighting fire and trying systematic forestry on its 70,000 acres of forest land.

## The Chicago District

The growth of the automobile industry in the Detroit-Cleveland district carries no promise that Chicago will be surpassed as the metropolis of the Lower Lake Region. Chicago exceeds Detroit or Cleveland in population because it has more reasons for being a big city.

Chicago's growth began with the beginning of steamboat traffic on the Great Lakes. One steamer reached Fort Dearborn (Chicago) in 1832; four in 1833. By 1848, 400 vessels, including sixty-four steamers, operated out of Chicago in the lake traffic. By 1852 the rate-war had cut the $25.00 passenger ticket from Buffalo down to $6.00 and $8.00. Chicago became the unloading point for settlers bound for the prairies and the shipping point for grain and live-stock bound for the East. It was natural that any railroad to the Northwest had to pass around the lower end of Lake Michigan, and any railroad anywhere near Chicago had to have a terminus at Chicago to receive and deliver freight at the port of commanding location. As the Central West grew she naturally became

[9] POPULATION (*thousands*)

|  | Detroit | Cleveland |
|---|---|---|
| 1900 | 285 | 380 |
| 1910 | 465 | 560 |
| 1920 | 973 | 796 |

the grain center, the meat-packing center, and later the agricultural implement manufacturing center for the wide farming region of the central plains. All this made her the transportation center of North America and the greatest railroad center in the world. The trunk-line systems join Chicago with both oceans and with the Gulf of Mexico. They have their connecting ramifications throughout Canada as well as the United States.

Chicago is the natural economic capital of the Middle West. The question uppermost in the mind of the wheat-grower of Kansas and South Dakota is, " What is the price of wheat in Chicago? " In Iowa and Nebraska it is, " What is the price of hogs in Chicago? " In Illinois, " What is the price of corn and oats in Chicago? " In Wisconsin, " What is the price of butter and cheese in Chicago? " For thousands of farmers in all these regions the event of the year is a trip to Chicago to sell something or buy something or see something — the annual grain show, land show or fat stock show. In a certain sense Chicago may be said to be the city of Iowa or Kansas because it performs in part the city functions of market, supply and factory for those states. Thus Illinois became 67.9% urban (1920), chiefly because of Chicago's population, while Iowa was 36.4% urban, Kansas 34.9% and South Dakota 16%.

After it had grown rich as a distributing center and grain and live-stock market, the refrigerator car (invented 1874) enabled Chicago to slaughter the meat animals which had previously been sent on to Eastern and even to European cities. Chicago, capital of the kingdoms of cattle and swine, quickly extended sovereignty over beef, ham, bacon and lard.[10] Chicago is the greatest food-distributing center of the world.

The Chicago packing plant is a marvel to match the Ford factory. The full utilization of the smallest piece of erstwhile waste has given rise to an almost endless list of side industries — soap, fertilizer, bone-products, oleomargarine.[11]

The great weight and low comparative cost of farm machinery gives an advantage in freight cost to the factory that is close to the market. This industry, keeping step with the strides of agriculture, rapidly passed from western New York, through Ohio and Indiana to the Chicago district, which is now the greatest farm-implement market and producing

[10] The record receipts at Chicago stock-yards for one day are cattle, 49,000; calves, 9000; hogs, 97,000; sheep, 72,000. The packing-plants have seventy million cubic feet of cold-storage space, some of it kept at 15° below zero.

[11] The oleomargarine business seems to have started the development of allied industries until the Chicago packers are often regarded with dread because of the power of monopoly that seems to lie in their hands. As producers of oleomargarine they soon handled butter also. They became owners of creameries and of milk condenseries as a natural next step. As vendors of canned meat it was easy for the packers to become nation-wide owners of canneries. As shippers of chilled meat they had to have refrigerator cars, and they soon offered nation-wide service in supplying refrigerator cars to shippers of perishable produce.

center in the world. These factories with many others demanded steel, so that Gary, Indiana, an economic suburb of Chicago, was selected by the United States Steel Corporation for the site of the largest and most complete steel plant in the world. The coal of Illinois and Indiana mingles with cargoes of Eastern coal, and the lake steamers here unload the ore immediately beside the blast-furnace, which hands its molten iron over to the steel converter. Thence the metal passes to the rolling mills

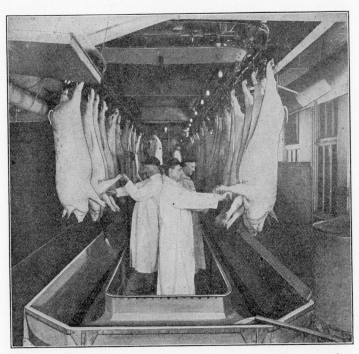

Fig. 197 — The Chicago pig, like the Ford car, rolls past a succession of finishers each with his small task to do. (Courtesy Armour & Co.)

and to the fabricating plants which turn out finished forms in great variety. On the other hand, the blast-furnaces pour their molten slag, often an earth-encumbering refuse, into cement plants that grind out this raw material of universal demand.

For the transfer of freight and the service of its factories, Chicago leads all the cities of the world in the development of belt-lines or railroads that run around the city and shift cars from road to road. They total 1400 miles in length. The outer belt-line starts at Waukegan, thirty-five miles north of Chicago, and swings around to Gary, Indiana. Chicago, the railroad center, close to the center of population, is the most commanding location for mail-order houses, which distribute their wares to every state. There is little doubt that the Chicago mail-order catalogue is the most read book (sad to relate) in thousands of American homes; and it also goes to foreign lands.

Because Chicago is on the plain expansion has been easy. But even though Chicago stands in a flat plain, it has had many physical problems to solve in its rapid growth. For a time its sewage was poured into the lake, while the city water-supply was drawn from places much farther out in the lake. The growth of the city made it impossible to continue to dispose of the sewage so conveniently. Owing to the flatness of the country, Chicago was able to divert water [12] from Lake Michigan into the Illinois River, a branch of the Mississippi, by digging a canal, the Chicago Drainage Canal. The Chicago sewage was then turned into the Illinois-Mississippi system. Chicago has the additional ambition to make of this route a Lakes to Gulf waterway.

GREAT MOMENTS IN CHICAGO HISTORY

MR. SEARS ROEBUCK AUTOGRAPHS A COPY OF HIS CATALOGUE FOR AN ADMIRER

FIG. 198 — *Life* has a little jest at America's most widely read book. (Copyright Life Publishing Co., 1924.)

Chicago is called the Windy City, because in addition to the normal wind of its latitude it gets from the lake the unbroken raw blasts of winter and the pleasant breezes of summer.

Occasional periods of southwest winds in summer drive Chicago's sweltering population to the lake shore for comfort which they cannot get, because the same wind blows the surface water away from the shore, replacing it with water from greater depth at a temperature of 50°, colder than most spring water. The people who swelter in the hot air immediately above the lake cannot bathe in such chill waters.

When the breeze happens to blow from the stock-yards, really a square mile of barnyards, across the city it is impossible for the people of Chicago to appreciate their greatest industry.

[12] The proposal to increase the amount of water diverted to this canal from 6000 (estimated) cubic feet to 10,000 cubic feet per second raises strenuous objections on the part of Canada, which claims that the diversion of lake waters already interferes with water-levels on the lakes and with water-power at Niagara and on the St. Lawrence. Lake outlets seem to be destined to cause disputes. Similar and even hotter is the clash between New York and Chicago over the St. Lawrence waterway, which promises to give Chicago a cheaper outlet by way of the Canadian ports than she now possesses by way of the United States ports.

When Mr. H. G. Wells, the English novelist, called Chicago a " lapse from civilization " he probably thought only of her money-getting.[16] Probably he was not fully aware of the great University in its heart or of the civic interest that beats against the unplanned chaos from which Chicago suffers along with every other big city in the world.

FIG. 199 — Packing Town. Chicago packing-plants in foreground and the cattle pens in the open-looking place. (Courtesy Armour & Co.)

Chicago's struggle for parks, playgrounds, and art centers has not been fruitless.[14]

Chicago, with its varied industries, suffers less violent fluctuations of fortune than Detroit. Like Detroit, it promises continued growth.

Mr. James J. Hill predicted that when the Pacific Coast has twenty

[13] The description of Chicago by her poet, Carl Sandburg, is in part:
" Hog Butcher for the World,
Tool Maker, Stacker of Wheat,
Player with Railroads and the Nation's Freight Handler;
Stormy, husky, brawling,
City of the Big Shoulders: "

From *Chicago Poems.*

[14] It is interesting, unique in America, and perhaps very suggestive that a group of her successful business men can paint pictures that are said to be worth while as pictures. The best known of them all is a fair musician.

million people Chicago will become the largest city in North America. He may be right.

Milwaukee (pop. 457,000) might be called a second Chicago, or side Chicago, in the economic sense. It shares in a smaller way the advantages of Chicago but is dependent much more upon manufactures than upon commerce. Meat, machinery, leather, shoes, and knit goods are her chief industries. The benefit of the lake location is well shown by her import of 5,000,000 tons of coal a year, a very fundamental need for a city whose cold winter calls for much house-heating and whose factories call for much coal-made power.

### The Ontario Section

The cities of the Ontario part of this region are also prospering, although tariff barriers prevent their full participation in the great ad-

FIG. 200 — There is not in all the world a rival of Niagara Falls in beauty or in easily obtained water-power. The death struggle is on, for using the power destroys the beauty. View from the American side, showing four power plants on Canadian side. (Courtesy Ontario Power Co., Niagara Falls.)

vantages of the American market. The Lower Lake Region has become conspicuous between 1910 and 1925 through the utilization of two economic factors. One is the standardized machinery typified by the automobile area, and the other is the cheap power supplied to Canadian cities by the Ontario Hydro-Electric Power Commission. The attempt to establish diversified industries in the towns of the Ontario plain led by gradual steps to the working out of a new system of power-supply. It is a kind of municipal partnership. Cities contribute money (as investors) to a central hydro-electric commission. The Commission, an arm of the provincial government, builds power plants and transmission lines from plants to cities. The cities then sell the power at cost which includes payments for interest, depreciation and sinking funds to retire the bonds. By this means the plants will be owned by the Commission (the cities) debt-free after a period of years. Since there is very efficient operation, no promoter's profits, and no watered stock, the manufacturers and householders in this region have power at low cost, much lower cost than prevailed before the operation of this system. For example, the householder charge in Windsor, opposite Detroit, was $5.90 per month in 1922 for 217 kilowatt hours instead of $17.36, the rate [15] under the old régime. In 1920 Toronto had three times as many lights as Buffalo, a city of about the same size. Buffalo paid $584,000 for light, while Toronto paid but $335,000.

The people of Ontario are dependent upon the United States for coal — a vital dependence that contributed to drive them to co-operative action. They believe that " whoever dominates power dominates industry " and are well satisfied [16] with their system.

The statistics of city growth show that the towns are prospering with manufactures much like the American cities across the boundary. Owing to tariffs, many American companies in the Lower Lake Region have Canadian branches also in the Lower Lake Region.

Toronto, the second city of Canada (pop. 521,000 — 1921), gained 38% in the last ten-year census period. This gain is not in the class of Detroit, but it compares well with the growth of other American cities at the same period — Buffalo (506,000), 19.5%; Milwaukee (457,000), 22.3%; Cleveland (796,000), 42.1%; St. Louis (772,000), 12.5%; Boston (748,000), 11.6%; Pittsburgh (588,000), 10.2%; San Francisco (506,000), 21.5%.

[15] 1922 Report Ontario Hydro-Electric Commission and Bulletin 88, National Popular Government League, 1923, Washington, D. C.

[16] Between 1907 and 1910, the people of twenty-nine Ontario municipalities voted three to one in favor of the system; in 1912 municipal balloting was at the ratio of six to one. Since that time the vote was fourteen to one, and in some places the vote has been unanimous. The service figures are impressive indications of success.

### The Growth of Hydro-Electric Service in Ontario

| | | |
|---|---|---|
| 1910 ..... | 750 horse-power | 10 municipalities |
| 1915 ..... | 104,000 " | 112 municipalities, 120,000 consumers |
| | | 18 townships |
| 1921 ..... | 302,000 " | 234 municipalities, 265,000 " |
| | | 44 townships |
| 1922 ..... | 544,000 " | 242 municipalities, 335,000 " |
| | | 74 townships |

## Agriculture

The agriculture of the Lower Lake Region is marked by four influences — the lakes, the North, intensification and, strange to say, abandonment.

The temperature control of the lakes in a latitude of severe winters permits the fruit industry in a latitude which otherwise would be too cold. This can be seen quickly by observing fruit areas at the latitude of Rochester on any map of fruit production. The lake influence on crops is well illustrated by temperature facts on the opposite shores of Lake Michigan. One winter day the United States weather map showed zero F. at Milwaukee, and 22° F. at a station on the opposite shore. The lake, being unfrozen, had the temperature of thirty-two degrees. The

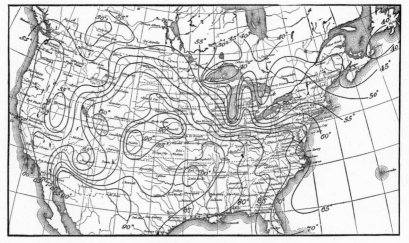

FIG. 201 — This map of temperatures at 8 P.M. on a hot May evening (May 13, 1915), shows in a remarkable way the influence of cold lake water on nearby temperatures. (Courtesy U. S. Weather Bureau.)

moderate west winds of the cold wave were warmed by passing over the lake waters (temperature 32°) so that the eastern shore was twenty-two degrees warmer than the western shore. This reduces winter-killing of buds. In the spring a warm southwest wind is cooled by the lake waters, giving much cloudy, foggy, cool spring weather to its eastern shore. Thus the fog adds its influence to temperature to hold back the blossoms. As a result, the eastern shore of Lake Michigan produces many peaches, apples, grapes and cherries.

The influence of the lake as a climate control also shows itself in a much longer growing season along the lake shore — one hundred and eighty days in the extreme southwest of Michigan, one hundred and fifty days at the northern part of the Lower Peninsula, while the interior of the peninsula has but one hundred and thirty.

Three small peninsulas getting the benefit of water on three sides [17] have marked industrial response to the water factor. Door County, Wisconsin, lies between Green Bay and the lake, while just across the lake is Leelanau County, Michigan, between Grand Traverse Bay and the lake. In both of these counties cherry orchards are important on the farms and cherry canneries important in the towns. On the south shore of Lake Erie is Ottawa County, Ohio, which includes several islands in the lake and the peninsula partly surrounded by Sandusky Bay. In

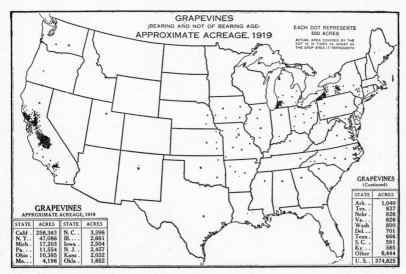

GRAPEVINES
(BEARING AND NOT OF BEARING AGE)
APPROXIMATE ACREAGE, 1919

EACH DOT REPRESENTS
500 ACRES

ACTUAL AREA COVERED BY THE
DOT IS 70 TIMES AS GREAT AS
THE CROP AREA IT REPRESENTS

GRAPEVINES
APPROXIMATE ACREAGE, 1919

| STATE | ACRES | STATE | ACRES |
|---|---|---|---|
| Calif . | 256,363 | N.C. . | 3,396 |
| N.Y. . | 47,086 | Ill. . . . | 2,681 |
| Mich . | 17,203 | Iowa . | 2,504 |
| Pa. . . | 11,554 | N.J. . | 2,457 |
| Ohio . | 10,385 | Kans . | 2,032 |
| Mo. . . | 4,196 | Okla . | 1,652 |

GRAPEVINES
(Continued)

| STATE | ACRES |
|---|---|
| Ark. . | 1,040 |
| Tex. . | 837 |
| Nebr . | 826 |
| Va. . . | 826 |
| Wash . | 800 |
| Del. . . | 701 |
| Tenn . | 666 |
| S.C. . | 591 |
| Ky. . . | 585 |
| Other | 6,444 |
| U.S. . | 374,825 |

FIG. 202 — The influence of the Great Lakes and the small Finger Lakes of central New York is clearly shown. (Courtesy U. S. Dept. Agr.)

1920 this county had 615,000 peach trees, while the county to the south of it had but 32,000.

The protective influence of Lake Erie also causes its southern and northeastern shores to produce most of the table grapes grown east of California, although Michigan is a rival. Three counties near Cleveland have a million vines each, but the New York end of Lake Erie has a greater concentration of the grape industry.[18]

[17] An even more striking example comes from Canada. "Districts along the shore of the Georgian Bay are remarkable in that the European plums and all varieties of pears and apples do extremely well, and peaches are found growing, though not in a commercial way. Again, on St. Joseph's Island, farther north, and on Lake Huron, a great many of our fruits are grown successfully; although they do not succeed in some of the higher sections inland and south." (Letter, P. W. Hodgetts, Director, Ontario Department of Agriculture, Fruit Branch. September 18, 1920.)

[18] In 1915 the growing season along the lake shore in northeastern Ohio was 190 days, while it was but 130 in the next county to the south, on the edge of the plateau.

The greatest fruit district in all this region is along the south shore of Lake Ontario. The Ontario part has a lake both south and north, but Lake Ontario alone gives enough frost protection to cause the Ontario plain in New York to be for many decades the leading apple district in the United States. You can ride for miles and be continuously in the sight of orchards of apples, peaches, cherries or pears. New York is second only to California as a pear producer.

### Intensification and Signs of the North

Signs of the North appear in the declining importance of corn and in the small acreage of improved land per farm. In these respects the Lower Lake Region resembles the North Central Dairy Region, not the Corn Belt. The smaller farm calls for more intensive use. Beef cattle and hogs are few, dairy cattle are important.

There are several important crops that bespeak the intensive agriculture. The potato is an important crop in lower Michigan and western New York. A hundred thousand acres of sugar beets [19] around Saginaw Bay made Michigan the second beet-sugar State in 1922. North of the latitude of Detroit a half-million acres of navy beans made her second only to California in bean production. In southwestern Ontario several thousand acres of tobacco are growing (Fig. 127).

In the Ontario plain of New York canneries vie with apple-storage houses and vinegar works to preserve food for future use. Fields of tomatoes, sugar-corn and green peas help to occupy the apple-grower's spare time and spare land. With fruit and truck crops this locality is one of the most productive agricultural districts in the United States. Aside from the above-mentioned centers of special crops, the dairy farm is the chief agricultural dependence. Markets, surface, soil and climate combine to make it so.

### Future

This region (except the Ontario section) started as a Yankee outpost of New England.[20] Its future is to continue its present. Does the United States want more meat? Chicago will slaughter it. More reapers? Chicago will make them. More mail-order goods? Chicago will keep them in store. More automobiles? Mr. Ford, Michigan and northern Ohio will make them. More apples, peaches, grapes, pears or cherries? The lake shore localities will grow them. Over-production or limited demand only prevents the extension of the fruit industry here. In the

[19] As evidence of the fitness of the beet for intensive agriculture, it yields eight or nine tons per acre in Michigan, and after the sugar is removed the pulp and tops have a forage value about equal to that of the average crop of hay in the United States.

[20] Every New England state sent a governor to Michigan, and five of them sent superintendents of Public Instruction.

summer of 1921 or 1922 orchards of perfect Dutchess apples were left unpicked in Michigan because the first shipments had netted a loss. In

June 1924, second-quality apples of the large crop of 1923 were being given away in western New York to anyone who would pay the cold-storage charges. These occurrences are not typical, but they are the factor [21] that controls production in a region that could produce more fruit. No lake-shore county has 10% of its area in apples. Ontario had less rural population in 1921 than in 1901, and Michigan with its extensive farm abandonment had the same experience.[22]

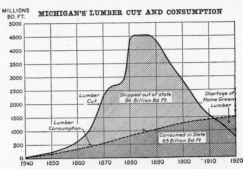

FIG. 203 — This record of frightful exploitation, accompanied as it has been by the burning up of the future supply, shows how this region has handicapped its own future. (Courtesy U. S. Dept. Agr.)

[21] " You would have enjoyed our forty-seven-mile automobile trip from Rochester to the home of Mrs. E., the route lying altogether through highly cultivated orchards, the trees loaded with fruit. There would have been a note of distress, however, for the economist in the fact that most of the orchardists were not picking their peaches. Here and there along the route we found baskets in front of farmhouses by the wayside offering peaches at $.15 a peck basket and plums at $.30 a peck basket. Most of the people, however, were not picking their peaches and plums at all, as there was no market.

" Mrs. E. stated that she would allow 300 bushels of peaches to go unpicked and one of her neighbors stated that he intended to treat 400 bushels in the same way. In the presence of this situation I saw a Greek fruit-store in Rochester displaying nothing but California fruit at ridiculously high prices." (Letter, Dr. Robert T. Morris, New York, September 22, 1922.)

[22] Chapter on Corn Belt gives some explanation of this.

Fig. 204 — "That looks just like Northern Canada," said Vilhjalmur Stefansson, Arctic explorer and son of an Icelander, as he stood before the original of this picture. "My, how I would like to be there!" he continued. Gray wolf group. (Courtesy of American Museum of Natural History, New York.)

# CHAPTER XXII

## THE GREAT NORTHERN FOREST

### The Indian's Country

THE white people of the United States and Canada seem to think that the whole continent of North America is theirs. Our maps solemnly aver that such is the case. But the fact is, there are several million square miles where most of the people are not white people. The land may be claimed politically, but it is not occupied by the white race. I was much surprised in 1920 to receive a manuscript map[1] from one of the bureaus of the Canadian Government, which showed that most of the area of British America has more Indians than white people living in it. The white people of North America have settled the arable lands whose climate permits a developed agriculture of the West European type.

North of the St. Lawrence Valley, the Lake, and Spring Wheat regions, is the Great Northern Forest. This land, too cold or too rough for European agriculture, remains therefore a land of the Indian. Its southern boundary is the northern line of Canadian agriculture, its northern boundary the limit of tree-growth. On the west it reaches up to the Alpine vegetation on the slopes of the Rockies. On the east it

[1] See Smith, J. Russell, *Human Geography*, Book 1, p. 44.

reaches almost to the Atlantic, but not quite, because the chill of Arctic waters, flowing down the coast of Labrador, prevents tree-growth for a short distance inland.

## Glaciation

This is the largest region we have considered, and the least well known. Even more than the Corn Belt it is glacier-made. And a bad job the glaciers made of it from the standpoint of human economics! The

FIG. 205 — The glacier annihilated economic vegetation 100%, and gave greatest possible aid to the economic geologist. A magnificent display of changed and twisted strata — the roots of a mountain of æons ago. The extreme of glacial scraping. Fullerton, Hudson Bay. (Courtesy Dept. Mines, Ottawa.)

Great Northern Forest is the place whence came some of the earth-material for the up-building and enrichment of the North Central Dairy Region and the Corn Belt. It is a case of robbing Peter (Canada) to pay Paul (the United States). Thousands of square miles of Quebec, Ontario, Manitoba and Saskatchewan are scraped bare to the hard rock, scraped down past the last fissure, so that the surface is smooth. If a little earth collects and a tree establishes itself it finds no crevice in which to catch a toe-hold. Standing thus in shallow earth, unable to grip the rocks, whole clumps of trees are sometimes overturned by the wind, with all of the thin mass of earth clinging to their upturned roots.

The surface of the upturned mass of roots and earth is left as flat and smooth as though the trees had grown on top of a cement floor.

The earth mantle is generally scanty and of the highly mixed character left by glaciers in rough areas. Most of its surface from the Gulf of St. Lawrence to the Rockies is of the old worn-down mountain roots described in the chapter on the Upper Lake Region.[2]

From Labrador to James Bay and James Bay to Lake Winnipeg, and from Lake Winnipeg to Great Slave Lake and the Rocky Mountains, is

FIG. 206 — Summer transport through the Great Northern Forest. An Indian family. (Courtesy Natural Resources Intelligence Service, Ottawa.)

a region peculiarly devoid of valleys. The glaciers filled them all up, so the present streams, without well-defined valleys, wander aimlessly around over a surface whose irregularities turn them into a multitude of lakes — Great Bear Lake, Great Slave Lake, Lake Winnipeg, Lake of the Woods, each of which is many hundreds of square miles in area. Besides these larger lakes there are hundreds, thousands of smaller lakes; lakes without names; lakes that are not on the maps; lakes that no white man has yet seen.[3]

[2] "The Bridge," 920 miles of the Canadian Pacific Railway from Kenora on the Lake of the Woods to North Bay, Ontario, is a traffic desert, devoid of farms. It has been described in six words — rocks, trees and water; trees, water and rocks. To build a railroad through the almost continuous rock was one of the greatest engineering feats.

[3] *The Geographical Review*, March 1918, p. 235, shows a map of unexplored areas made by the Canadian Geological Survey. An unexplored area lies more than fifteen miles from an explored route and has " no reasonably accurate survey " and " no records of the geography, life or general character of the region." Unexplored tracts varying from 8000 to 75,000 square miles covered most of the area north of the line running from Strait of Belle Isle to the south point of James Bay, and thence to the west end of Lake Athabasca and thence west to the Rockies.

## The Life of the Indian

This is the land of the life primeval, the land of the moose, the caribou, the mink, the marten, beaver, otter, wolf and bear. This is the land of the life of hunting; the land of the Indian, of the snowshoe, the land where the rivers are roads; the land of the birch canoe and the dog-sled. Up the rivers and across the lakes — that is the way to travel in the Great Forest. In winter the dog-sled follows the same trails over the ice of river and lake and across the snow of the same portages. Therefore travelers have seldom seen this land except along a few of the better watercourses.

The great commercial output of this forest region is fur. Those wonderful pieces of clothing and ornament in the shop windows of Fifth Avenue,

FIG. 207 — A trading-post is the commercial metropolis for thousands of square miles of wilderness. Fourteen thousand skins of bear, wolverine, etc., at Rampart House awaiting shipment to London market. (Courtesy Natural Resources Intelligence Service, Ottawa.)

New York, or State Street, Chicago, or San Francisco, by which people display their wealth, bedeck themselves, and keep warm while motoring, first entered commerce as a bale of raw furs lifted out of an Indian's canoe at a trading-post — on the southern edge of the Great Northern Forest. There and along the shores of Hudson Bay are scores of trading-posts. Upon his success in getting this bale of fur depends the prosperity, almost the life, of the Indian. He is not a man with a surplus, who can afford to have a poor season; he lives too near the margin of existence in his simple and direct combat with nature, in his lack of capital.

At the trading-post the two cultures meet — the white man of the complicated life of books, machinery and wide knowledge of many things, and the red man and the half-breed, of simple life, bookless, but with profound knowledge of the things of the forest. This man of the forest has no learning by which he could pass an examination to enter school, but he must pass a daily examination that decides whether or not he eats and is clothed or starves and freezes.

In summer the Indians come from the far woods and gather at the trading-posts. There they camp, enjoy a vacation, and transact the year's business by trading their furs. The men often work for the Hudson's Bay Company or other trading companies for a time during the summer camp. They may work the company boats for a month or two, or help to build an addition to the post, or help the fur-trader to lay in his annual supplies, thereby picking up extra cash to eke out the income from furs. But with the approach of autumn a camp of four hundred Indians will disappear even to the last family, each in its own canoe. Each goes back to its own hunting-grounds, for the Indians have property in hunting-grounds, with boundaries as clearly recognized as the sign-posts of the white man and often more scrupulously and honorably observed.

On the journey back from the post to the hunting-ground the entire property of the family, house, furniture, business equipment, is in their canoe. At every waterfall all must be unloaded and carried around to smooth water. At every portage, from stream-valley to stream-valley — portages are innumerable on some routes — all must be unloaded and carried. This is work, hard work. The labor of this transport shows why the Indian travels light. He cannot carry enough food for the winter, not even enough food for the journey, which may last for weeks. His purchases, if he has had furs with which to buy, are a tent, sheet-iron stove, stove-pipe, white man's clothing, except shoes (he prefers to make his own moccasins), steel traps, rifles, cartridges, axe, saw, knife and bucket. After the long journey is ended and the family has reached the home hunting-ground, they set up the winter camp, or the first winter camp, and there they live — fishing, hunting and eating the kill. The sheet-iron stove and the stove-pipe are great improvements to the tent, which may be pitched over three feet of snow, but a thick carpet of spruce boughs and the little stove keep it warm, even with a temperature 40° below zero outside.

From this base, the man makes his round — sometimes two or three days in extent — setting his traps and collecting his kill. Strong-smelling meat has been carefully saved and he drags it along the ground to draw animals to the traps. He uses a steel trap to catch the smaller animals — otter, beaver, mink, marten and muskrat. Sometimes he sets a deadfall to catch bears. A log pen is built, having a small door. As the bear gets to a certain position in entering the door he grasps the bait, thus releasing a string, which sets free a weighted log that falls upon him and breaks his back. The hunter makes the round of his traps on snowshoes and often he takes his dog-sled, on which the game is carried home to the squaw.   Her work it is to skin the animals and to prepare the flesh and the pelts.   As the pile of skins accumulates against the spring journey to the trading-post the family uses it for a bed.   The Indians often move their camps a few miles several times each winter to be nearer to unhunted game.

A land can support only a very small population on this basis of life, hence the Indians are few.   The lakes are rarely fished, so the fishing is usually good.   In winter fish is the great staple food of these people. In summer they have in addition many wild berries and water-fowl.   This does not sound like a balanced ration, nor is it.   It is poor food, and when the irregularity of supply is taken into account, we have an explana-

FIG. 208 — Winter transport.   Fur caravan crossing a lake in Great Northern Forest.   (Courtesy Natural Resources Intelligence Service, Ottawa.)

tion of the high death-rate of these people.   Ask an old Indian woman how many children she has had.   " Nine," or " ten," or " twelve," she will answer.   " How many are living now? " you will ask.   " One " or " two " is the usual answer.   Children die in infancy like flies in winter.   Sometimes the wolf or the bear gets the hunter, or he may get lost in a blizzard.   Then the wife and children, unable to subsist without his aid, may perish of starvation.

It is not an uncommon feat for a lone hunter, armed with rifle, cartridges, traps, blankets and warm clothing, to start in at the coast of Labrador in the autumn and come out upon the shore of the St. Lawrence in the spring, having spent all winter trapping, hunting, sleeping on the dry snow by camp-fires, and eating his kill.   We are forced to admire the nerve of such a man.   Think of the number of accidents that could cause that journey to wind up in one good meal for the wolf-pack that nightly sniffs about his camp-fire!

It is true that the Indian got along in the north woods for an indefinite period before the white man came; nevertheless, his struggle has been greatly aided by the white man's tools and weapons. It is doubtful, however, whether the Indian has benefited by the coming of the white man. These same weapons, in the hands of the white hunters, have reduced the game supply. The white man's forest-fires have done the same. Yet more, the white man brought the Indian the curse of strong drink and devastating diseases. Measles is often a fatal disease to the Indians, and the " flu " epidemic of 1918 was many times more deadly to them than to the white man, who is, after all, a very tough, enduring animal. The score of the Indian against the white man has one more item. The trading-post in the north woods is not often a competitive place. It is easy for the trader — how shall we say it? — to make large profits, or to cheat the Indian. The trader can price his stuff high and the furs low. Thus many a poor Indian is kept in debt for years, a kind of peonage not unlike Spanish-American peonage (p. 463).

## The Modern Epoch

If this Great Northern Forest region is used in the best way for the service of the white man, it will continue to be a land from which comes fur, but also it must be a land of wood, of water-power and of vacations. It is fortunate that these four utilities combine in demanding one common condition, namely, *forest protection*, of which unfortunately it has now but little.

### Agricultural Possibilities

This region with its rock base has two islands of softer earth which have possibilities of agriculture. One is the northward extension of the Prairie rock and soil formations in the Mackenzie Valley. The map (Fig. 209) shows that the land at the base of the Rockies has a much warmer summer than the land farther east. It is possible that many thousand square miles of the forest region here may some day become another Sweden — a land of wheat, barley, rye, oats, potatoes, hay and laborious farming — but that day is some generations away.

The same is probably true of the Northern Ontario Clay Belt (Fig. 209). This is a wide arc of clay laid down like the soils of old Lake Agassiz, now the Red River Valley. When the continental glacier, retreating to James Bay, held water between it and the height of land, the clay mantle was laid down on the old hard rocks.

The Canadian Government has put out many booklets praising agricultural opportunities in this clay belt — it is fertile but swampy, stumpy, and too often visited by summer frost. The census of 1921 showed 3000 occupied farms in the Temiskaming district. Between 1918 and 1922 the area increased from 40,000 to 59,000 acres, 47%; the area

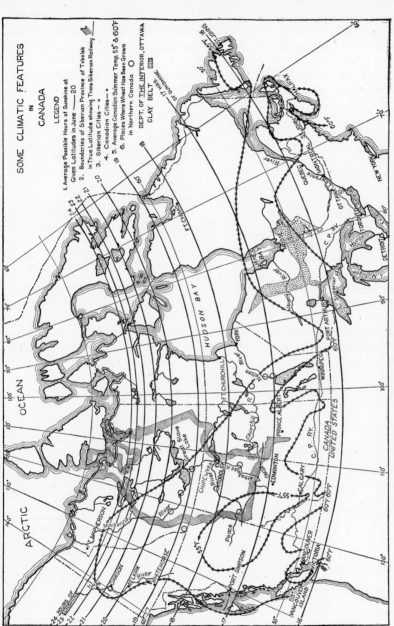

SOME CLIMATIC FEATURES
IN
CANADA

LEGEND

1. Average Possible Hours of Sunshine at Given Latitudes in June ──── 20
2. Boundaries of Siberian Province of Tobolsk in True Latitude showing Trans Siberian Railway ⟋
3. Siberian Cities ─ o
4. Canadian Cities ─ •
5. Average Canadian Summer Temp. 55° & 60°F ⊙
6. Places Where Wheat Has Been Grown in Northern Canada O

DEPT. OF THE INTERIOR, OTTAWA
CLAY BELT ▨

Fig. 209 — This map merits careful examination, especially the 55° line.

under crops increased from 28,000 to 54,000 acres, 95%, and cattle increased 94%. Perhaps this settlement will continue. Perhaps it is a land-reserve for the future like that of British Columbia, but with a colder, longer winter.

Small patches of similar clay are scattered through the whole region but especially west of James Bay where the surface is lower.

### Wood

We must keep in mind that this forest is little known, especially as to its wood resources. Wood is the great visible resource of this region, but its wood resources are more visible than real. The travelers have always gone along the streams, where the best trees are. Thus erroneous impressions of the forest riches have gone forth. Recent airplane surveys often produce sad disillusionment in regard to timber by showing sparse and scattering tree-growth on the inter-stream spaces and even bare areas with no trees at all. These facts are not discovered by the man who travels upstream in a canoe, because he cannot see beyond the fine growth at the stream's edge, especially as the creeping junipers beneath the spruce trees contribute to turn the forest's edge into a veritable evergreen hedge that offers great discouragement to inter-stream travel.

In a region so vast we should expect to find a great variety of conditions. Peat-bogs, called muskegs, are common in many places, and west of Hudson Bay they cover large areas.[4] They are often open or covered with trees of no commercial value. In recent years an insect, the spruce bud-moth, killing millions, has swept Canadian forests almost like a fire. Other places have fine stands of timber or pulp-wood.

I am greatly indebted to Mr. Roland D. Craig, Forest Resources Specialist of the Canadian Forest Service, for an estimate of the timber reserves of Canada, which he states may easily be reduced by more accurate knowledge.

|  | Softwood | Hardwood | Total |
|---|---|---|---|
|  | Million feet B. M. | Million feet B. M. | Million feet B. M. |
| Eastern provinces ..... | 300,000 | 100,000 | 400,000 |
| Prairie provinces ..... | 140,000 | 85,000 | 225,000 |
| British Columbia ..... | 360,000 | 1,800 | 361,800 |
|  | 800,000 | 186,800 | 986,800 |

Of species used for pulp-wood:

East Canada ............ 650,000,000 cords
West Canada ............ 690,000,000      "

Total ................ 1,340,000,000 cords,
of which 500,000,000 cords are saw-timber.

[4] Page 113, *Annual Report Topographical Survey Branch*, 1914–15, Ottawa.

Canadian timber resources are of vital interest to the people of the United States. Our own Forest Service reported in 1922 that already three-fifths of the original timber of the United States is gone and that we are using the remainder of it four times as fast as it is growing. To make matters worse, the remaining forests of the United States are so far away from the people who need the wood that wasteful marketing of the timber is necessary, and therefore the utility of the forests of the United States is lower than it should be. Can Canada supply us when we reach the inevitable end of our own virgin forests? We are increasingly calling upon Canada. She now supplies two-thirds of our paper. Many of our paper companies have leased large tracts of Canadian forests.[5]

## The Lumber Mine

The United States is now cutting about thirty billion feet of timber per year, which means that Canada has enough to supply us for about thirty years if we could use all that she has. Meantime, Canada is using on her own behalf about eleven billion feet per year, which would indicate that she has a ninety-year supply for her own needs. If she could reproduce her timber in ninety years she would be able to produce indefinitely her present consumption. But such reasoning is false. It supposes that all Canadian timber is available for use. A saw-log on the slope of James Bay, or a hundred thousand saw-logs on the slope of James Bay, is at present a questionable resource. I quote again from Mr. Craig's report:

" Under present conditions it is doubtful that more than one-half of the saw-material and one-third of the pulp-wood exclusive of the prairie provinces, can be considered commercially accessible. . . . Under the present systems of exploitation a great deal of the timber is wasted, and fire, insects and fungi are destroying many times the amount of timber used.

" In British Columbia, I estimated that fire had destroyed twenty-two times the amount of timber cut prior to 1917, and there is reason to believe that similar conditions exist in the other provinces. The spruce budworm has destroyed, it is estimated, at least 100 million cords of pulp-wood in Quebec, and fifteen million cords in New Brunswick during the last ten years. This is equal to twenty-nine times the annual cut of pulp-wood in the whole Dominion. Other insects are also destroying vast amounts of timber. No attempt has been made to estimate the damage done by fungi, but it would appear to be as great as that caused by either fire or insects.

[5] In 1922 a firm of Chicago publishers took a lease of timber lands from the Quebec government, secured after lively bidding, at terms which will ultimately net the government $3,000,000.00 and still leave it in possession of the land — an excellent policy for Quebec, especially if she can keep fires out of her forests.

" It is apparent to all who are familiar with the situation that the
timber resources within reach of the established industries, especially
in Eastern Canada, are being depleted to such an extent that unless
provision is made for the growing of new crops of timber, these industries are faced with the necessity of curtailment of production or entire
abandonment of their operations. The constantly increasing cost of securing supplies for the sawmills and pulp-mills is evidence of this condition
and has led to several of the pulp companies undertaking reforestation
measures."

It is plain that at the present time both the United States and Canada
are *mining* timber. Before many decades a change will force itself upon
both countries. Fire-protection and reforestation are most urgently
needed. Canada has an advantage in that 85% of her forests are
national possessions. This makes fire-protection easier, but the Canadian
forests are so large in area, so far away from large populations, that
fire-protection in Canadian forests is much more difficult than in the
United States; even in the United States it has thus far been almost
unattainable. From all parts of Canada, as from all parts of the United
States, returned travelers bring back tales of forests gutted by fire.
Government explorers in previously unexplored Manitoba report " fire-
killed timber," " small fire-killed spruce," and " surface soil seriously
damaged by repeated fires." The forest fire, set by Indian, camper,
prospector, hunter, lightning, travels so far ahead of the settler and so
far ahead of the possibility of commercial exploitation that it is one of
the most difficult problems facing our commercial civilization.

Forestry in the Great North Woods means protection from fire; then
Nature will make forest if she has the chance. The result will be the
lumber-camp once in twenty, thirty or forty years — great activity at
the cutting of mature trees, the logs and wood seeking cheap water routes
to market.

Pulp-wood holds out a ray of hope in the fight with fire and insects in
the coming era of forestry. The great increase in the use of cartons shows
that wood-pulp is competing successfully with sawed lumber and rapidly
replacing it for many uses. This is a great gain to man. Pulp-wood
can be made out of pieces the size of a man's thumb if we choose to
bother with them, and three-inch sticks are regularly used. To make
boards a saw-log is required, and to make saw-logs big trees are needed.
A tree that will grow to be four inches in diameter, twenty feet from
the ground, in fifty or seventy-five years, may need a hundred years more
to become a saw-log; it may even require more time in the cold North.
The interest-charge at the end of a century of conservation amounts to
something appalling, but for the shorter time needed to grow the raw
material for the pulp-mill the interest-charge is not prohibitive and the
business aspects of forest conservation are greatly changed. It is there-

fore natural that the paper companies, the chief users of wood-pulp, should be pioneers in forest-preservation and forest-planting in America.

The string of pulp-mills that lines the southern edge of this forest region from the Strait of Belle Isle almost to Winnipeg can function most economically only if the streams on which they are located keep on floating wood down to them.

## Water-Power

The Great Northern Forest region is second in North America only to the Pacific Mountains as a creator of water-power resources. Most of it is a plateau. It has tens of thousands of square miles of lake surface

Fig. 210 — Indians spearing fish near the Arctic Circle, Canadian Northwest Territory. Fish, like wood and water-power, go to waste in this region. (Courtesy Natural Resources Intelligence Service, Ottawa.)

(in some localities 25% of its surface), making natural reservoirs to produce an even flow in the streams that drain this region. Then, too, these streams, lately disarranged by glaciers, are tumbling over the edges of plateaus, making waterfalls, rather than running down forty-million-year-old valleys where they have had time to wear the rocks away and make an almost even slope, like those of the Potomac and James. These glacial streams give the hydraulic engineer his easy opportunities. The lakes not only make natural storage, but also offer the easiest possible opportunity for artificial storage. A little dam five feet high at the outlet of a lake may produce water-storage five feet deep on one hundred square miles of lake-surface. While five feet of flooding of the shores of a lake might work great devastation to houses or farms in Indiana, it would produce but little damage in a land with so few people as the Laurentian plateau.

Unfortunately, much of this water-power is far from centers of population; but now most of the eastern forest region is within power-transmission range of the shores of the St. Lawrence and the Great Lakes. The central part is within reach of Winnipeg (see page 363) and the Wheat Belt.

## Minerals

The mineral resources of this forest region may give it its largest population, at least for a time. The rich mineral region around Lake Superior has had approximately the same geological history as hundreds of thousands of square miles of the Canadian section. The Laurentian Plateau is therefore, theoretically at least, one of the finest mineral regions of the world. Some of it is easy to prospect because it is bare, but most of it is very difficult because the surface made by glaciation gives no idea of the character of the rock beneath. Sudbury Nickel, the world's premier nickel district, Quebec Asbestos, the premier asbestos district, and Cobalt Silver, one of the greatest silver camps, were all discovered by chance when the railroad was being built. The mineral output of the Canadian area has thus far been much less than that of the United States part of the Lake District. There is every reason to expect continued important discoveries [6] with increase of knowledge of the country. And for every mineral enterprise there will be a town, which will last months, years, decades or generations, according to the character of the deposit. But it cannot last like the well-kept forest or the cement power-plant at the base of the waterfall.

Probably the greatest excitement in regard to minerals for this whole territory will be furnished by oil. For years tar sands and flows of natural gas along the Mackenzie River about five hundred miles north of Edmonton have created considerable excitement. In 1789, seventy years before the first oil-well was drilled in Pennsylvania, Sir Alexander Mackenzie reported oil-seepages at Fort Norman, latitude 65°, on the river that bears his name. Indians at that time were gathering it from pools to smear on their canoes.

In August, 1920, a pioneer oil-well proved to be a gusher. It was capped in twenty minutes. What can you do with a gusher in an essentially uninhabited forest, several hundred miles from a railroad? Is this waiting volcano of oil worth a pipe-line that might cost $50,000,000? No one knows. But it is known that the rocks of the Devonian formations, one of the greatest of oil-producers, extend for a distance of six or seven hundred miles along the Mackenzie, thereby holding out the possi-

[6] For example, " A huge ore body (iron) on the north shore of Lake Athabaska " (London *Times*, November 11, 1922).

bility of a great oil region, which will, of course, be provided with outlets if valuable finds of oil are made.

We may, therefore, expect for a time the usual boom and shanty towns
of oil-fields to make a gamblers' paradise and a flare-up of city life in
this northern wilderness, only to be followed in a few years by a decline
and a return once more to the forest and the hunter.

### Future

Let them come — paper-mill, sawmill, power-plant, miner, farmer on
the clay belts, trapper for furs, trout fisherman, hunter for moose and

FIG. 211 — The beaver, industrious emblem of Canada, converter of poor
wood into fine fur, should be a permanent inhabitant of vast areas.
(Courtesy Natural Resources Intelligence Service, Ottawa.)

caribou, canoeist journeyer in the wild. If in years to come these
people should use this land to its best advantage, 95% of it will need
the forester. He is the backbone-man of this region. If he succeeds every
other industry is aided thereby.

The forester patiently watches the forest, and when fire appears he
fiercely fights it, that we may have saw-logs and pulp from a land that
appears to be good for little else. Good forest improves the storage
of water and the shelter for fur, game and fish. Good forest improves it
as a vacation land for the man who likes to paddle a canoe through uninhabited woods, to fish in little-fished streams, to hunt the moose, caribou,
deer and bear. It promises to be a permanent refuge for the Indian, and
a choice retreat for the type of man who loves to keep alive a spark of
the Viking spirit, a trace of the explorer's instinct. It will be a long time
before all of this region will be explored, with every stream and lake

properly located.   The enterprising, exploring geographic canoeist can go and add a bit to the map of the world, at the same time that he is toughening his muscles and calming his nerves far from the rack of city life.   The journey will also be enlivened by the contest to keep from being eaten alive, for in this mossy, marshy land of lake and stream the black fly eats you, if he can, in the first half of the summer and the mosquito eats the rest of you, if he can, in the second half of summer.   The best vacation season is the short autumn after frosts have laid the insects low and before the coming of ice and snow.

Fig. 212 — A Great Plains sheep herder often lives in a camp wagon and makes long journeys seeking pasture with his sheep. Flock of English blood. (Courtesy F. R. Marshall, U. S. Dept. Agr.)

## CHAPTER XXIII

### THE GREAT PLAINS

THE region of the Great Plains is a land of romance. Its most widely distributed product is fiction and movie plot, wild-west shows and Buffalo Bill, Indian fights, buffalo hunts, cowboy skill, round-ups and shoot-ups; has been stage hold-ups, escapes from prairie fires, wolves and rattlesnakes, wanderings in blinding blizzards, conquering bucking bronchos. The stories of these have gone far beyond the limits of the English language — and have raised the hair of youth in all continents.

The Great Plains region is a land of tragedy. For two and a half centuries the white man had marched westward, conquering the land, settling and making successful homesteads and building up communities. Thus he worked his triumphant way from the Atlantic to central Kansas and Nebraska. On westward, into the region of the Great Plains, marched this army of settlers, but here the battle turned against them and they were thrown back by hundreds of thousands. But this battle-field of their defeat, of the triumph of their enemies is not marked by tablets, monuments, and the usual signs of victory. A lion does not write a book, nor does the weather erect a monument at the place where the pride of a woman was broken for the want of a pair of shoes, or where a man worked five years in vain to build a home and gave it up, bankrupt and whipped, or where a baby died for the want of good milk, or where the wife went insane from sheer monotony and blasted hope.

From Plymouth Rock and Jamestown the westward march of the colonizing Americans had had two and a half centuries of unbroken success. There was a moment, that is to say a decade or two of alarm, when they first saw the prairies of Indiana and Illinois and thought they were

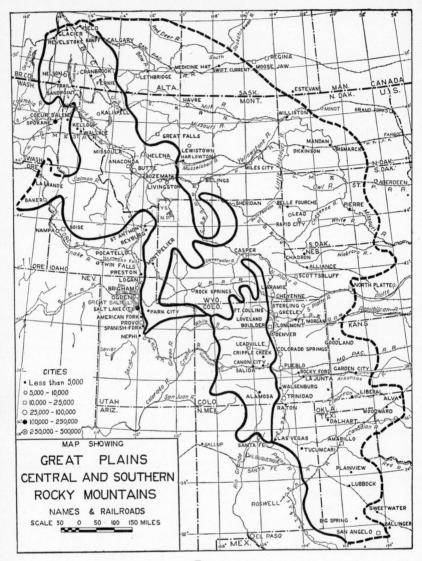

FIG. 213.

bad, but afterward found these prairies are good for the homes of men. Then from 1820 to 1870 there were two generations of quick settlement on the prairies of Illinois, Iowa, eastern Kansas, eastern Nebraska and the Red River Valley. West of the prairies stretches the country marked on our maps as the Great Plains. To settlers the land looked the same.

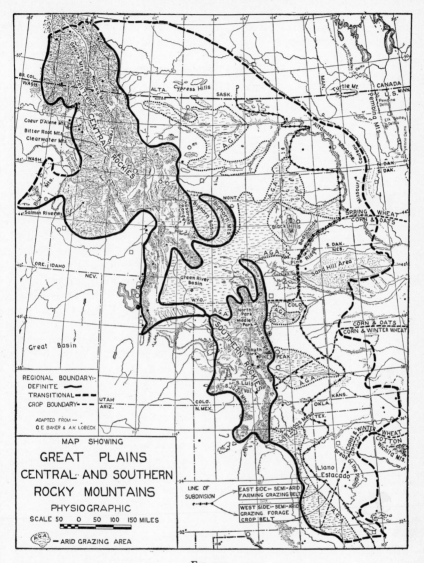

FIG. 214.

It had good grass. The brown soil was a sign of fertility, so they pushed on into the land where they were to meet defeat.

I knew one of these men. He started in Iowa with nothing, and saved a little money. One June day in the middle '80's he and some friends took a prospecting vacation trip out into Dakota. They traveled in .

wagons, camping as they went. Finally, one day, the beauty and promise of a particular place captured their fancy. The land was worth $30 or $40 an acre back home. They could homestead here for nothing. My friend picked his quarter-section on the shore of a little lake. All about was a sea of waving grass, bright with blossoms, as is the wont of the Great Plains in time of summer rain. Antelope occasionally scampered away in the distance. A railroad was being built but ten miles behind them. The next spring he took his wife and little girl to this place and there they built a shanty, broke a field and planted a crop with the team and tools brought from Iowa. The season was not very good, but they knew that the next would be better; they doubled the acreage, but the crop was again cut in half. The next winter the little lake in front of the house went dry and the jack-rabbits came by moonlight and dug in its bottom seeking food. The third year Simpson again doubled the acreage and the crop was again cut in half. The golden future had disappeared. He swapped his

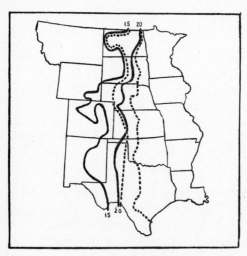

Fig. 215 — Annual rainfall figures are of varying value. The solid lines show amount of rainfall on the average. The dotted lines of equivalent crop-return show that more rainfall is needed for agriculture in the increasing heat and evaporation of lower altitudes. (Courtesy U. S. Dept. Agr.)

tools and horses for steers and heifers and sold them for enough money to get back to his wife's folks in Iowa. He found the ticket back cost a great deal more than the ticket out had cost. The railroads were encouraging settlement, not abandonment.[1]

These people had gone West to found a home and to be independent. They were bankrupt when the man was forty years of age. He was a man of parts but he never again succeeded in getting on his feet in a way that was satisfactory to him. His case is but the type. It is said that a quarter of a million people were similarly driven out of western

[1] " From the ninety-eighth meridian west to the Rocky Mountains there is a stretch of country whose history is filled with more tragedy and whose future is pregnant with greater promise than perhaps any other equal expanse of territory within the confines of the Western Hemisphere." (" Some Misconceptions Concerning Dry Farming," by E. C. Chilcott, *Yearbook* of Department of Agriculture, 1911, p. 251. Mr. Chilcott is in charge of Dry Farming Investigations, U. S. Dept. Agr.)

Kansas by a series of bad years in the 1890's. Eastern investors also lost millions that had been loaned on these farms. The record of the Great Plains is, to a great extent, a record of settlement and abandonment. Each wave of settlers intrenched itself a little better as it got away from the methods of agriculture and the seed that the first settlers brought from more humid lands (Fig. 64).

## Climate

The region of the Great Plains is characterized by rainfall insufficient for the agriculture of the corn and wheat belt types. It is a land of considerable variation in rainfall.[2] In some places the rain is only ten to twelve inches on the average. In other places it is sixteen, in others again eighteen — facts which make a very great difference in the lives of men.[3] But averages do not tell the whole. Averages rarely happen. The freaks of the season decide man's chances. Thus Montana had three splendid years in succession, 1914–15–16. It happened shortly after much talk about dry-farming and after a new homestead act (1909)

[2] It is also a land of temperature variation and extremes. Glendive, Montana, near the eastern border, recorded 117° F. in July 1893, and eighty miles to the west a temperature of —63° was recorded in January 1885. This is the coldest record in the United States, and Stefansson, in his interesting book, *Northward Course of Empire*, says it is colder than any record north of the mainland of North America. Winter changes are also very sudden. West Texas has a record of a fall of 63° F. in sixteen hours. A few days of hot wind will sometimes kill the corn crop even when the soil is moist.

The section at the foot of the mountains is warmer than the farther plains. The Black Hills even produce this usual influence of the mountain. Snow cover is often removed from this mountain base area by the " snow-eater," the warm chinook winds of winter.

[3] RELATION BETWEEN PRECIPITATION AND THE GRAZING CAPACITY OF RANGES

Table 1 — Arizona, New Mexico, Texas and Oklahoma, where grazing is possible for most of the year.

| Annual precipitation | Cattle per square mile |
|---|---|
| 0 to 5 inches | 0 |
| 5 to 10 inches | 9 |
| 10 to 15 inches | 15 |
| 15 to 20 inches | 24 |
| 20 to 25 inches | 32 |

Table 2 — In the Great Plains states north of Oklahoma, where there are usually periods of considerable length in the winter-time when grazing is not possible.

| Annual precipitation | Cattle per square mile |
|---|---|
| 10 to 15 inches | 19 |
| 15 to 20 inches | 38 |
| 20 to 25 inches | 76 |
| 25 to 30 inches | 265 |
| 30 to 40 inches | 409 |

(" Relation between the Annual Precipitation and the Number of Head of Stock Grazed per Square Mile," J. Warren Smith, *Monthly Weather Review*, U. S. Dept. Agr., June 1920.) *Annual average* precipitation does not tell the story. It is made of yearly figures that fluctuate greatly. The figures of the year do not tell the tale because the rainfall by months is so uncertain.

which let settlers have 320 acres instead of 160 acres. Settlers flocked into this area by tens of thousands.[4] On the basis of those three good crops, they built houses, schools, churches, sold bonds, and sold land at $30.00 and $40.00 an acre. On the last of these three good years

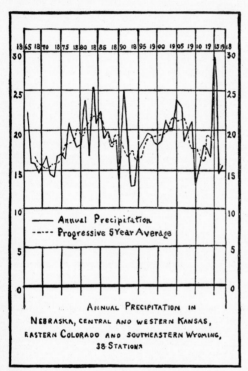

came the third homestead act letting one man have 640 acres. Also came World War prices for wheat. Then the three succeeding years w e r e periods of unprecedented drought and c r o p failure.[5] It seemed almost like a trap for the settler. Whole townships and counties could have been bought at $10 an acre. Some counties ceased to pay interest on their bonds. The United States government appropriated money to buy seeds for farmers, and the government of Saskatchewan did likewise. It is because of such cycles as these that some of the Great Plains area has been settled three times and abandoned twice (Figs. 18, 107).

FIG. 216 — If this showed *one station*, rather than the average of 38, the fluctuation would be greater.

### Erroneous Settlement

Then the land-shark has had a hand in this erroneous settlement, witness the farmer from Georgia who, after having been shown some Great Plains land by a real estate gentleman, said to me with real reverence: " Ain't it wonderful! The Lord just knows we needed more land and has gone and made it rain more out here in this country than it used to." The statement,

[4] Seventeen thousand eight hundred and sixty-five homestead entries were filed in Montana in 1912. A survey of former occupations of settlers in a Montana county showed that only half had been farmers. The list included musicians, butchers, bartenders, miners, deep-sea divers, maiden ladies, merchants, preachers, plasterers, printers, peddlers, gamblers and jacks-of-all-trades. Truly a democratic outpouring. Thirty per cent arrived with no capital, so we should not saddle the climate with full blame for all failures.

[5] Unfortunately Montana is not the only sufferer from such calamity. Western Texas had a similar drought about the same time, but it did not find so many trying to farm.

quite unfounded, that plowing the land increases the rainfall, has probably
made tens of thousands of sales and helped to wreck thousands of men.

The great railroads have had a great temptation to over-praise the

FIG. 217 — A good year at dry farming in the great spaces. Eastern Montana,
fifty miles south of Canada, eighty miles west of North Dakota. (Courtesy
Great Northern Railway.)

region. They had received large land-grants for building the roads. A
settler in the Plains region was worth $500 a year to the railroad in
freights in 1910.
He was worth sev-
eral hundred dollars
to the road if he
f a i l e d. I wonder
how many of these
men remember with
bitterness an adver-
tisement I saw in
an Eastern d a i l y
showing the Great
Plains farmer plow-
i n g t h e wide ex-
panse and turning
up piles of coined
dollars.

FIG. 218 — One of the processes of natural selection. A
long hard winter leaves thousands of skeletons like
this on the Plains, where forage is not provided.
This was one of thousands which perished in a wet
snow on the 8th of May when the emaciated animals
could not resist an ice-cold soaking. A few yards
back of these miserable remains is the edge of an acre
of dry and plantless alkaline mud, the bottom of
an ephemeral lake with no outlet. Alberta. (Photo
J. Russell Smith.)

*Stages of Develop-*
*ment*

The region of the
Great Plains began
its history as a roadway — people crossing to get to some other place —
to Santa Fe to trade with the Mexicans, to California and Idaho and

Colorado to dig gold, to the mountains to trade for furs. It began its modern epoch in 1869. In that year the Union Pacific Railroad was completed to the Rocky Mountains and California. At that time the roving Indians of the Sioux and other tribes still had possession of most of the Great Plains, and millions of buffalo made the annual migration northward from Texas and Oklahoma in the spring, returning southward from Canada in the autumn. Sometimes the trains of the Union Pacific Railroad had to stop while great masses of these cattle of nature shambled across the tracks, followed by Indians. It is no wonder that Plains Indians' law, religion and folk-lore centered in the buffalo. It was easy for them to kill buffalo and to dry the meat and use the skins for clothing, tents and tackle.

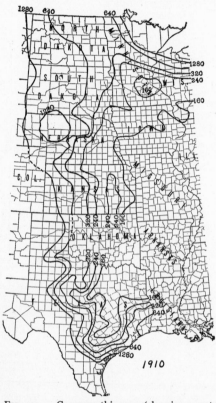

FIG. 219 — Compare this map (showing county boundaries) of average farm size (acres) with the U. S. Rainfall Map (Fig. 107). (Courtesy Nebraska Corn Improvers Association.)

In the four years, 1868–1872, the railroad, the repeating rifle and hunters from everywhere were too much for the buffalo. He was slaughtered by millions and the cowboy and white man's cattle took his place and that of the Indian.[6] The land belonged to the Government. No one wished to settle there and one of the easiest businesses in the world was to buy cattle, brand them, and turn them out to live as the buffalo had lived on his old pasture. The cattle picked their own living. In early summer a great drive was made, which rounded up all the cattle in a wide area. The cows were lassoed and

[6] Fortunately a few men of vision formed the American Bison Society and came to the rescue of the buffalo before complete extinction was his fate. In 1906, Dr. Hornaday, the learned director of the New York Zoo, reported that the bison in America numbered 506 or 507. In 1917 there were 5000, and they are now increasing steadily in many herds in national parks in the United States and in Canada and also in private hands. There is still one wild herd in the woods around Great Slave Lake. They may yet become the cattle of the Plains. They are superior to our

pulled out of the bunch, followed by their calves. To settle the question of ownership the c a l f w a s branded, and at the fall round-up the animals that were to go to Eastern markets were picked out. Cattle-men made g r e a t profits for a decade or two, until they overstocked the range, over-pastured it, and lost 50% or 60% of their cattle by starvation in the severe winters of 1886–87.

Then came the homesteader, trying his luck on the homestead defined by the Act of 1862 as 160 acres. In this region of little rain 160 acres was not enough. The homestead er failed, mostly through no fault of his own. He was in a strange land, very strange indeed, so far as farming was concerned. After tens of thousands of men had been failing for a couple of decades Congress waked up a little and enlarged the homestead to 320 acres (1909), and to 640 acres (1916). Experiment stations were established throughout the length of the Great Plains to gather facts for the farmer, decades after he first needed them.

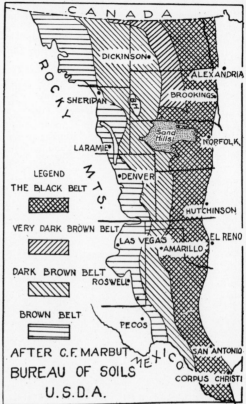

Fig. 220 — Compare with U. S. Rainfall Map (Fig. 107.) The color of soil in treeless areas depends upon rainfall. Much rain — much grass — many grass roots — black soil, and gradations thereof. Rain also affects *character* and *composition* of soil. East of the area shown on this map the rain soaks through and carries away its solutions. On the area mapped here solutions from the top soil are left in a hard limy layer as the water returns to be evaporated from the surface. Light rain leaves the hard lime layer near the surface. Mr. Marbut has repeatedly guessed the annual rainfall of Great Plains localities within one inch by looking at soil sections in a roadside. This is one of the best of all agricultural indexes. (After C. F. Marbut, *Annals of Association of American Geographers*, June 1923.)

breeds in ability to stand blizzard and drought, and maintain flesh under adverse food supply. They are bigger. The meat is said to be more digestible. The hide is thicker and stronger. The animal can be combed to yield wool that can be woven. (Information from Dr. Frank Speck, University of Pennsylvania.)

## Bounds

Now, forty years after the settlement of western Kansas, man has made considerable progress in adjusting himself to the conditions. What do we find? The eastern boundary of the Great Plains (Fig. 214) is shown as the place where pasture takes up more of the farm than do the cultivated crops.[7] This is one of the most important boundaries in American agriculture. It is, of course, a transition line. Fifty miles east of it the farm product in most counties in 1919 was over fifteen dollars per acre. Fifty miles west of it the farm product was under five dollars per acre. Fifty miles east of the boundary the average size of

FIG. 221 — There is no uncertainty as to the western edge of the Great Plains. The Rocky Mountain front stands up bold and sharp for hundreds of miles. (Courtesy Canadian Pacific Railway.)

farms was from 300 to 400 acres. Fifty miles west of it the average size of farms 'was from six to twelve hundred acres. Fifty miles east, the landscape looks like Corn Belt or Wheat Belt. Most of the land is in fields and crops. Fifty miles west it looks like open plains, with fences far apart and often lacking, most of the land still in the native grass, untouched by the plow.

This line at the edge of the Great Plains happens to divide the United States into two nearly equal parts. The eastern half is the land of humid agriculture and heavy population; the western half is the land of dry-farming, grazing, irrigation and scattered population. The

[7] Mr. O. E. Baker's careful and statistical study, " The Agriculture of the Great Plains Region," *Annals of the Association of American Geographers*, September 1923, also *Year Book* of Department of Agriculture, 1921, have been followed in this.

northern boundary is the Spring Wheat region; the western boundary is the foot of the Rocky Mountains and the western breaks of the Staked Plains.[8] (Fig. 39.)

## Surface of the Great Plains

The surface of the Great Plains can, in general, be spoken of as level or gently rolling, but in a land of such vast extent, fifteen hundred miles from north to south, and from three to five hundred miles east and west, there is naturally room for much variation. In northern Montana the surface is so high that there are frosts every month in summer, and hay is the only crop attempted. The rivers of Montana are in valleys five hundred to one thousand feet deep. The land comes down to them from the higher elevations in level benches edged by a series of hills, locally known as " breaks " or " bad lands."

The rock strata in most of the Great Plains are nearly horizontal, with softer material above and below. As the softer material is worn away cliffs or rows of hills are left with rocks sticking out from their sides and labyrinthine valleys cut into them. In such places it is hard for a wagon to get from one level to the next. Once the wagon has reached the top it may travel for days over a level or gently rolling surface. One well-known section, Goshen Hole, in western Nebraska and eastern Wyoming, is a lower area walled nearly all around by such a line of breaks.

At various places in the Plains, remnants of these old strata stand up as high hills, known locally as mountains. At other places ancient lava-flows and volcanic necks remain above the plain. The Black Hills were pushed up through the horizontal rocks of the plains by volcanic force. They are, therefore, ringed about by the upturned edges of the plains rocks, just as the western border of the plains at the foot of the Rockies has a similar upturned edge [9] where the granites of the Rocky Mountains were pushed through.

In southwestern South Dakota and adjacent parts of Wyoming and Nebraska there are two or three thousand square miles of Bad Lands. This land, which is mostly of heavy clay, is so steep that it washes badly and the earth absorbs so little water that it is bare of vegetation. But

[8] The wide-open plains of the Green River Basin and central Wyoming are not a part of the physiographer's Great Plains, but when considered from the standpoint of human use they are the same region. The Laramie Plain, of 2000 feet altitude has 15 inches of rain and is fine pasture. To the westward is a mountain-enclosed area with less than 10 inches of rain. It has shifting sand dunes and is called Red Desert. This Wyoming land is the drainage basin of the Colorado and has large possibilities from irrigation in the alluvial lands of an old lake bed in Green River Basin.

[9] This gives opportunity for the collection of artesian waters. These proved of great value for irrigation in North Dakota, until many wells ceased to flow — another case of wasted resources. In that state artesian wells are now controlled by state law, administered by the state geologist.

in among these bald, fantastic, bare Bad Lands are flats where good grass grows. The Bad Lands result from stream work in impervious clay.[10]

North and west of central Nebraska is an area of 18,000 square miles

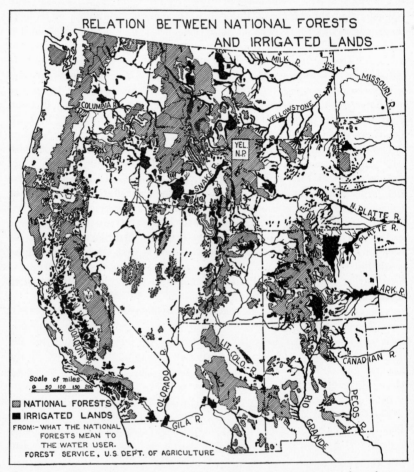

FIG. 222 — This map shows how much the citizens of one state are dependent on good forest cover in another state on land cared for by the National Government — a good example of the present economic complex.

of sand hills, apparently left by ancient stream-work, later blown around as dunes, still later fastened by grass into a rolling area and containing many pocketed valleys.

In Kansas, Nebraska and Colorado the surface is more level than it is

[10] The old resident on the Plains lives on soils of sandy loam. The hard soils are continually changing hands.

farther north. Much of it is outwash left by streams fed by Rocky Mountain glaciers in an ancient era of greater rain.[11]

The Staked Plain of western Oklahoma, Texas and part of New Mexico, despite its great elevation, is the largest tract of nearly level land [12] in the United States. Its base is a horizontal layer of limestone with " breaks " to the west and many breaks to the east, making an area of rough country in north central Texas.

## Rivers of the Great Plains

As most of the scanty rain falls in one season — fortunately for man it is the summer — most of the streams that rise in the Great Plains are dry a part of the time, and have channels choked with sand. The master streams, fed by Rocky Mountain snows and springs, naturally flow all the time, often with declining water content as the distance from the mountain increases. Man has now seized their waters for irrigation so that the Arkansas and the South Platte are dry a good part of the year and only the Missouri and North Platte continue to flow. Even the latter would doubtless have been dry at times if they had wide expanses of good, irrigable land to which their waters could be led by gravity.

From Saskatchewan to the Staked Plains, inclusive, there are many little inland basins without outlet whose waters are brackish, saline, or even alkaline.[13] This makes drinking-water scarce in this region. Many a rancher has wide acres all his own (really government land), because he owns the only water-hole where stock can drink. Farm wells are often several hundred feet deep.

## Natural Vegetation

The region is naturally treeless save for strips of cottonwoods and willows along the watercourses. Trees planted in the grass usually die. The grass gets the water-supply with its surface-roots before it reaches the roots of the trees. Cultivation makes many varieties of trees grow in the more humid parts of the area. (U. S. Dept. Agr. Bulletin 1113.)

The grasses fall into two groups, the short, surface-rooting varieties and the taller, deep-rooting varieties. In seasons of light rains the short surface-rooting varieties thrive and the deep-rooting varieties wait. In seasons of heavy rain the deep-rooting varieties can get moisture, grow tall and make seed.

[11] See Bowman's *Forest Physiography*, p. 417.

[12] " A place where you saw a visitor coming at sun-up and watched him all day, and then he didn't get to your place until half an hour late for supper."

[13] In the Sand Hills of Nebraska drifting dunes choked up most of the streams until this area is dotted with lakes from a few acres to two or three square miles in extent. A few have flowing outlets. More have outlets through the sand and are therefore sweet, but some are in basins without outlets and have collected enough potash to make them a considerable source of potash supply during the potash famine of the World War. Its cost, however, is many times that of mining the good deposits of Germany and Alsace.

As is the case with most arid regions, the grasses are very nutritious and hold their nutriment through the winter so that animals can find feed if their numbers are not greater than the food supply. Over-pasturing prevents the seeding of good grasses and has caused a great increase of weeds in some localities. In sandy locations over-pasturing breaks the grass-protection of old dunes; the sand being liberated is

again blown about. Thus the dunes may move to the next man's land and ruin it. Therefore, Kansas has a law that a man whose land is injured by drifting sand can collect damages when his neighbor has been careless and let his sand loose. Many parts of this area have had the pasture-value cut in half by over-grazing. The cure is to let the grass have a chance to seed before it is pastured.

*Agriculture*

Dr. O. E. Baker, as a result of his careful studies previously mentioned, clas-sifies the Great Plains into three main agricultural types: the farm-grazing,

FIG. 223 — We are destroying even the unplowed plain. Over-pasturing destroyed the grass so that the wind blew away the top soil save for the hummock which the horse is nibbling. (Courtesy U. S. Dept. Agr.)

the grazing-forage, and the arid-grazing (see Fig. 214).

(1) The farm-grazing belt is the eastern or more humid part of the Great Plains. It is about fifty to a hundred and fifty miles wide. In this area the crops are more valuable than pasture, but pasture takes up more of the land than the crops, only 21% [14] being in crop in 1919. The farm here needs to have one to two square miles, 640 to 1280 acres. In 1919 there were on the 81,000,000 acres of this land 90,000 farms using on the average 900 acres of land each. In the Dakotas it takes five to fifteen acres of grass for a cow or a steer; in Texas fifteen to twenty-five are necessary.[15] Live-stock is almost a necessity for the farmer here because

[14] In the different sections of this farming-grazing area the percentage of land in crop was as follows: spring wheat, 33⅓; corn, 29; corn and spring wheat, 22; cotton, 8.

[15] The line of fifteen acres per cow or steer crosses the Canadian boundary with fourteen inches of rainfall in northeastern Montana, and reaches the Gulf of Mexico near Corpus Christi with twenty-five inches of rainfall. The greater heat makes greater evaporation and less net effect of rainfall.

the frequent failures of grain-crops may leave him entirely without income, but if he has cattle his failed wheat-crop may be mowed for hay and his corn may make fodder if it does not make grain.

The crops in this long strip are in each case the same as the crops grown in the agricultural region to the eastward. The map (Fig. 214) shows the extension into the Great Plains of the spring-wheat area (also barley, oats and rye). Farther south there is a feeble extension of the corn-zone, then of winter wheat along with corn and sorghum. In the south, there is sorghum for the cattle and some cotton, but the cotton plants are small and the yield is low. Its chief advantage is that scanty vegetation cover and cold winter make it hard for the boll-weevil to survive the winter. (Fig. 127.)

(2) The grazing-forage section is separated from the farming-grazing section by the line [16] where pasture product becomes more valuable than crops. Crops here cover only 7% of the whole area. Most of the land is, of course, in pasture. It takes fifteen to twenty-five acres to keep a cow. The chief crops are corn and sorghum for winter forage, often with a field of wheat as speculation. If the weather is just right the crop will be fine, often far above the national or state average. If the weather is wrong the failure may be complete. On the average, wheat yields three-fourths as much as in the farm-

FIG. 224 — This ingenious photograph of two steers on the same scale shows the modern beef animal, weight 1000 lbs., and the now nearly extinct Texas longhorn, weight 500 lbs. The meager beast is the result of three centuries of buffalo life on the Spanish cattle from the Mexican settlements. (Courtesy W. H. Black, U. S. Dept. Agr.)

ing-grazing district, and three-fifths as much as it does in the wheat-belts to the east.

This belt had 120,000,000 acres of land and 98,000 farms in 1919. The land requirements are from two to four square miles per farm, 1280 to 2500 acres, provided there is no irrigation.

(3) The arid-grazing sections appear on the map in a number of

[16] The line is determined by the place " where wheat-growing ceases to be a good gamble and becomes a bad gamble." A Canadian saying.

" Last May 28 (1922) men and women of various creeds at New England, N. D., united in one common prayer for a bountiful harvest, following five successive wheat-crop failures. On October 31 they joined in a Community Thanksgiving." (*Philadelphia Evening Bulletin,* October 31, 1922.)

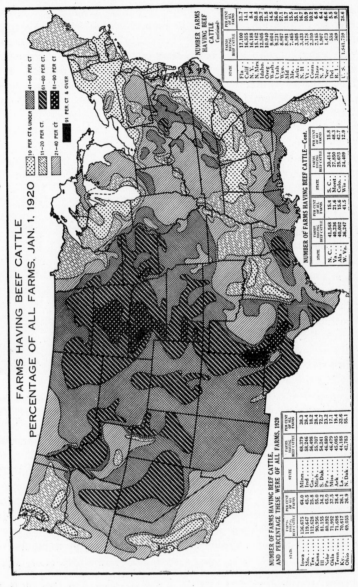

Fig. 225 — This map shows much regional geography. (Courtesy U. S. Dept. Agr.)

places. This is the rough land of the breaks and bad lands; the sandy lands of valley bottoms and the sand-hill country of Nebraska; and lowlands which are usually too arid for any agriculture except possibly here and there a little field of sorghum or corn-fodder. As compared to the highland, there is less rainfall in the lowlands and more heat and more evaporation. These tend to decrease the efficiency of the little rain that does fall.

The arid-grazing areas need twenty to forty acres to keep a cow and from twenty-five hundred to ten thousand acres for a one-family farm.

Fig. 226 — Ditching machine deepening irrigation ditch on Canadian Pacific Railway lands awaiting settlers, 1922, Brooks, Alberta. Another of the many cases where machine has replaced muscle and multiplied our powers and our riches. (Photo J. Russell Smith.)

Since sheep have cleft lips and can pasture closer [17] than cattle, and also need less water, these sections have more sheep than the rest of the Great Plains, which is largely given over to cattle. In the northern part so much of the land still belongs to the government as to interfere with satisfactory fencing, and the sheep travel in bands of one thousand to fifteen hundred, accompanied by shepherd and dogs. Most of them spend the summer in the Rocky Mountain National Forests, often above the timber-line. In winter the sheep go back to eat alfalfa hay and the dry nutritious grass of the plains. In Texas, where the land was given out in great Spanish grants,[18] it is all privately owned; most of the sheep-land is fenced in wolf-proof fences [19] and the sheep run at large. Incidentally

[17] Partly from this cause arose the bitter feud between sheep men and cattle men, resulting in the deaths of both sheep and men, and sometimes approaching the proportion of civil war.

[18] There is a sign on a Texas ranch reading, " seventy-eight miles to headquarters."

[19] Over nearly all this region the United States Government now maintains a staff of government hunters whose sole job is to exterminate predatory animals — wolves, coyotes, mountain lions, bear. One lone and wary she-wolf with only three toes on one foot, indicating trap experience, cost the cattle-men $15,000. She ranged a radius of forty miles and killed two yearling cattle a week for five years before she

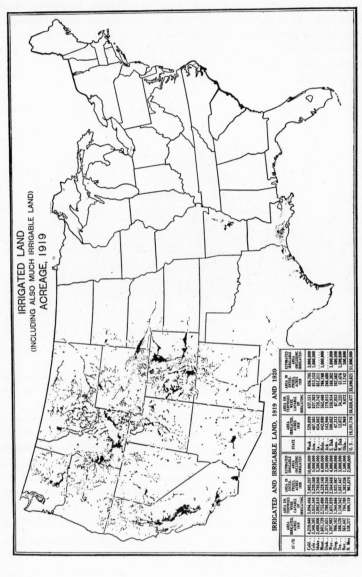

Fig. 227 — Owing to the difficulty of showing small areas, this map is not far from being a map of irrigable land. Irrigation cannot be the national panacea that many have hoped. Note the location of river valleys. (Courtesy U. S. Dept. Agr.)

the range on which sheep are free is twice as productive as a similar range in which they are herded in compact bunches because the trampling of great numbers of sheep injures the grass. The Sand Hill Country of Nebraska is unlike the other grazing sections in that its moist valleys grow enough forage to winter the stock, which is almost entirely cattle. The barbs of needle grass enter the skins of sheep.

These arid grazing areas, having the lowlands, contain nearly all of the irrigated land of the region. Owing to the deep, narrow valleys of the Montana streams, the largest irrigations are on the Bow (Saskatchewan), Platte and Arkansas rivers (Fig. 227). Irrigated land is usu-

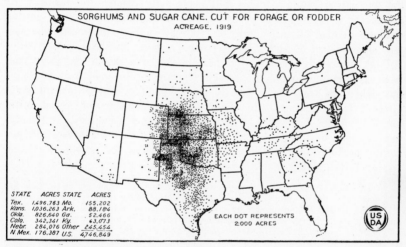

SORGHUMS AND SUGAR CANE. CUT FOR FORAGE OR FODDER
ACREAGE. 1919

EACH DOT REPRESENTS
2:000 ACRES

| STATE | ACRES | STATE | ACRES |
|---|---|---|---|
| Tex. | 1,496,763 | Mo. | 155,202 |
| Kans. | 1,036,263 | Ark. | 88,184 |
| Okla. | 826,640 | Ga. | 52,466 |
| Colo. | 342,341 | Ky. | 43,073 |
| Nebr. | 284,076 | Other | 245,454 |
| N.Mex. | 176,387 | U.S. | 4,746,849 |

Fig. 228 — Sorghum fodder for the ranch is a vital part of the live-stock industry.

ally put through a crop-rotation consisting of wheat, corn, beets or potatoes and alfalfa which stands for a number of years. The scattered oases of alfalfa render a great service by furnishing winter forage to the flocks and the herds that spend most of the year on adjacent pastures. It is in these better sections also that most of the dairying of the region is concentrated, because of the alfalfa hay and the corn and because of the physical fact that a dairy cow cannot easily make the daily mileage necessary to pick her living from twenty to forty acres of

could be killed. Another wolf in the bad lands of South Dakota was so well known that the farmers made up a purse of $1000 for his capture, and one Jim Young, government hunter, followed him for nine months across two states and finally got him.

The killing off of coyotes by white men removed the natural check from prairie dogs, which increase like rabbits, and by 1901 had completely taken about four thousand square miles of western Kansas. Just as men had begun to despair and fear that the dogs would take the whole plains, poison-gas warfare was discovered and the prairie dog ceased to trouble the ranchmen.

land and get back to the barn to be milked.  The Arkansas Valley
of eastern Colorado sends cantaloupes, Rocky Fords, late in the summer
to widely scattered markets.

### Agricultural Future

As prices and land-values rise there can be considerable extension of
irrigation by water-storage,[20] but most of this great region must continue
to be a land of farms and ranches, depending upon the rains of heaven,
rather than upon the waters of a ditch.

It must continue also to be a land whose yield is uncertain because of
the fluctuating rainfall.  This will perennially trouble the farmer.  At
present he is pressed also by two problems of adjustment: first, getting
the land divided off into family-size farms; and second, finding the system of agriculture [21] that fits his particular soil, climate and location.

First, the family-size farm.  It has already been shown that this varies
from six hundred to ten thousand acres, and if the man does not have
the right-sized tract he is greatly handicapped in conducting the right
kind of farm business, which may be grain farming or mixed farming or live-stock farming.  If the man needs twelve hundred, or twenty-
five hundred, or five thousand acres it is plain that the homestead law
permitting him six hundred and forty acres does not provide for satisfactory farms, which should be large enough to carry a hundred cattle.[22]

---

[20] The well-established fact that irrigation costs more than letting it rain has
helped to put a check upon the extension of irrigation for a time.

"Some irrigated land on at least fifty per cent of the farms of these three
states (Montana, North and South Dakota) is possible by making use of the flood-
waters from torrential rains and the melting snows in the spring.  In these three
states, where it is possible to soak the ground down four to five feet once during
the year, a good crop is almost certain. . . . Many farmers of the drought-stricken
'triangle' area of Northern Montana have taken advantage of this flood-water on
from one to one hundred acres of their farms and are receiving bumper crops from it.
The use of flood-waters for irrigation is not an experiment but has proven to be one
of the best practices of dry-land farming of northern Montana and there is no
reason why it could not be used in places with similar conditions." ("Use Flood
Waters for Irrigating Farms," Blaine Ferguson, *The Dakota Farmer*, July 15, 1923.)
The Montana station (Bozeman) has a bulletin on this.  There has been talk of
diverting Platte River floods to high plains.

This report and suggestion interest me greatly because it is a perfectly feasible,
tractor-road-scraper, edition of an age-old practice of the primitive agriculturist.
(See chapter on Southwestern Plateaus.)  It is real agricultural adjustment applicable
in all lands of limited rain.  It should spread as swiftly as styles in clothes.

[21] In western Texas a kind of crop-insurance is sought by planting alternate rows
of corn, one of an early, and one of a late variety.  They make different calls for
moisture.  It is being found in some places that corn in the fallow year of dry-
farming does not hurt the next crop much.  It is also being found that too much
tillage removes organic matter and soil blows away.  In some places blow-holes are
one hundred feet deep.  Verily this is a land of problems.

[22] "They thought, when the Kincaid law was passed increasing the homestead
allotments from a quarter to a full section, the people would make out better, but
they are disgusted right along.  They stick around two or three years, long enough
to prove up on their land and get title to it, and then they sell.  At the usual price

In 1924 the United States Department of Agriculture and the Montana Experiment Station started, with a 55,000-acre reservation at Miles City, Montana, to "experiment in stock raising and growing forage crops in connection therewith."

The whole region was settled first by the cowboy, who exploited the natural grass, and then came the bonanza wheat-grower, who exploited the good soil. This is a type of man who is willing to take a chance.

He hopes for the great crop of forty or fifty or even sixty bushels, which sometimes comes, and thereby makes him independent. Meanwhile growing wheat permits him to loaf for most of the year. Meanwhile also come the Department of Agriculture man from Washington; the man from the state college of agriculture; the county demonstration agent, the railroad representative and commissions of wise men[23] dinning in his ear the old sermon of diversified agriculture — corn-fields, hay-stacks, cattle, hogs, even cows with twelve months of work. The bonanza wheat-farmer has a saying to the effect that he would rather have four dollars from wheat than ten dollars from milking cows, so he takes another chance. This region hung on to its wheat acreage enlarged by the World War, when every other wheat area had reduced acreage. In many localities it is found that in a decade of change from bonanza wheat to live-stock farming the bonanza wheat-growers have sold out and gone away. They are to some extent a psychological type.

The Great Plains are a land that you love or you hate. In the winter come blizzards that are so blinding that you cannot see the length of your automobile and getting lost is most easy. In the spring there is usually a wind-storm or two in many parts of the plain strong enough to

---

for a section a man can just about consider himself paid for the time he put in on it, not considering the work done by the wife and kids.

"As the homesteaders quit, the ranches are getting back to their old size again. Ranch people buy up most of the sections. For a time there were mighty few really large ranches left. . . ." (J. E. Ogier of North Platte, Nebr., in Philadelphia *Evening Bulletin,* July 1924.)

[23] " . . . Your Commission concludes that a system of farm management in the Southwest (Great Plains section of Saskatchewan), to be reasonably certain of success, should be of a diversified character. The more the risk is divided the less heavily the losses will fall in any one season. There must also be live-stock of some kind to consume farm products, such as straw, corn, fodder, sunflowers, alfalfa, sweet clover, millet, low-grade grain, which are of a nature unsuited to direct marketing, and to employ home labor the year round. This live-stock must be an important and constant part of the farm and not merely a sideline. There must be grazing-land or access to grazing-land in order to take care of the stock during a part of the summer. There must be fodder and feed-crops. There must be summer-fallow or fallow substitutes. There should be a reserve of fodder and seed from year to year. There should be among the grain-crops a cash-crop and preferably an autumn-sown crop as well as spring-sown ones. There should be produced every year as much as possible of the farm family's needs, so as to reduce the outlay for supplies." (*Report of the* (Saskatchewan) *Royal Commission of Inquiry into Farming Conditions,* 1921, p. 55.) In 1924 unofficial reports credited Montana and adjacent states and provinces with a great increase in dairying.

blow half the water out of a bucket which you may be carrying. All summer long the wind blows and blows, and the sunshine glares. If the rain comes it is in showers which are soon over. Meanwhile there is little else to do but watch the weather. Many a settler's wife has paced the floor of her shadeless little kitchen until she wore it through, and there is a high record of women's insanity in some parts of the plain.

"Only six more months here until we prove up," exclaimed a pent-up woman in the sand-hills of Nebraska to a stranger who stopped for a drink of water. "Then you bet we're going to take title, sell out and leave this place." It *must* be miles to your neighbor if your farm has two thousand acres, but this poor woman was on a farm of only six hundred and forty acres where they needed twenty-five hundred. So they had to give up the struggle, as did many others who had tried to make homes in the sand-hills. Often the house was built of sod, and heated with "Hereford chips," dried cow-dung, made into a harmless chunk of cellulose by wind and rain and sun. This is the fuel of the dweller on treeless plains in all ages and in all continents.

On the other hand, there are people, especially I think men, who love

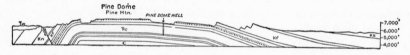

FIG. 229 — Cross section of a part of the Wyoming Plain showing how Nature collects petroleum; also how she makes escarpments. (Courtesy U. S. Geol. Surv.)

the plains. There is a charm, somewhat like the charm of the sea, about the endless, rolling hills and the horizon devoid of any objects. To some this gives a sense of space, of largeness, of being near to nature, to the Infinite, to God.

### Minerals

This region has great mineral resources and a small mineral industry. The Wyoming plain has several oil-fields, which produced twenty-six million barrels in 1922, or 4.7% of the American product. Of much greater permanent importance is the coal mined in Colorado, near Denver, in several counties in Wyoming and in Montana and Alberta. Much the greatest potential resource of the region is in the vast reserves of sub-bituminous and lignite in Wyoming, Montana, North Dakota, Saskatchewan and Alberta. The amount is estimated at three times that of the entire coal-wealth of Appalachia. Its production, of course, is an insignificant fraction of that of Appalachia, and any heavy utilization of it seems to await a rather distant future.

The Panhandle of Texas is the center of a huge deposit of gypsumanhydrate and salt. It is from three hundred to seven hundred feet thick, two hundred and twenty-five by one hundred and twenty miles long, and from four hundred to two thousand feet down. It runs from Salina, Kansas, through Oklahoma, Texas and New Mexico, to the Pecos River. It is geologically like the similar deposits on the Elbe in Germany, which have the world's chief potash deposit. There are excellent prospects as indicated by wells that potash will be found somewhere in this deposit, but it has not yet been found in commercial quantities.

## Cities

This region is not the natural place for the development of large cities. It has just enough towns to wait upon the country and the railroads. The first towns here, sometimes called " Hells on Wheels," were those interesting collections of technical skill, transient labor and floating vice that make up the construction camp of a frontier railroad. When a new section was begun, it moved on to the new site, leaving a lonely station-agent among the old tin-cans and refuse-heaps.

Today the chief town population within this region is at the places where railroads change crews and repair their equipment.

On the western margin are cities that are gateways between the mountain and the plain, and also metropolises of the irrigation centers that have been developed where the mountain waters first reached the level lands of the plains. The Rocky Mountain mines as well as the ranches of the plains give to Greeley, Pueblo, and especially Denver, a large distribution-trade. Mines with their expensive equipment made much business.

The remoteness of this population from the manufacturing East gives local enterprises a distinct advantage for the home-market. For example, Pueblo has the largest steel-plant west of Chicago, nearly a thousand miles from its nearest rival. Conversely this distance also makes it difficult for factories in these towns to export to outside markets.

The beauties of the Rocky Mountains bring to Denver and Colorado Springs a large tourist business. These thriving cities are in beautiful locations immediately at the foot of the mountains. The crisp dry air has made these cities a health resort to which people come on stretchers and remain in business. Denver's municipal automobile camp, with water, laundry, clubhouse, shower baths, steam table and other conveniences, is ahead of the inns of much of the world.

FIG. 230 — Corral, tank, and range of Angora goats, source of mohair, and beast of the semi-desert. (Courtesy Bureau of Animal Industry, U. S. Dept. Agr.)

## CHAPTER XXIV

### THE LOWER RIO GRANDE

THE horizontal limestone layers of the Staked Plains slope downward through the Edwards Plateau, south of the Great Plains, and finally end in a great fault called the Balcones Escarpment (Fig. 246). The dissected escarpment stands up like a mountain-front for many miles southwest of Austin. South of the escarpment the land is low and flat. The Lower Rio Grande Region lies between the Balcones Escarpment, the Mexican Uplands, the Cotton Belt and the sea. At its eastern edge it has a barrier beach, and behind the beach are the usual marshes. The summers are hot, very hot, but not humid. The rainfall is light and the region suffers from severe droughts similar to those that visit the Great Plains. Most of its area is sandy semi-desert, marked by cactus, chaparral, mesquite and other brush and bunch-grass.[1] Most of the area is fit only for ranches of low productivity and therefore of large size. These ranches are occupied chiefly by cattle, but also by some goats. This region is an arid grazing land with agricultural oases where

[1] Mr. O. F. Cook, of the United States Department of Agriculture, reports that mesquite and other brush and small trees have replaced large areas of grass in southern Texas since the white man came. This happened because in Indian days grass grew and waited for fires which killed the young trees. The heavier pasturing by cattle and sheep left no grass to burn and the bushes had a chance to live.

water can be had for irrigation.  The climate is hot enough and the summers long enough to make it, where water can be had, another Florida for f r u i t and truck, another C o t t o n  Belt for cotton.

## The Great River

The Rio Grande, the Great River of the Spaniards, is the great feature of this region, the Nile to t h i s near - Egypt. The Rio Grande is a ribbon of water winding through a maze of sand-bars, and then again it is a vast flood covering large areas of b o t h Texas and Mexico. In 1 9 2 4 p l a n s were under way to build levees for flood-protection n e a r Brownsville like those along the Mississippi.[2] As an international boundary it is a shifting failure (Fig. 231) and at low tide the Mexican can wade i n t o t h e United States. T h e R i o Grande system furnishes water to irrigate a number of

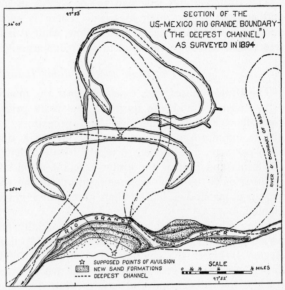

FIG. 231 — This reproduction from the United States boundary survey is a choice illustration of the fact that rivers are forever shifting their courses in flood plains and deltas, and leaving old channels which often become oxbow lakes, of which two are shown here. The speed of the process is surprising. One of the limitations of nations is shown by the fact that a major general in the U. S. Army reported the discovery on one of these surveys that rivers changed their courses. The statesmen (?) of a previous generation had made this one a national boundary. In practice this particular Mexican-United States aggravation is worked as follows: If the river slowly eats its way into the land and builds up the opposite bank, as shown in the area of "new sand" above, the boundary is changed. But the nationality remains unchanged if the river suddenly breaks across one of the narrow necks at a point of "avulsion," and thereby transfers a tract of land to the other bank of the river. Thus, El Paso has a piece of Mexico right in its midst. Nominees for Congress should be compelled to pass a stiff examination in Geography.

productive localities which support nearly all the population of this region. On the Mexican side 18,000 acres of cotton were the chief crop in the year 1921.[3]  Half of their cotton was destroyed by flood in June, but

[2] A part of this plan was to send some flood-water through an old channel reaching the Gulf forty miles north of the present mouth of the river.

[3] *Trade and Economic Review,* No. 20, U. S. Dept. of Commerce, 1922.

there was still time to plant corn, the second crop in importance, and expect a harvest.

The United States side had 170,000 acres of land under cultivation, and 400,000 under ditch in 1923. There is enough water to irrigate 200,000 acres by the river's normal flow, while it is estimated that storage reservoirs could raise the total to 1,000,000 acres.[4]

### The Fruit and Vegetable Industry

The United States side, especially near the mouth of the Rio Grande, experienced a land-boom during a few years prior to 1923. Owing to the influence of new railroads, land-speculators, and plenty of distant buyers, unimproved-land prices went up for a time to $400 and even $600 per acre, in a section so nearly frostless that it is a direct rival of California and Florida for winter vegetables and citrus fruits. The first carloads of citrus fruits were shipped out in the winter of 1921–22, and by 1923 one and a half million orange and grapefruit-trees had been planted.

Many winter vegetables are grown, especially onions, of which for a period in spring (beginning shipments about April 10th) the Rio Grande Region furnishes the chief national supply. Unfortunately, this region must share the dangers common to the truck-business, especially winter truck — limited demand and ease of glutted markets.[5]

The chief need of this region is agricultural adjustment. One method is to put the eggs into several baskets — grow staples, such as hogs, poultry, and dairy-produce. The production of these staples is increasing. In some cases the water-supply needs rearrangement.[6]

Many of the land companies had individual pumping-plants on the river, which often shifts its course, making trouble for the irrigator. By more comprehensive plans gravity can bring the water to the fields.

The long growing-season makes it possible to have a very rich agriculture here with one or two (or even more) summer crops, and also a winter crop of vegetables on the same land each year. Thus the

---

[4] *Circular,* U. S. Reclamation Service, April 1923.

[5] *The New York Produce Reporter,* May 3, 1924, told how the carry-over of old onions had made the shipment of new onions net a loss from the beginning of the season. "The average loss on old onions per car is rarely less than $750.00 and often as high as $1000.00 a car. Texas onions that cost $2.50 to $2.60 laid down here were freely offered Friday at $1.45 and less per crate."

[6] "Many farmers have been successful in this valley, while many others have failed and suffered heavy losses. The principal reasons for the failures in the irrigated sections appear to be over-exploitation and lack of operating funds, want of experience in irrigation and tropical farming, poor management, lack of marketing organizations, high freight-rates, the want of soil surveys and the determination of crops best adapted to the various types of soil; the high cost of water and, under some of the irrigation systems, the uncertainty of water supply." (*Irrigation Development in Lower Rio Grande Valley, Texas.* Reclamation Service, Department of the Interior, 1923.)

farmer can apply the much-preached diversification and still keep his specialties. Such diversification took place rapidly after the first rush of settlement.

This region has a social problem in that nearly all the laboring people are Mexicans who have found American wages and security much better than could be had on their own side of the river.

FIG. 232 — Typical landscape in the higher reaches of the central Rockies. (Courtesy Canadian Pacific Ry.)

## CHAPTER XXV

### THE ROCKY MOUNTAINS

THE Rockies are young mountains, geologically. There has not been time for water, frost, wind and the other forces of nature to wear them down. Therefore, like the Alps, they are high, sharp, rugged. Their tops are usually bare rock. They are high enough to be snow-covered late in the spring or early in the summer even in the south, while on the northern part, which reaches almost to the Arctic, the snow coat comes farther and farther down the slopes and lasts longer into the summer. In Colorado, Montana and Alberta interesting little glaciers hang in the high valleys, while below them are beautiful lakes which these same glaciers, in days of ancient greatness, gouged out with their feet and dammed up with their moraines.

In this upper realm beyond the timber-line there are large areas of so-called Alpine vegetation having midsummer foliage of strange beauty. It is a landscape that often fascinates the lover of nature, and it also pleases the sheep-herder because it offers rich midsummer pasture.

Below this comes the zone of forest, its upper cold-limit getting higher and higher as we go south. Its lower (dry) limit also gets higher as it goes south because of increasing summer heat and aridity.

Still lower down are mountain valleys, some of them deep with forest, impressive with cathedral gloom, others high with grass and blooming flowers; others again, shut off from good rainfall, show sagebrush, cactus and even the forbidding alkali, the sign of aridity.

These mountains first came to the attention of the people of the Mississippi Valley and the East as a source from which daring men brought furs in canoes down the Missouri River or on horseback across the Plains. They also figured largely in the minds of the publicists of the pre-railroad

FIG. 233 — Colorado mountain showing a beautiful illustration of the way the warm sun and evaporation make the timber line higher on the southwest (left) side. Wet Mountain Valley, 8500 feet. (Courtesy Colorado Agricultural College.)

age as an impassable barrier, the utmost possible limit of useful land, the boundary that God had set to the westward extension of the American people.[1]

These mountains still help to make a barrier as is shown by the shipment of Utah produce to the East by way of the Columbia River and the Panama Canal, and the corresponding shipment of Milwaukee produce to the Pacific Coast by way of New York and the Panama Canal. It costs money[2] to carry freight up and down three or four thousand feet.

[1] We in our wisdom who criticize those " ancients " should remember that we are thinking in railroad terms and terms of present knowledge, and that the " ancients " were thinking in pre-railroad terms, a thing we cannot do. In pre-railroad conditions, the " ancient " was not very far from right.

[2] The Canadian Pacific spent $6,500,000.00 (1913–16) in digging a five-mile tunnel under the Selkirks (one of the ranges of the Rockies) west of Banff to lower the tracks 552 feet to an altitude of 3795 feet. Work was started in 1923 on the Moffatt Tunnel under the Continental Divide west of Denver. It will shorten the distance from New York to San Francisco by seventy miles.

## Mining

Shortly after the gold-rush to California in '49, prospectors started through the Rocky Mountains, and for thirty years the chief output of this region was precious metal. In 1862 placers were found in Madison County, Montana, and in three years they were yielding $18,000,000 a year (worked out by 1900), in a locality 150 miles by wagon from Fort Benton, Montana, then the head of steamboat navigation on the Missouri.

Fig. 234 — Butte, Montana. The great copper deposits make a city where the smelter fumes kill every leaf and every blade of grass.

We would not think it was navigation now, considering the small size of the boat, the delays from sticking on sand-bars, and the cost of cutting wood to burn in the boilers, but there was no alternative save a wagon, which was a much more expensive means of transportation.

A few years later gold-placers were discovered at Idaho City, a short distance northwest of Boise. They yielded more than a billion before they were exhausted. Cripple Creek, Leadville and other mining towns are well known, but the most conspicuous aspect is the quick exhaustion of the mines [3] together with the abandoned town with shacks boarded up

[3] The Colorado Rockies, an exploited land with a riotous past and the promise of a conservative future. The riot is furnished by the frequent successions of booming prosperity of mining, followed by dead abandonment. In a 60-mile circuit from Boulder, Colorado, in 1922, there was never a mile of the sixty without sign of abandoned mining enterprise. Sometimes it was only a hole in the hillside with brown or white tailings spread out below it, and a tumble-down shack near by. Sometimes it was a sizable mill, with windows smashed and roof falling in; sometimes it was a whole village. Some remains of the earliest epoch showed only the foundations of buildings. An abandoned railroad added to the impression of ruin.

and a few lonesome burros browsing in the erstwhile streets. Here and there the mother-lodes that yielded the placers were found. These mines lasted longer, and made Colorado for many years one of the leading gold-producing States. Mining experts say that the best ores were near the top and are now gone; that means that most of the Colorado smelters are probably permanently closed. Fifteen mountain counties in Colorado lost in total population (1910–1920). One of them lost 67%. The golden age is past.

At the present time Utah has in Park City the world's largest lead and silver camp. After getting $250,000,000 worth of metal from sur-face-workings, deeper ores were found in 1922, and therefore this mining camp has the promise of several decades of prosperity.

The greatest of all the Rocky Mountain discoveries was the copper of Butte, Montana. There was a great hill of granitic rock, cracked by a labyrinth of fissures. Molten lava flowed into the fissures and the hot lava cooked out and concentrated the copper.

This hill has yielded a billion dollars since 1869 and has been the greatest copper camp in the world. In 1921 it yielded eight billion pounds, or 27% of the output of the United States, and it made the amazing total of eight million tons of freight. Its mines and smelters furnish the chief occupation of Butte, 41,000; Great Falls, 24,000; Helena, 12,000; Anaconda, 11,000. The city of Great Falls, with water-power plants, furnishes power and has smelters, while Anaconda counts itself famous for having the highest smokestack in the world. This is made necessary by the sulphur that is in the copper ores. Smelting turns sulphur into sulphuric acid, a gas so deadly that no green thing can grow for miles around. Hence a desolate neighborhood until improve-ments in smelting permitted plant growth to replace the artificial desert.

There are numerous deposits of coal in the southern central Rockies — probably of greater ultimate value than are all the high-priced metals.

## Future Mining

This region promises for the future two industries of gigantic propor-tions, phosphate and oil from oil-shales. When these industries shall come it is not yet easy to say. Some phosphate rock has already been dug, although there is no immediate prospect of a big industry. But the central Rockies contain the world's greatest known phosphate beds. The economic geologist tells us that in Colorado, Wyoming, Idaho and Utah (see Fig. 134) there are something like six thousand million tons of phosphate rock. Explorations are continually revealing more. This

---

The riotous past was further evidenced by the all-too-frequent signs of forest fires; fires recent, fires ancient, but always deadly. The conservatism of the future is indicated by the forest-ranger caring for the forest which must be the permanent use of nearly all this land if it is rightly used.

resource is of staggering importance in a world short of phosphorus and constantly losing it through a commercial agriculture which sends products to distant cities which in turn send their sewage to the sea. Of all the commercial fertilizers phosphorus is the scarcest. Without it all crops

Fig. 235 — "It was built in an hour of hope and visioning." The metal of ten million years' formation is often gathered quickly and then —. (Courtesy Anthony Euwer, Portland, Ore.)

fail. Here, therefore, is a great resource for the future. It is a misfortune that it lies so far from market. The phosphate would be immensely more valuable if it were on the banks of the Great Lakes, the Mississippi, or the Ohio, where it could float to the great sea. Fortunately, most of this mineral land belongs to the United States Government. Let us hope that it will be handled wisely. Royalties from it and the oil-shale might almost pay the national debt — or become the basis for a great trust. The choice depends upon our political sense.

## Oil-Shale

Great stretches of barren shale, cursed by stock-men because it produced no grass, and by farmers because it produced no crops, turn out to be rich with oil. The Colorado State Geologist says that in the north-

FIG. 236 — Hundreds of mine buildings, living and dead, cling to Rocky Mountain walls almost as bird nests stick to cliffs. Marble quarry near Denver. (Courtesy Denver Chamber of Commerce. Photo Charles S. Price.)

western corner of his state fifteen hundred square miles have commercially workable oil-shale beds containing thirty-six thousand million barrels of oil. This is about ten times as much as has been produced in the United States since 1859. Other Rocky Mountain states have part of this deposit. There is some of it out in Utah.

These shales will not be the scene of the oil-fever nor will they be the gambler's paradise. Those excitements gather around the wild-cat well which suddenly spurts forth its liquid fortune. Oil-shale must be mined or quarried like any other rock, and afterwards it undergoes laborious processes of distillation which require an extensive manufacturing plant. It is claimed that this quarrying and manufacturing enterprise can be so organized as to produce a barrel of oil as good as that of Pennsylvania, at from $.50 to $1.50, whereas the best Pennsylvania crude sells for several times that price.

### Minerals and Government

Rocky Mountain government from first to last has been strongly flavored by mineral influence. The gold-rush made into one group dozens, hundreds, even thousands of men, gathered from every class of society, from every walk of life, from every country, one might also add, from every jail in the world. A crowd like this when flung far into the wilderness must govern itself. When private shootings became intolerable or the sheriff could not keep order, the vigilance committee, the crudest but perhaps not the least fair of democracies, arose to handle difficult cases.

In the later stages, working the deep lodes required the great corporation. Millions of dollars came from New York or Boston, to erect smelters, crushers, concentrators and other huge works. Hundreds and thousands of men were employed. Most of the men were without families, and most of them were transients. Where men do not expect to remain they do not have much interest in government. On the other hand the affairs of the state government are usually matters of great importance to the corporation. Here we get prime conditions for political corruption, and by this, unfortunately, the Rocky Mountains have at times attracted much attention to themselves. The stake of the miner in the state is vastly different from that of the ranchman and the irrigator. The latter can succeed only by staying and they have the attitude of the homemaker rather than that of him who digs and runs.

### Rocky Mountain Valleys

The Rocky Mountains are not continuous. In central Wyoming there is a wide plain between the Laramie Mountains (8000 feet high) and the Big Horn Mountains (10,000 to 13,000 feet). In this gap are the Laramie Plains and the Green River Basin, both of which have been treated with the Great Plains. Within the mountains themselves are many valleys, some of which have been made by the filling of glacial lakes, some by the accumulation of soil washed down from the mountains. In Colorado these valleys are called "parks." North Park, which comprises 1500 square miles, is 7500 feet above the sea-level. Its high elevation prohibits the presence of trees, but it gives good rainfall and splendid grass, originally the food for thousands of antelope. South Park, forty by fifty-five miles, is 8000 to 9000 feet in elevation, and San Luis Park, the

largest of the parks, was once a lake.  It is drained by the Rio Grande
and is a fine agricultural valley [4] because it is made of water-borne soil.
Bitter Root Valley in Montana may be taken as a typical Rocky
Mountain valley.  It seems to have been formed by the settling of a
block of the earth's crust.  This process made the Dead Sea Basin.  A
lake filled this Bitter Root opening, and the lake in turn was filled
with mountain washings and drained when the river cut a gorge in the
surrounding rock walls.  Above the gorge are 511 square miles of valley,
sixty-one miles long and from three to fourteen miles wide.  As the
stream cut the gorge that drained the lake it made a series of terraces
at varying elevations.  These have frost-drainage excellent for fruit and it

FIG. 237 — The life history of a mountain lake.  The remnant of a lake that once
filled a Rocky Mountain valley.  The river that is filling it.  Witness the
marshes newly made.  In the foreground land firm enough for fields and town
site.  St. Joe River, flowing into Coeur d'Alene Lake, Idaho.  (Courtesy
B. H. Humphrey and Barrington Moore.)

is now the chief apple center of the whole Rocky Mountain region.  The
Kootenai Valley of Idaho, near the British Columbia boundary, had the
same origin as the Bitter Root Valley, but the outlet gorge is so narrow
that at times of flood the water dams up and floods some 60,000 acres of
valley land which is now being reclaimed by dikes.  Some of these valleys,
such as the Purcell Trench and the Rocky Mountain Trench, were so
scooped out by glaciers that they are open for great distances.

These mountain valleys have very different climatic conditions because
of differing elevations and differing rainfall resulting from the varying
height and direction of the enclosing mountains.  Some are too high for
agriculture (but excellent for summer pasture).  Many are dry, but
mountain streams often make irrigation possible.  Thus, the Missoula
Valley in Montana has 100,000 acres irrigated by one ditch.

[4] Pork produced in part by hogging down barley, is an important product here.

### Agriculture

Agriculture started in the Rocky Mountains when the farmers began to sell food to the miners. In the days when gold was king, thousands of men lived in camps in the wilderness. Their bacon, flour, beans, potatoes and apples came full a thousand miles across the plains. The railroads or even wagons brought the produce to the base of the Rocky Mountains. From there it was taken long distances by wagon or pack-mule to the various camps. The farmer who lived near one of these mining-camps and who had a little produce to sell got a price that was almost unbelievable. He received what the food was worth plus the charge for

Fig. 238 — Rocky Mountain Valley along Kootenai River. Bonners Ferry, Idaho.
(Courtesy Great Northern Ry.)

the long haul across a thousand miles of the plain. A Rocky Mountain garden patch in 1865 or 1870 was a source of income as good as a farm in Illinois at the same time. Under this profitable home-market, agriculture naturally expanded, but there came a day when the market was over-supplied. The surplus had to be sold in distant markets. The price that the farmer now received was the amount that was paid in the distant market, and from that amount three charges had to be deducted — the cost of the package, freight-charges to the distant market, and commission for selling the produce. If the distant market-price is one dollar, and it costs sixty cents to get the stuff to market, the price received by the farmer has dropped from $1.60 to $.40. This was a terrible day at the valley farms. It was indeed Black Friday and the catastrophe lasted through all the weeks and months and years.

This period of readjustment from import price-level to export price-level is one which has come to nearly all the Western country which started on some industry other than agriculture. As a matter of fact, the Rocky Mountain region is at the very bottom of the American price-level for farm produce because its location is most distant from all markets.[5]

The Rocky Mountain valleys and benchlands are excellent for the production of fruit. Peaches are a specialty in western Colorado. It is also excellent for staples, as is well illustrated by the Sweet Farm at Carbondale on the west slope of Colorado. Here tracts of well-drained benchland, irrigated by mountain streams, have this rotation: alfalfa, a perennial, standing three or four years, potatoes, wheat, barley and again, alfalfa. Wheat is sold. Barley and alfalfa are fed to sheep. Potatoes are sold. Potatoes yield sometimes five hundred bushels to the acre, and other crops several times the national average. The potatoes are of such excellent quality (being mealy when baked) that they are used on dining-cars and in New York hotels, but this is an exception. The region as a whole is so excellent for potatoes that the markets are often glutted, and therefore the chief produce must be meat and wool.[6]

In most of the region, animals pasture nearly everywhere at some time during the year — above the timber, in the timber, below the timber. Such distant locations always have an outlet for produce in the form of butter, cheese, dried milk and potato flour. But the time has not yet come for the large production of such intensive products.

In 1918 a man tried ten acres of lettuce in one of the high valleys of Colorado. He is said to have made $10,000. The news flew like rumors of gold. By 1923 the state had 7200 acres of lettuce, and markets had been glutted. Colorado suits lettuce because the plant requires cool weather, which is furnished by elevations of from 7000 to 10,000 feet. When the whole Mississippi Valley sweltered in a non-lettuce climate this mountain specialty supplied the summer market and the supply promptly caught up with the demand.

## The Northern Rockies

I separate the central Rockies from the northern Rockies at the Canadian Pacific Railway, which happens to be the northern limit of any important occupation by the white man. At this latitude, an elevation of

[5] For example, the average farm price of wheat December 1, 1921, was as follows: Colorado, $.76; Nebraska, $.83; Iowa, $.88; Illinois, $1.00; Michigan, $1.04; New York, $1.08; Maine, $1.75; California $1.07. Maine's small production, like that of California, placed her farmers in the same relative position as the Rocky Mountain farmer in the early days. They had outside market-price plus freight in.

[6] Some ranchers ninety miles from a railroad walk their produce to market.

4500 feet is fatal to agriculture. At Banff, where an old lake-bed affords several miles of beautiful alluvial soil, frost comes every month of the summer and people do not even attempt gardens. North of this is a little-explored land of wild mountains, peaks, snow, glaciers, lakes, lonely valleys, Indians, game and occasional prospectors. I make the region include a part of the British Columbia Plateau north of the Fraser Basin. It is a plateau with deep valleys, and geologically it is different from the Rocky Mountains. For the uses of man it is the same, an unexplored,

FIG. 239 — This noble beast shows the wild spirit of the caribou land in the cold highland of the Cassiar country, British Columbia mountains. Scene near Dease Lake. (Courtesy Bureau of Provincial Information, British Columbia.)

non-agricultural mountainous game-land which probably contains minerals. It may become a range, certainly a summer range, for some kind of foraging animals, other than those that now use it. The introduction of the reindeer and the semi-domestication of the bison [7] in various parks are very suggestive, and almost equally suggestive is the progress in taming the Rocky Mountain sheep. Now that the hunting has ceased, sheep have become so tame in the Canadian National Park, which includes the Bow River Valley, that they can be seen nearly every summer day on the road between Banff and Lake Louise.

### Forests

The southern and central Rocky Mountains have large areas of forest. It is often of poor quality and the timber is hard to get. Everywhere

[7] No hunting, protection and a few haystacks have raised a new problem in the Yellowstone Park — What shall they do with surplus elk and bison?

these mountains rise from plains that are too dry for forest. Therefore, forest is limited to a mountain-side belt with a transitional dry-line edge below and a transitional cold-line edge above. Both of these transitional edges produce little, poor, scattered, gnarled specimens of trees. In Yellowstone National Park forests begin at 5000 feet and disappear at 9800 feet on the south side and at 9300 feet on the colder north. On the Big Horns out on the plains the limits of forests are 6000 and 10,000 feet. In Colorado the limits are from 7000 to 11,000 and even 12,000 feet.

One can stand on Bald Mountain in south central Idaho and look away across the lava plains of farms and pastures. Turning east one looks over a mass of mountains worn into sharp peaks and sharp valleys, so narrow that for eighty miles there is not a single cabin. The Salmon River flows through this maze in a 250-mile canyon between the valley of the Snake, where there are farms, and the upper valley of the Salmon, where there is one of those inter-mountain valleys of good farmland.[8] Similar mountains of great roughness almost surround the Yellowstone Park.

FIG. 240 — The author of this book examining Engelmann spruce flattened by the wind at cold timber line on Pike's Peak. There were tall straight saw-log trees of this species on a protected place 500 feet lower down. (Photo Everett G. Rodebaugh.)

The San Juan Mountains of southwestern Colorado have many peaks above 13,000 feet high with a labyrinth of valleys at an elevation of 4000 to 5000 feet. It is plain that much lumber is in places where it cannot be got, even though Rocky Mountain lumbering makes use of chutes through which logs are slid down from high elevations and water-filled flumes that float wood out of many a gorge where even a donkey could not enter.

Conditions of tree-growth and wood-transportation explain why lumber is relatively unimportant in these states. They also point to pulp-wood as the most natural means of use, but there was only one mill in this region in 1924.

As in nearly all other parts of the United States, fire is here the terrible enemy of the forest. The following facts are sickening in their implications: Most of Pike's Peak and the vicinity were desolated by forest-fires between 1850 and 1860. Much of the land is still bare and just now is being replanted with trees the size of match-sticks. No man

8 Bowman, Isaiah, *Forest Physiography*, p. 323.

living is likely to see them attain saw-log size. Fortunately most of the forests of this area are now in the possession of the national government,[9] and nearly all classes of society want the forest preserved. Farmers who want irrigation water, city people who want lumber, water-supply and scenery are enthusiastically behind forest-fire protection. It is only the stock-man who pastures the mountain forests whose psychology is questionable. The vigilant National Forest Ranger Service succeeds in keeping the fires in national forests down to a small fraction of the area, in some areas as low as one-fifth of one per cent per year.[10]

### Scenery and Tourists

It is probable that the tourist is now, and will for a long time continue to be, the most important industrial resource of this region. He

Fig. 241 — A tense moment. Yellowstone Park Ranger making friends with his wards. (Courtesy National Park Service.)

is now the most rapidly growing industry.[11] The Denver Tourist Bureau reports that in 1923 $45,000,000.00 was spent in Colorado alone by tourists and that auto camps of that state give accommodation to

[9] Colorado, 20,700 square miles of national forest, one-fifth of state; Wyoming, 13,100 square miles, one-seventh of state; Montana, 25,000 square miles, one-seventh of state.

[10] A Forest Service tabulation classed the origins of fires in National Forests as follows: lightning 28%; campers, 18%; brush burning, 11%; incendiary, 11%; railroads, 9%; lumbering, 3%; unknown, 15%. Who set the incendiary 11%, and when will we treat it as a felony?

[11] Names reflect the change. Instead of Wildhorse Creek, Dead Man's Gulch, Rattlesnake Butte, names of the day of Bret Harte, the new places have soft-sounding names like — Idylwilde, Brookvale, Montrose. Red Bull Draw has become Antelope Canyon, and Skunk Canyon, Blue Bell. Alas for the passing of the Wild West!

643,000 campers. Whoever wishes to see the tourist attractions has but to write to any railroad crossing the Rockies, from the most southerly Santa Fe to the most northerly Canadian National, to receive booklets showing perfect and beautiful photographs of mountain scenery. He can also get an equally good or possibly better booklet by addressing the National Park Service at Washington. Fortunately for the people of this continent the United States Government and the Canadian Govern-

FIG. 242 — One of the mountain attractions for the nature lover and camera hunter. In the Canadian National Park at Banff the Big Horn or Rocky Mountain sheep have become as tame as bear and deer in the Yellowstone Park. (Courtesy Canadian Pacific Ry.)

ment vie with each other in setting off mountain lands as parks for the permanent possession and pleasure of all the people. Colorado contains the Estes Park and Rocky Mountain National Park; Montana, the Glacier National Park; the corners of Wyoming and neighboring states, the Yellowstone National Park, larger than Delaware and Rhode Island combined. Canadian parks are equally large. Arrangements are made, especially in the American parts, for the traveler *de luxe* in good hotels, and in camps for the traveler of simpler tastes or more moderate means. Here one may get all the pleasure of the out-of-doors, the wild, the unusual, the deep forest, the clear lake, mountain-climbing of all degrees of rigor, including the invalid's method of climbing by automobile. A good automobile road has been built to the top of Pike's Peak which makes one of the high mountains of the world accessible to anybody whose heart is not weak.

After wheat and hay are harvested out in the Great Plains and the Grain Belts, tens of thousands of farmers get into automobiles and cross the plains to the Rockies. All the continental railroads give very favorable summer excursion rates, and there is every reason to expect the tourist business to increase faster than the population of the United States, for the travel habit is growing upon us. It is a pity that these national playgrounds are so far from the great masses of our population.

### Future

This region has a good, wholesome, invigorating climate. The people are almost completely Caucasian, of industrious Yankee and European

Fig. 243 — The Pelton water wheel. It can use a 2000-foot head, but it revolves at such speed that only electricity can carry the power into use. (Courtesy Pelton Water Wheel Co.)

stock. What is to be its future? Its mountains are like the Alps. Switzerland has less than 16,000 square miles and nearly 4,000,000 people, or 243 to the square mile. The southern Rockies have about a quarter of a million square miles and about 600,000 people, approximately 1-100 as many per square mile as Switzerland. Like Switzerland this region has a great tourist business, but Switzerland probably has greater tourist possibilities because of the greater number of people living in the other countries which are near. Switzerland has a better commercial location because the Rockies are so far from large numbers of people.

The valleys of Switzerland are more uniformly well-watered, and much lower than those of the Rockies. The American region is richer than Switzerland in having phosphate, oil-shale and coal. It also has wood, iron ore, and water-power. Switzerland, with 243 people per square mile, is one of the most contented, orderly, well-educated, most civilized of countries. Certainly it is reasonable to expect that our Switzerland could be equally comfortable for man with one-tenth as many people per square mile, namely, twenty-five, or a total of 6,000,000 people. It could support

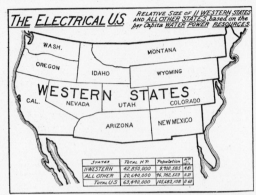

FIG. 244 — One method of showing how eleven Western states have more than twenty times as much water-power resource per capita as the rest of the United States. (Courtesy *Journal of Electricity and Western Industry.*)

varied industries supplying most of the needs of its people and pay for the rest with paper made of pulp-wood and money received from entertaining tourists. It would with ease supply six million people with apples, pears, grapes, peaches, cherries, small fruits, garden stuff, *all* the milk, butter, cheese and potatoes. It would also produce *all* the meat they would *need*, and most of the 36,000,000 bushels of wheat that they would use. Or, if more wheat were needed, a surplus of the near-by plains would probably supply it.[12] Such a population would be scattered in a host of small manufacturing towns like those of Switzerland, and on small farms. The whole population would live always in sight of a noble and inspiring landscape.

[12] The full utilization of so much steep land would probably find place for an extensive use of tree crops, as explained in previous chapters.

FIG. 245 — For unknown centuries the Indian of the Southwestern Plateaus has cultivated corn in the canyon bottoms. Outlook from Canyon de Chelly. (Courtesy Atchison, Topeka and Santa Fe R. R. Co.)

# CHAPTER XXVI

## ARID SOUTHWESTERN INTERMOUNTAIN PLATEAUS

THE Southwestern Plateaus are a highland and a dry land, an arid grazing region of vast extent. Everywhere the rain is so slight, the summer so hot, that the farmer with his plow is not the symbol of the settlement. Instead it is the cowboy with his lariat and the leather leggings that keep the cactus from pricking him. Someone has said that this is a region where there are more streams and less water, more cows and less milk, where one can look farther and see less than any other place in the world. The "streams" are the surprisingly numerous empty gullies (arroyos) where water runs only after occasional showers. The cows that do not give milk are the ranch-cows, whose milk is taken by the calf. "Looking farther and seeing less" refers to the clear air which lets you see great distances in a land empty of tree, home, field or man. In no part of this region is there any agriculture of importance in the modern sense save by irrigation, and the irrigated areas are small or very far between. Here, more than in any other region in North America, is the land par excellence of the large ranch, where animals must walk long distances to find enough scanty herbage to keep them alive. It is also a land where occasional drought brings death and starvation to beasts unless they can be carried in trains to places of greater rainfall. Thus, the state railroad commission of Texas, for itself and on behalf of the cattle-raising industry and the people of Texas, sent to the United States Food Administration in 1918 an expression of thanks for assistance in moving 1500 cars of live-stock from drought-stricken western Texas before the cattle starved or perished of thirst. Such droughts, often accompanied by the death of cattle, are common in all this region.

This region is a part of the vast domain where the Spaniard ruled the Indian. In the Mexican part of it the Spanish-American still rules him, but more than half the area was taken in the early part of the last century by the Americans. Everywhere are marks of its early Spanish occupation — Spanish names, the Spanish tongue, the Catholic church, the vast estate. In 1800 the Governor of New Mexico had 2,000,000 sheep with 2700 peons tending them. Up to the time of the confiscation of land under Obregon the Terrazas estate in Chihuahua extended for 200 miles and was larger than Massachusetts and Rhode Island together. In the

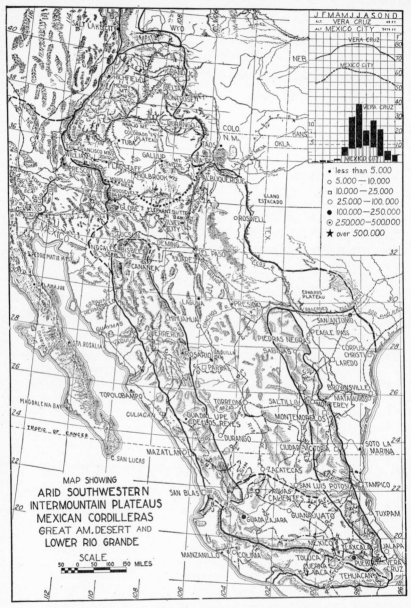

Fig. 246 — The dotted line shows the southern boundary of the nearly horizontal strata which make the Colorado Plateaus. Mexican states are indicated by abbreviations along boundaries. (See map in pocket.)

Edwards Plateau of Texas one ranch extends for forty miles on both sides of a creek and has a tract eight miles square as a sorting-pen for its cattle.

## Part I.  The Edwards Plateau

The eastern lobe of these plateaus, a limestone rock area sloping toward the south, is called the Edwards Plateau.  It is dissected in its eastern and southern parts by a multitude of little valleys.  Everywhere it is marked by very shallow soil.

Here the automobile often wears leather shoes with heavy steel bosses

Fig. 247 — As the stream cuts its channel in the steep land it flows swiftly. At the edge of the hills its velocity declines, it drops some of its load and spreads it out like a fan — " alluvial fan." Alluvial fans are spread out yards, miles, or leagues in width at the bases of elevations in all arid lands. (Courtesy Illinois Geol. Surv.)

to protect it from stones, cactus and brush.  This plateau is unusual in that it pastures sheep, goats and cattle.  It is the goat-center of the United States.  Most of the goats are Angora goats kept for their long fleeces of mohair.  The goats eat the bushes and the sheep and cattle eat the grass.[1]

[1] The coming of the white man has worked some strange freaks in nature's balance.  The Indians repeatedly burned the dead grass, which burned the bushes and kept this rough country in pasture.  When the white man came it was well covered with grass.  A farmer known to Professor Hartman, of the University of Texas, tells of having had difficulty in finding stones to mark the corners when making surveys.  Then the white man stopped the fires, and cedar bushes and trees grew up. They killed the grass.  The rain-water then washed the shallow earth mantle to the bottoms of the hills, converting areas into places of rocky desolation, where cedar-trees cling to the crevices in the bare stone hills and look down upon rich glades of good soil and grass.

## Part II. The Filled Basin Country

Most of this region, west of the Edwards Plateau and south of the Colorado Plateau, is land of filled basin formation — an arid land phenomenon. In regions of low but torrential rainfall the vegetation is scattered so that no mat of roots holds the land, and erosion on steep lands is therefore at its maximum.[2] As a result we often find bare, gaunt mountains, and between them wide stretches filled with waste washed down from mountain summits and slopes.

In old Mexico, as well as New Mexico and west Texas, many parts of this region have so little rain that the intermittent streams which wash

Fig. 248 — Semi-desert, pasture a part of the year. Near Silver City, N. M. Bloom stalks of agave. (Courtesy U. S. Forest Service.)

mountain-slopes to make filled basins cannot fill up their valleys and flow away to the sea. Therefore we have inland drainage-basins and salt lakes.

### A. THE TRANS-PECOS HIGHLANDS

The name Trans-Pecos Highlands is given to the ridge territory drained by the upper Pecos, the upper Rio Grande and streams in the many mountains between them. The Trans-Pecos ridges were made by the simple process of breaking up the earth's crust into great blocks and tipping them up — fault-block mountains, they are called.

The broken ends of the tilted strata face the west, so that the mountains

---

[2] The rainfall of a humid region supports a dense vegetation with an almost inconceivable mat of binding roots, and a mantle of small growth, leaves and leaf-twigs, all of which stop erosion very effectively. Desert vegetation, usually of the bunch-grass variety, affords little protection against washing.

have sharp western fronts and long sloping eastern fronts.  Such mountains are always in sight in most of the country between the Pecos and the Rio Grande and in some of the country west of the Rio Grande. The Rio Grande passes through these ranges in a series of gorges.[3]

Between the ranges are wide, level valleys.  Although the soil is fertile the valleys are not famed as the pleasant homes of men like the valleys of Virginia or eastern Tennessee.  Rainfall of eight, nine or ten inches a year, such as that of El Paso and other valley-locations in this territory, means desert.  The fitful rain that falls upon the mountains has long since washed the valleys full of loose and porous earth, and in this earth water promptly disappears, save in a few of the larger valleys where salt lakes or marshes occupy the lowest land.  There is a considerable area of inland drainage in these filled basins, here called " bolsons," the Spanish name for such a basin without outlet.  The longest of these basin valleys, close indeed to the Rio Grande, bears the suggestive name of Jornada del Muerto (journey of death), given to it by the early Spaniards.

What kind of country is this for the homes of man?  A New Mexican, describing the ranch-house of this region, answers:

" A ' dobe ' hut of one or two rooms, set out on a sun-blistered flat where bulls paw up clouds of pungent dust, while they bellow challenges at each other.  Miles away through quivering air dance the distorted outlines of the cool, timbered mountains. . . .

" A one-roomed log cabin with a ' lean-to,' in a beautiful mountain valley, but with every vestige of the native forest cut away from all around the house for fifty or a hundred yards on all sides.

" These are by no means the only kinds of ranch-houses, but they are by far the commonest. . . .

" The author also appreciates how the lack of control of land, the uncertainty of the returns for labor, the rough character of the work itself, the exposure it entails and the irregularity of habits which it engenders, all tend to render the ranch-house a mere ' permanent camp.' "[4]

Land-ownership here is in the same unsatisfactory state that we found prevailing in the dryer parts of the Great Plains, where the land belongs to the Government, since it will give but 640 acres to one man.  In the Trans-Pecos country of western Texas and New Mexico he needs from 2000 to 8000 acres to support a family.

So the rancher homesteads or purchases a piece of land with a permanent water-supply, which carries with it a more or less strategic command over an area of public land of varying size, giving him virtual possession of the produce of thousands of acres.  If he does not keep the land

[3] In such a mountain-break lies El Paso (" The Pass ").

[4] E. O. Wooton, *Tree and Shrubs of New Mexico*, pp. 11 and 12, Bulletin No. 87, N. M. College of Agriculture and Mechanic Arts.

stocked, someone's else stock may get in. As a consequence of this natural rivalry, the range is overstocked, the good grass is killed off, weeds are encroaching, and in seasons of dry years animals perish. The rancher says that it means less loss for him to over-stock the range and have his animals perish occasionally than to keep animals off the range and let someone else get it. This condition is characteristic of much of the arid land of the United States. We urgently need a land-policy that will enable the man who occupies the land to take decent care of it.

### Irrigations and El Paso

Here and there the greater rainfall of some upland makes possible a little dry-farming, but the chief escape thus far from dependence on the ranch and the occasional mine is afforded by irrigation in the valleys of the two main streams, the Pecos and the Rio Grande. By diversion and

FIG. 249 — The Elephant Butte Dam, holding more water than any other irrigation reservoir in the world, stores Rio Grande waters in the naked hills of New Mexico to grow crops on the plains of Texas, near El Paso. Power plant at foot of dam shows its size. (Courtesy U. S. Bureau of Reclamation.)

also by pumping, water is obtained to raise large quantities of alfalfa, which fattens the range-animals and carries them through periods of snow and drought.

One hundred and twenty-five miles above El Paso the Reclamation Service has built the Elephant Butte Dam, said to hold the largest artificial lake in the world, covering sixty square miles, having a shore-line of 200 miles and impounding water enough to cover the State of Delaware two feet deep. This water irrigates a half-million acres of land below the dam, in New Mexico and Texas. Elevation of 4000 feet gives this land a good healthful climate where wheat can grow in the winter and a crop of Egyptian corn can follow it in summer on the same land. Alfalfa for the range-animals is the chief crop, with long staple cotton pushing it for first place. Milk and vegetables for the city of El Paso may be expected to claim more land as the city grows.

El Paso, with characteristic Western hustle, boasts that it is the largest city within a radius of 500 miles, *i.e.*, between Los Angeles and San Antonio, that with eight railroads it is the greatest railroad center west of the 100th meridian, and that it is the metropolis of the richest mining region in the world, counting chiefly, of course, on the resources of the Mexican mountains. It also has smelters using coal from New Mexico and ore from both New and old Mexico.

## The Indian Culture

The white man, irrigating the valley of the Rio Grande, cannot claim to be a pioneer, for the first Spanish explorers nourished their famished bodies and replenished their stocks of food from the abundant harvests produced by the Pueblo Indians in the irrigated valley of the Rio Grande, where Indians had lived for unknown centuries. At Taos and a few other places we can still see the method of living these people had developed before the white man came. Many live under one roof. The pueblo is five or six stories high, the first story without windows in the sides. Rooms are entered from the top. The walls and roof are of sun-dried brick, supported on strong poles and piled thick with impermeable clay. If a young man wishes to marry, the fathers of the village point to a place where he may add rooms on the roof of the pueblo. The town of Taos now contains 300 rooms and about as many people.

It is greatly to be hoped that friends of fair play can keep these simple people from being crowded out of their water-rights and lands which are to them life. Many of the Indians are beginning to adopt the white man's ways — a practice of questionable benefit to them.

## The Many Cultures of New Mexico

New Mexico, with one of the sparsest populations of the country, can boast the greatest number of civilizations: (1) prehistoric, of which many cliff-dwellings and other remains abound, indicating a surprising culture. Dr. J. W. Fewkes, the ethnologist, has even found at Mesa Verde, southwestern Colorado (near the New Mexico line in the Colorado Plateaus), an astronomical observatory left by these remarkable people; (2) Indian, of which some towns remain and from which basketry and excellent blanket-work are increasingly thrust upon our attention; (3) Spanish, present in place-names as well as the persons and language of the Mexicans in the streets of Santa Fe and other towns; (4) the American culture which has had the good sense and taste to follow the native style of architecture. Its buildings are a blend of the Indian pueblo and the Spanish mission. This very pleasing type has been adopted with great enthusiasm. Witness the architecture of Santa Fe, where one sees apartments, office buildings and museums, even the United States post-office,

Fig. 250 — Indian pueblo. The poles carry the roof. Meat drying above. Bake oven. White man's windows. (Courtesy Museum of New Mexico, Santa Fe, N. M.)

all in this unique and useful style of architecture which so thoroughly fits into the climatic conditions of the country.[5] The thoroughness with which this new style of architecture has been adopted is well instanced by a public high school in Santa Fe, of which the earlier structure is thoroughly and hideously New England, and the new high-school unit beside it thoroughly and pleasingly New Mexican.

### B. THE MEXICAN PART OF THE SOUTHWESTERN PLATEAUS

Mexico is not separated from the United States by physical or even by racial lines, for many of the people of our own Southwestern Plateaus are Mexican in origin, and many speak Spanish. The American part is still substantially Indian, while across the Mexican boundary we find the population chiefly Indian and partly mixed, with a small percentage of Spanish. The boundary-line, which is strictly an imaginary line [6] for

[5] The plainer adobe house may look somewhat like a pile of mud, but it is in reality a comfortable house, cool in summer and warm in winter, because walls and roof are thick enough to turn both water and heat.

[6] Boundary troubles are ludicrously illustrated by an episode rehearsed at great length, with diagrams, in the correspondence between the United States and Mexico,

most of the way, is not much of a boundary even where it depends on the Rio Grande, for it is easy to cross the river at low water. Nevertheless the boundary has sharp political and cultural contrasts.

When you cross the river from El Paso to Juarez, you pass from a neat, orderly, clean, prosperous-looking town to one that is ill-kept, dirty, unsanitary, disorderly. There is no Eighteenth Amendment, not even as a sham, and most of the Ten Commandments appear to be in

FIG. 251 — Pueblo-Spanish-American architecture of the Southwest. Business building on central square, Santa Fe, N. M. The Pueblo influence is evident. (Photo Everett G. Rodebaugh.)

recess where the saloon, the gambling den, and the worst haunts of vice flaunt themselves. There are many such border towns, but we must not judge Mexico too much by them. Many of their patrons are people from the United States, who escape the restrictions of American law by a short sojourn across the boundary.

Mexico is also the land of the polite and cultured Spaniard, who salutes his friend by kissing him on the right cheek and turning his own left cheek to be kissed. Some of these people are educated in the United States and Europe, travel much and would belong in the educated circles of any capital.

This Mexican part of the Southwestern Plateaus, lying between the

in 1891. It seems that an Arizona sheriff in the town of Nogales desired to arrest a drunken man, who persisted in staying a few feet across the national boundary, which ran through the middle of the street. A confederate of the sheriff went across the street and "accidentally" bumped into the tipsy one, who went sprawling upon the ground, with his feet in Arizona and his head and shoulders in Mexico. The sheriff grabbed his feet, pulled him across, and locked him up in jail. Whereupon Mexico protested this invasion of her sovereign rights. The correspondence dragged on for some months and was never settled, for before the matter was concluded the Americans thought the intoxicated one had been in jail long enough and so he "escaped" and the diplomatic question remained unsolved.

eastern and western cordilleras, is from 250 to 300 miles wide, and 800 to 900 miles long. This great plateau, increasing slightly in elevation toward the south, has been built by the outpourings of volcanoes and by mountain washings. Therefore it is a vast sea of water-borne or volcanic soils with old mountains sticking out of it as islands. Fortunately for Mexico and the rest of the world, these islands of old rock contain much valuable metal and give rise to a great mining industry. As on the plateaus to the northward in the United States, but little agriculture is possible. In the north the River Conchos carries water from the western mountains to empty it into the Rio Grande. On both sides of the Conchos are areas of bolsons with salt lakes. Once the Rio Grande flowed into this territory, but a volcano threw a dam across its course, turning it to the present channel. These plateaus are walled in by the cordilleras so that some parts receive not more than four or five inches of rain. No parts have more than twenty inches.

## The Large Hacienda and the Peon

This is the land of the ranch, of the feudal ranch-estate, of the mine and the revolution. The traveler sees many signs of the civil wars (1911–1924) in block-houses along the railroad, unoccupied and ruined buildings, overturned locomotives and the wheels of burned cars. One who looks into the stormy history of Mexico and reads the chronicles of its civil wars wonders how the country can be as well developed as it is.

Climate and history combine to make the great feudal estates. The land is good for little but the ranch. Water is scarce, so the possessor of a few good water-sites has natural command of large areas around. In the politically disturbed times there was a real feudal basis — the landowner with his fortified house could protect his vassals. Certain it is that the American concept or the American ideal of the small farm occupied by its owner is almost unknown in this region. Instead, one vast estate succeeds another. When the Mexican owner visited the borders of his estate it often took several days, and he traveled with coach and six and retinue like a medieval prince, which indeed he was. The estate in Chihuahua has been mentioned. The Zuloaga family had two million acres. In the days of Diaz an American company bought an estate sixty by seventy miles in northeastern Zacatecas. It was occupied by 2000 people and 500,000 (estimated) head of live-stock. It was sixty miles from a railroad station to the manor-house, a large structure built around a *patio,* or open court. Near the manor-house was the church and a village. The peons lived in villages beside a spring or pond made by damming the channel of a stream to store its flood-waters.

Back and forth from thin and distant pastures to the stagnant waterhole moved the peon cowboy and the cattle. The house of the peon was made of sun-dried bricks. It was usually without a window, the door sufficing to let in such light as it could.   Some houses are even built without a door, entrance being made only through an opening into a wall, with another opening into an inner room.   The women and children must choose between the gloom of the " dobe hut " or the glare of the unshaded sun.   Here they were tied for life by peonage laws.

The peons are in reality medieval vassals, little better indeed than chattels, strangely like cattle.   Corn-cakes, fried beans and onions are the chief food.[7]   Their one ornament is the highly decorated and appallingly heavy hat; their one entertainment is the church procession, their one luxury to get drunk on fierce liquor — *aguardiente,* an un-

FIG. 252 — Homes of Mexican railway laborers, Lamy, N. M., near Santa Fe. The one-story, flat-roofed house of adobe looks next to nothing but is warmer in winter and cooler in summer than the most pretentious of elegant Yankee construction.   (Photo Everett G. Rodebaugh.)

believably strong alcohol distilled from mescal, a member of the century-plant family.   Such is the life of the poor peons — millions of them. They cannot get ahead financially.   They are quite unambitious — why should they not be?   They are also exceedingly conservative. They cut their grain with a sickle and shell their corn by hand, and only with the greatest difficulty can they be induced to use more efficient tools.

The American owners of the large estate just mentioned sought to improve the conditions and increase output by increasing wages.   The peons promptly cut down the number of days of work because the increased wage enabled them to live by their accepted standards with less days of labor.

### Cotton, Rubber and Ixtle

So far as area is concerned the ranch is far and away the predominant industry of the whole Mexican section of the plateau; but there are some other agricultural industries.   In the Laguna (lake) district around

[7] From the standpoint of *nutrition* this leaves little to be desired.

Parral there are 10,000 square miles of old lake-bed (not unlike the Nile delta), where the two mountain rivers, Nazas and Nievas, bring water from the western Sierras and permit rather extensive irrigation at the season of the summer rains. This locality commonly produces 100,000 bales of cotton, all used in Mexico. Much more land might be irrigated by pumping ground-water from a depth of six to thirty feet. In the eastern foothill region near Saltillo one or two million bushels of wheat are grown each year by dry-farming, unless there happens to be a drought.

In the neighborhood of Saltillo and Torreon there has been an interesting alternation of industrial output between ixtle and guayule. The ixtle fiber is taken from a plant that resembles the century-plant. It is exported to America and Europe for the manufacture of ropes, sacks, mats, brushes. The fiber business declined when, about 1905, it was discovered that the guayule shrub, growing extensively on the arid pastures, had about 10% of its dry weight in rubber. The shrub was rooted up far and wide and carried to Torreon and Saltillo, where factories chopped it up and dissolved the gum. For a few years there was a lively export of rubber. Then rubber declined in price, owing to rubber-production by cheap coolie labor in the East Indies. Guayule could not compete under the new conditions. Rubber factories were torn down and the workers turned to the fiber business, which again rose to its old proportions.

## Mining

Mines have furnished the chief export of these filled basin plateaus. The silver, gold, copper, zinc, and bismuth (chiefly silver), have far outranked in value the cattle, hides, rubber and ixtle. Some of the many mountains which protrude through the volcanic and lake deposits were the seat of a thriving industry in colonial days. The mining cities of Chihuahua, Zacatecas, San Luis Potosi and Aguascalientes are sisters in time with Plymouth and Salem, Mass., and Santa Fe, N. M. They are not mining-camps, but solid cities of stone, with fine churches and cathedrals, and good two-story houses of Spanish architecture, often surrounded, it is true, by acres of hovels. In Chihuahua stands a church, one of the finest pieces of eighteenth century architecture in all Mexico. It was built by a small tax that was laid on the output of the neighboring Santa Eulalia mine between 1717 and 1789. Near Zacatecas the Alvarado mine produced eight hundred million dollars' worth of silver between 1548 and 1867.

The mining industry prospered here during the colonial epoch and languished during the civil wars between independence, 1810, and Diaz, 1876. It rose to great prosperity under Diaz, and slumped again in the succeeding chaos. Mining revived a little under Obregon. In the days

of Diaz, American capital, American engineers and American managers
kept the Mexican peons digging quite as busily as they wished to dig,
often more busily.   There was at least one smelter in each of the four
above-mentioned cities, which had a prosperous trade in supplying
mining-camps and in handling ores.   Many peons starved in the hungry
days of the renewed civil wars, when the mine-mule was driven away,
the miner driven away, and the superintendent driven away (sometimes
shot).

The mines of this part of the plateau are not worked out.   They are
only waiting for the continued application of capital and labor to dig
deep where only surface workings have been possible by primitive methods.

### Future of the Mexican Plateau

This plateau must have peace.   Thus far it has been the source of most
of the Mexican revolutions.   It seems to be a matter of record the world
over that the desert and semi-desert are the places where armed uprising is easy and natural, and conquest is difficult.   Witness the determination of President Wilson to catch the troublesome Mexican Villa
(general? revolutionist? bandit?) in 1916.   We threw an armed force
into this region, equipped with the best we had and led by no less a
person than John J. Pershing.   Without making the slightest criticism
of Pershing or of the army, it must be recorded that they did not catch
the native half-breed, Pancho Villa.   In this respect we were exactly like
several Mexican governments, two of which bought Villa's good conduct
with heavy payments of cash.

The mind of the landless populace in a land of huge estates is a good
seed-bed for revolution.   Perhaps also revolutions arise on the plateau
in part at least because of the nervous irritation of hot and stifling winds,
a fact which is recognized in the Spanish saying, " Ask no favor while
the solano blows."   It is well known that any populace is likely to blame
the government for misfortunes the government does not create, such as
business depression.   The fluctuating rainfall of a desert's edge is continually causing poor grass, poor cattle and hard times.   Certain it is
that most of Mexico's revolutions have started in the dryer part of
this plateau and have swept southward and upward to the capital city.

If order and peace could remain for some generations in this region,
there is no reason to think the Mexican peon of the plateau would not
respond to education.   It should be remembered that he lives in a land
where the climate is wholesome and the nights are cool enough to be
invigorating.

Granted a government that could keep order, water could be stored in
the Sierras here as in our own mountains.[8]   This irrigation could greatly

[8] In 1922 and 1923 the Obregon government announced its intention of building
irrigation reservoirs in this region.   Between 1909 and 1915 a Canadian corporation

increase agriculture. Even without irrigation there can probably be some dry-farming, but it should be remembered that 95% or more of all the land is fit only for the ranch.

It is not likely that irrigation in this plateau will make Mexico an exporter of foods. She now imports pork, wheat, eggs and canned milk from the United States. Increased prosperity in Mexico means mines and a bigger home-market.

## PART III. THE COLORADO PLATEAUS

The northwestern part of this region, called the Colorado Plateau or Plateaus, has had a different geological past from that of the filled basin area just described. The strata, so nearly horizontal in the Edwards Plateau, so broken and tilted in the Trans-Pecos, are there again nearly horizontal. But the rock is broken by faults, and many wide areas, hundreds or thousands of square miles in extent, have been lifted up to various heights. Each differs in height from its neighbor and bears a different name — Kaibab Plateau, Kanab Plateau. High cliffs often separate these many plateaus from each other.

The rivers cutting into these high plateaus have made wide, deep canyons, the deepest in the world, but one may travel over the plateau-surface for long distances without any suggestion of being on high land or near deep canyons.

The two-hours railroad journey from Williams to the Grand Canyon takes you across a gently rolling country, past pine forests, sheep ranches, and prairie-dog towns, with no inkling of either elevation or canyon. Even a quarter of a mile from the Canyon brink, the view from the top of a forest-ranger's tower shows only a wide, level expanse of tree-tops with no hint that the world's deepest valley is within rifle-range.

This difference in structure of filled basins and high plateaus cut by canyons makes a very great difference in temperature and tree growth. In the lands of fault-block mountains and filled basins the mountains are narrow with sharp ridges or sharp peaks. Therefore there is very little room for forests at the elevation where increased rainfall and decreased temperature produce tree growth. On the contrary, the Colorado Plateaus with wide areas at the top have room for thousands of square miles of forest, and in some places the valleys are as sharp at the bottom as the peaks of the filled basin country are sharp at the top. Both types

---

built a ten-million-dollar dam at La Boquilla on the Conchos River, ninety miles south of Chihuahua (see map). It compares with Elephant Butte on the Rio Grande as follows: height 243 (Boquilla Dam) to 203 (Elephant Butte); area of lake, sixty-seven square miles to sixty square miles; water stored, 3150 million cubic meters to 3255 million meters. Up to 1924 (letter U. S. Consul, Chihuahua, May 21, 1924), it had been used only for power; 36,000 horse-power (enlargements in progress); 290 miles of line built or building carried power to Parral, Chihuahua and various mines. There is enough water to irrigate 175,000 acres of land, but the irrigation company had not got into operation in 1924.

of landscape have the entire series in the vegetative range[9] from the poor pasture of near-desert at low elevations to good forest at high elevations. The journey on the Santa Fe Railroad from the Rio Grande over to the Little Colorado River shows the sequence of vegetation. As the train climbs up from the Rio Grande, one looks back upon the river

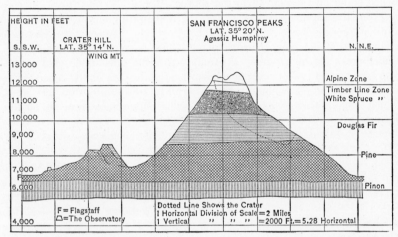

FIG. 253 — The San Francisco Peaks, built up by volcanic work on the treeless plateau, show a fine example of the zoning of vegetation. (From *Forest Physiography*, Bowman.)

valley and sees it as a streak of green trees and alfalfa in a brown and yellow land. For many miles up from the river the train passes through bunch-grasses standing on bare ground. For miles no houses are seen, no crop — only a cow-country where Hereford cows and their calves

[9] Botanists revel in the way the climate in the Colorado Plateau separates the plants into zones, one above another. These zones come close together on a steep slope where the climatic gamut is quickly run and Dame Botany is compelled to keep her classes close together.

First zone: 3000 to 5000 feet. Cottonwood and cactus and yucca. This is in the deep canyons. Cottonwoods are along the streams; the cactus and yucca are scattered along at intervals with a little bunch-grass and dwarf forms of sagebrush and greasewood.

Second zone: 5000 to 6000 feet. Sagebrush and greasewood. Here these desert plants are bushes four to five feet high, sometimes thick enough to make travel difficult.

Third zone: 6000 to 7000 feet. Piñon, the nut-bearer, and juniper, an evergreen bush — ten to fifteen feet high, and scattered.

Fourth zone: 7000 to 8500 feet. Yellow pine, solid forests of pine-trees, standing far apart, making a park landscape of great beauty.

Fifth zone: 8500 to 10,000 feet. Here are deep snows and cool summer days, showers and springs of water. Here, therefore, is the Engelmann spruce, a Northern tree, which often attains saw-log size. In the open spaces a rank growth of gooseberry, raspberry, grass and flowers in surprising profusion. Much of this timber, however, is totally inaccessible because the mountain-tops and mesas on which it grows are surrounded by labyrinths of rough land.

wander in a desolate land. Still climbing upward we enter the piñon country, and then an open forest of small pine-trees. We have passed the dry timber-line (nearly 7000 feet). Piñons and cedars are twenty feet high and give the impression of a forest. Trains loaded with good logs stand on a branch line. They have come from the Zuñi Mountains, which stand on the plateau to the south.

From this elevation of 7200 feet the downward journey begins. The railroad goes down a branch of the Colorado. Again the vegetation changes from big piñon to little piñon, then no piñon, then good grass, bunch-grass, no bunch-grass, but only scattering grass and small bushes and never a field to be seen in scores of miles. A few ranch-houses miles apart stand beside windmill reservoirs that store water for the herds, which find in this dear-bought water their only solace from the shade-lessness of the sun-scorched range.

### The Grand Canyon

The world of science and travel finds the Grand Canyon of the Colorado the most interesting thing in the Colorado Plateaus. The United States Government has preserved the canyon by making it a park, and the Santa Fe Railroad has made it accessible by building a branch-line rail-road to its brink. Even an invalid may make the journey to see the Grand Canyon. One needs to have only time and money. The tourist may live in comfort in good hotels that are well supplied with water brought more than a hundred miles in tank-cars, and with food assembled from almost half of the United States, so unproductive is the plateau itself. Automobiles make tours along the rim of the Canyon. Cowboys, bravely dressed but thoroughly tame, harmless, helpful and kind, lead forth trains of hand-picked mules upon which even the tenderfoot may safely ride down an appalling-looking trail. The trail is so steep and narrow that the mules seem to be going down a series of zigzag ladders. After three hours the bottom is reached, and there at the mouth of a side-ravine one looks upon the waters of the river that has carved this marvel of valleys. Coronado, the first white man who saw the Grand Canyon, said that the river had banks that " reached three or four leagues into the air, and were broken into pinnacles higher than the tower of the Cathedral of Seville." This river, loaded with sand, red with mud and therefore hiding its depth, roars over rapids, comes around a bend of rock where man could find no foothold, swirls on, foaming as it disappears around another wall of rock. Looking at the mighty creator of the canyon one muses upon the intrepid valor of Major Powell, one-armed veteran of the Civil War, who in 1869, taking his life in his hands, had the amazing courage to get into his boat and enter this gorge which ex-tended for hundreds of miles. From this hazardous trip there could scarcely be any returning except after a safe passage (or did he know enough about erosion to know that the river really has worn a course that could be navigated, though with risk?).

As you stand upon the canyon's rim and look down, you see that the canyon is not just a big hole in the ground. It is a steep and narrow valley with serrated edges where huge rocks stand in strange and fantastic forms. You are astonished to see red, white, green, brown and black rocks. You may be a visitor from the Atlantic Coast or from the Pacific

FIG. 254 — Cross-section showing process of making the Grand Canyon. (Courtesy Fred Harvey.)

Coast, but never before have you seen rock-formations with color like this. Looking into the canyon, you see a plateau part way down and you want to hurl a stone upon it. The stone sails out and then down, down, and finally hits the cliff almost directly below where you are standing. That plateau must be much farther away than it appears to be. You look closely and perhaps you see a moving speck. Your field-glass reveals a man on horseback. The plateau is 3000 feet below you, not just within a stone's-throw as you had supposed. Now the immensity of the canyon begins to dawn upon you.

You can sit in one place all day and make new discoveries, as the moving sun throws light where the cliffs had thrown shadows, and new shadows add blue haze where white light had been. Castles and cathedrals, ships and fortresses, river, ridges, buttes, cliffs and valleys change before your eyes. Then the next day you can sit somewhere else and see a different series of these moving pictures of nature. To many the canyon, as an emotional experience, is greatest in the gathering dusk of evening. Then red, white, brown, green — all colors — fade in the hazy shadows; pinnacle and cathedral lose their form, and distance multiplies immensity. You think that you can hear the river grinding its granite bed. While distances across the canyon appear to grow greater, I know that this great gorge from which I have just climbed with such effort is a narrow valley and therefore that it is one of the youngest of valleys, not one of the oldest. Old valleys are wide, not narrow. They have gentle slopes, not steep walls. What is time? And there are the abandoned holes of the miners by the trail and that cliff-dweller's ruined house I saw far above me on the canyon wall in the afternoon. Where is he, and the nomad from whom he fled to that refuge? And how long shall we stand triumphantly on the top of the plateau?

The formation of this world-wonder is explained by the character of the rock. As the stream saws its way down through the nearly horizontal strata, the rocks stand up almost like the side of a pile of lumber. If there is a soft layer beneath a hard layer, the soft part is worn away more easily, and this undermines the hard layer so that the bottom of the hard layer goes as quickly as the top of it (Fig. 254). This process of earth-sculpture makes buttes and straight-walled canyons in lands of horizontal rocks. Thus the walls of the Grand Canyon fall away in sheer cliffs. A man may travel for twenty miles along the rim and find no place where he can climb down.

### Other Canyons and the Ancient Culture of the Plateau

The plateau over which the tourist goes *de luxe* is not the whole of the plateau, nor is the canyon the whole of the canyons. These famous

FIG. 255 — San Juan Canyon, one of the lesser canyons of the Plateau, but a wonderful exhibit of process and structure. (Courtesy H. H. Vinson, U. S. Geol. Surv.)

parts of the region are indeed but a corner of the whole. The Colorado Plateaus section alone is as large as the United Kingdom. Its western edge overlooks the Arizona desert from the Grand Wash Cliffs, a wall of rock 1000 to 2000 feet high and 150 miles long and which continues to the south under other names.

To the eastward, plateau rises above plateau with bare rock wall hundreds of feet high and tops with hundreds, and even thousands, of square miles extent. Through all this high, dry land of flat, hard rocks are the deep-sawn canyons of the Colorado and its several branches.

These various streams come together above the Grand Canyon. We may think of that canyon as a wrist and of the other canyons as outstretched fingers. The Grand Canyon is 6000 feet deep and 125 miles long, but before reaching it the Colorado flowed through the Marble Canyon, sixty-five miles long, and the long Glen Canyon. The Dolores River reaches the Grand River (a branch of the Colorado) in a canyon 2000 feet deep, and if America had no other canyons like those of the Green River or Grand River they would be considered world-wonders. Because travel is so difficult, this is the least-known part of the United

States. For this reason it is the site of the oldest civilization and the place where native culture reached the most advanced stage. Building a civilization takes time, much time. Rare is the human mind that devises something really new, and slow is the process of building upon it and improving it until finally industries, arts, crafts, customs, law and order are evolved. Many successive generations must combine their efforts before culture reaches an advanced stage.

The situation of cliff-dwellings in canyon walls or the pueblo on the mesa-top gave the necessary natural protection.

It is far back in the plateau that the greatest ruins are found, and these ruins show evidences of the most advanced native culture.[10]

### The Navajo Country

The Navajo country may be taken as a type of the central part of this region, indeed of most of it. The term " Navajo country " is applied to the land between the Colorado River and its two branches, the Little Colorado and the San Juan. It embraces the northeastern corner of Arizona, the northwestern corner of New Mexico and a little of southern Utah. It is a land of high plateau, flat-topped mesa, high, inaccessible butte, sharp, deep canyon, and sandy and gravelly wash. The wash is a valley or canyon whose rock-bottom is covered to a depth of ten or a hundred feet with sand, soil, or gravel, over which the water rushes after rain. Above the plateau stand volcanic remains, sometimes cores of old volcanoes, sometimes wide runs of lava which make level-topped uplands, with steep faces.

As the general level of this perpendicular plateau country is about 5500 feet with canyons cut 2500 feet into it, the climate at its tops is like that of the Colorado mountains, and at its bottom it is like that of the Navajo Desert. Here, as elsewhere, elevation is a great controller of rainfall. Holbrook on the Little Colorado, elevation 5000 feet, has a rainfall of nine inches. At Flagstaff, 6900 feet, the rainfall is twenty-three inches. The rain has two seasons, one in the winter and one in July and August, with April, May and June as the driest seasons of the year. This summer rain comes as showers, which is the common desert type of rain. It is caused by the air near the surface being heated by the hot earth. The heat expands the air. This makes it light and it rises. As it rises the hot air is cooled sometimes to the point of condensing its moisture, which falls as rain, sometimes fairly coming down in torrents for a few moments. The climate further troubles man because the scanty rainfall, like the rainfall in all arid lands, is very fickle and irregular. Hundreds of square miles of the Navajo country have no

---

[10] Dr. J. Walter Fewkes reports finding pre-Columbian pottery with paintings showing a game of draw-poker. (1923 Meeting, American Association for Advancement of Science.)

cover of vegetation.[11]   The ripping waters and the hard winds have carried away every vestige of soil, and the surface consists of bare rock and blowing sand.   Patches of this bare rock are scattered almost everywhere.

It is often only thirty minutes from sunshine to sunshine, during which time it has clouded up, rained half an inch and cleared off.   As a result of downpours, water rushes down steep slopes and carries gravel, sand or stones, which fill up watercourses with wide, level stretches of sand and gravel " washes."

These watercourses are nature's roads.   Sometimes the traveler innocently going over them with his pack-train, is overtaken by a rush of water from a shower miles upstream, and he has to scramble in order to escape drowning.   The Colorado River sometimes rises twenty feet in a night.

The larger streams and their branches have cut the country into a labyrinth of canyons.   The land of the Navajos is pre-eminently a horseback-country.   A pack-train is the only type of outfit which offers freedom of movement.   Quicksand is to be expected in all stream-channels and in the beds of " dry lakes." [12]

Water is scarce in this Navajo country.   As one enters it from Gallup, N. M., on the Santa Fe Railroad, there is only one permanent stream in the first thirty-five miles.   Plateaus with an area of 100 and 200 square miles without any permanent water are very common.   Only five per cent of the Navajo country has permanent streams, and man and beast must therefore depend upon pools, water-pockets, or tanks — left in the beds of streams and carefully enclosed by artificial dams.   The Navajo has a saying, "Where feed (grass) is, there is no water; where water is, there is no feed."   He says this because the water is in a few deep canyons and the grass is far away on the higher land where winter snow gives moisture for grass-growth in spring.

In this country are about 20,000 square miles of the Hopi and Navajo Indian reservations, containing about 30,000 Indians, 500 whites who belong there because of their official relationships with the Indians, and a number of interloping whites who have no right to be there.   Life in this country is hard.   Professor Gregory calls it heroic.[13]

[11] As to bare places John Van Dyke, in his book *The Desert*, says of the Painted Desert northeast of the Grand Canyon: " In spots not a living thing of any kind is seen: where there is nothing but dry rock in the mountains and dry dust in the valleys."

[12] All crossings should be tested before wagons or pack-trains go over.   Owing to the possibility of a sudden rise of water, streams and dry washes should be crossed at the earliest favorable opportunity and camp should never be pitched on the floor of even the most innocent-looking dry stream-bed or " adobe flat."   (*The Navajo Country*, Herbert E. Gregory, Water Supply Paper 380, U. S. Geol. Surv.)

[13] " To my mind the period of direct contact with nature is the true ' heroic age ' of human history, an age in which heroic accomplishment and heroic endurance

## The Hopi and His Farm

The Hopi people of the Reservation still live in the fortress-homes built by their ancestors on the easily defended tops of the mesas. The situation afforded protection against the hungry raiding nomad tribes, probably Apache and Navajo. Here for many centuries two great treasures have been guarded with most solicitous care — the big jars of water and the piles of corn. These two treasures, if sufficient in quantity, would enable the walled village to live through any siege that men of bows and arrows (Stone Age) could maintain. The spring or water-hole from which the water-jars were filled was usually far away, perhaps a mile or even more, and often down hundreds or thousands of feet from the lofty village. The cliff-dwellers worked hard in carrying the jars of water on their heads or shoulders from the spring to the village, but in the jars was the issue of life.

To these people climate was, and is, fate. In their mythology, folklore and religion, water is ever uppermost. The snake-dance is really a prayer for water. The dancers grasp the loose skin of live rattlesnakes with their teeth and carry the serpents around, importuning the snakes to tell the spirits of the underworld the needs of men.

The Hopis may be classed among the world's dryest farmers. They have developed plants from which we shall yet profit greatly and devices that we will adopt if we ever adjust ourselves to the dry environment half as well as they have done. The way a Hopi can make corn, beans, melons and squashes grow in a sand-dune is amazing. Most of the farming is irrigation-farming — flood-irrigation. Often to get water for his crops an Indian must go ten or more miles from his village to his fields.

In May or June, a few weeks before the summer rains are due, he goes to some wash and there plants corn about twelve or fifteen inches deep so that it will be well established before the season of July rains. Planting is a great Indian ceremonial. When the rains flood the wash the corn gets one or two good soakings. If water runs too deep the corn may be buried, or it may be washed away. So if he is a careful Hopi he will watch his corn during the period of the rains. He may be seen wading around in the water with shovel or stick or even with bare hand, building little dams and opening little channels, and sticking in brush barriers that the water may wet his corn but not bury or wash it away. The remains of old dams to impound the water near the cliff-dwellings indicate that 1000 years ago the Hopi ancestor raised his corn and cotton by the same methods. Full-grown Hopi corn is no more than knee-high.

are parts of the daily routine. The activities of people in this stage of progress deserve a place among the cherished traditions of the human race." (*The Navajo Country*, Herbert E. Gregory, Water Supply Paper 380, U. S. Geol. Surv.)

It needs no great expanse of leaves in so dry a climate.  Hopi corn has become a wonder by developing a long, underground stem so that it can be planted deep for moisture and then sprout through three or four times as much earth as the corn of Illinois.

When the white man came to the Indian's country he brought great gifts — sheep, goats and cows to a people who had only dogs and fowls. Sheep have been a boon to the Hopi and even more of a boon to the nomad Navajo, the traditional enemy of the Hopi.  Now the Navajo follows his flocks and herds from water-hole to water-hole, and derives from them his chief support.  At a recent count they had per capita fifty sheep, and ten horses, mules, or burros.  The Navajos learned a

Fig.  256 — Zuñi corn and canyon landscape near Zuñi, New Mexico.  Corn grown by flood irrigation.  (Courtesy U. S. Bureau Plant Industry.)

little about farming from the Hopis, and the United States Government Indian Service is trying to teach them better ways of farming.  In caring for their flocks and their patches of corn, beans, squashes and melons, and in weaving their blankets, the Navajo men, women and children lead a busy life.

## Let the Indian Alone

The two great hopes for these native people are that we shall not steal their land and that we shall let them continue to be Indians and not force them too rapidly into the ways of the white man.  While helping the Indians we should be very careful that we do not destroy their civilization and their very remarkable culture.  It would be all too easy to destroy what they have developed — a fate that has happened to most of the primitive peoples of the world who have come in close contact with the white man.

The observation and recommendations of Theodore Roosevelt (in the *Outlook* magazine) as he visited these people may well be quoted at length:

"We dropped down from Buckskin Mountain, from the land of the pine and spruce and of cold, clear springs, into the grim desolation of the desert. We drove the pack-animals and loose horses, usually one of us taking the lead to keep the trail. It was a land of wide spaces and few people, but those few we met were so friendly and helpful that we shall not soon forget them.

"At noon of the first day we had come down the mountain-side, from the tall northern forest-trees at the summit, through the scattered, sprawling piñon and cedars of the side slopes, to the barren, treeless plain of sand and sagebrush and greasewood. At the foot of the mountain we stopped for a few minutes at an outlying cow-ranch. There was not a tree, not a bush more than knee-high, on the whole plain round about. The bare little ranch-house, of stone and timber, lay in the full glare of the sun; through the open door we saw the cluttered cooking utensils and the rolls of untidy bedding. The foreman, rough and kindly, greeted us from the door; spare and lean, his eyes bloodshot and his face like roughened oak from the pitiless sun, wind, and sand of the desert. After we had dismounted, our shabby ponies moped at the hitching-post as we stood talking. In the big corral a mob of half-broken horses were gathered, and two dust-grimed, hard-faced cow-punchers, lithe as panthers, were engaged in breaking a couple of wild ones. All round, dotted with stunted sagebrush and greasewood, the desert stretched, blinding white in the sunlight; across its surface the dust-clouds moved in pillars, and in the distance the heat-waves danced and wavered.

"During the afternoon we jogged steadily across the plain. At one place, far off to one side, we saw a band of buffalo, and between them and us a herd of wild donkeys. Otherwise the only living things were snakes and lizards. On the other side of the plain, two or three miles from a high wall of vermilion cliffs, we stopped for the night at a little stone rest-house, built as a station by a cow outfit. Here there were big corrals, and a pool of water piped down by the cowmen from a spring many miles distant. On the sand grew the usual desert plants, and on some of the ridges a sparse growth of grass, sufficient for the night-feed of the hardy horses. The little stone house and the corrals stood out, bare and desolate, on the empty plain. Soon after we reached there a sand-storm rose and blew so violently that we took refuge inside the house. Then the wind died down; and as the sun sank towards the horizon we sauntered off through the hot, still evening. There were many sidewinder rattlesnakes. We killed several of the gray, flat-headed, venomous things; as we slept on the ground, we were glad to kill as many as possible. Except this baleful life there was little save the sand and the harsh, scanty vegetation. Across the lonely wastes the sun went down. The sharply channeled cliffs turned crimson in the dying light; all the heavens flamed ruby-red, and faded to a hundred dim hues of opal, beryl and amber, pale turquoise and delicate emerald; and then night fell and darkness shrouded the desert.

" The landscape had become one of incredible wildness, of tremendous and desolate majesty. No one could paint or describe it save one of the great masters of imaginative art or literature — a Turner or Browning or Poe. The sullen rock walls towered hundreds of feet aloft, with something about their grim savagery that suggested both the terrible and the grotesque. All life was absent, both from them and from the fantastic barrenness of the boulder-strewn land at their bases. The ground was burned out or washed bare. In one place a little stream trickled forth at the bottom of a ravine, but even here no grass grew — only little clusters of a coarse weed with flaring white flowers that looked as if it throve on poisoned soil. In the still heat ' we saw the silences move by and beckon.' The cliffs were channeled into myriad forms — battlements, spires, pillars, buttressed towers, flying arches; they looked like the ruined castles and temples of the monstrous devil-deities of some vanished race. All were ruins — ruins vaster than those of any structures ever reared by the hands of men.

" There were little water-holes, usually more or less alkaline, ten or fifteen miles apart. At these the Navajos were watering their big flocks of sheep and goats, their horses and donkeys, and their few cattle. They are very interesting Indians. They live scattered out, each family by itself, or two or three families together; not in villages like their neighbors the Hopis. They are pastoral Indians, but they are agriculturists also, as far as the desert permits. Here and there, where there was a little seepage of water, we saw their meager fields of corn, beans, squashes, and melons. All were mounted; the men usually on horses, the women and children often on donkeys. They were clad in white man's garb; at least the men wore both shirts and trousers and the women bodices and skirts; but the skirts were often green or red or saffron or bright blue; their long hair was knotted at the back of the head, and they usually wore moccasins. The well-to-do carried much jewelry of their own make.

" This northern Arizona desert was less attractive than the southern desert along the road to the Roosevelt Dam and near Mesa, for instance; for in the south the cactus growth is infinitely varied in size and in fantastic shape.

" Soon afterwards a Navajo family passed camp; they were traveling in a wagon drawn by a mule and a horse, and the boys of the family were driving a big herd of sheep and goats. The incident merely illustrated the real progress the Indians are making, and how far they already are from pure savagery.[14]

" Next day at noon we climbed the steep, narrow rock-ridge on whose summit rise the three Hopi towns, at one of which, Walpi, the snake-dance was to be held. The clustered rock villages stood in bold outline, on the cliff-top, against the blue sky. In all America there is no more strikingly picturesque sight. We walked up the precipitous cliff-trails to the mesa-top, and visited the three villages thereon. We were received

FIG. 257 — This picture taken near Denver is an admirable example of a mesa. The top is a naked remnant of a horizontal layer of rock. It has protected the earth under it from erosion, but the exposed part is worn away to a steep slope. In the background, plateau top of the same hard rock. (Photo Everett G. Rodebaugh.)

with friendly courtesy — perhaps partly because we endeavored to show good manners ourselves, which, I am sorry to say, is not invariably the case with tourists. The houses were colored red or white; and the houses individually, and the villages as villages, compared favorably with the average dwelling or village in many of the southern portions of Mediterranean Europe. Contrary to what we had seen in the Hopi village near Tuba, most of the houses were scrupulously clean; although the condition of the streets — while not worse than in the Mediterranean villages above referred to — showed urgent need of a crusade for sanitation and elementary hygiene. The men and women were well dressed, in clothes quite as picturesque as, and quite as near our own garb, as the dress of many European peasants of a good type. There were several rooms in each house; and the furniture included stoves, sewing-machines, chairs, window-panes of glass, and sometimes window-curtains. There were wagons in one or two places, for a wagon-road has been built to one end

14 I regret that the hero of San Juan Hill used that word of ignorance. I think he was in a hurry.

of the mesa; and we saw donkeys laden with fagots or water — another south-European analogy.

"Altogether, the predominant impression made by the sight of the ordinary life was that of a reasonably advanced, and still advancing, semi-civilization; not savagery at all. There is big room for improvement; but so there is among whites; and while the improvement should be along the lines of gradual assimilation to the life of the best whites, it should unquestionably be so shaped as to preserve and develop the

FIG. 258 — Indian woman weaving a Navajo blanket by hand. Being creative artists, the Indians can rarely be persuaded to make two blankets alike.

very real element of native culture possessed by these Indians — which, as I have already said, if thus preserved and developed, may in the end become an important contribution to American cultural life. . . . The effort should be to develop the existing art — whether in silver-making, pottery-making, blanket and basket weaving, or lace-knitting — and not to replace it by servile and mechanical copying. This is only to apply to the Indian a principle which ought to be recognized among all of our people. A great art must be living, must spring from the soul of the people; if it represents merely a copying, an imitation, and if it is confined to a small caste, it cannot be great.

"Of course all Indians should not be forced into the same mold. Some can be made farmers; others mechanics; yet others have the soul of the artist. Let us try to give each his chance to develop what is best in him. Moreover, let us be wary of interfering overmuch with either his work or his play. It is mere tyranny, for instance, to stop all Indian dances. Some which are obscene, or which are dangerous on other grounds, must be prohibited. Others should be permitted, and many of them encouraged. Nothing that tells for the joy of life, in any community, should be lightly touched.

" As an example, take the case of these Hopi mesa towns, perched in such boldly picturesque fashion on high, sheer-walled rock-ridges. Many good people wish to force the Hopis to desert these towns, and live in isolated families in nice tin-roofed houses on the plains below. I believe that this would be a mistake from the standpoint of the Indians — not to mention depriving our country of something as notable and as attractive as the castles that have helped to make the Rhine beautiful and famous. . . . Our own ancestors lived in villages as filthy not three centuries ago. The breezy coolness of the rocky mesa-top and the magnificent outlook would make it to me personally a far more attractive dwelling-place than the hot, dusty plains. Moreover, the present Hopi house, with its thick roof, is cooler and pleasanter than a tin-roofed house. . . . Give him a chance to utilize his own inherent sense of beauty in making over his own village for himself. Give him a chance to lead his own life as he ought to; and realize that he has something to teach us as well as to learn from us.

" Arizona and New Mexico hold a wealth of attraction for the archaeologist, the anthropologist, and the lover of what is strange and striking and beautiful in nature. More and more they will attract visitors and students and holiday-makers. That part of northern Arizona which we traversed is of such extraordinary interest that it should be made more accessible by means of a Government-built motor-road from Gallup to the Grand Canyon; a road from which branch-roads as good as those of Switzerland would gradually be built to such points as the Hopi villages and the neighborhood of the Natural Bridge."

### A Little-known Land

It is not surprising that this is the least-known part of the United States, and that in some of the remote sections the wild stallion still gallops at the head of his bunch of mares. In the fifties and sixties many exploring parties were sent through the country looking for railroad-routes to the Pacific coast. None was found here amid the steep-walled canyons. Railroads, those lovers of the plains, have scrupulously avoided crossing this region. The Santa Fe skirts its southern edge, the Denver and Rio Grande its northern edge. North of Flagstaff, Arizona, there is no railroad for 300 miles, nor is there likely to be one in any predictable time. The country is too profoundly broken and cut up. It was only in 1909 that the white man first saw the greatest natural bridge in the world, the Rainbow Bridge in southeastern Utah, which even now only a few dozen white men have seen, so difficult is the saddle journey to it.

Fig. 259—The sharp cliff, the edge of the arid plateau, overlooking the Grand River valley in western Colorado. Grand Valley Irrigation Project. Some water passes to lower irrigation canal through power plant, center foreground, where pumps lift water through iron pipe to high-level flume at extreme right. A, mouth of tunnel carrying main water supply; F, intake for water-power pumping plant C. The water then goes to fields through canal B. D, pipe through which water is pumped from C to flume and high level canal E. (Courtesy Smithsonian Institution.)

## Modernization

Most of the Colorado Plateau must continue as now, either as the Indian's or as the white man's ranch — a ranch of low productivity. Wide-reaching national forests cover the western and southwestern edge of the Colorado Plateau (Fig. 222).

Here the elevation contrast, produced by the sudden rise from lower lands, wrings enough moisture from the southwest winds to make large areas of open forest. The prevailing type of tree is Western yellow

FIG. 260 — Steam shovels working at four levels on an Arizona hill of solid ore. (Courtesy Phelps-Dodge Corporation, New York City.)

pine, and this plateau forest of Arizona and New Mexico is said to be the largest pine-forest in America. It lies in the most accessible part of the region.

The first impression one receives is that this land, so nearly devoid of minerals, should be left for national forests, parks, and Indians. But it has resources also for gigantic enterprises of the age of scientific engineering. The rock walls of the canyon are the most perfect sites for reservoirs in which to impound water for irrigation and power. Some parts of the upper valleys of the streams in New Mexico and Colorado, Wyoming and Utah (Fig. 227) are level enough for irrigation, and ultimately hundreds of thousands of acres within this region may be used for irrigation. Applications have already been made to the United States Government for permits to develop 4,500,000 horse-power of hydro-electric energy. (See chapter on the Desert.)

### Part IV. The Arizona Highlands

The Colorado Plateau is a plateau because the rocks are high above sea-level and almost horizontal. Lower than the Colorado Plateau and to the south and southwest of it, where the rocks have been broken into blocks and tipped at considerable angles, we find a different kind of country called the Arizona Highlands. Here the steep faces of the blocks of rock, miles in length, face the plateau and the gently sloping faces are toward the Pacific. The country resembles the Trans-Pecos High-

Fig. 261 — Open stand of nut-bearing (piñon) pine on rolling plateau near Santa Fe. If every tree were grafted to the best piñon known, this would be valuable property. (Photo Everett G. Rodebaugh.)

lands. This labyrinth of mountains and valleys is drained by the Gila River and its branches. It is a land of heat, drought, and ranches where many acres are needed for a cow. Some of the lowlands are bare rock, some of them bare desert, others are thick with cactus, while better grass and bushes grow up on the slopes of the mountains. Some of the mountains are high enough to have bits of isolated pine and even spruce upon their crests. At their western edge these highlands merge into the Arizona Desert (see next chapter), where only isolated mountain-tops stick up above the plains of sand and clay which the torrential rains have washed down from the highlands.

These Arizona Highlands have one feature which the Colorado Plateaus do not have — towns, mining-towns. Here are Globe, Bisbee, Douglas, and other towns, thriving when copper is high, depressed when copper is low, dead when the copper is gone — such is the fate of the mining-town. Already in this district railroads have been pulled up and sold for old iron.

## Future Tree-Crop Agriculture

The greatest possibility of increased agricultural production in the Southwestern Plateaus, after irrigable areas are used, is in tree-crops, which may be capable of a greater product than that which can come by irrigation. This development is a long way in the future, awaiting improvements in technique, land-values, and point of view. It should be pointed out that this region has already made a start in both crop and technique. The piñon pine grows almost everywhere that any tree will grow. It is the first tree at the dry timber line. The piñon tree grows

FIG. 262 — A lesson from North Africa. The Berbers of Matmata, central Tunis, build loose stone dams across gullies (arroyos) which hold rich soil, to be soaked by every rain, thus supporting olive trees of great vigor in a section having rainfall of ten inches or less. (Photo J. Russell Smith.)

wild in the dryer edge of all forest-belts from central Mexico to Utah and Colorado. It is one of nature's great gifts to man. For an indefinite time it has been an important source of food-supply in this region. Piñon nuts are rapidly coming into world-trade, and shipments from New Mexico alone were about 7,000,000 pounds in the good crop-year of 1921. Most of these nuts were gathered by Indian women and children. Large quantities went to waste or supported myriads of squirrels. Like most of the other fruit- and nut-yielding trees the piñon is in all probability capable of great improvement.

The process of flood-irrigation developed and practiced for ages by the cliff-dwellers and now practiced by Hopi, Navajo and the people of the Mexican Plateau in regard to corn has much greater possibilities when applied to tree-crops. Plant the trees in the gulches, build loose dams to catch the fertile silt so that summer showers must saturate the earth in which the tree-roots stand, and we have the possibilities of tens of millions of crop-yielding trees. This differs but little from the flood-irrigation now being used in Montana (chapter on Great Plains). This is not a " pipe dream." It has been going on for centuries. I have seen it among the Matmata of central Tunis. These Berber tribesmen have worked out by this means an agriculture in a limestone plateau where the rain, which falls only in the winter season, is about seven or eight inches. Their main crops are olives and dates, scattered up their gulches. The natural conditions seem far less favorable than that produced by the summer rain of our Southwestern Plateaus.

What the possible crops are is now quite unknown. There are native candidates in piñon, mesquite, screw-bean, honey locust. Possibly the olive might thrive. Search and investigation alone can tell, but certainly my observation of the splendid, big, prosperous-looking olive-trees in the earth collected above loose rock-dams in the gulches of Matmata makes me quite sure that there might some day be many millions of fruitful nut, fruit or bean-trees fed and watered by run-off from the showers of our Southwestern Plateaus.

# CHAPTER XXVII

## THE GREAT AMERICAN DESERT

FOR the last hundred years the American maps have been showing the Great American Desert in retreat. On grandfather's map, the desert had a bold stand as far east as the Mississippi Valley. When men learned

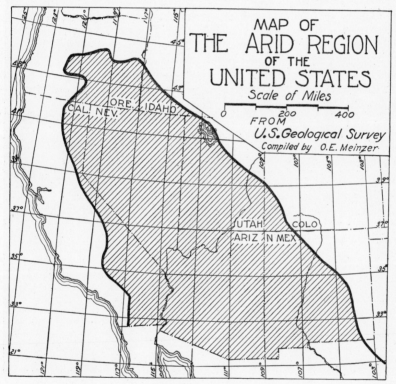

FIG. 263 — The area of our arid region as classified by the U. S. Geol. Surv. For the area of *desert* as classified by the U. S. Dept. Agr., see Map, inside back cover.

that Kansas grasslands would grow corn and that Colorado brushlands would feed sheep, maps were changed to accord with the newer knowledge. " The Great American Desert " has retreated toward the west and southwest, shrinking as it went. Unfortunately, this retreat will not re-

485

Fig. 264 — Alluring, weird, deceptive land — the giant cactus, its smaller thorny brethren and the scattered bushes of the Arizona deserts hide the bones of dead men, men to whom the land could give neither food nor drink. (Courtesy Chamber of Commerce, Phoenix, Ariz.)

sult in an evacuation, for the desert has made a last stand. The United States Geological Survey maps show it (Fig. 263) as covering a wide triangle with its western edge following up the Sierra Nevada mountains to central Oregon, and its eastern edge passing through Salt Lake City and Santa Fe southward to the mouth of the Pecos River.

Most of this desert area has a rainfall of less than ten inches per year and is therefore of little value, although most of it is more or less used for pasture. However, one part is even more unproductive than the rest, for sixty or seventy thousand square miles, with Yuma, Arizona, roughly in its center, is so dry and so hot that it is not pastured at all, except along the streams and in high mountains. This chapter discusses this unpastured desert region which extends far down into Mexico and may truly be called desert. The pastured part, we call arid.

The hottest temperatures in America, 115°–120° F. in the shade, prevail for days and weeks at a time near the mouth of the Colorado. This place has more sunshine (90%) than any other part of the United States.

This Great American Desert region has many names. Northeast of Los Angeles it is called the Mojave Desert; northwest of Yuma the Colorado Desert; west of Yuma the San Bernardino Desert; east of Yuma the Arizona Desert; east of the Gulf of California the Sonoran Desert. Lower California is also properly included in it.

## Water Work in the Desert

Most of this desert is lowland with a mountain rim to the east and a mountain rim to the west. The mountains on the western rim shut out the rain-winds from the moisture-giving sea. Many people think of a desert as being entirely without rain, but this is a mistake. Observation of rainfall taken for a period of thirty-six years near Yuma shows an annual average of 2.7 inches of rain. One year (1902) there was no rain at all; in the year of greatest rainfall (1904) there were seven inches. Here rain comes in two seasons, about half of it in the winter and half in July and August, when the great heat of desert earth makes the air above so hot that it expands and rises to such great heights that clouds form and rain falls.

From river bottom to upland rim the rainfall increases to as much as ten inches in the higher places. In the southwestern section, elevations above 6000 feet are forest-clad and appear as green plant islands in a brown waste. If we should start from the Arizona Plateau or from the mountains behind Los Angeles and travel for a day down toward the floor of the valley, we should see a striking contrast. There is good forest of pine at the top, which soon gives way to smaller pines and cedars; then comes the bunch-grass, the yucca; and suddenly the giant cactus, like a beheaded tree, rises by the roadside, the sentinel outpost of the desert. Along with it are sagebrush, mesquite, and other low desert bushes which spread themselves ever farther and farther apart as we descend into the land of lesser rain and greater heat.

Since but few plants can grow where the rainfall is so scanty and irregular, there are but few roots in the desert earth, and they are often large rather than fibrous. Having no roots to hold it in place, the desert soil is always moving and locally disappearing.

The wind, blowing away particles of dust, leaves the heavier, coarser pieces, so that wide stretches appear to be a solid gravel bed. In reality the gravel is only a thin layer that keeps a bed of fine soil beneath from blowing away. At other places the surface is bare rock from which every movable particle has been shaved off by the wind-blown sand and by gravel, scraping over it at the time of torrential rains. The mountains are mostly bare and nature breaks them up rapidly with winter frost and summer heat. Summer temperatures of 130° or 140° F. by day and 40° to 60° at night make great surface expansion which cracks the rocks so that sometimes the surface breaks off in flakes or even sizable layers. But as there is no vegetation to hold the soil, wind and water carry the mountain waste away, and it is never made into clay soil, rocky but rich, like the granite formations in the eastern United States. The work of wind and rain on desert mountains weathers their bare forms into weird and picturesque shapes. Throughout this desert region, sprinkled with old mountains buried hundreds of feet in rock waste, fantastic remains of weather-beaten mountains appear as pinnacles, spires, round-topped haystacks or sharp and jagged chains. To survive in this dry land the traveler must know which rock it is that hides one of the few drinking-places. He must be able to follow a dim trail to the next water-hole, and the next, and the next; if he does not know these things he will succumb to the ever-present menace of the desert — death from thirst.

### The Desert Charm

No other landscape affords such a wealth of color. Brown and yellow and tawny reds predominate, touched up with black and gray. The brilliant reds and yellows of midday may be turned to violet in the softer light of sunset or dawn. Something in the desert sunrise and sunset makes colors that are never seen in the lands of plentiful rain. Look across the desert landscape and it draws you. You want to go out into it. You want to go back to it when you have left it. This quality is not peculiar to the American Desert alone. I found that the people of Algeria feel that way toward the Sahara.

Add the lure of gold, with its appeal to our deep-set instinct for taking a chance, and you can see why men have gone to the desert, even though it has claimed many victims who have died the terrible death of thirst — the price of being lost in the land without water. It was therefore a humane act when in 1916 the American Congress appropriated money to provide for the survey of the wells and springs of the desert and for marking the highways with signs so that travelers could find the nearest drinking-place. The survey of 60,000 square miles of this region has been completed and the results published in bulletins of the Geological Survey, which has planned to render the same service for the whole of the arid region west of Salt Lake, Santa Fe and the mouth of the Pecos.

### Surface and Streams

Only a small proportion of the surface of this desert is made up of areas of entirely bare sand, bare gravel, bare clay, bare rock, or is so poisoned with alkali that no plant can grow. Indeed it has a most surprising, though economically useless, scattered vegetation. Near Yuma there are

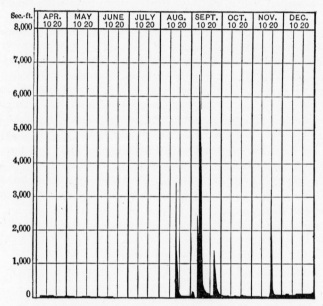

FIG. 265 — This graph of the flow of the Gila River gives a view of the problems of irrigation and water storage. (Courtesy U. S. Geol. Surv.)

140 species of plants and seventy-five varieties of cactus, the most conspicuous being the tall giant cactus. When some spot has the fortune to be wet by a shower or two of rain, the annual plants, such as grasses and flowering herbs, spring up quickly, bloom with amazing suddenness in the fearful heat, ripen their seed and in a few weeks again resume the brown of winter. The bushes which live through often have a large development of root to seize and hold moisture when opportunity offers. This fact, in combination with the greater rainfall of the mountains, makes the inhabitants tell the Easterners that this is a country of contraries. For example, " we have to dig for wood and climb for water " —

the wood of roots, the water of a mountain spring that flows a few feet
and sinks into sand or gravel.

Many of these little mountain streams start down toward the desert
only to be promptly swallowed by the sands and coarse soil at the base
of the mountains. It is easy to understand this when we consider how
rain falls in a desert. It falls as showers, almost cloudbursts, very irregular in times and amount. Sometimes, after a year or two years almost without rain, there may come a torrential downpour — a cloudburst.
The sky seems fairly to pour water, almost to dump it. A wash that
has been dry for years becomes, for the moment, a rushing river. Often
a mountain torrent will gather up great masses of rock and mud which
it carries along for a short distance like a rolling wall. But even a torrent cannot carry such heavy material very long, so, as the water spreads,
it begins to drop the heavier parts of its load. Soon pieces of rock,
some as big as barrels, are dropped; the water rushes on, dropping more
of its load as it goes, and finally carrying only the smaller particles
forward to the master river. By this process a loose soil of great porosity
is spread out like a fan at the foot of the mountains. Any small flow
like that from a spring, on reaching this porous wash, sinks quickly out
of sight and works along through subterranean channels (Fig. 247).

Water for irrigation purposes is frequently raised from dry river beds
by piling rocks and brush in the stream bed so as to compact the underlying sand and thus bring the water to the surface so that it can be led
away in ditches. The amount brought to the surface in this way is
sometimes surprising.

Along streams that may be without surface-water for months at a
time there is often a strip of tree-growth fed by the seeping underground
water. The stream bank is often brilliant with the light green foliage
of the cottonwood, one of the most rapid-growing trees and of great
value in such a country. Only five living streams cross the 700 miles
of the American boundary between the Rio Grande and the Pacific Ocean.
In the Piedmont area of Pennsylvania and Virginia one would have difficulty in traveling five miles in any direction without crossing five
streams. On the east coast of the Gulf of California, between the
Colorado and the Yaqui, a distance of 500 miles, there is no living stream,
and the west side of the Gulf is no better. Indeed, only one or two
living streams come down from the one snow-capped mountain in the
peninsula.

The subterranean streams of the desert sometimes support agriculture.
The Coachella valley, to the northwest of Salton Sea, has developed a
substantial agriculture solely by artesian water, some flowing, some
pumped from many wells fed by the White River on the slope of the
San Bernardino Mountains.

Only a small part of the desert drains into the master stream, the

Colorado, which lives by the rain of distant and more humid regions. Most of the desert is a series of inland basins where there is not enough water to fill them and overflow to the sea. Some of these basins, now dry, tell of greater rainfall in the past, for they show unmistakable signs of being old lake beds with the usual desert-lake remains of common salt, soda, borax, alkalies and other salts. One of these valleys, the one nearest the Sierras, with mountains towering 10,000 feet above it, is a kind of aristocrat among desert valleys because it contains Owen Lake,

FIG. 266 — Rough crust of impure salt on the floor of Death Valley, California. (Courtesy U. S. Bureau of Soils.)

a fine body of water, fed by the melting snows of the Sierra and wasting its vapors into desert air; at least, that is what it did until the city of Los Angeles, in order to double its population, built the longest aqueduct in the world to divert the water from the lake and carry it under mountain and over valley for a distance of 240 miles. In time Owen Lake, with its water-supply diverted to good works, will doubtless become a dry bed like most of the others.

A little farther to the east is the famous Death Valley, properly named because of the fate of the expedition of forty-niners who got lost in it. While it has high mountains upon its edges, the valley itself goes down to 256 feet below sea-level. It is at this point that the United States strikes bottom. There is a rainfall of two or three inches per year, which, falling in the winter season, leaves it indeed a desert.[1] But such is the ability of plants to adapt themselves to environment that even here there is vegetation. Death Valley is so nearly without water that many miners have died there of thirst while seeking its fabled gold. There is a story of one miner who knew of a secret spring, perhaps one little spot behind a rock, where he could drink. He thus lived while picking over ores in some secret ledge. It was the secret spring that enabled him to sneak away without being seen and then to appear from time to time with enviable stocks of gold.

## Desert Lakes

One of these old lakes, Searles Lake, is now a plain of salt crystal, but if you take up a shovelful the crystals are found to be lying in liquor,

FIG. 267 — A small part of the waters of Salt River in flood, tearing out the causeway at one end of the bridge at Phoenix, Ariz. The Roosevelt Dam was built to conserve the water of these occasional, destructive desert cloudbursts and to make their water useful. (Courtesy Chamber of Commerce, Phoenix, Ariz.)

the remnant of a lake saturated with borax and potash, estimated at about thirty million tons each. This basin was the site of one of our feverish war industries when we tried to reclaim the potash, but it could not compete with the vast and solid layers of potash salts that can be so easily dug up near the banks of the Elbe in Germany and the Rhine in Alsace.

Another of these old lake beds is called Borax Lake. For many years,

[1] " League upon league the infinite reaches of dazzling white alkali laid themselves out like an immeasurable scroll unrolled from horizon to horizon; not a bush, not a twig relieved that horrible monotony. Even the sand of the desert would have been a welcome sight; a single clump of sagebrush would have fascinated the eye; but this was worse than the desert. It was abominable, this hideous sink of alkali, this bed of some primeval lake lying so far below the level of the ocean." (*McTeague*, Frank Norris, Boni & Liveright, pp. 424–25.)

there was a desolate camp upon its arid shore.  Men lived there and shoveled up borax that was hauled for several days across the desert in great wagons drawn by many spans of mules.  It was advertised as Twenty Mule Team Borax.  Like the potash of Searles Lake, this deposit is no longer able to compete with more available sources, although the advertisement, having established a brand, still continues to be used.

### Resources

" This region is by no means devoid of natural resources or human activity.  It contains prosperous cities, fertile agricultural districts,

FIG. 268 — A gorge in the solid rock eighty miles upstream from the level Phoenix plains furnished an excellent site for the Roosevelt Dam.  The power plant at its base shows the size of the structure, and utilizes a by-product of power, as the waters flow away to feed crops on the fields eighty miles downstream.  (Courtesy U. S. Reclamation Service.)

forest-clad mountains, a large aggregate number of watering-places, some rich mines and an unknown wealth of mineral deposits.  But the localities that have water supplies are widely separated oases in a vast expanse of silent, changeless, unproductive desert, whose most impressive feature is its great distances and whose chief evidences of human occupation are the long roads that lead from one watering-place to another." [2]

In a country so dry as this, chances for a living are indeed small, and Bowman (*Forest Physiography*) points out that there are not one hundred permanent inhabitants in a strip of land twenty miles each side of the boundary, six hundred miles long, save for the oases of irrigation and the exotic settlements of the mining-camp.

[2] *Routes to Desert Watering-Places in the Salton Sea Region, California*, U. S. Geol. Surv., Water Supply Paper 490-A, p. 1.

But for the rivers that flow into the desert from the mountains and plateaus beyond its rim, the record of human activities upon its surface would be short indeed, limited to a few small oases and to mining enterprises which sooner or later result in abandoned towns, like Tumco, north of Yuma. There $12,000,000.00 worth of gold was dug out and three thousand people drank water from a pipe-line extending thirty miles to the Colorado and hauled their food and wood many miles. Before the

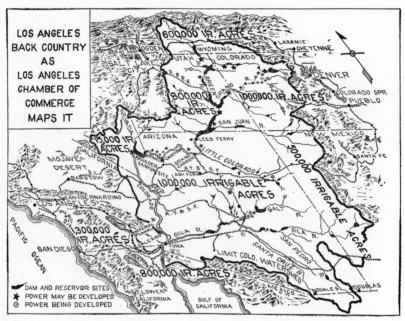

FIG. 269 — This map made by the Los Angeles Chamber of Commerce shows the vital interest of that city in the Colorado Basin.

year 1900, when the workings ceased to pay, the people vanished to the last man. Then came the scavengers, hauling away the lumber of the shanties and digging up the floors of the cabins, looking for buried gold. Of the town nothing now remains in good order except the graveyard. Grass does not grow over desert graves and even a wooden cross is long immune to decay in the dry air.

### Irrigation

But for the rivers this land indeed would be much like the Sahara; and as in the Sahara the River Nile carries the water which sustains kingdoms, so into the American Desert flows the water of the Colorado and the Gila. Long ago the Indians seized upon these waters as a source of life, and developed irrigation to a high degree of perfection and

practiced it for unknown
centuries. We can still see
their ruined canals extending for scores of miles. In
the Salt River Valley alone
t h e r e are 150 miles of
these ancient canals [3] still
visible, enough to have irrigated 250,000 acres, although there is no evidence
that they were all used at
o n e time. (U. S. Geol.
Surv. Water Supply Paper
365.) On the Pima In-
dian Reservation there still
stands a three-story adobe
fortress - granary t h a t i s
thought to be 1000 years
old. It was built for the
defense of grain and man
against nomad raids.

After hunting for gold
f o r h a l f a century the
white man, about the be-
ginning of the twentieth
century, invaded this re-
gion with plans for large-
s c a l e engineering irrigation. The Salt River Val-
ley was picked out as one
of the units to be devel-
oped under the Reclama-
tion Act of 1902, and by
1920 it was pointed out as
the one really successful
enterprise of t h e m a n y
that have been built under
this law.

Few rivers have given
man a plainer call to come

[3] Of this 150 miles, forty
miles are now incorporated in
the present irrigation system,
for our engineers were unable
to improve upon the survey of
the ancients.

Fig. 270 — The red granite mountain remains
naked, unchanged. The alluvial desert plain
was changed by irrigation, first to a barley
field (center), and then to an orange orchard
(bottom). The rows of trees in the distance
mark the course of the irrigation ditch. Three
pictures taken on the same spot, near Phoenix,
Ariz. (Courtesy U. S. Reclamation Service.)

and control them than has the Salt River.  Here was a wide, rich valley
with hundreds of thousands of acres of level, water-borne soil, rich with
the unleached fertility of arid lands.  For ages streams coming down from
the mountains have been filling the valley with rich soil which in some
places has no rock for at least 1200 feet.  Dr. Willard Smith of Phoenix
is authority for the fact that a good piece of pine was brought up from a
depth of 702 feet from a well at Glendale, near Phoenix.

### The Roosevelt Dam and Salt River Valley

With rich soil, continuous heat and sunshine only water was lacking
and there was the Gila-Salt River, with a wide channel, which was
sometimes almost dry, and sometimes turbulent with an appalling and
uncrossable flood.  In the year 1903 the river discharged at Yuma
60,000 acre feet of water and in 1905 sixty times that much.  In some
years a single rain would send down more water than all of the rain in
the low year (1903).  If only the flow would be regular!  Then the reclamation engineers, climbing around the defiles of the mountains in the
Arizona Plateau, found an ideal site in which to build a storage reservoir.
Here stands the now well-known Roosevelt Dam, which can store so
much flood-water that the rains of 1930 will feed the crops of 1932 on the
hundreds of thousands of acres of land many miles downstream.

The creation of the Roosevelt Dam is one of the spectacular stories of
the development of the West.  There was no natural road leading to
the site, so for twenty miles the road was built through the waterless
desert; then for forty miles the road was blasted through rock walls
of canyons at a total cost of millions.  The hundreds of thousands of
barrels of cement needed were made in a cement plant that was built
for the purpose.  Power with which to quarry, lift, and haul cement
material and dam material was produced by a temporary hydro-electric
plant built for the purpose.  The plant received its water through a
nineteen-mile cement-lined canal.  For many months the 3000 people
connected with this enterprise toiled; finally they left a huge structure of
solid concrete that can last almost as long as the mountains stand.  At
its foot a power-plant develops 6000 horse-power, some of which is used
to lift irrigation water to lands which canals cannot reach.  The water-
power derived as a by-product from irrigation works becomes more
valuable with the increase of population.

In 1923 the people of the Phoenix region were much excited over the
plan to erect two more power-plants (nearly completed in 1924) producing a total of 65,000 horse-power.  Power can be sold for light, transportation, manufacturing and pumping purposes at a cost which will
enable the water-users of the Salt River to maintain their canals and
actually get the water to their own fields for nothing.

This is heralded as the most successful of the Government's irrigation enterprises, but it can scarcely yet be said to have found itself, if finding itself consists of settling down to an established type of agriculture with more or less fixed rotation such as that which we find in the Eastern States or the Corn Belt. In the early days of the Salt River Unit it seemed as if the successful alfalfa crops were making an established dairy industry by the rapid increase of cows and shipments of butter. Then came the war, with the unheard-of prices of $.50, $.75, and even $1.00 a pound for long-staple cotton. Experiments with Egyptian cotton had shown that the African resemblances held true here also, and that long-staple Egyptian cotton, so highly prized by automobile-tire manufacturers, could be grown as well in the Salt River Valley as in any other Egypt. Visions of wealth from cotton-crops picked by cheap Mexican labor began to fill the minds of men. By comparison the steady income and unending labor of the dairy looked small and prosaic. Cows by thousands were dumped upon the market and cotton fields rose where the alfalfa had been. The $600,000.00 creamery owned by Armour & Co. was shut down. Two large crops of cotton were sold at high prices. In 1920 there was a great acreage of cotton produced at a cost of $.40 and $.50 a pound, but it sold for only half that much. Despondency filled the valley. By 1922 the farmers were beginning again to build up their dairy herds.

This is a place where a great variety of products will grow, including alfalfa, forage grains, early vegetables, olives, and many fruits. But the vital question is, what can be grown that will sell at a profit? The location is very remote and the Imperial Valley to the west sends vegetables into the markets a little earlier. In 1922 considerable acreages of young oranges were being planted in one part of the valley near Phoenix, where a high granite mountain called the Camel Back protected groves from the north winds and permitted them to bear crops, while orchards on similar slopes and soil five miles away, but unprotected by the Camel Back, were frozen out.

The promoters in Phoenix are hoping that their place will become a winter resort for people from the East. They say that Phoenix is much more delightful than southern California, because it is almost rainless, with bright sunshine and crisp and invigorating air. They admit, however, that for four months in summer " the climate hasn't much edge on hell." (The words of a leading citizen.) When I was there in July it was not particularly hot, but the bed burnt my body and sleep seemed only possible by the breeze of an electric fan. In the streets of Phoenix no gentleman needs to wear a collar; propriety permits him to seek comfort by rolling in the neckband of his shirt and giving himself some approach to the comfort of the costume of women.

### The Colorado River

The Colorado River, the greatest source of life in all this region, drains nearly a quarter of a million square miles.  The Colorado is 1750 miles long, coming from the high Wyoming valleys where there is freezing weather every month of the year, and flooding the hot, subtropic delta where vegetation grows twelve months of the year.  Eighty-five per cent of the water of this stream comes from the snow-fed tributaries in the Rocky Mountains of Colorado and Wyoming and the Wasatch Mountains

Fig. 271 — Basin irrigation and two-story agriculture in the Imperial Valley.
(Courtesy Yuma Commercial Club.  Photo W. L. Jacobs.)

of Utah.  For 600 miles in its lower course it has no branches worth mentioning.  It is best known for the Grand Canyon, one of the marvels of geology and one of the wonders of the world.  More and more the river assumes importance as a source of water-power and irrigation.

At Yuma the river loses the last vestige of the canyon form.  Indeed, it flowed into the Gulf of California at that point but yesterday, geologically speaking.  But the river that has made itself world-famous by cutting the deepest of gorges, also, and for that reason, holds the world's record as the greatest carrier of mud and sand in proportion to its bulk.[4]

What did the canyon-cutter do with all the mud and sand it had dug out of the plateau?  It dumped this into the Gulf of California and built a delta that reached across the Gulf, a huge dam that shut off the upper end completely.  Across this delta, which appears to be flat, the river, with many channels, twists and winds, filling up old channels and cutting new ones, and leaving ponds, sloughs or empty channels.  When the river chanced to turn to the right it flowed into the end cut off by this delta and filled it up so that it overflowed across the delta.  This high

[4] Circular 159, University of California, 1917, says the river carries sediments to the extent of 3.2% of its volume, but D. T. McDougall, Director of the Carnegie Institution's Desert Station at Tucson, says (*Geographic Review*, vol. 3, p. 372), in speaking of the Salton Sink: " The silt-laden water of the Colorado River deposits about 6% of its volume as dry soil."

level is marked by a clear-cut beach about twenty feet above sea-level. When the river turned to the left after some flood it flowed to the Gulf. While this was happening the water of the part cut off by the delta, now called Salton Sea, dried away. When the white man first found it, it was a salt-encrusted lake of small area. Back of the Salton station on the Southern Pacific Railroad, eighty old beaches are clearly marked, one having been made every time the lake remained a while at one level and the waves beat its shore.

Fortunately for man, the river has for a long time been flowing into the Gulf. White settlers found the Salton Sink almost dry. Thus several hundred square miles of the richest soil were below sea-level, but dry and offering one of the most productive opportunities in the world for irrigation. In the year 1900 not a single civilized person lived in this valley. Then a company of enterprising Americans dug a canal carrying water from the southeast corner of California through part of Mexico, to irrigate the rich lands of the old sea bottom southeast of Salton Sink, known as Imperial Valley. The through line of the Southern Pacific Railroad was already there. Settlers flocked in. They planted and tended crops which grew prodigiously in a climate which boasted of eleven months of summer and one month of late spring. The boom was on. More water was needed, so the promoters made a new irrigation canal. This was the beginning of tragedy because the river was higher than the Salton Sink, and flowing in one of those temporary channels which the river has been for ages making and unmaking in the porous, light, river-borne material of the delta. The river flowed into the canal, turning it into a raging river. The descent to Salton Sea was steeper than the descent to the Gulf of California, so the canal cut deeper and deeper until it had at one time 87% of the water of the river. Salton Sea rose, flooded the railroad tracks, compelled the re-location of the Southern Pacific; and only after most desperate labors and the expenditure of $2,000,000.00 was the break stopped and the river sent back in its old course toward the Gulf.[5] By this time, 1907, the Salton Sea had increased from about 200 square miles to 450 square miles. Ten years later it had shrunk to 300 square miles.

Under the Reclamation Act the United States Government created the Yuma Irrigation Unit, on the Arizona side of the Colorado, and the Imperial Valley Unit on the California side. And then the problems began to arise. In 1915 the river did not carry enough water to irrigate the land then under ditch. Nevertheless between 1915 and 1922 on the lower Colorado, 60,000 acres in the United States, and 150,000 acres in Mexico had been put under irrigation. With all that land in use the people lived in fear and trembling lest another dry year should come. If, for a moment, they forgot the menace of drought, they remembered

[5] Epes Randolph, the engineer who did it, was venerated for the rest of his days.

the flood that broke into Imperial Valley and worried about that. Meanwhile there was trouble farther up the river. Water was being diverted from the headwaters of the Colorado and used to irrigate land in Utah, Wyoming and Colorado.

There were eight such diversions, carrying water through the Rocky Mountains in Colorado. All this made the fear of a dry year an endless nightmare to the people at Yuma and the Imperial Valley. What would they do if, as was sure to happen, the low waters of 1915 came again? There are few places in the world where it is more necessary

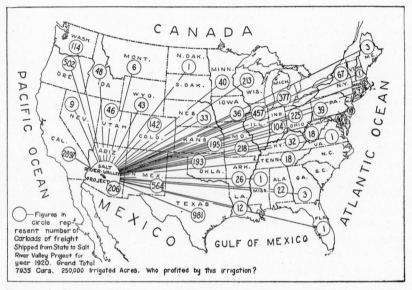

FIG. 272 — If anyone knows of a better evidence of the present economic interdependence, the author of this book begs that it may be sent to him.

for a man to live by his wits, his large-scale wits, than in this region of Colorado waters. Then the fear of flood rose higher and kept increasing thousands uneasy. There are dikes along both banks of the Colorado and along both banks of the Gila, yet the river is always choking itself with mud and raising its channel higher and higher. From the Mexican boundary the river flows seventy-five miles south to reach the Gulf. From the same place it flows seventy-five miles to the Imperial Valley. There is a thirty-foot fall down to the Gulf, but in the other direction there is a 250-foot fall to the Imperial Valley. If a big flood came, the river would doubtless rush down the steeper grade and perhaps overwhelm the Imperial Valley and the Yuma lands. Meanwhile millions of horse-power of water-power were wasting themselves in the canyons above and capitalists were asking for permits to build dams and power-plants. Would the dams make power-sites and also store water for irrigation and end the flood danger as well?

From the consideration of these dangers, needs, and undeveloped resources it became plain that here was another of those economic enterprises that require a large-scale, comprehensive plan. The interests of seven states conflicted. The Secretary of the Interior, Mr. Hoover, representatives from the seven states involved, and the engineers of the Geological Survey held many conferences on ways and means of meeting the problem. As a result a four-page interstate agreement, " The

FIG. 273 — Thus Yuma boasts of her winter climate. (Courtesy U. S. Reclamation Service.)

Colorado River Compact," was signed at Santa Fe Nov. 22, 1922, by all of the states except Arizona.[6] This is really a kind of treaty between the states in which they agree in a general way regarding the division of the river's resources. Much study will be needed to determine the final plans, but preliminary suggestions are somewhat as follows: In the lower part of the Grand Canyon to build a dam, the Boulder Dam, to impound 21,000,000 acre feet of water which can be used for irrigation. The dam can store temporarily half as much more water in time of flood, thus giving protection against overflows downstream. It will also develop 600,000 to 700,000 horse-power (the amount is uncertain because of the uncertain influence of irrigation). Shall a certain reservoir be emptied in one month to water alfalfa or the next month to make power? This proposed dam — the Boulder Dam — would be only 299 miles from

[6] " There are those living in Arizona who believe that the Colorado River is in a considerable degree our own property. There is a tendency on the part of Los Angeles to annex Chicago, New York and London as suburbs." (A leading citizen of Arizona.)

Los Angeles — a great market for power. Many more smaller reservoirs are planned farther upstream, and several more power-plants are projected for various places in the Grand Canyon so that altogether full utilization of the stream would require the expenditure of hundreds of millions. Two or three generations would be required to complete the project which calls eventually for the irrigation of 4,000,000 acres in the upper basin — Colorado, Utah, Wyoming, Arizona and Nevada. In the Lower Basin (below the Grand Canyon) the United States is to irrigate 1,220,000 acres and Mexico 800,000 acres. It is estimated that water-power could be developed as follows:

|  | Horse-Power |
|---|---|
| Green River Basin | 1,390,000 |
| Grand River Basin | 210,000 |
| Colorado | 4,410,000 |
| In round numbers | 6,000,000 |

Full irrigation would reduce this to 3,400,000, thereby raising an interesting question of relative value for some supreme command to settle.

### The American Egypt

What will be grown in this American Egypt, this land which boasts a climate of eleven months of summer and one month of late spring; a land where the sun sometimes makes the water from a pipe buried in the earth so hot that one cannot bathe in it; a land where the farmers regularly forgo the August irrigation of the alfalfa for fear that a little water may be left standing in the field when the sun strikes it? When this latter occurs, the alfalfa is cooked and completely killed. If this land is properly used all the heat, moisture, and fertility have great possibilities for production. These climatic conditions admirably suit the date, which the Arab says wants to have its feet in the water and its head in the fires of heaven. Date plantations of the Coachella Valley (the part of the old Gulf depression northwest of Salton Sink) are said not to have missed a crop in ten years. In 1922 the harvest yielded 300,000 pounds. Here is doubtless enough date land, if fully utilized, to furnish all the dates we can use, perhaps many more.

While there are many possibilities, there is, as yet, no established agriculture. At the present time the principal income is from lettuce and cantaloupes for the markets of Eastern cities and from meat and dairy products. Lettuce is ready to be shipped in January, but risks in marketing may be encountered. In January 1921, almost a whole crop was plowed under because there was no market for it. They plowed up lettuce to plant cantaloupes, which begin to be ripe about May 20 and for a time monopolize Eastern markets, but it is easy to oversupply the market with 500 cars a day and then the cantaloupes must rot, as not infrequently happens. Grapes ripen here in July — and monopolize the

market. In 1919 and 1920 this section went through the same cotton
boom that cursed the Salt River Valley.

Meanwhile the chief acreages are Egyptian corn, sorghum (it is too hot
for the American corn to fer-
tilize its blossom) and alfalfa,
which yields on the average six
cuttings and four to five tons
to the acre (Circular 159, University of California). Much
of this alfalfa is baled and sent
to the cows in Los Angeles territory. Many carloads of manure are also sent there for fertilizing orange orchards. There
will probably be worked out a
safe balance between d a i r y
acreage and vegetable acreage
with slowly increasing acreages
of dates and fruit. Meanwhile
the farmers here are developing
their problems. To mature an
acre of alfalfa hay from 300 to
1000 tons of water are required.
Four acre feet of water build
up the level of the land a quarter of an inch. The muddy
water carries fertility as does
the Nile, but it also fills the irrigation d i t c h e s with sand.[7]
The sand has been lifted out
w i t h big scrapers drawn by
tractors. It is injurious to put
it on the land and it has made
such piles on the banks that
the scraper will no longer clean
the ditches. What next?

FIG. 274 — The writer of Genesis placed
Adam and Eve in a date oasis. The
date growers of Arizona and California
have made a successful introduction of
the main crop of the Garden of Eden.
Imperial Valley, California. (Courtesy
Yuma Commercial Club. Photo W. L.
Jacobs.)

In some places the raising of
the ground-water level is creat-
ing alkali soils, a common trouble in most irrigated places. This trouble
shows that the great ditch cut by the runaway river of 1906 has benefited
the lands near it because it furnishes them with drainage.

[7] The analogy with Egypt here breaks down. We must shift to Mesopotamia.
The Nile is ideal with its *thin* coat of rich mud. The Tigris and the Colorado, fresh
from the canyon are ditch chokers. See Newbigin, M. I., *Man in Mediterranean
Lands.*

The Mexican boundary cuts through the middle of the Imperial Valley lands, creating interesting but troublesome situations of a political origin. Arizona wants a port on the Gulf of California, but Mexico will not hear of selling the strip of land and Arizona does not dare build a port in Mexico.[8] The irrigation canal in the Imperial Valley runs through Mexican land, but the corporation that owns it is in turn owned by the American irrigation district. The fear of civil wars and trouble in or with Mexico has caused serious consideration to be given to a very expensive plan for an all-American canal to the Imperial Valley. At the time when the international boundary was being surveyed, it is said that when the American surveying party reached the east bank of the Colorado after many weeks in the desert they heard of a Mexican town a few miles upstream. Thither they went for a little vacation. When ready to resume work, some one said: " Oh, what's the use of going down the river? The country's no good anyhow. Let's go on from here." They did, and that accounts for the jog in the boundary at that point. To straighten that line now millions of dollars might be cheerfully paid. In the beginning it could have been done by a few hours of walking.

Boundary influence is curiously shown in one town which is divided by the boundary. The northern half is named Calexico, the southern half is Mexicali. All the store business is on the American side, because it is cheaper to carry into Mexico a basket of shopping than it is to buy at a Mexican store which has already paid the tariff and must take a profit on the same. The managers of all the enterprises on the Mexican side live in Calexico. Mexicali is chiefly peopled by Japanese and Chinese who cannot be admitted into the United States. In 1920 a 200,000-acre tract of land on the Mexican side was bought by an American-Mexican Corporation.

It is a question who will live in this American Egypt a hundred years hence. At the present time there are more Indians, Mexicans and Orientals than people of North European stock. Many of the Imperial Valley dwellers are recently from Mexico or Japan. Which element in this diverse population will increase? It remains to be proven whether North European stock can hold its own for even a few generations in such a climate as this.[9] Perhaps we shall some day have to choose between letting a given acre foot of water support Caucasian families in Wyoming or families of other races in the Colorado delta.

[8] A news item of Sept. 20, 1924, reported that the Colorado River Land Co. (note the language of the name), owners of 800,000 acres on the Mexican side of the boundary had announced its plans for building a new railroad through its lands to the Gulf — 138 miles of line. Traffic in cotton from Imperial Valley, bananas from the south coast of the Gulf and machinery from the East was expected.

[9] According to Dr. Charles E. Woodruff in *Medical Ethnology*, the population must at least be brunette, if not colored. The striking resemblance of climate to that of Egypt gives the Egyptian native a peculiar interest to us.

### Lower California

Lower California, a peninsula 750 miles long and 30 to 150 miles wide, is also a part of the Great American Desert. Most of it is high, bare mountains, very steep on the Gulf side, sloping away more gently toward the Pacific. Upon their heights are some pine forests, quite out of the reach of the lumberman, but sending down a few streams to water a few acres for beans, garden stuff and alfalfa for a few thousand people,

FIG. 275 — These seven-foot conduits for irrigation water in the Culiacan Valley, built about 1922, show that Mexico is not all chaos and cactus. (Courtesy U. S. Dept. Commerce.)

mostly Indians, who live in this little-known part of the Great American Desert. There seem to be possibilities for considerable water-storage and irrigation of frost-free lands.

Lower California, like the mountains of Mexico itself, is supposed to have much mineral wealth, but the only enterprise of note is the Boleo Copper Company at Santa Rosalina, where for many years a French company has operated a plant with imported machinery, imported fuel, imported food but with native Mexican labor. The company had twenty-eight miles of narrow-gauge railroad and twenty-three miles of six-inch water-pipe, bringing from a mountain spring the possibility of life into a hot and desolate place. At last accounts the town had 11,000 people, about one-fifth of all those reported to live in this long peninsula.

### Eastern Coast of Gulf of California

Far down the coast of the Gulf of California the desert fades away into a land of greater rainfall. As the Mexican mountains are higher here the streams reach the sea, and some have so much water that there are several valleys in the State of Sonora and more in Sinaloa with considerable irrigation and greater possibilities to be attained by storage water if the day comes when there is better government.[10] This country is chiefly inhabited by Indians, with a few Mexican and American enterprisers. The chief crops are corn, sugar and chick peas or garbonza, all of which are shipped to the interior of Mexico. Bananas grow from San Blas to Mazatlan. Before the Mexican disturbances began, in 1911, the people shipped winter vegetables, cantaloupes, tomatoes and early oranges, to the United States before our own were ripe. This is a trade for which there are excellent physical possibilities, but the political problem furnishes a great embarrassment in a country where revolutions can confiscate anything, impress anybody, and cause the destruction of railroads, as has happened for many miles in the southern part of this district.

### Future

The big thing in this region is the Colorado irrigation. Next comes the irrigation along the eastern shore of the Gulf of California. There will be other irrigations, some of which have already begun.

Interesting discoveries of water are being made in the Mohave Desert. Some of its basins are underlaid with artesian water.

At Richardson a well ran useless soda water. This was cut off and farther down a smaller flow of sweet water was found — excellent for drinking-water or for irrigation. It is known that there are many of these artesian areas, and now the traveler may see from the car window the strange contrast of the black-green foliage of a pear orchard standing trim and alone in the flat gray desert. Is there any reason to expect these people to be wiser with artesian water than their neighbors in Dakota? If not tragedy awaits many, if not most, of those who settle here, for they will probably send too many wells into this precious accumulation and run it out several times as fast as it soaks in. With care the irrigation and the water-power should last as long as climate lasts.

Lastly, minerals. More careful exploration may be expected to reveal many mineral deposits that will give rise to temporary industries — lasting a year or a few generations.

[10] In 1923 the interest rate at Manzanillo was 10% per month, but the Mexican Government was making surveys for irrigation units costing millions and duplicating the Roosevelt dam in miniature.

Fig. 276 — One of the striking monuments of natural history which tell a part of the recent geological history of the Great Basin area. In the background, the naked and sharply eroded mountains of aridity. In the foreground, the basin filled by mountain wash. The terraces in the center record the wave work on the shores of a lake, which stood at different levels as it dried away in an era of declining rain. Since that day the mountain rains have cut an arroyo in the terraces. Perhaps Sherlock Holmes started as a geologist. (Courtesy U. S. Geol. Surv.)

## CHAPTER XXVIII

### WESTERN ARID INTERIOR PLATEAUS

BETWEEN the Rocky Mountain system and the Pacific Mountain system, and north of the Great Desert, lies the wide stretch of the arid Western Plateaus. Only the height of the land saves this region from being like its southern neighbor, the Great American Desert.

Because these plateaus are higher than the desert they receive more rain, therefore most of the area can be, and is, pastured. Three or four million sheep and some cattle crop the scanty bunch-grass and the scattered sagebrush. But the poverty of the pasturage is shown by the fact that the United Kingdom, somewhat smaller in area, has about ten times as much livestock. There are many regions that are wholly desert and are so named by the people who live there; at best this region should be called semi-arid, always remembering the rich oases.

It differs also from the Desert in having much, rather than little, of its area covered with mountains. The mountains, having more than desert rainfall, therefore produce enough vegetation for upland pasturage, although rarely enough for forests. It differs from the Desert in having no great inflowing master stream, no Nile (or Colorado). The nearest approach to such a stream is the Snake River which flows across one corner of the region. Again it differs from the Desert, its neighbor region, in having several small rivers that flow into its eastern and western margins, making possible considerable oases of irrigation and thus becoming the chief basis of man's support.

Mountains on three sides and at many places within the interior; upland summer pastures for sheep and cattle; winter pastures on the

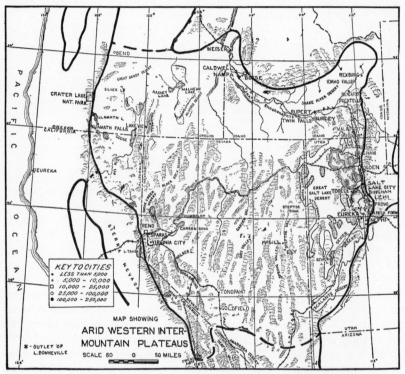

Fig. 277 — This map shows the ancient boundary of one prehistoric lake. If the scale were large enough, many could be shown.

lower plains and stacks of alfalfa in many scattered oases of irrigation — these, plus mining camps, are the main features of the Western arid Interior Plateaus (Fig. 39).

### The Great Basin

The Great Basin which includes a large part of the entire region is very definitely a basin, or rather, many basins. The high Sierras shut off the sea-winds and there is so little rainfall that not enough water can gather to fill the valleys; so the water lies in the basins below the level of the rims and never flows out to the sea. Shut off from the moisture-giving sea by the highest part of the Sierras, a considerable area in Northwestern Nevada has less than five inches of rainfall. Only in the northwestern part of California and Oregon, and in the higher lands of east-central Nevada is the rainfall over ten inches.

The Arid Plateaus have been vividly portrayed in fiction with tales of burning thirst, heroism, loss and death in the desert. Man is con-

FIG. 278 — Idealized diagram to show Sierra Nevada and Wasatch Mountains with block mountains and waste-filled valleys between.

tinually striving to get water, to save water, to use water to the best advantage.

The Great Basin is the geologist's delight. The geologist is a kind of detective looking for signs. He can study a region and know what acts Nature committed there millions of years ago with water, earth, and rock. Geologists have figured out an interesting story here. They tell us that apparently there was once a great arch extending from the Sierras to the Wasatch Mountains in central Utah. The middle parts of the arch have broken into many pieces and have fallen down. The two bases of the old arch, the Sierras on the west and the Wasatch Mountains on the east, stand with their steep fronts facing each other, 400 to 500 miles apart. In the intervening space many parts of the original arch lie tipped so that the pieces become mountain ridges with one front, usually the eastern front, steep, while the other, usually the western, slopes gradually away as does the Sierra Nevada. Everywhere this region is much eroded, and since the streams have no outlet to the sea the eroded material remains and fills the spaces between these basin mountains to great depths, often one, two, and three thousand feet.[1]

The waters that have filled these valleys with mountain washings, having no outlet to the sea, have spread out in shallow lakes. As the water in the lakes evaporated, ever-increasing quantities of salt, alkali and other materials that the water had dissolved from the earth collected in the beds of the lakes. Great Salt Lake is estimated to have 400,000,000 tons of common salt. The leachings of the volcanic soils of western Utah have produced a lake containing millions of tons of soda. Some of the basin lakes, however, are as fresh, pure, and clear as any other lakes, because they are up high enough to have outlets. Such are Utah Lake

[1] An artesian well-digger at Huxley, Nevada, on the Central Pacific Railroad, brought up pieces of well-preserved redwood from a depth of 1900 feet. (*United States Geological Survey*.)

in Utah, and the beautiful Lake Tahoe on the western edge of the basin in the slopes of the Sierras.

It is the habit of desert-basin lakes to fill their beds so full of mud that they become almost level, having only the slightest curvature of bottom. Thus they become very large and so very shallow that they dry up quickly. Then the sun bakes the mud of the bottom into a veritable pavement which resounds almost like metal beneath a horse's hoofs. These dry beds seamed with cracks are called " playas." One of the playa lakes in southeastern Oregon is called Alvord Desert; it covers fifty or sixty square miles. In the spring its water is from a few inches to perhaps two feet deep. In the summer it is a dry, smooth, hard surface on which the mirages play. Black Rock Desert in northwestern Nevada becomes in the spring rains 450 square miles of lake only a few inches in depth. But soon it is shining white with the crystals of alkali that remain after the water has dried up, leaving a typical " alkali flat."

Even Great Salt Lake is approaching this stage and its changing levels show how it, like every other desert-basin lake, fluctuates with the amount of rainfall. Its average depth is from fifteen to eighteen feet; its maximum depth is less than fifty feet. Its area in 1850 was 1750 square miles, but by 1869 the size of the lake had increased to 2170 square miles. From 1900 to 1904 much of its bed became a salt desert and it was feared that the lake would disappear entirely.[2] Since that time the water-level has risen to such an extent that large engineering works, like the Lucien cut-off of the Southern Pacific and the roadbed of the Western Pacific, are endangered and may have to be abandoned.

During the heavy rains of the Glacial Epoch the Great Basin lakes rose to overflowing and expanded so that many basins became one of huge size. The geologists call the expanded Nevada glacial lake, Lahontan; that of Utah they call Bonneville. Great Salt Lake is now but a diminutive remainder of that great body of water. In its prime it was 1500 (now fifty) feet deep and discharged through a notch in the divide between its basin and the Snake River valley. Dr. Ellsworth Huntington says that if the rainfall of Nevada were doubled we should again have Lake Lahontan, and he makes the appalling statement that Bonneville may return. Man in arid countries wishes for an increased rainfall, but a heavy increase in rain would be a sickening catastrophe to the inhabitants of Utah; only a moderate increase of rainfall would turn the fertile irrigations and the adjacent deserts into a billowy inland sea.

" About the borders of the basin of Great Salt Lake may be seen shore features associated with the ancient lake levels and still in an almost perfect state of preservation. Upon the surrounding slopes and up to elevations of 1500 feet above the surface of Great Salt Lake are

[2] The limitations of irrigation will prevent the drying up of the lake. United States Geological Survey, Bulletin 612, p. 95. Farmers cannot use all the water.

well-defined deltas, bars, beaches, spits, capes, cliffed promontories, and bottom deposits, all formed by or associated with the ancient lakes whose waters once stood at these high levels. . . .

"Important changes in the outline of some of these lakes have taken place since the settlement of the country. In the early days of Lake View (in southern Oregon near the Nevada boundary) the town was on the edge of Goose Lake, but it is now six miles from it. . . .

"After the exceptionally dry season of 1887–8, Silver Lake dried up, its·bed was cultivated by farmers, and one season's crops were gathered before the lake again occupied its floor." [3]

## Mineral Wealth

Save for the Mormon settlement at Salt Lake City, this plateau region was of interest·to white men first as a mining country. Mining has had its ups and downs. In 1859 the Comstock lode, one of the world's most famous silver mines, was discovered near Virginia City, Nevada. This mine was so hot (140° F.) that great expense for ventilation was necessary in order to make work at all possible, and three shifts of workers kept it going night and day. As they worked they drank ice water by the gallon and perspired almost beyond belief. The period 1860–64 was one of great speculation. The Comstock mine went down in the late '60's and rose to great prosperity again after new discoveries of ore were made in 1873. In '79, Sutro Tunnel, finally nine miles in length, was dug through the hills to drain and ventilate this mine. During the period 1875 to 1877 Nevada's production of gold and silver was greater than that of all the remaining United States, including California.

In 1877 the output of the Comstock mine was $36,000,000.00 and Virginia City was a thriving mining center. Its fate, as the mines were worked out, is indicated by the experience of a miner who was planning to go back to Iowa to live, but who wished to stay a couple of months after his job ended. For these two months he bought for $32.50 a substantial two-story brick house that had once cost $2650.00. But even a good brick house in an abandoned town has small value. By 1900 the mines were virtually worked out and Nevada's population was declining. Shortly after 1900 new discoveries were made elsewhere and the boom returned. The fate of a region entirely dependent upon mines, as was the case in Nevada prior to the recent large-scale irrigation, is shown in the population of that state which was in 1860, 6000; 1870, 42,000; 1880, 62,000; 1890, 45,000; 1900, 42,000; 1910, after the new discoveries, 82,-000; 1916, estimated 107,000; 1920, 77,000. Despite this small population, Nevada was admitted to the Union in 1864, with only a handful of people. Two more votes were needed to put some desired reconstructive legislation through the Senate of the United States. Nevada was the

[3] Isaiah Bowman, *Forest Physiography*, pp. 212–6.

only chance, and President Lincoln is reported to have said sadly as he signed its admission, " It is either admit Nevada or raise another million men." Thus, our most scantily peopled state came into being.

In the year 1900 gold and silver were found at Tonopah in southern Nevada near the California boundary. In two years it yielded $7,000,000, and the desert settlement had 4000 more people. Two years later good deposits were found twenty-four miles south at Goldfield. In 1904 deposits were found at Bullfrog, sixty miles southeast of Goldfield. Although it was one hundred miles from the railroad, in ninety days the town had an electric-light plant, an ice plant and a hotel. These discoveries made Nevada boom as a gold-producer.

It is a great misfortune for the mining industry that in such a region railroads must be built to serve the mines alone, whereas in lands of rainfall there may be farm produce, manufactures and other freights for them to carry. When there is nothing at the end of ninety miles of railroad but a mine, it makes the mining expensive. Thus the construction of the Steptoe concentrator marked the expenditure of about $20,000,000.00 in placing the Nevada Consolidated and Cumberland Ely mines on a producing basis. This amount included the purchase of the mines and cost of development, the construction of the Nevada Northern Railroad, the building of the immense plant at McGill, towns at the smelter and mine-shafts. The railroad which joins these mines at Ely with the outside world joins the Southern Pacific at Cobre, a distance of 141 miles.[4]

While the western part of the Great Basin has been having its ups and downs in the mining industry, the eastern or Utah part has had a later start and had not yet reached the working-out stage. The desert ranges of that state are rich in metals, and the great copper-mines at Bingham, sixteen miles from Salt Lake City, are really a mountain to be scooped up by steam shovel. In 1920 Utah produced $21,000,000.00 worth of copper, $11,000,000.00 of lead, $14,000,000.00 of silver, $2,000,000.00 of gold, $1,000,000.00 of zinc. Many of these deposits are of large extent and promise great output, though the quality of the mineral is low-grade. The mineral industries are greatly aided by the fact that just across the edge of the Great Basin in the Colorado Plateaus of north-central Utah there are extensive coal-fields in Carbon County which produced $19,000,000.00 worth in 1920. Already the Geological Survey reports at least 13,000 square miles of coal in this state, and the estimate is constantly enlarged. While but little of this coal is within the Great Basin proper, it is such a short distance away that it may

---

[4] More than 99% of its freight is from the mines. Another railroad, eighty-six miles long, and connecting with the Southern Pacific at Palisade, Nevada, cost the smelting company $1,500,000.00. " The first year this railroad operated it paid for itself and the second year the Mills Building was erected at 30 Broad Street, New York City, out of the profits made from this road." (From a private letter.)

be counted as one of the assets of the region. The extreme south-eastern part of the Great Basin in Iron County, Utah, has deposits of iron reported to be " almost inexhaustible." This must not be considered as the basis of an immediate industry, because iron-smelting requires a large population to furnish the necessary labor, and a large market easy of access to take the product. None of these conditions are to be found in the Great Basin, but it is a comfort to know that the iron is there waiting the day when we may have it manufactured with Rocky Mountain coal and carried two thousand miles to centers of population.

## Climate and Settlement

Aside from mining, how does this plateau appeal to home-seeking man? The climate is so dry that the plains are treeless. Many of its northern and southern ridges are stark bare; only a few go above the dry-timber line, and at best the forest growth is scattered and open, and the trees are of such slow growth that the timber is crooked, knotty and of small value for lumber. The few trees are of several varieties of pine, with poplar or cottonwoods in the moister canyons. As is the case with all dry countries, the climate is subjected to great variations not only between day and night but also between winter and summer. In parts of the earth where there is moisture the land is kept warm by the moist atmosphere and particularly by blankets of clouds, neither of these conditions being present in dry lands. The blazing heat of the noonday sun radiates rapidly, and at night temperatures of 50° or even less follow a noonday temperature of more than 100°.

The climate of this plateau is further complicated by the fact that it is a plateau, a rather high plateau. Elevation alone tends to make climate changeable. Thus while flowers bloom every month in the year at Portland, Oregon, in the moist seaward part of the state, there is frost every month at Lakeview on the shores of Goose Lake in the Great Basin near the Nevada boundary, and at Truckee, 5800 feet altitude, near Lake Tahoe, temperatures of −25° F. are met in winter, and summer temperatures above 100° are to be expected almost everywhere. Sparse population is inevitable in a region where such conditions prevail.

The first extended contact of the white man with this region was his attempt to cross it. It lay in the path of the forty-niners who tried to cross the continent to California by wagon, and who suffered so dreadfully and in some cases perished so terribly in these deserts. Crossing the Basin was made possible for many by the accidental fact that the longest river in the Basin, the Humboldt, happens to flow (or furnish a string of water-holes) nearly in an east-west line almost on the line between Salt Lake and Reno, most of the way across the Basin.

The year before the forty-niners set out the Mormons fled to this desert around the Great Salt Lake. By a remarkable journey across plains and mountains they had fled to be forever beyond the reach of the people of the United States who had successively driven them out of various places in Illinois, Missouri and Iowa.

### Basin Lands and Irrigation

The newly arrived Mormons diverted the mountain streams to the fertile plains at Salt Lake City, thus making themselves self-sustaining in the desert. Theirs was the first irrigation of any importance in the United States. The people from whom the Mormons had fled crossed the continent in the rush for gold in '49; they were greatly aided in their project by being able to buy supplies from the thrifty Mormons. These people of Teutonic stock had farming well under way the first year, and they did a thriving business with their erstwhile persecutors.

From 1848, until the completion of the first transcontinental railway in 1869, the Salt Lake settlement was indeed buried far in the wilderness, but buried in a land of agricultural plenty. By 1889, 260,000 acres were under cultivation. In the next decade they doubled it. The chief extension of agriculture in this inter-mountain region has come since 1900, but unfortunately irrigation can never reclaim any large area here. It is a great misfortune for the race that the water-supply is so scanty in a region where the valleys are so extensive. It is a fact that the land of the filled valleys which characterize the arid basins everywhere is peculiarly adapted to irrigation. There are several reasons for this. In the first place the stream-filled arid basin lands are almost level, so that it is easy to lead water, if there is any, to the desired spot. Also the soil is rich in these dry lands. It has not been robbed of fertility by the presence of plants or by the leaching action of water. The land is indeed suitable for irrigation. Only water, the great indispensable agent, is wanting from most of the Great Basin valleys. The lack is fatal. It should be noticed that the important irrigation enterprises of the Great Basin are immediately along the edges, so that the snow-water from the Sierra Nevada and Wasatch Mountains may flow into them. A number of small irrigations are scattered about the bases of Basin ranges where small streams give water.

Utah has been accurately described as " an oasis at the foot of the Wasatch," [5] and in Nevada the railroads are as valuable as farms, towns and live-stock combined. The Wasatch Mountains, the steep western front of a high plateau, rise abruptly 4000 to 6000 feet above the level plain in a precipice called Hurricane Ledge, which extends from near the Colorado River in Arizona far up into central Utah. In many places the Wasatch Mountains, two miles back from the foot of the plain, are a mile high. Wherever this wall is cut by a canyon from which flows a

---

[5] Mark Jefferson. This explains the small value of Great Basin farms.

mountain stream, there on the plain at the mouth of the gorge, living from its waters, is a settlement (oasis) such as Salt Lake City, Ogden, Provo and other towns. If there could be more water, the settlements could extend farther out into the desert. The scarcity of water, the necessity of heavy engineering works and the limitations of the Great Basin are well illustrated in the greatest Utah irrigation unit, that of Strawberry Valley, which has been built by the United States Reclamation Service. The water is furnished by Strawberry River on the east side

FIG. 279 — Weeding beets in the Strawberry Valley Irrigation project. This characteristic basin landscape at the foot of the Wasatch is irrigated in part by water brought by tunnel under the range. (Courtesy U. S. Bureau of Reclamation.)

of the Wasatch, where a 6800-acre reservoir stores 110,000 acre feet of water which is conducted through a 19,000-foot tunnel under the crest of the mountains from the Colorado Basin over into the Great Basin. There it is poured into a branch of the Spanish Fork River and thus carried down to irrigate 60,000 acres of land on the plains around Utah Lake. This water storage and others like it that have been, and may be, built will be a great help in this region because the streams reach their maximum before the crops need so much water. The flow in June is four times the flow in August, when the demand for water is greatest.

Two other large irrigation units have been established by the United States Government in the Great Basin: one the Klamath, Oregon-California, and one of the Truckee and Carson rivers, western Nevada, where water stored in Lake Tahoe (193 square miles) is carried by a thirty-one-mile diversion canal from one river valley into another, there stored in an artificial reservoir and finally turned out upon the plains around Carson City where it is hoped that eventually 230,000 acres will be brought under irrigation.

### Land Injury by Alkali

One of the dangers of irrigation in Basin regions of this character is that the land may be spoiled with alkali. The repeated evaporations of the lakes in their basins mean that the beds for great depths down are alternately layers of sand, clay, mud, salt and alkali. When water is poured on the surface by irrigation it soaks down to a considerable depth and dissolves salts. The salts rise to the surface by capillary attraction, and when the water evaporates they remain encrusted on the surface. Thus many a field, promising and fruitful in the second and third years of irrigation, has been ruined in succeeding years because alkali killed the plants. Also waters from irrigation canals along higher levels have come in and ruined many a lower-lying field. The only cure is to wash the alkali out. To do this, ditches are dug in the field. The field is then flooded with water which soaks down and flows out through the ditches, leaving the top part of the soil free of alkali. Thus every irrigation enterprise in the Great Basin needs some lower place to which to discharge its alkali waters — a kind of agricultural sewage disposal. The playa lakes are well adapted for such a service. It is quite conceivable that even a moderate increase in rainfall might cover these playas and the irrigated lands along their shores. Such a calamity would rival the flood of Noah, and its effects would last much longer.

### Corn and Alfalfa

Corn will not ripen well in the cool climate, but, as in New England, it reaches a point where it is ready for the silo, and dairying is increasing. Seventy per cent of the farmers in the Newlands Reclamation Project, western Nevada, are dairymen. Alfalfa, wheat, beans, sugar beets, potatoes, tomatoes, melons and vegetables thrive. The yields of all crops are very high, in large part owing to the fact that the soils are quite new, unleached and very fertile. The early settlers of Truckee, 1906 and 1907, met an interesting but, to them, alarming illustration of the disturbance of the life-balance due to the intrusion of man. When by irrigation man raised fine fields of alfalfa and potatoes, certain desert-burrowing mice found unexampled opportunities for food. They burrowed from potato plant to potato plant, eating and breeding as they went. The alfalfa fields were their delight. They ate the plants, tops, roots and all, and attained numbers estimated from 8,000 to 12,000 per acre, utterly annihilating the crops. Man had further aided them, of course, by destroying hawk, shrike, snake, and above all foxes and coyotes, all of which had preyed upon the mice. The Government was appealed to. Experts studied the situation and extensive poison enterprises were undertaken which finally left man a chance to harvest his own crops.

## Dry Farming

Much has been said in the agricultural press of the country for the last fifteen years about dry farming in Utah by the summer fallow system, but after all it is a limited resource. The low plains are too dry. Some of the highlands are too frosty. Sandy soil is too porous and dries out. Clay soil bakes. Only a sandy loam soil will do for dry farming, and it must be rich and deep. The area of such soil is limited to mountain slopes and mountain valleys. As long ago as 1917 nearly all such land was in use. (Bulletin 883, Utah Experiment Station.)

This system of agriculture was tried as early as 1850 but without material success until 1890. It was not taken up as a deliberate series of experiments by experiment stations until 1913. The chief crop of this kind of farming is wheat. The reasons are two; it is the most valuable of the grains, and since 85% of the rainfall of this region falls in winter it is perfectly adjusted to the needs of winter wheat.

## The Snake River Valley — Land of Lava Soils

The Snake River country has an origin quite different from that of the Great Basin, and to understand its use by man we must first understand how it was made. To the geologist nature tells the following story very clearly in the walls of the banks of the Snake River: For more than a hundred miles south of Lewiston, Idaho, this river has a gorge 4000 to 6000 feet deep which is a worthy rival of the Grand Canyon of the Colorado. In one place the wall of this canyon shows the section of an old mountain with cliffs and sharp peaks reaching many hundred feet above the bottom of the canyon. Upon the top of the mountain are layer after layer of lava, and then layers of sand and mud that were placed there in the bottoms of lakes, then more layers of lava, and layers of volcanic dust, until finally the old buried mountain has on its head 2000 feet or more of volcanic stuff and lake-bed stuff. These deposits make up the whole area of the upper Snake Valley (Fig. 277). The surface of this valley is a series of gentle swells, each with its center over a vent from which lava has rolled and flowed away in all directions, making a gentle slope which

FIG. 280. — A dry farming exhibit. Mr. F. A. Wyatt, of Utah Agricultural College, under direction of Prof. L. A. Merrill, traced the roots of a wheat plant. It had hundreds of roots, six to seven feet long — a total of more than half a mile.

merges into the slopes from other vents. This lava contains much of the mineral augite which melts at a very low temperature for minerals and therefore made the lava run almost like water. In several places a hundred of these old flows can be seen, one upon the other, in canyon walls.

Such a flood of lava would dam a stream and turn it into a lake where sand and mud collected before the next lava flow covered it up. An interesting example of this process can now be seen in Lakes Harney and Malheur in southeastern Oregon. One of the most recent lava-flows dammed two streams, whose waters collected to make these lakes now only ten or fifteen feet below the elevation of the lava dam. Before this occurred 400 square miles of land drained into the Snake. Now it is a part of the Great Basin.

The volcanic processes were not limited to the Snake River Valley. Lava seems to have poured out of fissures at the base of the Cascades. Volcanoes threw showers of dust and ashes into the air and they were spread so thickly that much of Oregon is of volcanic origin. Some of it is so sandy and dusty that a considerable area (150 by 30 miles) bears the name of Great Sandy Desert. This soil is so porous that no water lies on its surface, and there is no water fit to drink within the area. The winter rain, however, which is more than ten inches, is sufficient to cause a good growth of grass which is sometimes uneaten over large areas because no animals can come, owing to the lack of any opportunity to drink in that region.

Lava-flows also cover large areas in the Columbia Basin. The total of this northwestern lava field amounts to about a quarter of a million square miles, making it the largest of its kind in the world. Lava flowed around old hills, leaving them as islands of older rocks in a sea of basalt (solidified lava). Old ridges became capes and peninsulas, while the Blue Mountains, an outlying part of the Rocky Mountain System, stand now as a great island in a sea of basalt. Most of the basalt has weathered into soil, but some of it is still hard rock, being but a few hundred years old. The plains around the Blue Mountains are from 4000 to 6000 feet high. The mountains rise to 8000 or 9000 feet.

Lava dammed the streams that flowed away from the mountains and turned the mountain valleys into lakes. With time the lakes have become filled with sand and clay through which the streams wander as the Mississippi wanders on its mud plain. Where these streams reach the lava dams, they cut sharp gorges in the newer material.

### Surface and Water

The Snake River Valley is much like the oasis strip of Utah except that it has more water and a rich soil of volcanic origin rather than of mountain washings. On both sides of the Snake Valley are mountains. Those on the south afford rich summer pasture but no forests, while the great mass of the Salmon River Mountains and the Clearwater Mountains on the north, and the Bitter Root Mountains on the east have forests, above 5000 feet, and snowfields which melt just when the settlements below are in greatest need of water for irrigation.

The Snake River runs for more than 300 miles in a great curve across the state of Idaho, but its valley, with all of its rich soil, suffers the misfortune of having the river at the bottom of a sharp canyon 400 to 1000 feet deep.[6] For 250 miles in the eastern part of the state there is no branch that reaches the river from the north. All the streams sink into the lava. This water difficulty is shown by the Minadoka irrigation unit, one of the first built by the Reclamation Service. There it was necessary to pump water for all the land on the south of the river, although gravity served to supply the lands on the north side with water from a branch of the Snake.

This irrigation unit on the Snake River illustrates in an interesting way some of the problems and unexpected things that happen where the maintenance of life depends upon irrigation. In most parts of the valley, farmers had to dig 300 to 400 feet to find water, but it was different in a large part of the Minadoka unit. It so happened that there was an old lake-bed with tight bottom thirty or forty feet from the surface. Irrigation water was turned on and in a few years it became so full that water came to the surface of the land. Then ditches had to be dug at a cost of $18.00 an acre to drain it.

On all sides of this unit is a sea of sagebrush which for a generation or two has been free range for flocks of sheep; but since laws have been passed which give the settler 320 acres or 640 acres of land for a farm, much of this has been homesteaded by the dry farmers. Many fail and move away. Others stay and work, hoping for luck, increase of knowledge and better prices. It is too soon for the fate of dry farming in this region to be fully known, but the price slump after the World War caused many to give up.

Higher up on the edges of the valley the rainfall is better, the evaporation is less, the loss from drought therefore less, but here the summer frosts furnish an uncertain element whose limits can be determined only by years of experiment.

### The Live-stock Industry

The one sure thing in the Snake River Valley is the live-stock industry. It thrives on the sagebrush plains and mountain pastures and the alfalfa rick. Indeed, you would think it was the agricultural Eden to hear a valley irrigation farmer brag about how he makes his living turning on the water to irrigate his alfalfa. He sits on the porch two or

[6] There is no valley land for irrigation west of the mouth of Malad River 100 miles (on east-west line) from the east boundary of Idaho.

three weeks waiting for alfalfa to grow, then he works busily for a week
cutting and putting it in the stacks, and irrigating the field again. Then
more weeks on the porch, then a second cutting and then a third. In
the autumn come the sheep-owners to dicker for the alfalfa. They drive
in their flocks and the animals eat the alfalfa where it stands. Meanwhile the alfalfa owner spends the winter in California or Florida, or
takes a look at the Great White Way — if prices are good enough.

### Electricity on the Farm

The use of electricity as a farm and household convenience has perhaps reached a higher development here than in any other part of the
United States. Mountain streams whose waters finally irrigate the land
have falls, and the Reclamation Service has built power-plants to make
power for the use of the people in the irrigated land. In some cases
power is used in the summer for pumping water. One thousand of the
2200 farms have land so situated that water can be lifted a few feet
from the main gravity ditch to irrigate their fields. In one case a man
added twenty-two acres with a $900.00 pumping plant. It is common
for the farmers to have co-operative power lines; a hundred or two of
them living in a certain locality will have a line that taps the main
transmission line. Since water for irrigation is not needed in winter
there is a surplus of power for sale, and it is used for heating houses at
a price from one-quarter to one-half cent per kilowatt hour. In the
towns of Rupert and Burley half the houses are heated by electricity.
The typical farm-house has an electric washer in the basement and in
the kitchen an electric hot-water heater, ironer, vacuum-cleaner, and
range. Halfway between the house and barn is a cement creamery
heated by electricity, while the separator and churn are driven by
electricity. The barn is lighted by electricity and an electric pump with
automatic control furnishes water supply for both house and barn.

I regard this as typical of a development which from now on is likely
to take place with great speed throughout the more populous and progressive parts of the civilized world, where power resources promise henceforth to be not only one of the bases for manufacturing industry but
also a factor in the development of agriculture and in improved living
conditions. It will be merely an application of known technique.

### The Influence of Freight-Rates

The farmer of this region is far from markets. It is much more than
a thousand miles to Chicago.[7] Therefore it is plain that he faces a high

[7] As there is not enough irrigable land to use all the water in the Snake it
promises to be permanently navigable from Pittsburg Landing, about seventy-five miles
from the southwest corner of Washington state. This fact should play a large part
in the future of Idaho.

freight-rate for his product. The force of circumstances has turned him to concentrated products, of which meat and wool are excellent examples. The sugar-beet crop of this region is far more valuable than the wheat crop. The natural conditions for producing sugar are admirable. The soil is deep and loamy in the one-time desert valleys, a heavy crop is made possible by irrigation, and the comparatively high value of sugar makes the freight-rate seem small. (Fig. 127.)

The necessity for concentrated products shows itself in the development of a dairy industry for which the silo and the alfalfa stack are the great raw materials.

## Cities

The cool Salt Lake City, with a population of 118,000 (1920), the largest city between the Rockies and the Pacific ports, is larger than the next four cities of this region, combined, yet it has no great manufactures. It serves as a distributing center for the sugar industry, and the farms and ranches over a wide territory, and for mines in both Basin and mountain. Immediately above the city towers the Wasatch, several thousand feet high, giving Alpine scenery and an abundant supply of clear drinking water. A few miles away is the Great Salt Lake, whose waters are so heavy with 22% of salt that a person cannot sink in them. The salt water is evaporated in ponds beside the lake and there is a considerable salt industry for which the city is a distributing center.

The people of this city have unusual facilities for bathing, with the lake on one side and hot sulphur springs within city limits. These springs belong to the city and are much utilized for bathing purposes and are a rather important source of income. Salt Lake City boasts that a quarter of her population is constantly in school and that education takes more money than all other city expenditures combined. The leadership of this territory in education for everybody is very striking in Huntington's map of civilization. (See *Civilization and Climate*, E. Huntington.)

## Future

The future of the Arid Plateaus promises to be one in which for a time the great resources of minerals will give rise to a greater and greater mining population, especially in periods of high prices. These people will continue to live as now, in places which look to the tree-lover scarcely at all like home, for the desert mining settlement is usually without tree, grass or flower, utterly shadeless, burning hot on summer days, severely cold in winter, wind-swept, dust-blown, desolate. Its delights are gold, humanity and mechanism, unless the untouched desert, scrubby or bare, a hundred yards away happens also to be a delight; and the desert *has* great charm. This mining town, which can scarcely have a vegetable garden in its whole length, is an excellent market for the produce of irrigation settlements. However, the time must come when the mines will follow the fate of the first Nevada mine and be exhausted, leaving man to fall back on the scanty resources of pasture and the richness of the oases.

The pastures which have been injured with over-grazing may be improved a little with care. In the northern parts of the Basin the grass cannot now be used because there is no water fit to drink, but animals might live there if a simple African cistern were used. It was first built by the Romans and ever since has been utilized in parts of Tunis where there is no surface drinking water available, and the wells are all alkaline.

It is plain that the chief economic basis for the future of the Great Basin is in irrigation, for which it seems reasonable to expect that man will eventually use almost every barrel of water that gets into the Basin streams, thus causing most of the lakes to become dry because water is more valuable in the irrigation ditch than in any other place. The Snake River Basin and the Great Salt Lake Basin apparently have more water resources than land that is suitable for irrigation.

The selection of plants for their resistance to alkalies, salt and drought affords another interesting line of possible extension, but there is small reason to expect this region to support a population many times its present population, which is less than a million.

The three states, Utah, Nevada and Idaho, which make up the greater part of this region, have three distinct flavors arising from their history. Utah was settled by Mormons, people who believe ardently that the best community is composed of land-owning farmers. They shunned mining as much as possible and made excellent laws for the distribution of water among the people. Nevada would have many more farmers and much less wasted water if she had Utah's water-laws. Nevada suffers in part because of the lack of scientific policy in the management of public lands. For example, the man who owns a spring may automatically have a monopoly on the pasture of thousands of acres of land because there is no other water within reach.

Idaho came quickly through the stages of the gold rush, sheep ranching and homesteading to the last stage of scientific, large-scale irrigation. This leaves a newness, a frontier spirit not found in Utah.

Fig. 281 — The agriculture of the Columbia Basin is typified by three pictures: The giant harvester on the far-reaching wheat lands; the sheep lands (Fig. 284) of greater aridity; and the apples (Fig. 285) of irrigation. (Courtesy Chamber of Commerce and Inland Automobile Association, Spokane, Wash.)

## CHAPTER XXIX

### COLUMBIA–FRASER VALLEYS

THE territory from the Blue Mountains (south of the Columbia River) northward to the northern part of the Fraser drainage and between the Rocky Mountain system and the Pacific Mountain system is drained by two great rivers, the Columbia and the Fraser. These rivers barely escape through the coast ranges to the sea, through gorges so narrow that in these gorges even road-making and railroad-building have been most difficult.

The greatest handicap of this large region is low rainfall. The Cascade and Coast mountains have squeezed out so much of the moisture from the rain-bearing west wind that the lowest lands along the rivers, except where irrigation is practiced, are arid expanses of sagebrush and poor pasture, with lakes of salt or alkaline water. Climbing upward from this dry bottom zone of poor pasture to altitudes of greater rainfall and less heat, we pass through zones of dry farming, humid farming, upland pasture and finally forest. If the slope is gradual, as is sometimes the case, the zones of production grade insensibly into each other. The farming zones eastward from Pasco, Washington, to land of greater elevation are typical: (1) There is an area with soil so light and rainfall so scant that it has never been farmed; (2) then dry farming begins where a crop of wheat is grown every two years. The dry farmer plows his land in the spring of the first year, tills it in the summer to conserve moisture and destroy weeds, and plants wheat in the autumn of the first year or the following spring; (3) a little farther to the east it has been the custom to raise two crops in three years. One year the land is summer-fallowed, the next year it is in wheat, the next

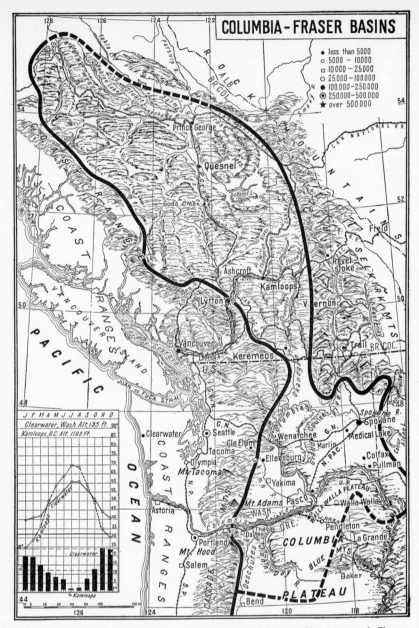

Fig. 282 — It takes close looking to see the rainfall facts of Kamloops and Clear-water in the climate graph. Both the temperature and the rainfall of these two stations show well the climatic differences between the oceanic-windward and continental-lee sides of a high mountain system in middle latitudes.

in wheat, oats, or barley. Near the Idaho-Washington state line peas have been grown in a two-year rotation with wheat. In other localities less susceptible to frost, beans and wheat may form a two-year rotation, but the area adapted to beans is limited. Some farmers can grow three crops to one summer fallowing.

Above the dry timber line is the upland pasture and forest zone. Here the greater rain of higher altitudes makes fine pasture, but the summer frost of high altitudes often cuts off crops before they can mature so that even where the land is arable it can be used only for pasture.

Going upward from the master streams and along the slopes of elevations within these valleys we find these zones in ever-varying width. In a brief summary of the region, one more feature must be mentioned — the oases, where the farmer irrigates the dryer lands by mountain waters. It is fortunate that nature has given great allowance of streams to this region, where man's greatest physical problem is the watering of arid land.

## PART I. COLUMBIA BASIN

The differences in rainfall between high and low elevation are well shown by the facts of rainfall eastward from the crest of the Cascades. At Marlin, Washington, alt. 2777 feet on the east slope of the Cascade Mountains, the rainfall is 80 inches, eighteen miles east, at Cle Elum, 1909 feet, 25.91 inches; twenty-two miles farther east, at Ellensburg, 1510 feet, 9.79 inches. In the lowest part of the Columbia Basin, at the mouth of the Snake River, the rainfall is but six inches. A large area in central Washington and adjacent parts of Oregon has less than ten inches, and some parts are called deserts by the people who live near them.

The aridity of this central lowland is further shown by many little inland drainage basins. " The central and eastern part of Washington is largely a great lava plateau . . . now dotted with literally hundreds of small inclosed basins, due primarily to inequalities in the lava surface; . . . some of these depressions now carry permanent or intermittent lakes; most are slightly or moderately saline. So far as known none drain an area of over a few square miles." (Bulletin 54, United States Department of Agriculture, p. 55.)

Most of the rain of this region falls in the winter. At this season the cyclonic storms draw the moist Pacific winds inland with greater force than in summer, and as the land is then colder than the sea it is natural that rain is most easily and therefore most abundantly produced in the winter season. This bit of meteorology explains the fact that all west coasts in lower middle latitudes have most of their rain in the winter season — witness Portugal, Chile, South Africa, Western Australia.

In the winter the farmer can work out-of-doors most of the time. Temperatures of twenty degrees below zero come occasionally, but the cold waves of winter are of short duration, because the wind blows from the west (the warmer Pacific Ocean) most of the time. The warm chinook wind often comes over the mountains and eats up the snows almost as quickly as they fall. In April, May and June, the healthy young wheat gets soaking rain. July and August are almost rainless, and tempera-

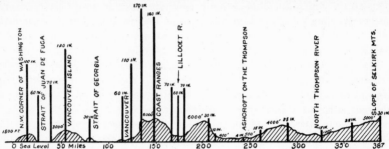

FIG. 283 — This graph is a wonderful exhibit of climate. It shows rainfall and a generalized topographic profile along the straight line from the Pacific to the Selkirk Mountains and crossing a long series of heights and depressions.

tures above 100 degrees are common at all lower elevations. This perfectly wheat-adjusted climate is one reason why Washington, a state with low rainfall, leads the country in wheat-yields.

Columbia Basin soil is also responsible for heavy wheat-yields. Nearly all of the Columbia Basin is of the lava formation described in the last chapter. The lava flowed out from great fissures in the earth and remained in layers often 3000 to 4000 feet deep. Eight different flows can be recognized in the Yakima Valley. In most parts of the Columbia Basin the lava is old enough to be deeply decayed. There is often sixty feet of decomposed lava, rich soil, on top of basalt (solidified lava). The lava flowing from under the earth-crust is fresh earth stuff, and mostly rich with the elements of plant food. The scanty Columbia Basin rainfall could not leach away much of its richness, to carry it off to the sea, so this fertile volcanic soil patiently waited, smiled when introduced to the plow and responds annually with a golden harvest. Hence the sound basis for Washington and Oregon boasting. Despite the low rainfall the rolling wheat-fields of the Columbia Basin yield more per acre than those of any other wheat-growing state.[1] It is a great

[1] WHEAT PRODUCTION AND YIELDS

|  | Washington | | Kansas | | Minn. | | U. S. | |
|---|---|---|---|---|---|---|---|---|
|  | million bu. | bu. pr. acre | m.b. | bpa. | m.b. | bpa. | m.b. | bpa. |
| 5-year average..... 1918–1922 | 40.6 | 16.6 | 131.3 | 13.6 | 38. | 12.7 | 878.7 | 13.8 |
| 10-year average.... | 43. | 20.4 | 106.3 | 14. | 51. | 13.4 | 802.6 | 14.6 |

misfortune to man that so much of the Columbia Basin is too dry for wheat, so that its total production is much less than that of Kansas.

The largest block of wheat-land, as the wheat map shows, is on the wide plains at the base of the Blue Mountains and on corresponding plains north of the Snake River with Spokane as their metropolis. On the steeper slopes of the Cascades and the mountains of the northern part of Washington there is only a narrow belt of land with enough rain for dry farming or rotation farming, between the sagebrush pasture of low elevation and the rough land of the forest at high elevation.

The southeastern part of Washington has a large area of hills that are thought to be of windblown formation. The prevalent southwest wind coming across the volcanic dust-areas of north-central Oregon and adjacent parts of Washington has picked up volcanic dust and fine particles of soil, drifted them along, mixed them with local soil, and built hills after the pattern of sand-dunes, with gentler slopes (twenty to twenty-five degrees) toward the wind, and steeper slopes (of forty, sometimes even fifty degrees) away from the wind.

Where the rainfall is sufficient these hill lands are also in wheat. In the dryer parts a column of dust sometimes marks the location of the plows and harrows long before they can be seen. Despite the steepness of these windblown hills the largest harvesting machines on earth swing round and round their smooth slopes. These machines are the combined harvester and thresher, often drawn by twenty or thirty horses, or by tractors. It is only because of the rainless, stormless summer of this region that the wheat will dry out so thoroughly as to permit this large-scale method of threshing. In most of the wheat-growing regions of the world there must be an intervening period of curing in the shock or stack.

It is in this Columbia Basin that one of the interesting and suggestive triumphs of plant-breeding has been wrought. Because of the almost rainless summer, the farmers can let the wheat stand in the field for a month after it is ripe. The harvesting can accordingly be extended over a period of several weeks, and comparatively few men can thus take care of vast farms. But it was necessary to accommodate the wheat to this schedule. The wheat-breeding work was undertaken at the State College of Washington, about 1900. At that time some of the winter wheats yielded well, but their straw was so soft that when their yield was heavy they would break down before becoming ripe. The grain would also shatter from the heads of these winter varieties soon after ripening. Some of the spring wheats had stiff straw and would hold the wheat kernels but they yielded poorly and if they were planted in the autumn they would frequently winter-kill. A spring variety and a winter variety were crossed and a new variety was developed that would yield well, and hold the grain after becoming ripe, and that would not winter-kill.[2] It also had a stiff straw that would stand up so that the harvesting season could be prolonged. With this new frost-resistant, grain-holding variety a large increase of wheat harvests was possible on the wide fertile lava lands of the Columbia Basin. This is merely an illustration of man's new-found ability to apply science to everyday affairs, that is destined to enrich every land in the world. The fairy tale has come true.

## Problems of the Wheat Farmer

All the land in the Columbia Basin that is good for wheat was under cultivation by 1900, or earlier.

On the Columbia Basin wheat-lands, as in all other wheat regions, the earliest grain farmers expected to raise a crop of wheat every year. Experience has shown, however, that where the rainfall is less than eighteen inches a crop of wheat cannot be grown every year. In such places the farmer raises wheat by the farming system of a fallow year alternating with the crop year.

The wheat farmer is not without problems, even though he is on land with more than eighteen inches of rain. The plowing that prepares the earth for the planting of the wheat in the autumn also encourages the growth of various weeds. In time these cultivated weeds choked the wheat to such an extent that an occasional fallow year, when the ground was cultivated to sprout and kill the weeds, became common in the lands with more than eighteen inches of rainfall. This expedient of the Columbia Basin farmers is but a temporary phase of the one-crop plantation system which must everywhere give way to crop rotation. In 1915 a study was made of 2,000,000 acres of Oregon and Washington land near the Blue Mountains and the Columbia. It had been under cultivation for thirty years. In that year 30% of this land was found to be in fallow chiefly to kill weeds, so that a good crop of wheat could follow. This study also showed that the wheat-yields were declining because the soil was being exhausted, and that the removal of humus by continuous wheat-growing was making the soil get harder and harder, and thus becoming less suitable for tillage. As a result of this investigation, the United States Department of Agriculture recommends [3] that the farmers of this region keep their land in small grain for half of the time and for the other half in some legume — clover, peas, beans or alfalfa. There is nothing new about this medicine. It is the experience everywhere on the frontier of agriculture as the second stage, the crop-rotation stage, is entered. The first stage is the continuous cropping, soil-robbing epoch, which is often necessary to make new lands profitable to the settler.

[2] Winter-killing is different from frosting. Frost injures the wheat when it is in bloom, damaging the future kernel.

[3] Bulletin 625.

The natural next step is crop-rotation, the growth of clover and other crops. Almost any crop-rotation usually includes hay and calls for beasts. With a live-stock industry the sunflower may be the great dependence for silage. It can stand early frost, one of the drawbacks of this region (as corn cannot), and survive with less moisture than corn. Experiments at the Washington experiment station at Pullman show that the sunflower makes twice as much silage as corn at that place.

### Skimming the Cream

It is plain that the Columbia Basin lands of Oregon and Washington have passed the cream-skimming stage. The declining fertility of the better agricultural lands — those which can produce a crop every year — is not unique. It is true of all lands that have passed the frontier stage.

A bulletin [4] of the Washington experiment station tells of declining yields in the dry-farming lands also. It tells of efforts at soil improvement by plowing in straw, which failed because there is not sufficient rainfall in these dryer lands to cause straw to decay and mix satisfactorily with the earth. This is, of course, also true of similar lands in Oregon. The investigators arrived at the depressing conclusion that this decline of fertility must continue (unless costly commercial fertilizers be used) until a maintenance-level is reached. At this point, unless fertilizers are employed, each crop must use the fertility produced by earth decomposition since the previous crop. Long continued tests at the experiment station at Rothamstead, England (a land of satisfactory rainfall), showed the maintenance-level crop at that place to be about ten bushels of wheat per year.

The cream-skimming aspect also appears in irrigated lands. Naturally the lands that could be most easily irrigated have been first used. Further irrigation will be more expensive than earlier enterprises. The usual waste of some irrigated land by " drowning out " and destruction by alkali has followed a few years of irrigation. (See chapter on Western Arid Interior Plateaus.)

Long ago the ranges were overstocked. In 1905 a bulletin of the United States Department of Agriculture said that owing to " gradual lowered carrying capacity of ranges in the State of Washington investigations were begun in the spring of 1901." The recommendations were essentially similar to those discussed in connection with the Great Plains and the Trans-Pecos Highlands, *i.e.*, give the grass a chance to seed itself.

### Glaciers and Irrigation

The northwestern corner of the State of Washington was overridden by a great glacier that flowed down the Okanogan Valley and pushed on

[4] No. 156, p. 54.

across the Columbia. This great glacier dammed up the Columbia valley at Great Bend and forced the river out of its bed and across the plateaus east of its present course. As the waters found their way back to the old channel below the glacier they plunged over a precipice, making a cataract which far outdid Niagara. It was 400 feet high. Niagara is 160 feet high. It cut a gorge fifteen miles long. That of Niagara is but seven. Then the glacier retreated and the river reclaimed its old channel. The old falls are called Dry Falls. The ancient river gorge is known as the

FIG. 284 — Pasture, alfalfa stacks, sheep — the cycle of mutton. Hay Creek ranch near Deschutes River, an Oregon branch of the Columbia, on the slope of the Blue Mountains. Characteristic Merino sheep and treeless pastured hills of this region. (Courtesy Chamber of Commerce, Portland, Ore. Photo, Gifford.)

Grand Coulee, a valley now so dry that the small lakes in its base cannot overflow to the river. However, several of the series of lakes occasionally overflow into those toward the south end of the valley, so that the lakes in that direction become increasingly saline and alkaline. The last one is called Soap Lake because the waves beat its shores into masses of foam produced by the carbonates and sulphates of soda which are in the water. Think of the relief to mothers if all small boys could swim in that lake!

Far more important to Columbia Basin farmers, this ancient glacier scooped out a series of mountain valleys. Then with the scoopings the glacier dammed up the lower ends of the valleys, so that today we have the beautiful glacial Lake Chelan and three other beautiful lakes in the upper Yakima. These Cascade lakes make admirable water-storage reservoirs for the irrigation of valley lands below.

### Irrigation and the Famous Apple Valleys

The most extensive irrigation in the Columbia Basin is at the foot of the Cascade Mountains. Here are Yakima, Wenatchee and Okanogan Valleys, the centers of irrigated apple orchards, among the best-known places of their size in the United States. They became known through early advertising and later performance. These valleys are the land of the apple. The early successes of a few orchards which supplied near-by markets led to a great orchard boom. For several years before and after 1910 the populous centers east of the Rockies were flooded with the most beautiful prospectuses telling about fortunes to be made in Western apples. They were often put out by Eastern promoters, appealing to the teacher, the preacher and other professional people of intelligence and limited income. These people were told that five or ten acres of apple orchard in Washington, Oregon or Rocky Mountain states could be easily cared for by absentee management and would make them financially comfortable for the rest of their lives.[5] Most of these Western orchards that were sold to absentees in five- or ten-acre units were not in the hands of the original purchasers at the end of a decade. Many trees were planted on unsuitable land. The difficulties of business administration of these far-away orchards were great. Apple prices had declined. Some orchards were pulled up. Others were united into larger ownerships.

The fate of particular investments should not be confused with that of the industry at large, for by 1920 Washington State led the United States in apple-growing. Irrigation guarantees heavy crops and the high sunshine of a naturally dry country gives beautiful color. Nevertheless, many Easterners declare the flavor of the Western irrigated apples to be inferior to the Eastern flavor of *their* apples. However, the apples of the Northwest have captured Eastern markets through marketing enterprise vastly superior to that prevailing over any large area in the East. By early failures and losses the Northwestern farmers were forced to build centralized packing-plants. Each grower then handed his crop over for the central plant to pack, thereby removing himself from the temptation of making a poor pack and from the difficulties of making a good one. Centralized selling agencies were equally important.[6]

Another factor helping to explain the leadership of this region in the apple industry of the country is the fact that it was newly settled by a select population — the progressives from the East, who were not en-

[5] Mr. David Fairchild, the creator of the plant introduction work of the U. S. D. A., has emphasized the fact that tree agriculture is one of the most natural and easy bases for the development of over-enthusiastic hopes. It is so easy to find some phenomenal tree, apply the processes of multiplication and have a product that is unattainable in practice, because the phenomenal tree is unusual and has unusual opportunities. The promoter selects an unusual, not an average harvest from this tree, multiplies it by a number much greater than can grow on the acre, and the result is wickedness approaching fraud, although it may easily happen that the man who puts forth the scheme is himself deceived and is undertaking it honestly.

About the time of the Western apple boom there was a similar pecan boom in the Southern States with identical results. There will probably be others as agricultural science advances.

[6] In 1924 Washington State apple-growers combined to place a single order for 100 cars of apple-wrapping paper, $500,000.00 worth.

cumbered with local precedent or held back by their conservative brethren whom they had left two or three thousand miles behind them.

The Hood River Valley of Oregon, in the eastern margin of the Cascades just south of the Columbia, is another famous apple valley. It has been through experiences very similar to those of its sister valleys to the north. Its water-supply is derived from the natural storage of the

FIG. 285 — The people of Hood River Valley are proud of their landscape, green with apple trees on its floor, green with evergreens on its sides, white with the snow sentinel, Mt. Hood, at the south. (Courtesy Truman Butler, Hood River, Ore.)

perennial snow-fields and glaciers on Mt. Hood. The land of this valley is not a level flood-plain, but high ground, as rolling as the Piedmont of Virginia, several hundred feet above the Columbia. A great deal of work has been done to get the water by pipe, ditch and flume over the hilly land and properly distributed to the trees.

If a man seeks a beautiful home in the country, the Hood River valley offers him the site. Its rolling landscape, its well-kept orchards are everywhere in the immediate foreground. Not far away to the west are the green slopes of the Cascades. To the south stands the towering snow-capped Mt. Hood. To the north, across the Columbia, is the similarly towering and similarly snow-capped Mt. Adams, and there are few landscapes that exceed the snow-capped mountain-peak for variety of effect as the sun works around from the surprise of sunrise to the glow of sunset.

In the days of boom-beginning, the orchardists of the apple valleys expected to produce apples only, just as the cotton-grower of the South and the wheat-grower of Alberta and eastern Washington started with one crop. But experience has proved the unwisdom of a sole dependence on apples.  Crop-failure and flooded markets are the nightmares of the one-crop farmer.  Now everybody, from banker and railroad man to state experiment station expert, is advising the Columbia Basin farmer to diversify his crops.

### Unused Irrigable Land

Irrigation is sure but it is also costly.  The balance of supply and demand is indicated by the land situation on the Government reclamation units.  A bulletin sent out from the United States Reclamation Service in 1923 showed that the Okanogan Reclamation Unit had 5300 acres of cultivated land and 2700 acres capable of irrigation, ready for settlers,

Fig. 286 — Once all this landscape was bald and treeless save for willows and cottonwoods along the stream.  Then the settler with his irrigation ditch made this general farm, with orchards, vineyard, and stacks of alfalfa. Pigs and sheep pasture the hills and eat the alfalfa.  (Courtesy Chamber of Commerce, Wenatchee, Wash.  Photo B. C. Collier.)

but unused.  Settlers are advised to bring with them at least $5000, preferably $10,000.00, cash.  The Yakima unit had 107,000 acres cultivated, and 344,000 that could be irrigated.  This unused irrigable land cannot yet be profitably farmed.

### Resources for Manufacturing

What are the possibilities of manufacturing?  The Columbia Basin is surrounded by a rim of forested mountains and therefore has large supplies of wood.  Its wheat-fields produce grain.  Its ranches produce meat, wool, and hides.  Power-lines can easily carry cheap hydro-electric power from marginal mountain and central master-stream to every square foot of the region if it is wanted. It can be fairly deluged with power. There are many unused power-sites in the Rockies to the east of it and millions of horse-power in the Cascades to the west of it. Even the little River Deschutes, hard to find on the map, is said to have a million horse-power because it flows down east of the Cascades into the Columbia with a swift descent of 3000 feet and remarkably even flow. This even flow is produced by two factors — the slow melting of Cascade snows, and the natural water-storage of porous volcanic dust-soil. Will this power be used in this region?

The people in the United States part of this region like to speak of it as " the Inland Empire." Because of its great undeveloped resources it has rivaled California in advertising for settlers.[7] Spokane is its economic capital, located immediately by a waterfall where the Spokane River leaves a wide-open valley and tumbles into a canyon en route to the Columbia. But Spokane shows no signs (nor does any other Columbia Basin city show any signs as yet) of extensive export of manufactures to other regions. Spokane commands the resources for factories, but its population is still scanty. It is much like Corn Belt cities in this respect. Other places have equal resources and more accessible locations.

Spokane has half as many people as Akron, Ohio. It is about the same size as Reading, Pennsylvania. Spokane is a distributing center for the wheat country, for the ranch country, for the lumber-camps and mines in the mountains to the east of it. It is a railroad center, a natural place for railroad repair-shops, but railroad freight-costs tend to limit its factory market to the region near it. That region is not populous, nor does it show signs of multiplying many fold in population. During the decade 1910–1920 eight counties in central and southeastern Washington lost population, and Spokane County increased less than 5%.

### Future

The future of the Columbia Basin is plain. Scarcity of water is its greatest limitation. Therefore most of it must, alas, continue to be a grazing land — ranches. Some of it will continue to be dry-farming land, with a tendency toward declining fertility. Several million acres with good rainfall will be rotation-farming land, in which there can be great increase in intensity of cultivation and value of output of wheat, animal products and fruit if needed. There remains the great dare — can we use the waters of the mighty Columbia, one of the great rivers of the world, carrying down to the sea sufficient water to irrigate millions of acres of high rich land, which need only the water to blossom with harvest? But the river is in a canyon a hundred to a thousand feet below this rich land. Can man get the water up and on to the land —

---

[7] The town of Walla Walla used to put out attractive booklets with the slogan, " What Walla Walla wants is *you*."

land which is much more rolling than might be desired by the irrigator? Unfortunately this land has not a level, water-built surface like the plains of the Great Basin. That is the great dare that the river holds out to man. Since this region is a place of good climate, peopled by energetic and intelligent men, I think that some day they will take the dare, get the water up, and reduce the area of range-land and hazardous dry-farming land by making thousands of farms, highly productive, but expensive to water. Increasing population makes increasing food-costs and land-values and therefore will permit greater expenditures to reclaim land.

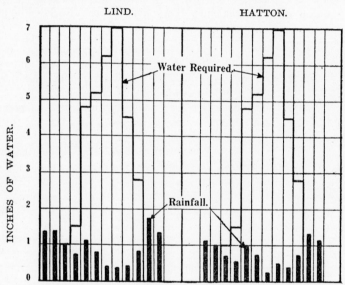

FIG. 287 — The rainfall by months and irrigation water-needs by months at two villages in the dry part of the Columbia Basin show very clearly the basal pinching fact of irrigation — the necessity of concentrating a deficiency until it is turned nto a surplus.

A substantial start toward taking the great dare is involved in the plan of the Columbia Basin Irrigation League. To avoid the Columbia Canyon they propose to take the water of a branch stream, the Pend Oreille, at a point just east of the Idaho-Washington boundary, and lead it thence via Spokane through aqueducts, tunnels, canals, and reservoirs to irrigate 1,753,000 acres of the three million acres lying between the Columbia and the Lower Snake rivers. The cost is estimated at $254,-000,000.00, or $145.00 per acre — excellent proof of the end of the era of cheap land in America.

It is interesting to speculate for a moment upon what would have happened if the Pacific mountains were absent (in the same latitude of Europe where there are fortunately no coast mountains), and if the

mountains between central Colorado and latitude 55° could have lain
east and west as do the Alps. In that case the cyclonic rain-bearing
storms would have swung into the Columbia-Fraser Basins as they do
into Europe, where in similar latitudes we find such magnificent agricultural lands and such human hives as the United Kingdom, France, Holland, Belgium, Germany, Switzerland and Northern Italy.

PART II.  THE FRASER PLATEAUS

The Canadian geographers mark off on their maps an area of about
60,000 square miles of plateaus, lying between the Rocky Mountain

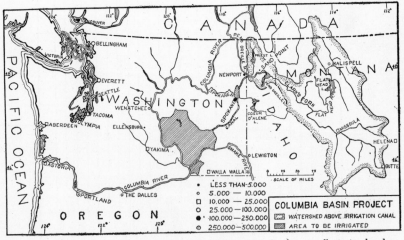

FIG. 288 — This map typifies the large scale of many of the future efforts to develop
the continent.

system and the Pacific mountains, and between the United States
boundary and 55° north. Nearly all of this area is drained by the Fraser
River, but the southern tip is drained by the Okanogan into the Columbia,
and the northern tip sends its waters down the Skeena.

Like the Columbia Basin, the Fraser Basin is shut in by the Pacific
mountains. Indeed, the Fraser Canyon through the Pacific mountains is
so sharp that the recommended Canadian transcontinental auto-road in
1922 had as one of its links a railroad haul for the car through these
mountains, where no suitable road had then been built.

Being thus shut away from the ocean by a high mountain mass, this
area, like the Columbia Basin, has little rain at low elevations. Many
of the lower parts have less than ten inches. Near Basque, close to the
Fraser River, there is a salt lake, somewhat like Searles Lake in California. It is covered with salt and the liquor beneath contains Epsom

salts.[8]  In 1922, at the town of Kamloops, there was a poster in the shop windows telling about a picnic excursion " across the desert to Everett." The word " desert " was properly used, for in some years the rainfall at Kamloops has been less than five inches.

The Fraser Valley is connected with the Columbia Valley by the open valley of the Okanogan. The two areas are much alike save for two great exceptions: (1) the Fraser has no lava plains; (2) most of the Fraser area is a plateau cut through by many long, rather narrow valleys. These valleys have low (generally arid) areas of alluvial soil. Higher

Fig. 289 — Fraser River Valley. At left, the scattering small trees of dry interior; at right, the horizontal white streak in center of picture shows surface of a tract of typical terrace or bench land. (Courtesy Geol. Surv., Ottawa.)

up in the valleys are many terraces or bench-lands formed by the lakes of the glacial era. These bench-lands have enough rainfall to permit some dry farming. Above the terraces are uplands with a great variety of soil, much of it glacial till marked by both fertility and stones.

Most of the Fraser Plateau is covered with forest of mediocre quality,[9] much of it open forest with grass.

As a result of surveys the government of British Columbia reports many million acres of land suitable for agriculture, but most of it should be thought of as a land-reserve to be used after more accessible and better lands of the east, south and central sections of the continent are in use and selling at higher price-levels than at present.

[8] *U. S. Commerce Reports*, Nov. 11, 1919.
[9] Less than 5000 feet BM of lumber per acre. *Forests of British Columbia*, Whitford and Craig.

AGRICULTURAL COMPARISON OF BRITISH COLUMBIA AND WASHINGTON STATE

| Cows (thous.) | Other Cattle (thous.) | Sheep (thous.) | Hogs (thous.) | Horses (thous.) | Apples (thous. (bu.) | Wheat (acreage thous.) | Total Acreage in Wheat, Barley, Rye, Oats (thous.) |
|---|---|---|---|---|---|---|---|
| 1923 | 1923 | 1923 | 1923 | 1923 | 1922 | 1922 | 1922 |
| 71 | 192 | 53 | 42 | 54 | 1,027 | 46 | 116 |
| 283 | 253 | 520 | 217 | 278 | 25,678 | 2426 | 2721 |

The comparison of Washington State and British Columbia is not an exact comparison of the Columbia and Fraser Valleys. Each has a coast-region with some agriculture, but the figures tell much, for the present at least. British Columbia has less than one-fiftieth as much land in wheat as Washington has. The figure is startling. Kamloops, the metropolis of the Fraser Valley, has 6000 people. Spokane, the metropolis of the Columbia, has 104,000.

The leading agricultural development of the Fraser Valley is apples, which are nearly all grown south of latitude 52° and chiefly along Okanogan Lake, a glacial lake forty miles long, much like the glacial lakes of Washington. It is probable that the climate of this section is one of the best climates in the world for apples, because there are no midwinter thaws. British Columbia apples often win prizes in competition with those of Washington and Oregon.

To find the climatic counterpart of the Fraser Valley we must go to Europe. If one takes into consideration the many mountain-like plateaus, the valleys and slopes and ancient glaciers, and the temperature,[10] it is instructive to think of this section as another Switzerland, but it has no such large proportion of humid valley-lands and it has no such tourist possibilities, and the location for commerce is not so good. It should always be kept in mind that the climate of the Fraser section, much like that of Central Europe, is one of the best in the world for the production of energetic human beings.

Like Switzerland the Fraser Basin is well supplied with water-power. If the Fraser Basin is ever used as fully as Switzerland, it might with equal ease support fifty to seventy-five people per square mile, but such efficient utilization of these plateaus and sharp-cut valleys will not come until the United States and Canada have four or five times as many people as they now support. The present meager development of transportation here and the advantage of shore locations for manufacture is such that there will be a strong tendency, because of inland location, for the Fraser Valley to have but few more people than it can feed. When it comes to the full utilization of its agricultural lands, Northwest Europe probably shows the type of agriculture for most of it — barley, oats, clover, root crops.

| | [10] Jan. temp. | July temp. | Annual temp. |
|---|---|---|---|
| Kamloops (alt. 1193 ft.) ........... | 24.7 | 69.7 | 47.7 |
| Lucerne, Switz. (alt. 1480 ft.) ..... | 29.7 | 64.9 | 47.3 |

Fig. 290 — Typical orange groves at the foot of barren mountains near Los Angeles.
(Courtesy Los Angeles Chamber of Commerce.)

## CHAPTER XXX

### VALLEY AND COAST OF SOUTHERN CALIFORNIA

Los Angeles, the metropolis of southern California, is the center of the greatest tourist district in the United States, and of the world's moving-picture industry. The city is also distinguished by being the center of the most fully developed region in the continent of North America. The region which I shall discuss as Southern California is only a few thousand square miles of land beside the sea. This small but populous region lies on the edge of a million square miles of desert and semi-desert which radiates inland from it in nearly all directions. Southern California is rescued from the desert by the green wall of the San Bernardino and San Jacinto ranges, which reach up high enough to make clouds and snatch moisture from the passing wind. Rain makes possible the homes of man where otherwise there would be only jack-rabbits, pastures and a little extensive farming.

This bit of good land, walled off from the desert by the mountain arch, faces the sea, and the winds blow from this sea with great regularity, making the land warm in winter and cool in summer.

A man in San Francisco, the rival city, says: " Half of it is wind, and the other half's water " — the " wind " being salesmanship, the "water" being irrigation. The two great California cities maintain a riotous rivalry.

### Climate

Briefly, the climate of this part of California, and also of the central part of California, may be described as subtropic because it will grow oranges and lemons, and as semi-arid, because irrigation is needed for most crops. The climate is called the Mediterranean type, which means that nearly all of the rain falls in the winter and the summer is virtually

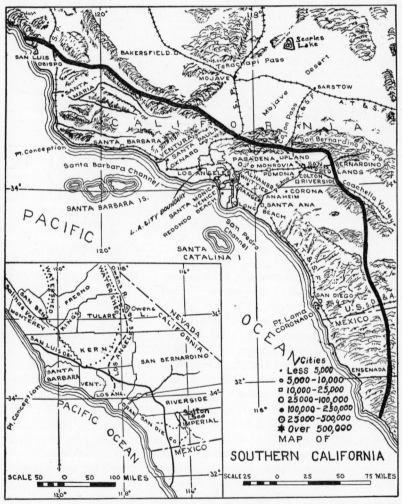

FIG. 291 — The dotted lines connecting with Salton Sea are streams of occasional flow.

rainless. Because of its many virtues and its many economic results this type of climate may be called the greatest resource of the region. The residents allow no traveler to overlook it. (Figs. 18, 128.)

### Stages of Industry

Southern California, like the central part of the state, has had a most varied industrial history in a very short time, as human history goes. The Spaniards made their first real settlement when in 1769 they founded missions or monasteries. By 1800 there were eighteen of these and more were established later. The missions were really economic enterprises, as they had to be self-supporting in this far country. The Spanish friars transplanted the products of their Mediterranean homeland to the monastery gardens in California, where there are still some famous specimens of ancient vines and orange, lemon, olive, cork oak, carob and other trees of the Mediterranean region. This early start with growing fruit was an invaluable guide in getting California's greatest industry — fruit — under way. On grassy uplands the friars grew wheat

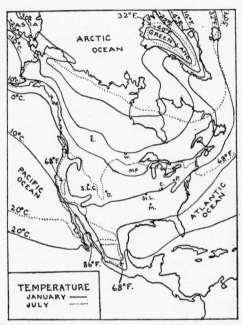

FIG. 292 — This map of average monthly temperature shows clearly the tendency of California's winds from the ocean to maintain an even temperature.

and barley for their bread (getting crops in years of better rainfall). By 1834 the friars owned 420,000 head of cattle, while herds of wild horses and wild donkeys were so plentiful as to be a veritable nuisance. At this time the hides were the chief basis of California trade. Yankee ships were gathering up hides at San Diego and other ports as described in Dana's classic, *Two Years Before the Mast*. The old missions are now little more than carefully preserved historical curiosities and penny-catchers, like the well-preserved Revolutionary bullet-holes of New England. The Spanish occupation left its mark in other ways. These people gave the Spanish names to the California settlements and they helped to create a style of architecture very different from that of the Eastern United States.

" California may be said to have ' found itself ' architecturally, a thing not yet true of the East. Of course, it is impossible to say whether the current development in California is a fashion or an architectural style; it is to be hoped the latter, since climatic conditions, local materials and historic tradition alike point to the development of a school of architecture of southern characteristics. California, indeed, the whole Southwest, requires heavy overhanging eaves as a protection against the sun; thick walls as insulation against the heat; comparatively small window areas because of the intense brightness of the air; low-pitched roofs are rendered appropriate by the absence of snow. These requirements are identical with those which built up the Italian and Spanish country schools of architecture, and even had there been nothing to copy it would seem natural for such buildings to have been developed in the Southwest, so that in principle the Italian type of building, which is generally out of place in the Eastern and Northern states, is eminently fitted for the Southwest." [1]  This is a nice recognition of geographic influence.

By 1860 the ranges had begun to suffer from over-pasturing. Drought killed hundreds of thousands of cattle in the early '60's and the people turned to raising sheep, which will survive on poorer pasture.

Between 1870 and 1890 California went through a period of bonanza wheat-growing.[2] The treeless plains and foothills were most easy to cultivate with machinery. Maximum production was reached in 1882, and for many years much wheat was exported in sailing vessels around Cape Horn to Great Britain. The twenty years from 1870 to 1890 were also a period of experiment in horticulture — the industry which helped to cause a decline in wheat to one-tenth (1913) its former acreage.

Long before the American flag waved over California, the mission gardens had produced an abundance of grapes and fruit, and showed clearly the possibilities of indefinite expansion if there were a market. But in that day marketing fruit in California was like marketing building-stone in the heart of a mountain.

The opening of the first transcontinental railway, 1869, suggested a dim possibility, but it was only in 1876 that California sent her first car of oranges to market.

Since 1890 there has been a very important horticultural industry developed in Southern California, in the Great Valley and the Coast Range Valleys.[3] In Southern California there has been an even more

---

[1] " Modern American Country Houses," Aymar Embury, the *Architectural Forum*, March 1923.

[2] Its smaller area made Southern California but a small participant in this wheat fever, which was centered in the Great Valley of California.

[3] California, with only 3.2% of the population of the United States, produces 5.4% of the farm products of the country; pays 5.5% of the income tax; has 6.5% of the automobiles; and owns 8.9% of the homes wired for electricity. (*California Development Board*.)

remarkable economic development — I refer to the utilization of the climate as a dominating factor in business enterprises, a factor of greater economic value than that of their orchards and vineyards.

### The Tourist Era

We might call the period from 1890 to the present time the period of the boomers and builders. The resources utilized were the beauty of the country, the pleasant qualities of the climate and the excellence and variety of subtropic crops. This land has great attractions for the traveler from the cold East and Middle West. Few persons, when they no longer enjoy coasting, really care very much for snow, blizzards or a January thaw. These things are apt to happen from Montana to Tennessee and Maine, but meanwhile roses bloom in San Diego and in Los Angeles and people who live there can, with pleasure, be out of doors most of the time.

The landscape offers the varied charm that can be found only where sea and mountains are near neighbors. In Southern California you can after a few hours' journey climb a mountain or take a dip in the ocean. The trees are the wonder and admiration of visitors from the East. The lovely drooping pepper tree with its sweep of feathery foliage is everywhere. The palms and the ever-green orange trees offer contrast and great charm.

The whole region is threaded by good roads which make traveling by automobile a joy.

In summer it is rarely hot near the sea, and even farther inland the dry climate makes a blanket necessary at night even though the day is very hot. But if the day is hot it is also dry, and the heat is of a less wilting character than that of the land east of the Great Plains. San Diego properly boasts a climate which for forty years did not go below freezing or for more than an hour above 90°. No one will dispute San Diego's boast of having winters like Egypt and summers like Alaska.[4]

All these qualities are naturally attractive to the tourist and the vacationist, and the facts have been most diligently spread before the world by the activities of railroads seeking traffic, of business men's organizations wanting their towns to grow, and of land-boomers wishing to retail at profit. In gathering information for this chapter I have collected a pile of material two feet high, much of which is of an advertising character. In striking contrast the material I found about the mighty and fully occupied Corn Belt contained almost nothing of the advertising sort. The West hustles to advertise. As an example of Western hustle, I recall the complaint of an Eastern railroad traffic manager. In attempting to get Easterners to help him get up an exhibit for the New York Land

---

[4] The same is true to a lesser extent in places near San Francisco Bay.

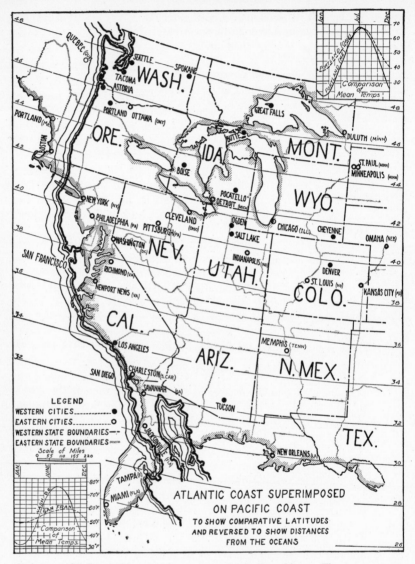

FIG. 293 — Study of this map shows many interesting things. The temperature graphs are especially instructive.

Show of 1911 he complained that " the Western states, railroads, and business organizations have secured over four-fifths of all the available space."

Every one will recall having seen much magazine advertising calling attention to a great variety of opportunities in Southern California, as well as in the rest of the state.  Looking over the business opportunities in the Sunday edition of the Washington *Star*, August 19, 1923, I found this:

" One acre will produce independence, immediate income and permanent prosperity in glorious California.  Write for particulars.  Pacific Homeseeker, Chamber of Commerce Building, Los Angeles, Calif."

Many California counties maintain publicity departments under the direction of able men, and Chambers of Commerce have reached a degree of activity unknown in any other part of the world.  That of Los Angeles claims the greatest membership in the country.  Its various departments are run by able assistant secretaries.  Are you interested in agriculture? You can get real and, I am glad to say, honest information from the man now in charge.  Do you wish to write about Southern California?  The Chamber of Commerce will get you the facts if possible.  The pictures you want will be taken.  The things you want to see will be shown you by an officer of the Chamber in an automobile of the Chamber, or perhaps some leading citizen, *who really knows*, will take you out.

As a result of this publicity we all hear of California before we get there, and hear of it continuously when we do get there.  Indeed, the residents seem to think that you are stupid if you do not want to live there, once you come.  They are partly right in assuming that once you come you want to stay.  Thousands have come for the journey, fallen in love with the country, and bought a home — some to live on their accumulations, some to try making a living.

Said a man at Santa Ana, a few miles south of Los Angeles:  " I jest got tired of crawnchin' through the snow back in Ohio, feedin' hawgs before daylight of winter mornings, so I am out here finishin' up my days raisin' alfalfa."

The people of Southern California make you welcome, and try to make you feel at home.  They take you to their picnics and parties in a whole-hearted way that is not to be found in the older communities of the East.  Perhaps the visitor may be pardoned if sometimes he wonders if the whole thing is a conspiracy to sell, and if everybody he meets isn't to some degree at least an assistant advertising agent.  The people really do sell their climate as the Swiss sell their Alps.

For the ever-increasing thousands who can take a tour, and as a place in which to live during years of retirement, Southern California is probably without a parallel in the United States.  Why should the retired farmer stick in the black mud of Illinois or face the cold winds of Iowa, Minnesota or Manitoba, if he can spend the winter or his declining years in this land of gentle climate? [5]  Indeed, many a Western bonanza farmer who has made a good crop goes to California for the winter and

[5] Some prefer the more changeable and stimulating climate of the San Francisco region.

returns home for the spring planting.  Why should the retired school-teacher or other person of small fixed income spend the years after he or she has retired from business in New York flats or in Chicago or Des Moines?  Thousands of such people have gone to Southern California, where more people live without working than in any other part of the United States.  People who go to Southern California from other states often form state societies.  Not long ago the Iowa Society held a picnic at Pasadena.  The 27,000 people who attended grouped themselves under county banners so that their friends might find them in the great crowd.[6]

### The Health-Seekers and Over-Population

Then there are the health-seekers, especially those who have some pulmonary or respiratory trouble in the more rigorous or humid East. These people find that they can live in Southern California.

Sometimes people who come for love of the country or from the necessity of ill-health are capitalists, and as a result of all these factors outside capital has poured into this part of California as into no other part of the United States.

Many who love the climate or who must stay there on account of their health have a few acres of fruit as their means of livelihood.  In the San Fernando valley near Los Angeles there is a settlement of five-acre units, covered with fruit, mostly apricots.  The houses are buried in fruitful shade; each " ranch " has a large hennery with a thousand or two of white Leghorns, whose eggs are sold in New York at top price through the co-operative egg-marketing associations.

As a result of all these things, Los Angeles and its vicinity grew, between 1910 and 1920, as no other part of the United States, save the automobile boom-town of Detroit (see percentages given below).[7]

Los Angeles is surrounded by suburbs or semi-suburbs.  The convenient little bungalow, bowered in vines, flowers and shade-trees, is more universally attractive than the small home in any other part of the country.

---

[6] There are forty-seven state societies with headquarters in Los Angeles.  Hawaii and Alaska also have societies, and some states have more than one.

[7] THE GROWTH OF METROPOLITAN DISTRICTS CONTAINING NEARLY ONE-FOURTH OF ALL THE PEOPLE OF THE UNITED STATES.

|  | 1910 | 1920 | Per cent Increase |
|---|---|---|---|
| Greater New York...................... | 4,766,000 | 5,619,000 | 17.9 |
| Greater New York (and 9 near-by counties). | 7,037,000 | 8,524,000 | 21.1 |
| Chicago District (5 counties).............. | 2,660,000 | 3,422,000 | 28.6 |
| Boston District (4 counties).............. | 2,025,000 | 2,315,000 | 14.3 |
| Phila. District (3 counties).............. | 1,808,000 | 2,187,000 | 20.9 |
| Detroit (Wayne Co.)..................... | 531,000 | 1,177,000 | 121.5 |
| San Francisco District (4 surrounding counties)................................. | 746,000 | 968,000 | 30. |
| Los Angeles (Riverside, Orange, S. Bernardino and S. Diego counties)............. | 691,000 | 1,233,000 | 78.4 |

This is a new country but it is no frontier. In many respects it is quite as up-to-date as New York or Chicago. Its newness is shown in the absence of social stratification and the ease of social mingling. Nevertheless some of the characteristics of an old community are present. The labor market is somewhat depressed. Many who have gone to California seeking health or pleasure need to supplement a small fixed income by additional earnings. So many enter the professions, or take clerical jobs or part-time work that the demand is more than supplied and wages are lower for that kind of work than in many other parts of the United States. This would indicate a good place in which to start

FIG. 294 — The beautiful homes of Southern California charm thousands and turn visitors into residents. (Courtesy Los Angeles Chamber of Commerce.)

manufacturing, but thus far the cities are not much marred by smokestacks and big factory buildings. Manufactures, now on the increase, were for a long time strangely limited to the local needs, save for the great exception of moving-picture films.

## The Moving-Picture Industry

Film is by far the leading manufactured product of this territory. Its 1920 films were worth 150 million dollars; iron and steel products forty-four millions; auto trucks and parts, thirty-three millions; chemicals and soaps, twenty millions. The finished film is often worth more than its weight in gold. The surface and climate of Southern California are the resources which have been most instrumental in making it the moving-picture center of the United States and of the world. The producers can stage an out-of-door scene and photograph it without the intervention of unexpected showers. The dependable weather of the long, dry summer is a decided asset. Winter is mild enough for much out-of-door work, and there is very little strong wind.

This locality offers wonderful settings for great varieties of pictures. Do the producers want seashore, mountain, plain, farm, village, city, orchard, palm, pine, sand dune or rocky cliff? All are within easy reach of Hollywood and the other studios. Just a short trip by automobile takes the actors to the desired spot.

As is usually the case, the picture industry brought subsidiaries with it. If a scene with the period furniture of the time of Queen Victoria or Cleopatra is wanted, it can be hired from firms whose business it is to rent furniture for this purpose. If the hero wishes to wear the shoes of

FIG. 295 — One of the ways by which a movie play costs its much advertised million. This one-faced shell appears as a perfect reproduction of the public square of Monte Carlo when seen by the eye of a properly placed camera. (Courtesy Los Angeles Chamber of Commerce and Universal Studios.)

Charlemagne or Caesar, there are shoemakers who have the patterns and can make the shoes; he can hire clothing and uniforms for almost any country or period of history. Does the story call for a bowl of bread dough to be smashed over the head of the hero? Behold a manufacturing plant that specializes in soft and friable pottery! Another plant makes furniture which harmlessly breaks when used. One of the studios even maintains a private zoo, with chimpanzee, lions and other animals awaiting the call. One morning a thousand gray-haired women were desired for a great scene. By noon they were assembled with the aid of a card catalogue — already on file. Ten thousand maidens can be obtained in a few hours, for nearly everybody wants to get into the movies. Los Angeles is forever having to deal with the penniless, deluded persons who without qualifications have come from the ends of the world to star in the movies. The unemployed population of Los Angeles furnishes plenty of material for mobs and supers.

To succeed in this industry more is needed than an artistic temperament and a desire to act. Plenty of hard, careful work is necessary. One day a movie queen forgot to wear a locket that had a vital part in the plot. Not until the end of a day's work was the omission discovered. The whole day's work went for nothing; it had to be done again, although the actual cost of the complete staff of actors, supers, photographers and rentals was $10,000.00 a day. So thoroughly organized has the movie industry become that it is less dependent on California climate than it used to be. Buildings are being made in which players can enact scenes previously done out of doors. The industry seems to be more firmly established by these buildings than it was before they were built. It is probably true that Hollywood is the greatest single center of influence of thought for the average man. From this town come most of the films at which 50,000,000 people spend an afternoon or evening each week in the United States alone.[8]

The moving-picture industry is in the control of a group of New York ex-clothing dealers who have had the foresight to seize upon the picture industry. This is another example of the inpouring of capital to Southern California. The films are made in Hollywood, but financed and distributed in New York.

## Agriculture

The agriculture of this region is marked by its intensive character. Los Angeles County leads all United States counties in value of farm produce and in number of farms. The latter is chiefly because they are small. It has the largest gross return per acre, partly because it has so many acres of oranges, lemons, walnuts, apricots, market gardens and truck-farms. Much of the produce is consumed by the local markets, and a great deal is sent to the Eastern markets. In the winter-time 4000 acres of cauliflower and 4500 acres of lettuce are produced. Riding south from Los Angeles toward San Diego, one rides much of the time through orchards.

The region is one of great variety of rainfall and frostiness or frost exemption and therefore has great variety of crops in different places. San Diego has 9.5 inches of rain, Los Angeles has 16.4 inches, but on

[8] Many movies go to foreign lands, and what do they tell of the United States? Says the London *Evening News:*

"It is inhabited in the East by unscrupulous but enormously successful business men, who devote their nights to squandering in cabarets their ill-gotten gains of the day before. In the West 'bad men' rob stage-coaches and banks and shoot sheriffs and their partners in crime and spend a good deal of time rolling on the ground in attempts to gouge each other's eyes out. The North is peopled by bearded scoundrels, who go there to escape from the law, to steal mining claims and to menace lonely girls snowbound in log cabins. The South is notable for cacti and half-breeds. The last-named have no particular vice; they are just bad."

the mountain slopes it sometimes increases ten inches in a single steep mile. Thus Riverside, 850 feet elevation, has 10.5 inches of rainfall; San Bernardino, ten miles away, elevation 1050 feet, has 15.5 inches. On the mountain rim of the valleys it runs up to twenty, thirty and even to forty inches.

The fact that rain falls chiefly in the winter-time makes one of the limitations of the region, and presents to man a great problem, that of storing the water for several months [9] until it can be utilized for growing plants. On the bare humid slopes the winter rain is sufficient to raise a crop of winter wheat and winter barley or barley hay. Certain coast districts have a peculiar combination of qualities that especially suit lima beans. The soil is mostly " doby," a heavy clay that holds water well. The ground cracks open eighteen inches deep in the summer-time and gives itself a supply of air as is the case with certain lava soils of India. Where this soil is near the sea it has the benefit of night fogs throughout much of the growing season. Sometimes these fogs are so heavy that they not only stop all evaporation while present but wet the plants and even moisten the ground. These bean-fields cover large stretches,[10] and often between Los Angeles and San Diego one sees only a field of beans or wheat between the Pacific and the pastured hills.

Aside from these, all other important crops depend upon irrigation, which is here carried on with greater intensity than in any other part of the United States. The large income of orange, lemon and other valuable crops makes man strive indefatigably for water. He uses canal, reservoir, wells (surprisingly deep) and even tunnels dug back into the hills to intercept ground waters. To preserve this water-supply weeds are pulled

FIG. 296 — Lima-bean fields in Southern California sometimes reach almost as far as you can see. Young English walnut tree by roadside at left. San Fernando Valley in Los Angeles County. (Photo J. Russell Smith.)

and the ground covered with earth mulch by repeated cultivation.

To take advantage of frost drainage the crops are laid out upon the sloping sides of valleys in zones or bands according to their ability to withstand frost. For this reason the lowlands of Southern California are in alfalfa, grain and sugar-beets because these groups are little injured

[9] In San Diego County water is sometimes stored for several years.

[10] Irrigation improves the yield but large acreages are grown without it. They are even grown without rain after planting in land that is plowed in the autumn to make it hold all that is possible of winter rain.

by frost. Farther up the slope come grapes and peaches; then the more sensitive orange; then the still more sensitive lemon, and in a few localities where the elevation is sufficient for the cooling effect of altitude to operate there are wide expanses of apples. The irrigation ditch that is the highest one on the slope divides the green of the irrigated lands from the brown of the unirrigated lands. This zonal distribution of crops

FIG. 297 — The perfectly clean tillage clear down to the roadside in this lemon orchard shows the intensiveness of some California agriculture.

is really remarkable in the region of San Bernardino, Redlands and Riverside. There the valley bottom is quite without orchards, while a few feet above it is a great horseshoe of rich, black-green orchards, which make the city of Redlands boast that it ships more oranges than any other city in the world.

As Southern California is the least frosty [11] part of California, it contains most of the 40,000 acres of lemons that are grown in the state and includes also more than half of the oranges. The growth of the California citrus fruit industry to the point where it is shipping in normal years more than 40,000 carloads of oranges and about a fifth as many lemons is the result of much work in overcoming difficulties both of production and of marketing. After fighting frost and drought, another of the episodes of production is to fight to control certain bothersome insects which if left undisturbed greatly injure the trees and which the usual methods of spraying do not affect. Gangs of men with trucks and tents make regular rounds, throwing a high canvas tent over the orange tree and releasing under the tent the deadly fumes of hydrocyanic acid

[11] Equal or better frost immunity is claimed by certain foothill sections on both sides of the Sacramento Valley, such as Porterville and Maxwell, where lemons are grown. Southern California has a destructive freeze about once every ten years. That of 1922 did twelve million dollars' worth of damage. (U. S. Weather Bureau.)

gas, which annihilates the insects, and holds their numbers in check for a time.

The marketing of the California orange is one of the finest examples of co-operative marketing. The grower picks his fruit and takes it to the co-operative packing-house. The central organization grades, packs, ships, advertises and sells his product for him. The scope of the organization may be measured by the fact that several years before the World War it took an expert from the Department of Agriculture at Washington and paid him $10,000.00 a year for advice about the best methods of handling and shipping oranges. The expert was thought to have been an excellent investment.

Like nearly everybody else in California, the orange-growers are capitalizing California's sun by giving the name " Sunkist " to their oranges. Everywhere they advertise the superiority of their product. The organizations selected localities in which to advertise and an increase in the consumption of oranges resulted. After that large sums of money were spent regularly to make us believe in and eat the " Sunkist " oranges. One of the last moves was to put an orange squeezer for the making of orangeade in thousands of drug stores. It is almost amusing to see the peculiar wrath of California people at the mention of the Florida orange, and *vice versa*.

The way natural factors control California crops is well shown by the absence of orange trees in front of the Cajon Pass, where the Santa Fe Railroad crosses from the Mojave Desert into the San Bernardino Valley. Cold winds sweep through the Pass, bringing freezing weather in winter and beating the trees about in summer, so there is a break in the orange orchards opposite the Pass. With all the care that can be observed, frost frequently injures the crops in small areas and sometimes does great damage even in the favored locations. At times there has been widespread use of fires, smudge-pots, small metal stoves. The stoves burn crude oil and scores to the acre are used on cold nights to keep away the frost. This is ultimately a poor dependence, uncertain, expensive, for what will be the future price of oil?

The orange has been one of the baits by which many a green Easterner has been lured. Sometimes one sees a rascal hauling rich-looking dirt to cover up a barren piece of ground, in which he has planted worthless seedling oranges merely to sell this worthless bargain to some Eastern greenhorn. This has been done over and over again.

One of the most expert orange-growers in this region says that the orange orchards of California may be divided into three groups. One-third of the orange trees produce from three-and-a-half to four boxes per tree per year, which is a profitable crop. One-third were worthless from the start because of poor soil, poor water-supply or frosty location. These trees were set out (often by non-residents) to catch suckers, which they have done, often repeatedly. The other third have been neglected or mistreated by people who did not know or would not observe the proper rules for orange culture.

## The Intensiveness of Agriculture

The increasingly intensive nature of the agriculture is shown by a marked decline of butter-making in this region since 1905. Indeed, to get a sufficient supply of fresh milk is becoming a problem. Milk is now being brought by the train-load from Bakersfield and other points in the Great Valley. Alfalfa cost $24.00 per ton at Los Angeles in 1923, and only $16.00 at San Francisco. Intensive agriculture is also shown

FIG. 298 — Celery field in Los Angeles County. (Courtesy Los Angeles Chamber of Commerce.)

by the absence of weeds in the fence rows, often by the absence of fences; by the cultivation of the ground right down to the edge of the road; by the rows of grafted English walnut trees beside the road, and by the fact that the house often stands in the orchard and is shaded by fruit trees. (Fig. 116.)

Nowhere in the United States is it more difficult to draw a line between city life, suburban life and country life, because the farms are so small, the roads so good, and the automobile so universal that large numbers of people are making their living by growing fruit, vegetables and poultry so near other people's farms that together they make a small city. The small farm suffices because the regular climate, irrigation and the high value of crops permit a small area to produce a great return. But shortage of irrigation water here is complete calamity.

The market gardener has the advantage of a very long season because things grow for at least ten months in the year, and under irrigation he can get several crops from the same land.[12]

[12] But here too the glutted market menaces. In April 1921, half of the cabbage crop was abandoned.

This condition of intensive agriculture and the small neat home, bowered in fruit trees and other shades, is not universal. There are still some of the old Spanish grants, and on the road between Los Angeles and San Diego the Santa Fe Railroad track runs for twenty miles through one estate, which has thirty miles of ocean frontage and is much larger than the average county in the United States. Some of these big estates are rented, and the standardized, unkempt dwelling of the tenant plainly shows that he is a tenant, and the mile-long stretches of sugar-beets and lima beans or wheat offer, with their wide expanse, a great contrast to the bungalow areas of semi-suburban orchards. (Fig. 127.)

### Future — Agriculture

The agricultural future of this region depends upon the better use of resources, of which the cream has been already taken. Many resources, especially forest and soil, have been injured or destroyed. Agriculture here is full of problems. There is some truth in the saying that " God never intended Southern California to be anything but a desert. Man has made it what it is." Man still has many adjustments to make before he can make full use of Nature and get her aid without catastrophe. For instance, the agriculture even of this region has not yet got down to the basis of established rotations. Instead of following the dictates of the science of agriculture the people are still raising this and that, according to individual whims or in response to market reports.

Already in the process of irrigation alkali has ruined,[13] permanently or temporarily, thousands of acres of splendid land. Even in some of the most densely peopled parts of this region, lowlands which look as though they should be the best of land are unproductive and worthless (for the present at least) because they have become alkaline by nature or as a result of seepage from irrigations and ditches higher up. The truth is that in America we have not yet learned fully how to practice irrigation as a fine art.

Wells and pumps are being more used for irrigation in Southern California than in any other part of the United States. The ground water is slow to accumulate, but the electric pump works rapidly. As a result, in 1922, at the end of four dry years, the people of many localities were in a condition little short of panic. Near San Bernardino the water in some wells had gone down sixty feet, greatly increasing the cost of pumping and promising the complete exhaustion of wells which were really using up an accumulation. The seriousness of this problem is shown by the following quotation from the United States Geological Survey Water Supply Paper 468, " Records of Water Levels in Wells in Southern California," p. 5: " Most of the water supplies, whether used for domestic

---

[13] In this respect most other irrigated areas are greater sufferers.

purposes or irrigation, are obtained wholly or in part from ground water. In 1905 Mendenhall estimated that two-thirds of the land at that time under irrigation in this region obtained its water from subterranean sources during the protracted period of low run-off then prevailing. Since that time much more land has been brought under irrigation, and the proportion of land supplied with ground water has probably been increased."

### The Alluvial Fan and Subterranean Water Storage

There are two cures for this exhaustion of the ground water. One is to pump out less water; but the other, and better, cure is to get more water into the ground. Man can do this to some extent by diverting

FIG. 299 — The victory of destruction. The alluvial-fan process working too fast for man. Because the hills in the background were burnt bare the heavy rain ran away so quickly as to make a flood and cover hundreds of acres of alfalfa fields with the unproductive sand shown in foreground. Along the San Diego River, Southern California. (Courtesy U. S. Bureau of Forestry.)

mountain streams at the foot of the mountain in such a way that water will run into the ground. This is made possible by the geology of these valleys. They are made of mountain wash, brought down by the streams and spread out at the foot of the mountain. If a swift mountain stream strikes a valley its speed slows up and the load begins to drop. The heaviest material drops first; the water spreads out the finer stuff in deltas or alluvial fans, as such formations are called. They are essentially like the Colorado delta already explained, the only difference being that the upper end of these fans is often of surprisingly coarse material. For example, on the upper end of the Mill Creek fan near San Bernardino there are hundreds of acres of rough bouldery land, composed of coarse sand, gravel and stones, some of which were as big as bushels and gradually reducing in size, with increases of distance from the foot of the canyon. But the fan extended three or four miles before the soil got fine enough for any kind of tillage and then the fact that most of it was waste land was shown by little patches here and there set to orange after the stones had been very laboriously picked up and the sandy soil thus made available. The journey down the fan showed increasing areas of tillable land, but it was several miles before I reached soil so fine that the whole of it was in farms, chiefly oranges. Down the center was a sandy watercourse, now dry, but spanned by a very wide bridge speaking effectively of winter floods and wasted waters (Fig. 247).

The coarseness of the earth at the top of the fan allows water to soak into it very rapidly, a fact of great importance to the irrigators, who can pump it out months later, and perhaps at a place miles away down the slope. The stream is spread over the top of the fan by little dams and canals so that the water may sink into the earth.

In one place in Southern California 800 acres are being used for spreading water on such land. Observations below show the flow of water as it slowly works through the subsoils and accumulates in wells.

### Mountain Reservoirs

Many more reservoirs can be built in mountain gorges to hold water for irrigation and also to prevent floods. In winter raging torrents rush down channels which for months of the summer are only dry white sand. Even parts of the city of Los Angeles itself have often been flooded in winter. Much of this could be prevented by storing the flood waters for irrigation.[14]

### Social Control of Water

The problem of the use of water, with its troubles of over-pumping, alkali land, over-irrigation and failure of supply at critical times, requires handling in a large way, by the kind of social organization of which the twentieth century must work out many types if our efficiency in the use of resources is to pass 25% or 50%. Progressive men of the territory around Los Angeles have formed the Water Users' Association, whose membership includes County Farm Bureaus, Chambers of Commerce and private individuals. For example, there are 1100 irrigation projects in the San Gabriel Valley alone. Some of them are just a farmer's well; others, a well that is owned by several farmers; others, the simple diversion of a stream; others, reservoirs with canals. Most of those who use the water have less water than they need. Sometimes they wake up in the night from dreams of dry ditches. Even now the failing well barely waters the alfalfa, and the truck field and orchard. The man who finds his well going dry is in a position to listen to reason and to be amenable to the idea of applying the law of eminent domain still more

---

[14] In 1924 Los Angeles County voted thirty million dollars for flood control.

to water supply and irrigation problems. The great need is to increase the supply and make its distribution and use more effective. This means less of our beloved American independence for the individual, but such sacrifice seems less terrible when it holds out the possibility of supplying the failing well with water from the top of an alluvial fan, miles away, or bringing it by a new ditch from a reservoir not yet built. This Water Users' Association is confronted with a big and knotty problem of engineering, of agriculture, and above all, of dealing with human nature. The Association must get the people working together, as it tries to apply and bring conviction back of its motto, "It must become a crime to waste water."

These people are also deeply concerned about their forests. Places where, a generation or two ago, good forests stood, have been burned down to the subsoil, almost to the rock, by repeated forest fires. There are thousands and tens of thousands of acres of such ruined forest land. The effect of this forest destruction and its relation to the problem of water supply is well shown by the following California facts:

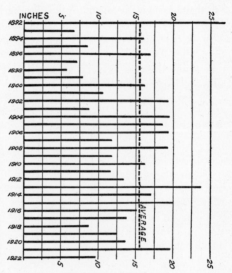

Fig. 300 — Compare the fluctuation of amount of annual rainfall of Los Angeles (type of the west coast) with that of Philadelphia (type of east coast, Fig. 73), and see one of the great problems that climate forces upon man.

"The north fork of the Yuba River in the Sierras of California is forest-covered, and the south fork has been denuded. The first has a watershed of 139 square miles, and the second a watershed of 120 square miles. The first, well covered with timber and brush, gives a minimum run-off of 113 cubic feet per second. The second should have given a minimum run-off of about 100 cubic feet per second, but is said to be practically nothing for four months in the year." (Charles R. Van Hise, *The Conservation of Natural Resources in the United States,* p. 249.)

The agricultural value of the water from a small effective watershed is astounding. In 1915 the San Antonio watershed [15] in Southern California, with an area of only twenty-four square miles, furnished irrigation

[15] *What the National Forests Mean to the Water User.* U. S. Forest Service, 1919.

water for 25,750 acres devoted to citrus fruit, alfalfa, and sugar-beets, and producing 5.4 million dollars' worth. The same year, the San Dimas watershed, eighteen square miles, watered 5800 acres of citrus fruits, with crop value of 2.6 million dollars.

### More Intensive Agriculture

The possibility of better use of land and water is well indicated by the yields of many farms which here, as often elsewhere, are far above the average of their locality. American agriculture, even in Southern California, is still far below its possibilities.

It is true that the yields per acre in Southern California are better than the state average, but the table of yields from a University of California Bulletin is very suggestive of the difference between average and reasonable possibility:

AVERAGE, PROBABLE, AND POSSIBLE YIELDS IN CALIFORNIA

|  | Average yield per acre | A safe estimate for business purposes | A good yield which competent men may hope to attain | Yield not infrequently obtained under favorable conditions | Possible but extraordinary yield |
|---|---|---|---|---|---|
| Wheat, bu................. | 13 | 20 | 25 | 40 | 50 |
| Oats, bu.................. | 31 | 45 | 60 | 90 | 120 |
| Barley, bu................ | 25 | 40 | 50 | 75 | 100 |
| Potatoes, bu.............. | 125 | 175 | 200 | 300 | 500 |
| Alfalfa, ton.............. | 3.5 | 5.0 | 6.0 | 9.0 | 12.0 |
| Cotton, Durango, lb........ | 300 | 400 | 500 | 800 | 1200 |
| Rice, rough, lb........... | 1500 | 2200 | 3000 | 4500 | 6000 |
| Beans, field, lb........... | 1100 | 1200 | 1400 | 2500 | 3000 |
| Sugar beets, ton.......... | 9 | 13 | 18 | 25 | 30 |
| Butter fat, per cow, lb...... | 150 | 225 | 300 | 350 | 400 |
| Oranges, box.............. | 150 | 225 | 300 | 450 | 600 |
| Lemons, box.............. | 175 | 225 | 300 | 450 | 600 |
| Raisins, Muscat, ton....... | 0.5 | 0.75 | 1.00 | 1.25 | 2.00 |
| Raisins, Seedless, ton..... | 0.75 | 1.00 | 1.25 | 1.50 | 3.00 |
| Grapes, shipping, ton...... | 3.0 | 5.0 | 7.0 | 10.0 | 15.0 |
| Grapes, Interior, wine, ton . | 3.0 | 5.0 | 7.0 | 10.0 | 15.0 |
| Grapes, Coast, wine, ton... | 1.5 | 3.0 | 5.0 | 7.0 | 10.0 |
| Olives, ton............... | 1.0 | 1.50 | 2.0 | 3.0 | 5.0 |
| Walnuts, ton.............. | 0.4 | 0.5 | .75 | 1.0 | 1.5 |
| Almonds, ton............. | 0.4 | 0.5 | .75 | 1.0 | 1.25 |
| Prunes, dried, ton......... | 1.25 | 1.75 | 2.5 | 3.0 | 5.0 |
| Plums, shipping, crate..... | 250 | 350 | 450 | 650 | 850 |
| Apricots, dried, ton........ | 0.75 | 1.0 | 1.25 | 1.75 | 2.5 |
| Apricots, shipping, crate.... | 250 | 350 | 450 | 650 | 850 |
| Pears, ton................ | 4.0 | 5.0 | 7.0 | 10.0 | 12.0 |
| Peaches, dried, ton........ | 0.75 | 1.0 | 1.5 | 2.0 | 3.0 |
| Peaches, shipping, box..... | 300 | 400 | 600 | 800 | 1000 |
| Apples, box.............. | 200 | 300 | 500 | 900 | 1200 |
| Cherries, ton.............. | 1.25 | 2.0 | 2.5 | 5.0 | 8.0 |

## The Practice of Economy

Considerable increase in the capacity to sustain increased population in all parts of the United States can result if we learn to cherish economy rather than to adhere to the grand, extravagant manner which so marks the traveling American, and so shocks nations that for generations have been taught to save.  For example, in 1922 Southern California plowed under 60,000 tons of cabbage when it was selling at two to four cents per pound.  On a wager, to prove that the American people do not want to b u y cheap things, Dr. Clements of Los Angeles had two large trucks loaded with these cabbages accompanied by salesmen a n d placarded t o a n - nounce that it could be b o u g h t f o r a cent a pound.  One went north- w a r d through the city, the other went s o u t h.  O n e s o l d o n l y fifty pounds, and the o t h e r 112 pounds, one of the many e v i d e n c e s that might be adduced to show that the American people have an instinct to buy the expensive rather than the economical thing.

FIG. 301 — Stripping cork bark in Portugal.  California forests might contain millions of acres of cork oaks.  (Photo J. Russell Smith.)

## Relative Freedom from Cold Waves

A factor in the future of this region is the rela- tive immunity from cold waves; it has fewer cold waves than any other important part of the United States.  But they do come even here.  For forty years San Diego had no temperature below freezing.  Then in January 1913, the ther- mometer dropped to 25°.  That one cold wave is estimated to have done $40,000,000.00 damage to oranges and other California crops.  There is probably no escape from the occasional recurrence of such destruction, to which in some form every part of the world is heir.

### Extending Agriculture Through Non-Irrigated Tree Crops

Dr. Coit, formerly Professor of Citriculture in the University of California, reports that large areas of land situated above the possibility of irrigation and having as much as twelve inches of rain may be developed as possible residence sites and also made to produce a valuable crop, if planted to the carob tree. He thinks there are half a million acres of

FIG. 302 — This hill on the Sorrento Peninsula, overlooking the bay of Naples, shows America what man can do when good climate and steep land are used scientifically. In the background every tree, even at cliff bottom and cliff top, is a grafted olive. The larger trees of the foreground are grafted English (Persian) walnuts, whose product comes to the United States. (Photo J. Russell Smith.)

foothill land in Southern California suitable for this crop. Dr. Coit has found some seedling specimens of this tree in California, which produced regular crops of beans to the amount of 600 to 700 pounds of beans per tree, per year. For centuries these beans have been used in Europe as food for stock. The beans resemble corn in chemical analysis and price. Dr. Coit is planting considerable areas of these trees, which he expects to yield four or five tons to the acre, with, of course, occasional failures.

Much of this same land might grow the olive, but with the present prices of $175.00 a ton for best pickling olives and $40.00 a ton for common oil-olives, olive oil cannot be produced in the United States in competition with European olive oil or with other vegetable oils. Olives might be grown on much of the rough land near the heads of alluvial fans. There are a few orchards in such locations now and the fact is suggestive.

## Future of Cities and Towns

Los Angeles is a hustling city. It boasts a greater expenditure for schools than any other city in the country. The organized promoters are working for the third epoch of the city's industrial history. First, the city was an agricultural center; then it became a tourist and residential center; now they want to make it a manufacturing and commercial center. Los Angeles needed a harbor. The people reached out with comprehensive plans. There used to be a little place south of Los Angeles called San Pedro. It had a breakwater and poor harbor. Los Angeles annexed San Pedro, dug out its muddy creek and made it a good harbor. The port was only 10% used in 1918 but by 1922 the people claimed that it was 100% used. Los Angeles had persuaded an amazing number of the shipping lines of the United States to call at its port, even Shipping Board ships which had service to one hundred important ports, including those on the east coast of South America. As a result of these lines Los Angeles is rapidly becoming to the trade of Western Mexico what Seattle is to the trade of Alaska. Because of these shipping lines to Mexico, Los Angeles boasts that when the señorita of Mazatlan steps forth on the street she looks like the models of the best Los Angeles stores, whence her clothing comes. The harbor of Los Angeles gives access like that of Boston or New York to the world highway to cheap ocean transportation, which brings the product from anywhere.

## The Imported Water Supply

For a decade the economic interests of Los Angeles have almost paid worship to a man named Mulholland. It is said that the city guaranteed a life salary of $10,000.00 a year to Mulholland because he was the prophet who foresaw a way out of the painful restrictions of limited water-supply. By 1900 it was realized that Los Angeles and vicinity could never pass a million population while depending upon the water supply within the basin. It was Mulholland, city engineer, carrying his levels over mountain and valley, who, in 1908, figured out the route for a 225-mile aqueduct which brought the water from the east side of the Sierras through a twenty-five-million-dollar structure of cement and steel. Through canal, siphon and tunnel; across desert and valley, and finally under the mountain, into the Los Angeles Basin came the precious fluid.

Now the city of Los Angeles could take care of twice as many people and was able to meet the demands of the Goodyear Rubber Company when it asked for a guarantee of 6,000,000 gallons of water per day, as a necessary basis for the founding of a new $20,000,000.00 factory on the Pacific Coast.

One of the conditions of the contract whereby Los Angeles got the Owens Valley water was that the water must all be used in Los Angeles; so Los Angeles promptly enlarged itself to make use of the water. At a single sweep it took in over fifty thousand acres of dry wheat land in the San Fernando Valley. This tract is now laid out with water-mains sufficient for intensive irrigation of fruit and vegetables. It is a kind of semi-suburb of fruit and poultry farms. People in Los Angeles think that this San Fernando Valley will become a city. Strange to say, it is figured that the same amount of water will supply this land whether it is used for residence or for irrigated agriculture.

Already studies for a future supply for the yet greater Los Angeles water-supply are in progress. One plan is to get it from the Colorado River. As a part of the Marshall plan the water is to come from the Kern River Valley on the west side of the Sierras, where it will be impounded in five reservoirs, passing through power-houses as it goes from reservoir to reservoir. The water will finally pass through the Sierras to the Mojave Desert in a tunnel thirty-three miles long, from which it will enter the Basin of Southern California by another tunnel nine miles long. The longest tunnel in the world is eighteen miles long but it does not daunt the Californians to anticipate making one thirty-three miles long, and there is no reason why it should.

Southern California will continue to be a desirable place of residence. It will continue to be a place for the health-seekers and it has great advantages necessary for becoming a manufacturing center.

### Power

In the early days the possibilities of manufacturing were greatly limited for want of power. Coal is so scarce on the Pacific Coast that there has long been regular import from Australia and from the Atlantic Coast, even in the days of sailing vessels around Cape Horn. Then came the discovery of oil in 1892. Oil became industrially important in 1894, and it has given the Pacific Coast the great boon of cheap power, and the great stimulus that comes from an oil boom, with its few big stories of fabulous wealth and its many little stories of lost savings, and cheap oil for everybody. Important fields have been found in the city of Los Angeles itself. This of course is very accessible, as is the oil of wells actually standing in the edge of the ocean to which pipe-lines must be built if an oil-field is productive. In 1922 Los Angeles and Orange counties alone produced 41,000,000 barrels of California's total product of 139,000,000 barrels. It is, however, almost appalling to think that

FIG. 303 — The oil-field game of checkers at $25,000 to $40,000 a move, and nearly all of them absolute waste so far as the American people are concerned. This double line of oil wells marks a tract boundary. Every time one owner put down a well his neighbor matched it to get his share of the oil. Question: Could there be a better argument for the nationalization of all undiscovered oil? (Courtesy U. S. Geol. Surv.)

California alone uses over 100,000,000 barrels at the present time, and we know, of course, that the life of oil-fields is short.

The oil has served, however, to give manufactures of this region a start. Already power comes from plants in the Sierras, and negotiations are under way to bring hundreds of thousands of horse-power from the Grand Canyon.

### Human Energy

Granted mechanical energy, the final question for this region is, will it continue to develop human energy? This point will be discussed in another chapter. The fact is that Southern California has thus far grown up on imported brains as well as imported capital. Most of the adults of this region were born in some other place. Most of its activities are being run by " a lot of imported Yankees still running with the energy that results from their having been wound up somewhere else." It is impossible to calculate the influence of a few dozen captains of industry who, having made themselves nervous wrecks somewhere east of the Rockies, came to Southern California to get well, and who have then turned their unusual and unused talents to the development of the region. This territory has another great advantage in that it has been settled by the progressives from other states. The " stick in the mud " has stayed at home so that he does not block the wheels of California progress — as yet. It is plain that Southern California has an assured future along her present lines. Just how far she will go is an interesting question which no one can answer today. It depends *so much* upon highly imaginative enterprises of large scale.

## *The North Coast Strip*

Three counties along the coast north of Los Angeles are commonly spoken of as being in Southern California. These counties, Ventura, Santa Barbara, and San Luis Obispo, have beautiful shore lines, cool climate, and picturesque mountains, with scraggy forests on their tops and pastures on their slopes. Between the mountains are valleys — dry, narrow, meagerly supplied with water for irrigation. Fruit is grown in the valleys and wheat and beans are grown along the shore as they are in the similar area at the south end of this region toward San Diego.

This area is not included in the big water-borrowing scheme of Los Angeles, and its limited resources are shown by the small population of the counties, 91,000 in comparison with thirteen times that many in the four counties to the south, which gained nearly twice as great a percentage in 1910–1920. (Fig. 291.)

Fig. 304 — The future development of California depends on things like this. The Don Pedro dam and power-house furnishing power and water to Modesto district. Note sparse tree growth on west Sierra foothills. Altitude at dam crest, 1480 feet. Height of dam, 283 feet. (Courtesy Modesto Chamber of Commerce. Art Craft Studio photo.)

## CHAPTER XXXI

### THE SIERRA NEVADA MOUNTAINS

THE Sierra Nevada Mountains,[1] seventy-five miles wide, extending north and southeast of the Great Valley of California, may in an economic sense be called the mother of the Great Valley, and also its nurse, for they give it both life and health. The prosperity of the Valley lies in the lap of the mountains. From them it must draw great draughts of water, the life of its fields, water and water-power for town, farm and city. From the ridges, valleys and peaks of the mountains also comes wood; and to an increasing extent they furnish recreation for vacation-seekers.

But water is the chief product. The Sierras have a long gradual western slope and a short eastern slope. This is fortunate indeed for the Great Valley of California. The long western slope gives space for the wringing of much moisture from the moist west wind. The big resource of the

[1] Physiographically, the Sierras and the Cascades end at the Feather River, so that Mount Lassen, the volcano, is in the Cascades. But this is an economic rather than a physiographic discussion, and this chapter deals with the mountains to the east of the Great Valley.

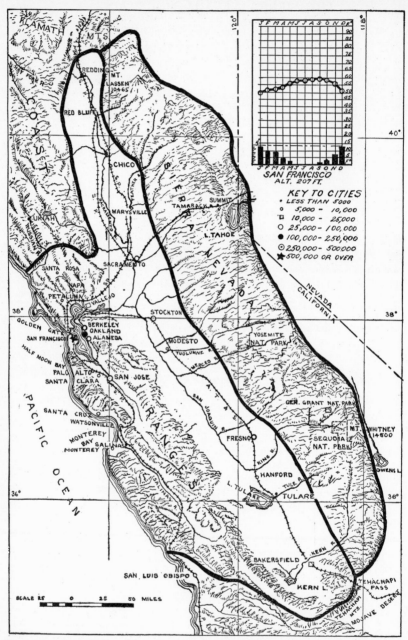

Fig. 305 — Map of Sierra Nevada and Central California regions. The graph shows the seasonal type of rainfall for both regions, and the remarkably even temperature of San Francisco.

mountains is rain, two or three times as much rain as falls in the Great Valley, a short distance to the west, and five or ten times as much as falls in the Great Basin east of the wind-barrier of the Sierra Nevadas.

The heaviest Sierra rainfall comes in the winter season, and, fortunately for the farmer's summer crop, much of this winter rainfall is in the form of snow. These mountains are deluged with snow. At Summit, on the Southern Pacific Railroad, elevation 7017 feet, the record for forty-four years averaged 419 inches of snow. On March 10, 1911, snow at Summit lay twenty-five feet, seven inches deep. Ten feet of snow is common over considerable areas of the Sierra Nevada Mountains. It often reaches the eaves of one-story buildings.

Strangely enough, forests survive even in these areas of heavy snow. Broad-leaved trees are broken to pieces, but a few varieties of evergreen

Fig. 306 — The plight of these one-story houses, buried in snow on the top of the Sierra, bespeaks abundant harvests for the Sacramento Valley in the ensuing summer. (Courtesy U. S. Weather Bureau.)

endure in a peculiar manner. Each winter the snow breaks off all side-limbs of these hardy trees. Each summer the trees push on farther up until finally they are little spindling bare rods, fifteen feet long, with small bunches of foliage at their tops.

Such snow is appalling to the railroad operator. To combat it he must put his railroads in houses — snowsheds — which cover thirty-two miles in the Sierra section of the Southern Pacific. Before the war, these sheds cost $42,000.00 per mile on single track, and $65,000.00 per mile on double track. Even though built of heavy timber these sheds are not absolute protection. The snow sometimes gets so deep on them that men must shovel it off, and occasionally the snow smashes through. They make crossings dangerous. They are liable to burn, and they also shut out the view.

The valley-dweller is so keenly interested in Sierra snow that it is news in California papers.  Much snow on the mountain in March means much water for the valley in June, while little snow promises water-famine.  The snow supply is far from regular.  Loose snow means quick melting and floods.  Tight snow means slow melting and long irrigation.

In the winter of 1912 Summit had 284 inches of snow.  Five years before there had been 602 inches.[2]  At best the mountain snow has usually melted and run off through the soil and down the streams by the end of June.  As a result many an acre of Great Valley farmland gets a June watering but can have none in July.  Plainly the farmers need water-storage.  The building of reservoirs in the mountains has already begun.  In 1923 the Don Pedro Dam on the Tuolumne River was finished.  It is 283 feet high (the famous Roosevelt Dam is 280 feet in height) and will give an all-summer water-supply to thousands of acres which had often gone dry during the latter part of summer.  This is merely one of many dams, and there will be more.

These mountains have for the Valley another creative gift, without which the Valley would lose its greatest industry — fruit.  The fruit industry of the Great Valley thrives because the mountain wall shuts out from the warm valley the cold winds from the interior of the continent.

## Water-Power

In addition to furnishing life and protection and wood for the farmer, the Sierras also furnish light and power to farmer and townsman alike.  Hundreds of thousands of horse-power are carried across the valley on wires from mountain power-plant to seacoast city.  Man cannot lift himself by his boot-straps, but water is more agile.  Water falling through a mountain power-plant generates energy that may lift water from the same stream a hundred miles away, put it on the land, and by so doing turn poor pasture into productive orchard.

## Zones of Vegetation

The long western slope of the Sierra Nevada Mountains gives room for changes in temperature and moisture to separate natural vegetation into clearly marked zones.  The first zone, up to 1500 feet, includes the rounded foothills of the mountains, grass-covered foothills because the low altitude has scanty rain.  In the moister spots are scattered oak trees.  In the forest transition-zone, 1500 to 3000 feet, better rainfall encourages scattered trees, especially yellow pine, the drought-resister.  Drenching rain between 3000 and 6000 feet makes a third zone of heavy timber, thick forest.  The fourth zone, 6000–8500 feet, has much rock-surface, with here and there poorer forest stunted by the cold at the upper limit.

[2] Snow facts from *Scientific American Supplement*, Feb. 5, 1916.

The high Sierras contain Mount Whitney, 14,501 feet, the highest peak in the United States. The tree-line on the dry east side is much higher than on the wet west of the mountains.

The heavy timber-zone is the home of the sequoia. This may well be called the Emperor of trees, for it makes the king of forests. Standing in the presence of these giants, you may be silent with a sense of awe and come to understand the meaning of the word "majesty" far better than by the view of kings. The presence and acts of kings after all show them to be strangely human, little unlike millions of others, but the sequoia towers in a class alone.[3]

These trees attain their great size by a combination of qualities. They have a thick, spongy bark, which holds water, rendering it almost fireproof. The wood is almost fireproof, insect-proof, fungus-proof. The trees stand in sheltered valleys where there can be no strong winds to break them down. Thus they can stand for millenniums and grow, and grow, and grow. The whole tree is not gigantic in proportions. The amount of foliage-bearing

Fig. 307 — The citizen who likes to think of the United States as a land of abiding riches and power should read and ponder the legend on this (rather small) Sequoia log.
923 A.D. Center
1066 Battle of Hastings
1215 Magna Charta
1492 Discovery of America
1620 Landing of Pilgrims
1776 Declaration of Independence
1860 Civil War
*When will we get another crop?*
(Courtesy National Park Service. Photo Ansel Hall.)

branches is no greater than that of many smaller trees. What they have actually done is to add rings of growth on their trunks, century after century, and become great collections of wood — overgrown trunks,

[3] Tree-lovers need to keep watch on legislation at Washington lest some of these groves be even yet handed over to private ownership — the axe of the plunderbund which never sleeps.

twenty or even thirty feet in diameter — which Nature has not at that point been able to smash down, as she does in nearly all other parts of the world.

## Volcanic Energy

This mountain barrier also contains Mount Lassen, our only United States volcano, which awoke in 1914 after an unknown period of slumber and blew off a slight eruption (for a volcano) of steam which swept away forests of trees six feet in diameter, with the same ease that a person can blow small bits of paper off a table.

In the locality of Mount Lassen there are many hot springs. Here an expert fisherman could catch a trout in one stream and swing him into the boiling water of another pool without moving. Far more important, however, is the possibility of using this earth, hot with volcanic heat, as a means of boiling water, making steam, and running engines, as the Italians have done for nearly a decade in Tuscany.

## Recreation

The Sierras have wonderful resources for the vacationist. Greatest of all these resources is the Yosemite Valley, although other Sierra canyons are almost as beautiful. These canyons are midway in the mountains, not in the foothills, nor yet at the crest. They were dug out chiefly by glaciers. Some of them are half a mile deep. The Yosemite, such a puzzle to the non-technical observer, was dug out of granite rocks. Granite usually has joint seams in it at short distances apart. Occasionally a place can be found where these seams are absent and the granite is just one solid piece. Such solid pieces are exceedingly resistant even to glacial digging. Such are the great domes at the sides of Yosemite Valley, which the glaciers could not dig. The valley floors are large areas of ordinary granite, with cracks through it at short intervals. In this granite the glacier could dig, much as a man with a pick might dig a stone wall to pieces. The valley walls and domes are granite monoliths which ice and water erosion could not destroy.

This slight difference in the rocks has made one of the most impressive of valleys. The wonder of the visitor is increased by the waterfalls of great height and properly famed beauty, produced by branch streams plunging over the edge into the master valley.

## Future

As population increases the water resources of the Sierras will be more effectively used, as one gorge after another becomes a water-storage reservoir.

The slopes of the Sierras should stay in forest. Much of the area is now a national forest, and none too soon, for the destruction by the axe and fire of heedless lumbermen and of cattle-men and sheep-men, primarily interested in grass, was indeed frightful before the nation took charge. Forest destruction is bad enough now, despite the best efforts of forest-rangers to fight fire. Nature alone with her lightning starts enough fires to make one wonder how there is any forest left. There is a record of one cyclonic disturbance with little rain and many lightning storms, which started seven hundred forest-fires in three days in the Southwest.

Some of the Sierra forests promise to remain forever inaccessible to the sawmill, under present conditions of moving logs, because they stand behind precipices over which the most ingenious American cannot handle saw-logs. But what choice opportunities these forests, untouchable by the lumberman, offer to the camper, with knapsack or burro train, who wishes to climb and camp in the forest primeval, to fish in rarely fished pools, and to be in the presence of untouched nature!

Fig. 308 — The rainless summer, with the relentless heat, sometimes makes the bed burn you in the Great Valley. It is a great commercial asset, for it dries hundreds of millions of pounds of fruit which goes to every hamlet in the United States, to every continent in the world. (Courtesy Southern Pacific Co.)

## CHAPTER XXXII

### CENTRAL CALIFORNIA

THIS region, which includes the Great Valley of California and the Coast Ranges, with their enclosed valleys, had the same early history as Southern California, and is therefore supplied with a great number of Spanish place-names. These, with the Spanish architectural influence, are about all that remains to speak of Spain.

Gold populated Central California with amazing speed. The city of San Francisco, now the metropolis of this region, is situated on a point of land. Its location it suitable for trade rather than for a self-supporting mission settlement. San Francisco, therefore, was not an early Spanish mission center, but was founded by an Englishman in 1835. After thirteen years it had only two hundred houses, and less than one thousand people. Gold was discovered. The amazing story spread abroad, and 90,000 people landed in a single year. By the fall of 1849 San Francisco had 15,000 people gathered from everywhere. The life there at that time will probably be remembered as the world's classic gold rush. A city was built almost overnight, in a place where it was difficult to build and in spite of great shortage of supplies. In this land of cattle ranches, there had been just enough agriculture to feed the few people. Then suddenly came these thousands of interlopers, greedy for gold and demanding to be fed, clothed and housed.

Ships rushed from various parts of the world with supplies, but no contract could keep the sailor from dropping overboard at night and swimming for shore. There he could dig for gold and get $10.00 and $15.00 a day like the rest of the gold-seekers, including most of the United States Army garrison. This was indeed a golden age, not only of income but of independence, for the gold was stream-gold, and to get it every miner had his chance. He took his pick, shovel and pan and dug for himself. A few of the less adventurous took the more certain jobs of running restaurants and engaging in transportation. There are records of a man and mule making $3000.00 a month. For a time three men ran a ferry across the San Joaquin River and made an income of $500.00 to $1000.00 a day by charging $2.00 for passage for a man and horse. The price was reasonable enough where wages and earnings were $10.00 to $15.00 a day, and ferries were few.

In San Francisco people lived in everything that could be lived in. They even made homes of piles of store-boxes, boards around three sides of an enclosure, or a piece of canvas on four sticks. A tent 15 x 25 feet was rented by gamblers for $48,000.00 a year. Bayard Taylor, who visited the country about this time, said that the effort expended to build San Francisco and to house 15,000 people so far from supplies would have created a comfortable city for 100,000 people on the Atlantic seaboard.

By 1853 the gold output was $57,000,000.00. By 1857 it had gone down to $49,000,000.00 and thereafter the exhaustion of the stream-gold was rapid. It was not many years later

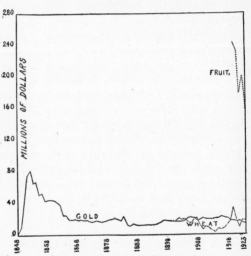

FIG. 309 — Gold is more romantic than fruit, but the figures of the value of California's products show things in their economic light.

that California gold was chiefly derived from mines of rich ore far back in the mountains where the mother lode had been found. Today gold-mining ($14,000,000.00 in 1923) is a minor industry of the state.

## The Coming of Oil and Fruit

Sixty years after the gold, oil was found. In the southern end of the Great Valley around Bakersfield, there was all the intense excitement of striking oil. The value of the yield of oil exceeded, for a time, the value of gold, when gold was at the peak. But the oil industry will never give California history the flavor of the famous gold-rush. The oil has been an important export and a great stimulus to manufacture in the coast cities, but it is not a great or enduring industry of the valley. Not oil, but vegetables and fruit now symbolize the Great Valley, once famed for the gold of its foothills, and their value far outranks that of gold or oil at their height. Fruit and truck, though less romantic than gold or oil, are *permanent* industries. At no other place in the world is there so large an area that can be depended upon to produce such variety and quantity of fruit as in Central California. California has had good reasons for boasting that she can grow anything that the temperate zone produces and subtropic crops in addition. Consider this fact of great variety of product, the big trees, and the great distances in California, the speed with which changes of industry have come, and we can see how it happened that some one said of California: "They cultivate, irrigate, exaggerate." Nature set them the example of exaggeration.

California, when she was an almost unsettled frontier, was the world's greatest gold producer. Now she is the greatest exporter of fruits and vegetables in the world. The change has indeed come with great speed. As I rode past the city of Modesto in 1922 I looked out and saw a great factory which, I thought from its size, must be railroad repair-shops. It was one of the several canning factories owned by a single company. An old man sitting by my side remarked: "I remember when that town was a wheat-field. When I came here in 1867 I used to see herds of a hundred antelope on both sides of the river here, and elk as late as 1870. The whole country was a cattle-ranch. Wheat began in 1868 and they sowed the grain after a chisel cultivator and harrowed it in and got good crops. Later they had to plow it. Then came the irrigation. Now that sandy land is worth $200.00 or $300.00 an acre. It will grow alfalfa, grapes, fruit and cantaloupes." [1]

This Great Valley lies between the Coast Range and the Sierras and is entirely surrounded by mountains save at the Golden Gate. The valley is 500 miles in length, twenty to fifty miles wide and includes more than 17,000 square miles.

## Great Valley Climate

What makes the Great Valley a fruit and vegetable region, with such an amazing variety of product? It has a climate much like that of Southern California — a warm winter, winter rain and summer drought. This is a wonderful climate for crops, if water can be had. The remarkable feature about Great Valley climate is the amazingly warm

---

[1] Between 1900 and 1910 the San Joaquin Valley, where irrigation was increasing, gained in population more rapidly than the Sacramento Valley and the rest of the state. In the next decade the boomers of Southern California made their section the most rapidly growing part of California.

winter, considering its latitude. The northern end, in the latitude of New York, is about as warm as the southern end which is in the latitude of Cape Hatteras. This happens because of the tempering effect of the warm ocean to the west, and equally important are the protecting mountain walls to the north and east which keep away the cold winds from

FIG. 310 — In honor of a belated winter rain. If the winter rains are delayed a downpour is the subject of general rejoicing, and is news for California papers, announced by headlines, editorials and cartoons. (Courtesy *San Francisco Chronicle*.)

the middle of the continent. As a result, oranges and olives grow in the northern part of the Sacramento Valley, in the latitude of New York. The city of Sacramento, in the latitude of Louisville, Kentucky, sometimes passes a whole winter without a frost. But after such a winter it once had a killing frost on May 7, showing that even here the weather is not absolutely reliable.

The Coast Ranges keep away the sea breeze, and in summer the Great Valley is *hot*, hot from end to end. At times the summer temperatures may reach 100° anywhere at all. At Fresno the average of the hottest part of the days for July is 100°, although the minimum night average of 64° shows the cooling influence of the dry climate. Bakersfield is hotter than Fresno.

The rainfall increases from five inches at the south to twenty-five inches at the north, because of the near approach to the center of cyclones which pass to the north of the state. Such low rainfall makes the country treeless except along the streams, and too dry for any important agriculture without irrigation, save wheat and barley. There are some parts, especially in the south, where even barley can be grown only in very rare seasons of exceptional rain. (Fig. 107.)

The hot summer is not so humid as the Mississippi Valley, but the heat blocks this region from even thinking of itself as a residence region for the retired Easterner. It is to be the home of those who have business there; and this business is, and will continue to be, chiefly agriculture — an agriculture where the farmer has difficult problems both in production and in selling. The energetic people have set world examples in the solution of some of these difficulties.

On the production side the farmer's great problem is the struggle for water and the study of how to use it most effectively. In many parts of the Great Valley the first comer got first use of water, the second comer got the right to the leavings and the later comers got the right to further leavings if there were any. As a result there is much land that may or may not be irrigated, depending on the abundance of rain that season. The total flow from the Sierra ranges amounts to about twelve inches for the whole of the valley surface. This is not enough. Most of it comes in the northern part of the valley, where the mountain rainfall is greater [2] than in the south. Fortunately the surface of the valley favors the farmer greatly in his problems of cultivation and irrigation.

## Surface, Soil and Waters of the Great Valley

The Great Valley was once an arm of the sea, like the Gulf of California. It has been filled, all save San Francisco Bay, by alluvial fans, a multitude of them. To get an idea of the construction of the valley, lay your hands on the edge of the table, spread out your fingers, let the thumb of each hand touch the other thumb and imagine a whole row of such hands. Think of the wrists as the mouths of canyons that have

[2] From King's River south, 5100 square miles produce 3,000,000 acre feet of water, while from the King's River north 7500 square miles of Sierra watershed give three times as much, namely, 8,500,000 acre feet.

spread out their fans like the fingers of your hand, each fan merging into the fans next to it. This will be the east side of the valley. A row of child hands on the other side will represent the smaller alluvial fans on the west side, built by the smaller streams from the less humid coast-ranges. Being water-borne, these fans are of soft earth material, easily plowed. Being water-borne, they are of gentle, even slope, easily irrigated. (Fig. 247.)

Near the master-streams, San Joaquin and Sacramento, the ascent toward the mountains is but five or six feet to the mile in the lower valleys, steadily increasing to twenty or thirty feet near the mountain. The soils get finer and finer as the distance from the canyon mouth increases, because of the declining carrying power of the water. The work of fan-building and its natural overflow is sometimes unfortunate for the farmer. Go back to the simile of the outstretched hands. Let an extra big hand represent the fan of King's River as it spreads out from the southern Sierras and you have the explanation of the fact that its fan, being higher, has cut off Lake Tulare from access to the San Joaquin. It is an inland basin. Sometimes it is a lake (1922), sometimes it is

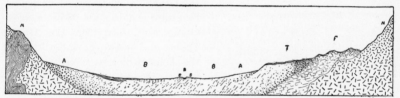

Fig. 311 — Section of the Great Valley of California as shown in a bulletin from the University of California. *MM*, mountains, old rocks; *F*, more recent sedimentary rocks, foothills; *T*, old terraces, parts of ancient fans now cut through by present streams; *AA*, upper slopes of fans now building; *BB*, flat lands near valley center; *R*, river; *SS*, natural levees which make river banks higher than *B*.

wheat-fields (1918–21), depending upon the rainfall. South of Tulare, in another basin, is Kern Lake. The waters which once supplied Kern Lake have been carried off to an irrigation reservoir and that lake is permanently dry.

In the lower Sacramento Valley the river, overflowing, has built natural levees, and its branches coming from the mountains have done the same, thus enclosing basins without outlet. These basins have been diked, ditched and pumped to make available their rich alluvial lands. Such are the bottom lands of Sutter Basin, American River Basin and others. In some places units of as much as 50,000 acres have been reclaimed.

An alluvial fan, with its layers of clay, layers of sand and a water-supply at the top, is a natural place for the accumulation of artesian waters, which underlie some 4500 square miles of the San Joaquin Basin alone. For a time it had flowing wells, but most of them have ceased to flow and 10,000 pumps were lifting water to the fields in 1923.

A layer of artesian water is really a river flowing along beneath the ground, and it must finally get somewhere. Usually, by way of pump and well, it gets to the irrigation ditch. But sometimes its disposal is not so useful. Where can artesian water go in the lower San Joaquin Valley, a great flat, with a horseshoe of mountains around three sides? There it is easier for the water to come to the surface than to flow away underground. This slowly moving water brings up with it the things it dissolved beneath the ground and they are left on the surface as the water evaporates, thus making " the great alkaline areas of the east slope of the valley trough." (U. S. Geol. Surv. Water Supply Paper 222, p. 26.) Thus tens of thousands of acres are at present virtually worthless. Some of the land is spoiled by hard pan, an impervious layer of clay.

### Great Valley Agriculture

This valley of warm climate, low rainfall, alluvial fans and artesian waters has not yet settled to a standard agriculture. Traveling through the Great Valley reveals a varied agricultural landscape. The railroad climbs northward from the Mojave Desert and enters the valley through the Tehachapi Pass. Near the summit of the pass, the valley widens and small mountain streams and wells irrigate pear orchards. Then for 3000 feet of descent not a drop of summer water is to be seen. The train finally rushes out beside a sandy stream-bed into a flat plain. The bright sun-glare on yellow, dead grass, almost blinding, stretches away for miles. Even up to the pasture foothills the dead grass stretches. But, far out in the valley, a dark green streak is seen. It is the green of irrigated orchards. There are miles and miles of orchards, then miles of wheat stubble, more miles of orchards,[3] and so on and on through county after county. There are stretches of wheat-land sometimes as far as one can see, with ranch-houses very far apart; stretches of alfalfa land, marks of the dairy industry; stretches of orchard land with houses close together, the mark of intensive agriculture; and stretches of pasture-land show where the

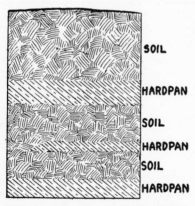

SOIL

HARDPAN

SOIL

HARDPAN

SOIL

HARDPAN

Fig. 312 — This drawing from a University of California Bulletin shows one of the troubles of California flat lands and the flat alluvial lands of all arid or semi-arid regions.

---

[3] A forest of oil-derricks bristles in the glaring landscape about Bakersfield.

land is of low value or where it is not yet in full production. Northward without a break the San Joaquin Valley merges into the Sacramento Valley with its miles of wheat and barley fields and the green areas of irrigated rice, alfalfa and orchards. On clear days the mountains are in view in both directions. From the center of the valley in summer-time one often sees beyond the low dry valley-bottom low, rounded foothills, often somewhat gullied and brownish yellow with stubble of barley or dry grass. The more distant foothills are cut by streams. Not so dry as the valley bottom, they are sharply topped with light grayish earth, dotted with the black green of bushes. Back of the foothills is the third

FIG. 313 — The scanty rain of the San Joaquin Valley leaves the hills along its margin treeless. The seeping moisture once fed scattered oaks in the lowland. Then the running water in man's irrigation ditch, supplied by electric pump from shallow artesian wells, made the sharp line of contrast along the foothill between brown pasture, worth $25 an acre, and black-green orange orchard, worth $1000 an acre. Palms are a common ornament around well-kept California homes. (Porterville, Calif. Courtesy Southern Pacific Co.)

horizon, dark green with forest. Across the country a column of yellow dust sometimes marches along in the center of a whirlwind, blending with the yellow of the wheat and strangely contrasting with the bright green of the irrigated fields.

The lack of uniformity in the use and the degree of intensity of use of the Great Valley agricultural lands results from the curse of big estates, a misfortune inherited from Spain, whose kings and royal governors handed out land in California and elsewhere to their friends in such blocks [4] that there are still original tracts of 100,000 acres in the valley

[4] This is very different from the democratic ideal that has dominated the American Congress in its attempt to give away homesteads of the proper size to support one family.

of California. Most of them have already succumbed to the high land-value and have been subdivided into small farms, a process which yields great fortunes for the holders of the big estates.

Particularly conspicuous among large estates is that of Miller and Lux. These men (now dead) were cattle-kings of the early days. They were men of energy, ability and prophetic foresight. They obtained old Spanish land-grants when land was cheap, got large tracts cheaply by reclaiming swamp and overflow land, and bought soldiers' scrip after the Civil War. The scrip entitled the holder to land, which Miller and Lux added to their holdings. So great was their accumulation of land that it is said that cattle could start at Bakersfield and march into San Francisco, sleeping each night on Miller and Lux lands. In one case these estates included the banks of the San Joaquin for sixty miles. The fore-sighted Miller and Lux dammed the river and turned the whole of its waters on their land, pretending thereby to irrigate and by that process to establish a claim to the whole river. As late as 1922 their assumption caused whole counties to pause in their development because, while the county needed irrigated land, and the water was in the river, the Miller and Lux claim (now Miller and Lux, Inc.) might finally get the water and thereby ruin any irrigation works that others should build. In 1922 a method of utilizing the river was finally agreed upon.

As these vast ownerships were usually much easier to operate as cattle ranches or wheat farms than they were under more intensive agriculture, large areas which might be irrigated are still (1924) being dry-farmed to wheat and barley.[5] Some of it is being plowed for the first time and large areas are still in cattle ranches, which are often overpastured.[6]

The artesian waters beneath the valley floor and the waters of many mountain streams flowing into the valley have made it easy to irrigate a portion of the Great Valley. As a whole, California increased her irrigated area[7] more rapidly (71%) between 1910 and 1920 than her population increased (44%). Much the greater part of this increase of irrigated land is in the Great Valley. Farmers in California and also in the East, having succeeded in producing crops, have another, and often a more difficult problem in marketing the produce. The programme of the Counties Convention of the California Development Board held

[5] The very low rainfall of 1923 caused the abandonment of half the wheat acreage of the state. Much of it was in the old bed of Lake Tulare, gone dry as a result of irrigation.

[6] The condition of these overpastured lands and much of the foothill country is such that they are thought to be capable of at least 25% improvement; hence the University of California has recently established a professorship of Range Management. " Probably no grazing region in the world needs the rehabilitating influence of a sound and far-sighted range-management policy quite so much as the ' blistered ' foothills of California." (G. Cecil Alter, *National Wool Grower*, June 1922.)

[7] California put it spectacularly by saying that the number of farms increased forty-four times as rapidly in California, 1910–1920, as in the rest of the United States.

at San Diego, November 12 and 13, 1915, started as follows: " The grower can produce almost anything in California and in unlimited quantities; but he cannot sell it at a fair price, and in some cases cannot sell it at all." Unfortunately that statement has much perennial truth in it, especially for the growers of fruits and vegetables, there and elsewhere.

## The Marketing Problem

Considering the problem of marketing in the Great Valley of California before the year 1900 — and to some extent the facts still hold —

FIG. 314 — Preparing fruit in one of many California canneries. (Courtesy California Packing Corporation.)

it might be said that there is nobody (less than 1% of the population of the United States) between the Sierra Nevada and the Rocky Mountains, so produce cannot be sold there; there is " nobody " in the Rocky Mountains; there is " nobody " in the Great Plains Region. So California, during most of her history, has been obliged to disregard her excellent agricultural opportunities and export hides, gold, wool and wheat. The horticulture of the last epoch could be developed only after a great struggle to overcome the difficulties of marketing somewhat perishable produce in places 2000 to 10,000 miles distant.

Because of these marketing difficulties the California fruit and vegetable business has been developed in specialized centers. Around Fresno the greater part of all the grapes of California are grown. Melons will grow nicely in many parts of the valley, but Turlock is the center of most of the acreage. Free-stone peaches are grown in one place; cling peaches are grown in another place. Santa Clara Valley is an almost continuous prune orchard. This centralization gives the grower the advantage of trained labor, for everyone knows how to work on the one crop

of the neighborhood and the town near by carries supplies. Every man
has the stimulus of keeping up with his neighbor and the growers can
get together and exchange information and ideas, for agriculture is
scientific and the " shop-talk " is interesting. Above all, the compact
group of growers has the great advantage of selling [8] through co-operative
associations, which alone have brought the fruit industry of California
from chaos to the highest degree of development to be found anywhere.

The raisin industry may serve as a type of Great Valley horticultural
localization and marketing methods. Fresno County is the second richest agricultural county in the United States. Its county-seat, Fresno, is
the capital of the raisin world. I rode out from the city eight miles to
the east, four miles to the south and back again. I estimate that 95%
of the land was in grapes, a veritable sea of grapes, and yet the county
planted 7000 acres more in 1921. (Fig. 202.)

Some of the vineyards are thirty-five to forty years old and are being
pulled up and renewed. Such continuous cultivation has resulted in
declining yields and low humus content of the soil. The county agricultural agent believes that increasing exhaustion of the soil will make
necessary an eventual agriculture with more provision for soil renewal.
Such an agriculture, according to the agent, will have 75% of the land
in grapes. The remaining 25% will be in alfalfa to feed dairy cows and
make manure to fertilize grapes.

For the present some of the raisin-growers have developed a fertility
method which permits 100% of the land of the farm to support grapes.
If there is water enough every alternate space between the rows of vines
is planted to sweet clover, a diligent gatherer of nitrogen and maker
of humus. In the other spaces between the grape-rows trays filled with
grapes are laid to dry. The following year the spaces reverse their
occupations and the mat of fertilizing clover is plowed under.

A typical successful Fresno grape-grower had forty acres in grapes.
He hired one man and had time enough left to participate in civic
matters.

[8] As examples of aids to selling, note the following quotations from the supplement to the 1918–19 Annual Report of the California Development Board covering
1920:

" Opening prices named by the California Almond Growers' Exchange for 1920 on
September 13th were . . .

" The Central California Berry Growers' Association, through whose auspices 90%
of the crop in Central and Northern California is marketed, estimate the following
production for 1920. . . .

" Opening prices, California Peach Growers, Inc., for Blue Ribbon Brand peaches
in cartons were named July 22nd. . . .

" Opening prices by the California Prune and Apricot Growers' Association on
August 12th were . . .

" Demand was strong at the opening prices fixed by the California Walnut
Growers on Oct. 7th. . . .

" California Co-operative Honey Producers' Exchange standardizes high-grade
white orange blossom and white sage honey under ' Sunni-Hunni ' brand."

Grapes will live and yield without irrigation, but irrigation will double the crop, so the grape-area is covered with canals and also with pumps. Pumps are needed because the surface water is exhausted early in summer, after the melting of the snows.

Here, as in many other places in California and elsewhere in the United States, water is often shamefully wasted because the proprietor can get

it by an old claim without paying for it and lets too much run on to the land, often spoiling the land by bringing up alkali.

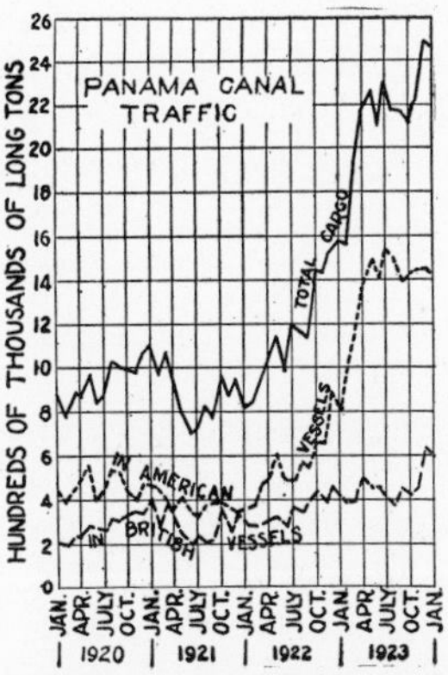

Since the grape is an old-world industry, Fresno County has attracted many foreigners. It is indeed a veritable melting-pot, if variety of races makes a melting-pot. Thirty-three different nationalities with more than 100 of each nationality were in that one county in 1920. Armenians led with 5000, and Mexicans and Italians came next with more than 300 each.

FIG. 315 — The very rapid increase in Panama Canal traffic promises that the waterway will henceforth play a great part in California trade.

The most conspicuous thing about the raisin industry is the work of the Raisin Growers' Association. It was formed when 50,000 tons of raisins were overstocking the market and making low prices and unprofitable farming. Then the growers began to standardize and to advertise. Who has not heard of " Sun-Maid

Raisins "? I saw the raisins going into bright red boxes with Chinese inscriptions on them.[9] Who has not bought " Sun-Maid Raisins " because of the advertising of this association? In 1922 the association had 14,000 members, or about 85% of the raisin-growers of the state.

Each member of the association dries his own grapes in the vineyard beside the vines. He brings or ships them to the Fresno raisin plant, a huge structure of concrete and steel which is owned by the association. This building has every mechanical convenience. The raisins are never lifted by human hands from the time the lug-box is lifted out of the truck or car in the receiving shed until the raisins go into the final package. The use of elevators, conveyors and specialized machinery is amazing. Men worked for years to develop a seeding machine, which takes raisins and, by a process similar to that of the cotton gin, puts the raisin in one place and the seed in another place. In the busy season 1600 people are employed and the factory runs eleven months of the year.

[9] " Ralph P. Merritt, president and general manager of the Sun-Maid Raisin Growers, is on his way to the Orient seeking new markets for California raisins." The *Washington Star*, March 12, 1924.

In a few years, advertising and standardized product had raised the demand for raisins from 50,000 tons to 200,000 tons a year. This campaign resulted in an increase of price for the consumer and in an increase of prosperity for the grower. Meanwhile a few growers and independent packers remain outside the association, profiting by the advertising without helping to pay for it, so that in the winter of 1921–22 the independent packer paid the independent raisin-grower $.09 to $.10 a pound, while the Association could only pay its members $.06 to $.07. The Association members were held in by contracts, most of which expired while this situation continued. Naturally many of them thought it would

Fig. 316 — Strawberries. No other part of the world has such wide expanses of truck crops as some of the flat lands of the Great Valley. The wooden flumes crossing the rows at right angles deliver water to each furrow. (Courtesy Southern Pacific Co.)

be profitable to drop out of the Association and sell to the independents. This short-sighted policy would of course soon have resulted in chaotic marketing and slump of prices. As is usual in such cases, the raisin-growers had great difficulty in holding their organization together, and virtually resorted to compulsion.[10]

[10] One who was there and knew the facts wrote as follows (spring, 1922):

"A well-organized campaign was conducted to 'influence' growers to sign up with the association. Indeed, the 'influence' was in the form of guns, rough boards, etc. It was a picnic to us who remember the old college days.

"As a result nearly 90% of the growers have signed up with the association for the next five years. The association will be able to keep the prices up and assure fair returns to the growers, for as certain as the campaign had failed the raisin-growers of this valley would again be at the mercy of the independent packers.

"The association has 80,000 tons of raisins in storage at present, and had the campaign failed, bankruptcy would have been in order and that tonnage would have been thrown on the market at once, whereas now it may be sold to suit the demand that will result from the advertising that has been done throughout the world.

"You will readily see that much has been at stake here recently, and if ever guns and rough boards were properly brought into play it was in this fight.

"The association is now advertising that if any grower in the Valley will make affidavit that he was coerced into signing he may be relieved of his contract with the

They held the organization together, but the spring of 1924 saw consternation in the raisin camp because of huge unsold stocks remaining from the crop of 1923. Co-operation is not an ultimate cure for over-production, but it may increase markets greatly and sell to good advantage.[11]

### The Truck Industry

The newest, the lowest, and the flattest land in the valley has been laid down by the Sacramento and San Joaquin Rivers, where they flow into the Bay. Indeed, most of this land was swamp a few years ago, flooded in the season of melting snow and covered with grass and reeds the rest of the year. This swamp-land was a haunt of waterfowl which divided their time between it and Alaska. The soil is black loam, often peaty, and of excellent quality for truck crops. Hundreds of thousands of acres have been diked, drained by pumps,[12] and laid out in some of the largest

Fig. 317 — The man who has abundant irrigation water, and whose land is very flat and water-tight below, can turn wheat fields of low yield into rice fields of larger yield. Near view of rice field, Sacramento Valley. (Courtesy Southern Pacific Co.)

fields of celery, asparagus, spinach, and other vegetable crops to be found anywhere in the world. As one looks down the straight rows it seems that they reach almost to infinity.

---

Association, but I am quite sure that the first one to make such a move will lose his vineyard, for the white people of this valley have their minds made up.

"Of course, it may be said that this manner of procedure is illegal and wrong. It is illegal, of course, but certainly ruin would have come to the raisin industry and many farmers and their families would have gone hungry had the recent effort failed. In view of that fact, it may not have been wrong to adopt the K. K. K. on these foreigners who for the most part are mighty poor citizens — indeed, most of them are not citizens at all."

[11] Fresno, Calif., Oct. 19. — It would be folly for a single additional vine of raisin grapes to be planted in California until present growers are assured a living, says Ralph P. Merritt, president of the Sun-Maid Raisin Growers' Association of California. Up to January 1924, he pointed out, the maximum consumption of raisins was 140,000 tons per annum. Heavy plantings from 1919 to 1922 brought the raisin acreage from 100,000 acres to 300,000 acres, with a normal production this season of 300,000 tons. He said the demand had been increased to 200,000 tons per annum and that the remaining 100,000 tons might be sold as by-products. (Special to Business Section, Philadelphia *Public Ledger*, 1924.)

[12] In the spring a little irrigation is sometimes needed. This is had by siphoning water over the dike.

Raise your eyes in the street-cars of Eastern cities and brightly colored advertisements will invite you to eat Del Monte canned peaches, Del Monte this and Del Monte that, including Del Monte asparagus tips. This branding and advertising is not a co-operative enterprise. It is the work of a private commercial corporation which has the advantage of growing fruit and vegetables on large areas of uniform soil. The result is standardized agricultural output on a large scale — large enough to make national advertising pay, as it does in the case of Sunkist oranges and Sun-Maid raisins.

The centralization of Great Valley agricultural production applies even

Fig. 318 — A part of San Francisco harbor and in the distance the Golden Gate — that romantic Mecca of the Pacific. (Courtesy San Francisco Chamber of Commerce.)

to rice, which has had a meteoric career in this territory. Successful cultivation, using Louisiana methods, began only in 1912. By 1920 162,000 acres were grown, almost entirely in the Sacramento Valley. The rapid rise of rice-growing here may be partly explained by the high yield, 52.8 bushels per acre, 1918–1922, in comparison with 38.7 bushels for the United States. In 1920 more was planted than could be harvested and the crop resulted in great loss (Fig. 72).

Most of the vegetable growers are tenants — Japanese, Hindus, Mexicans and other foreigners. In 1919, Portuguese were renting alfalfa land from the Miller and Lux estate and other estates, sometimes paying $25.00 to $35.00 per acre a year, and Japanese at Turlock were paying from $45.00 to $60.00 an acre per year for cantaloupe land.

## Labor and Immigration

It is easy to see how the immigration problem first assumed acute forms in California. The Oriental, willing to work longer hours than we, willing to live on less, could pay more for the land which he bought or leased. What race, what culture, shall own California? Shall it be the economically efficient Mongolian or the less economically efficient Caucasian? This question pressed for an answer. Since self-preservation is the first law of all nature, the answer is perfectly plain. It carries with it the explanation of the movement for the exclusion of the Chinese and Japanese, largely at the insistence of California and other Pacific states. It should be noted that the same feeling against the admission of foreign peoples whose standards of living are low has finally seized upon the whole country. The result has been the limitation of immigrants to numbers which we feel that we can absorb into the mass of our people.

The fruit industries of California have joined the lumber camps of the mountain in making manifest another social problem — that of floater labor. The grape-grower or peach-grower or apricot-grower who has no hired man at all for most of the year may need five or six helpers at harvest-time. He is very glad to see the floater or " itinerant " coming along in his decrepit Ford. He also, of necessity, welcomes the Indian, the Mexican, and the bum who beats his way on the freight-train. All these floaters are not particularly good for the social life of the rural community, where they are much more conspicuous than in the lumber-camp far away in the forest or in the segregation of city slums.

## The Central Coast and Coast Range Valleys

Between the Great Valley and the Pacific are several ranges of mountains (the Coast Ranges) and between these ranges are several small valleys, notably the Santa Clara and Salinas, south of San Francisco, and the Napa and Santa Rosa (sometimes called Russian River) Valleys, north of San Francisco. These smaller valleys have more rain than the Great Valley because they are nearer to the sea. For the same reason they have less heat, at least in some parts, and several very pronounced agricultural adjustments result. For example, most varieties of grapes do not do so well in the cooler air and their yield is less than in the Great Valley, so the grape-crop is unimportant in the immediate vicinity of the sea. The artichoke, however, loves the cool salt air and sea-breeze. It is therefore a coast-crop. From Half Moon Bay, thirty miles south of San Francisco, to Santa Cruz there is an artichoke center. Ten miles from Monterey Bay is Watsonville, which is by far the greatest apple center in California, because the coolness of sea-air makes an ideal apple climate, which is rather rare in California.

The Santa Clara Valley, which is really the southward extension of an

FIG. 319 — The growing vogue of the stewed prune and the stewed apricot has made orchards of these fruits fill the Santa Clara Valley, climb up its slopes and overflow into other sections of California. Panorama taken at plum (prune) blossom time. (Courtesy Southern Pacific Co.)

arm of San Francisco Bay, is the most productive of the coast-range valleys. It is near enough to the sea to have a summer temperature that rarely goes above 90° and winter temperature that rarely brings frosts. It seems to be a kind of fruit Paradise, as is proved by the great quantity and great variety of product.[13]

[13] ORCHARDS AND PRODUCTION, 1921, SANTA CLARA COUNTY

| | Acres | Tons | | Acres | Tons | | Acres | Tons |
|---|---|---|---|---|---|---|---|---|
| Apples | 1,200 | 10,000 | Prunes | 80,000 | Dried 60,000 | Limes | 10 | |
| Apricots | 7,000 | 25,000 | Plums | 11,500 | 37,700 | Oranges | 40 | |
| Cherries | 4,000 | 1,000 | Almonds | 400 | 200 | Figs | 40 | |
| Grapes | 10,000 | 40,000 | Walnuts | 1,000 | 300 | Pomelos | 10 | |
| Peaches | 5,000 | 25,000 | Olives | 250 | | Berries | Chests | 65,000 |
| Pears | 3,500 | 18,000 | Lemons | 200 | | | | |

VEGETABLE PRODUCTION

| | Tons |
|---|---|
| Sugar beets (for refineries) | 150,000 |
| Beans (canning) | 500 |
| Peas (canning) | 150 |
| Spinach (canning) | 1,000 |
| Tomatoes (canning) | 60,000 |
| Potatoes (fall) | 1,000 |
| Potatoes (early) | 1,500 |
| Other vegetables (cabbage, cauliflower, celery, artichokes, lettuce, squash, corn, onions, etc.) | 2,500 |

(Statistical Report of the Calif. State Board of Agriculture, 1921.)

The floor of the valley has fifteen to sixteen inches of rainfall and there is a rather rapid increase in amount on the foothills. With this rainfall, orchards can live without irrigation, but small applications of water are so profitable that everywhere the pump is busy, and as a result the water-table is sinking alarmingly. This valley is as exclusively devoted to orchards, chiefly prunes and apricots, as is the plain around Fresno to grapes. The people of the county frankly say that the young man of Santa Clara who desires to grow prunes must go somewhere else to do it. There is no more room in the valley. The automobile journey from San Francisco to San José, the valley metropolis, leads for a number of miles through suburban lands where there is no water for irrigation

Fig. 320 — The first settlers found the Great Valley a land of grass, interspersed with oak trees. Many of the oaks have been permitted to stay in the wheat and barley fields which cover large areas before the land is given over to irrigation, with its more intensive and speculative crops. Los Molinos, Sacramento Valley, a very characteristic and beautiful Sacramento Valley landscape. (Courtesy Southern Pacific Co.)

and which are therefore but little used for agriculture. It is a beautiful locality with its parklike expanses of oak trees. Then, within a space of two or three miles, orchards suddenly increase until the good cement road extends between solid masses of prune and apricot trees, often with a row of grafted English (Persian) walnut trees by the roadside for ornament. Many roadside booths sell fresh fruit, so that one need not be hungry if he has small change.

Ordinarily the weather is perfect for drying prunes. The fruit ripens fully, falls to the ground, is dried on the trays of the grower, and taken to the central plant to be sorted, graded, packed and sold by the association. Our prune export of seventy-five million pounds per year is a marvel for a country which imported most of its supply a generation ago. Once in the last twenty-five years there was a heavy rain in this valley before the prunes were picked. It was a calamity. The whole valley became a stench of rotting prunes.

San José, the center of the Santa Clara Valley, is one of the leading fruit cities of the world. Its canneries, dryers, and packing-plants have developed to such an extent that carloads of peaches and other fruit are hauled to San José from points as much as 200 miles distant. At the un- loading platforms trucks and trains are disgorging thousands of boxes of fresh fruit. It is rolled into the factory door in quantities that seem truly appalling. Hundreds of men and women are busy paring, cutting, skin- ning, scalding and packing.

Walking through the storeroom of one of these factories one wonders where on earth the people can be who eat so much canned fruit. Cases of it are piled tier on tier, and the trucks roll in more from the factory alongside. There is even an industry which thrives by manufacturing charcoal from the hulls of peach seeds, after the kernels have been used for the manufacture of oil.

In the process of making us eat their fruit and vegetables, the Cali- fornians have gone after us so systematically that we can scarcely open a national journal or lift our eyes in a trolley-car without seeing " Sun- Maid," " Sunkist," " Del Monte " or some other California trade-mark which has become so thoroughly standardized that we can know what we buy without looking into the can. The Santa Clara Valley people make us long for " Sunsweet " prunes. The Californians certainly make the sun do the work.

Opening into Monterey Bay south of San Francisco is the Salinas Valley, a hundred miles long and six to ten miles wide, with alluvial land at the bottom and rolling hills at the sides. Fruit, truck and alfalfa grow on the easily irrigated lowlands, grain on the slopes and pasture on hills.

The Russian River Valley, north of San Francisco, like the Santa Clara Valley, is much given to fruit, but the town of Petaluma has de- veloped a world's record with the standardized hen. The business of this town and its environs is as thoroughly dominated by chickens as the en- virons of San José are dominated by prunes. There are literally millions of single-comb White Leghorn hens, all alike, laying eggs that are all alike, which the association sells in New York at prices much above the average.

The handicap of scanty water resources of the Coast Ranges limits irrigation in these Coast Range valleys. This is reflected in the popula- tion. In 1910–20 the increase was less than one-fourth as great as that of the state as a whole.

### San Francisco

The gateway of all these Central California valleys is San Francisco. It was once the unrivaled city of the Pacific Coast, but it has now had the humiliation of being surpassed in population by Los Angeles. So keen is the rivalry between these two cities, each the metropolis and publicity center of its region, that hard indeed is the way of the California politician; for if he pleases Southern California he almost automatically displeases Northern California. Jest has it that there is on foot a movement to divide the state into two parts, the northern part to be called California and the southern part to be called Cafeteria. Certainly no other part of the world has better earned the latter name.

In comparing Los Angeles and San Francisco it can be pointed out that both lack coal and depend on the same imported supply. Los Angeles is a little nearer to the California oil fields than is San Francisco, but

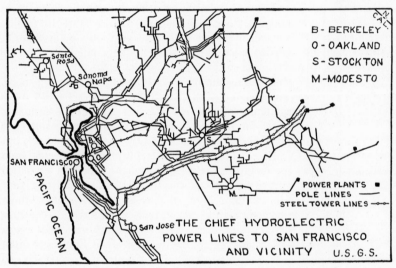

FIG. 321 — This map shows how San Francisco factories are children of the mountains.

this difference of accessibility is unimportant. Both cities depend upon distant mountain water, for San Francisco has been compelled to spend more money than even Los Angeles did to obtain a new water-supply from the Hetch-Hetchy Valley in the Sierras. Both cities depend upon distant sources of electric power. San Francisco is nearer to the water-power of the Sierras, but this is not a great deal superior to the Grand Canyon water-power sources for which Los Angeles is planning. Nonpartisan observers declare that Los Angeles is out-hustling and out-doing San Francisco at the present time and that the business men of Los Angeles are invading San Francisco territory. This is perhaps the natural result of the greater ability of Los Angeles to import outside talent, for there is no question that Los Angeles has the more pleasant

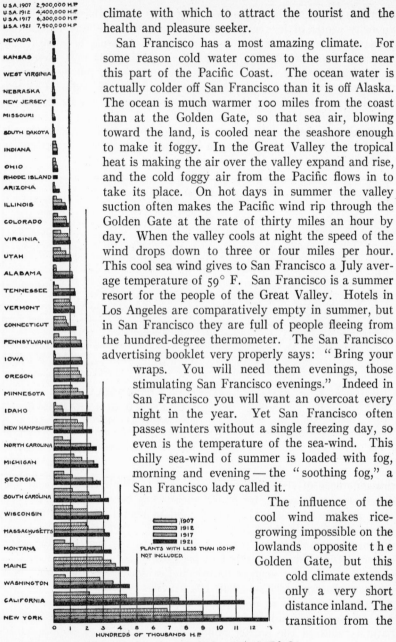

climate with which to attract the tourist and the health and pleasure seeker.

San Francisco has a most amazing climate. For some reason cold water comes to the surface near this part of the Pacific Coast. The ocean water is actually colder off San Francisco than it is off Alaska. The ocean is much warmer 100 miles from the coast than at the Golden Gate, so that sea air, blowing toward the land, is cooled near the seashore enough to make it foggy. In the Great Valley the tropical heat is making the air over the valley expand and rise, and the cold foggy air from the Pacific flows in to take its place. On hot days in summer the valley suction often makes the Pacific wind rip through the Golden Gate at the rate of thirty miles an hour by day. When the valley cools at night the speed of the wind drops down to three or four miles per hour. This cool sea wind gives to San Francisco a July average temperature of 59° F. San Francisco is a summer resort for the people of the Great Valley. Hotels in Los Angeles are comparatively empty in summer, but in San Francisco they are full of people fleeing from the hundred-degree thermometer. The San Francisco advertising booklet very properly says: "Bring your wraps. You will need them evenings, those stimulating San Francisco evenings." Indeed in San Francisco you will want an overcoat every night in the year. Yet San Francisco often passes winters without a single freezing day, so even is the temperature of the sea-wind. This chilly sea-wind of summer is loaded with fog, morning and evening — the "soothing fog," a San Francisco lady called it.

The influence of the cool wind makes rice-growing impossible on the lowlands opposite the Golden Gate, but this cold climate extends only a very short distance inland. The transition from the

DEVELOPED WATER POWER BY STATES-1907,12,17&21.

FIG. 322 — The growth of California product is conspicuous. (Courtesy Baum's *Atlas of U. S. A. Electric Power Industry.*)

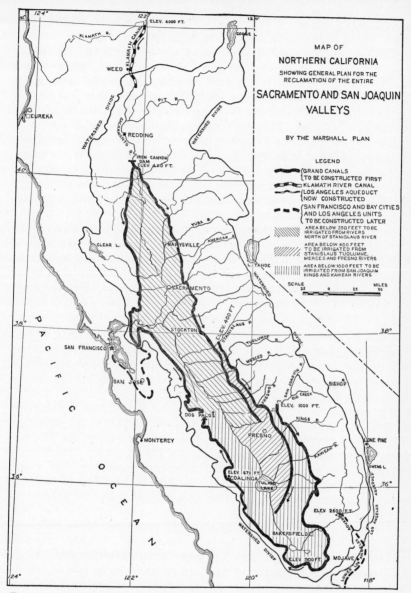

FIG. 323 — The Marshall Plan. Some say it is a pipe dream — but there is water going to waste, and there is land idling in the sun.

cold breeze of the sea to the hot sunshine of the valley is made so suddenly that it is like going from a cold cellar into a hot room.

This cool climate, limited to the small area in the immediate vicinity
of San Francisco, is claimed by San Franciscans as an industrial and
intellectual asset because it is a good temperature in which to work.  It
is better, they say, for mind and body, than the more even and warmer
climate of Los Angeles.  Such forces can work their full result only over
a long period of time.  They are constant, like the pressure of water.

Like Los Angeles, San Francisco is trying hard to develop her manufactures, but aside from food products she is still chiefly in the home-
supply stage of manufacture.  One of the local products of export is an
electric heater, a natural development of the local market in a town where
thousands of people want temporary heat for a part of the day.  Her
chief exports are foods from the valleys.

In 1906 San Francisco had the great misfortune to be wrecked by an
earthquake which destroyed the water-works, set the city on fire and
burned most of the business section.  With characteristic hustle San
Francisco was quickly rebuilt, and became a much finer city than before
the catastrophe.  Unfortunately earthquakes are a habit of nature much
less subject to control than fires.

### Future

When it comes to back country (hinterland) whose trade may support
a metropolis, San Francisco is far ahead of Los Angeles.  The mountain
rim is close to Los Angeles so that the acreage of possible agricultural
land in Southern California does not begin to approach the 12,000,000
acres of the Great Valley.

The greatest factor in the future of the Great Valley, and probably also
of San Francisco, is the question of water-supply for valley irrigation.
The state is making a careful water-survey as a result of the Marshall
plan.  This plan is a piece of daring constructive imagination which would
apply large-scale engineering to the water-supply problem.  At a cost
of $750,000,000.00 or $1,000,000,000.00, Mr. Marshall would have the
canals skirt the foothills of the valley on both sides and carry water to all
lands and cities (Fig. 323).

The plan provides for reservoirs above the canals and below the canals
and power-plants wherever they can be utilized.  Lastly, Southern
California must co-operate with Northern California in this plan.  Under
the Marshall plan the waters of the Kern River are to be held in a series
of reservoirs and taken under the mountains to Southern California;
perhaps that will enable Los Angeles to double her population again.
We can be sure that Los Angeles will co-operate, if Mr. Marshall's
statement is correct.  He says, " If Southern California does not join the
large scheme at the beginning and Kern River water is once used in the
Grand Canal system — a use which will affect the entire plan of con-

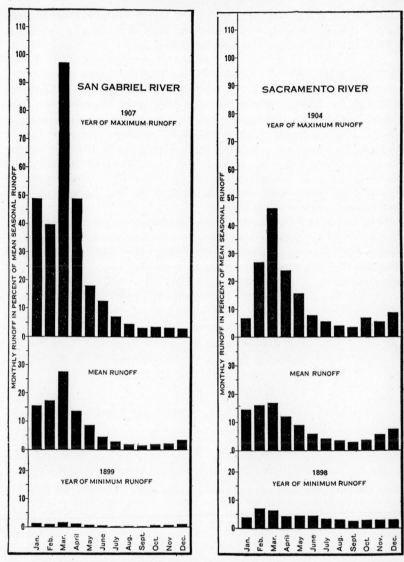

FIG. 324 — These figures, showing fluctuating annual run-off of particular streams, in which are a stern and alarming call to big action. (Courtesy California Water Resources Investigation, Bulletin No. 4.)

struction — then Southern California cannot get the Kern River water in the future." The necessity of great works in water-control is shown by this statement about the water-supply in California streams. "The total run-off in successive seasons there fluctuates between limits, one seven times the other, and the value of any one season lies at random between them." (*Water Resources of California*, 1923, Bulletin 4, p. 30, Dept. Pub. Works Div. Engineering and Irrigation, 1923.)

There is no hurry about the Marshall plan. The full utilization of California water will take decades of time, and the details will doubtless be different from those of the original plan. It would be a great calamity if it were made effective now, because there is no present need for it. California's greatest problem is to sell what she has, not to grow more. For example, on August 5, 1923, when the cantaloupe crop near Turlock was half harvested, the association stopped shipping to the East because the markets were being supplied by Delaware, Maryland, Michigan and Arkansas. Losses on California fruit and vegetable shipments, as on similar crops from other parts of the country, are very common, because the markets are often over-supplied.[14]

In 1922 the city of San Francisco raised $400,000.00 to advertise the resources and opportunities of California. This was particularly inspired by the fact that many counties in the Great Valley had completed large irrigation works but needed settlers to come and use the land and the water.

The various counties put out magnificent illustrated booklets, from which I quote:

" Monterey County, California:

> " A Heaven Favored Land,
> Bathed in Warmth of Summer Sun,
> Kissed by Ocean's Cooling Breeze —
> Beauty, Life, and Wealth in one."

" Stanislaus County, where water, sunshine and climate unite to make wealth, health and happiness."

" Alameda County possesses a temperate climate without variations of seasons in respect of temperature. Regarding humidity, little rain falls except during what in less temperate climes are called the winter months."

---

[14] The large carry-over of canned goods in the season of 1922 caused California canners to make a mid-July reduction of prices for best-grade cling peaches from $40.00 to $30.00 per ton; of freestone from $35.00 to $25.00 per ton. In the middle of August the failure of wholesalers and jobbers to place orders caused canners to stop buying even at these low prices. (From *Weather, Crops and Markets*, U. S. Dept. Agr., Oct. 6, 1923.)

Some of the results of this are shown in the following quotation from a personal letter from near San José, California, Sept. 5, 1923: "Your father has been helping John haul truck-loads of the nice cling peaches from a neighbor's ranch to feed the hogs. It seems such a shame to see them go to waste, but it was the same way with apricots. Price was so low it did not pay to pick them. Labor is so high they have nothing left." This sounds like New York or almost any other fruit district at times.

Markets for farm produce may be classified as depressible and gluttable. Meat, grain and cotton are depressible but fruit and vegetables are gluttable. California depends upon gluttables to a perilous extent.

The high rent of land and the high cost of land and irrigation equipment show that California is no longer a promised land for the farmer without capital. It seems plain that the Great Valley and lesser valleys will remain lands of agriculture with a tendency toward increasing the production of fruit, for which they are so well suited. The factories of the valley will be largely limited to preserving the fruit and vegetables,

FIG. 325 — A state-wide system of roads, perfect for the automobile, combined with varied and beautiful landscape, enable the traveler to see California with more thoroughness, pleasure, and ease than most states can afford. These roads pay good dividends to the stockholders, the California tax-payers, through the expenditures of travelers. The roads are often tree-lined. The native black walnut of the early plantings here shown is often being succeeded by rows of English walnuts. (Courtesy Southern Pacific Co.)

as is now the case. The more movable types of manufactures will continue to establish themselves around San Francisco Bay with its ships and its coolness.

Above the line of irrigation Sierra foothills and Coast Range foothills offer extensive possibilities for an increased yield through dry-land tree-crops — almonds, olives, carobs and perhaps other crops as has already been discussed in connection with Southern California. This will of course be much less productive than irrigated land.

It will probably be found that Californian agriculture will increase less rapidly in the future because it will have to await the growth of a demand from other parts of the United States and foreign countries. California's prosperity depends upon the ability of distant people to buy her products.

FIG. 326 — The cool, moist summer like that of Northwestern Europe makes the Puget Sound-Willamette Valley a great center of production for berries and small fruits. (Photo Asahel Curtis.)

## CHAPTER XXXIII

### THE PUGET SOUND–WILLAMETTE VALLEY

FOR three hundred miles north of the Great Valley of California, the Klamath Mountains spread themselves over all the country between the Cascade Mountains and the Ocean. Then, lying between the Coast Ranges and the Cascades, another Pacific valley appears, the Puget Sound-Willamette Valley. Like the Great Valley of California, it is composed of two parts: the southern Willamette Valley, and the northern, more humid, Puget Sound Valley.[1]

The region, like the Great Valley of California, has soils that have been washed into it from the surrounding mountains. Nevertheless the two valleys are very different because of climate. This northern valley has more rain than that of California, and enough of it falls in the summer to make the valley greener. (Fig. 19.)

### *The Willamette Valley*

For most of a summer day you may ride in an express train through the Great Valley of California. All day you will be looking at a brown

---

[1] For convenience in discussion, I make this term cover all the land between the Puget Sound and the Columbia River. Although a part of it is drained by the Cowlitz flowing into the Columbia, and a part by the Chehalis flowing into the Pacific, it is in reality one valley. It takes close observation to tell when you pass from one drainage-system into the next.

and yellow landscape with green patches on it — brown pastures, yellow wheat-stubble, green irrigated alfalfa and still greener rice-fields and orchards, and occasional whirling columns of dust. The next day, as the train goes north, you look from the car-window upon a green land-scape. The train has entered the Willamette Valley. This is a region of farms and also of trees. It may indeed be called a vale of spires, so numerous are the beautiful, sharp-pointed fir-trees. They shade the homes of the val-ley, mark the fence-rows and stand in clumps at such frequent intervals that one has the impression of being in the center of a clearing a few miles in extent and surrounded by the firs. Such is the result of a climate that is more humid and less hot than that in the Sacramento Valley. You see other signs of moisture in the ferns by the roadside, moss on house-roofs, fields of potatoes, stream-beds with water in them. (See general map.)

### Good for the Early Settler and the General Farm

The Willamette Valley is a good country for general farming, a much better country for the pioneer farmer than was the Valley of California. In its early history, the Valley of California had

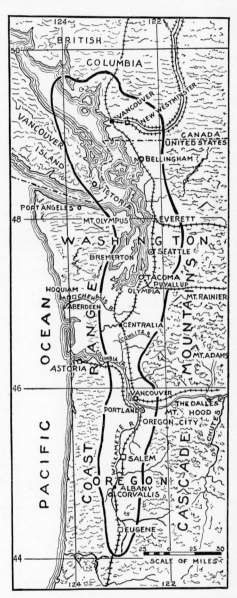

Fig. 327 — Map of Puget Sound-Willamette Valley. City symbols same as on other maps. It is a pity that we have so little level land in such a favored climate.

ranches and bonanza wheat. In the Oregon Valley the settler from Missouri, Illinois, Kentucky found a land that reminded him of his home-country. The floor of the valley was flat, much of it unforested or park-like — smooth, rich, easy to settle. The settler could grow wheat, clover, potatoes. It reminded him of the old home.

In the frontier days this Willamette Valley was the goal of the Oregon Trail, the longest of the overland emigrant trails. The trail started from Kansas City or Omaha and went up the North Platte to Fort Laramie, across the South Pass, down the Snake Valley, down the Columbia Valley, through the Columbia Gorge in the Cascades, and on to the good lands of the Willamette. The journey by wagon took five months. In 1842 a hundred settlers covered this route, under Elijah White, but they could not get their wagons through with them. The next year a thousand went through, cutting down thickets, chopping trees, filling gullies, making the rough semblance of a road over which they could with care take their wagons and drive their cattle. In 1844, 1400 adventurous souls made the journey; in 1845–1847, there were 9700.

These people were driven by many motives, one of which was patriot-ism. They wanted to settle and get possession of Oregon. Britain claimed it, and the popular cry in America at that time was "54° 40′ or fight." Some were Abolitionists getting away from slave neighborhoods. Business was bad in the East, and some were fleeing hard times. Those fleeing hard times were certainly successful. The country was good for wheat, so the settlers planted and sold wheat to the Russians, to the fur-traders and to the Hawaiians. Then came the California gold-rush and the people of the Willamette Valley rivaled the Californians in reaping the fruits of California gold. About half of the Willamette farmers sailed down the coast to California or rode down the old fur-trail through the mountains. Those who remained got even richer by selling produce to the Californians. They had a 10,000-mile advantage over their nearest competitors, the farmers of the Atlantic Coast. Fifty cents for an apple and prices of other crops on the same scale made fortunes for farmers in a year or two. This agricultural prosperity arising from its excellence for the all-round farm gave the Willamette Valley an early agricultural advantage over the Great Valley, which it maintained until the rise of the fruit industry in California.

### All-Round Agriculture and Fruit

But this valley of all-round excellence is no longer the giant of the Pacific Coast. It was good for the early settler, and is still good for general farming. The people boast that they can grow as great a variety of products as any part of the temperate zone, but actually the farming is of the Corn Belt type with the corn left out — general grain, grass, hay and live-stock farming. But in this agriculture there is no great staple which appeals to the world-market as does California fruit. But now the Willamette Valley is competing with California with fruit-industries that are increasing in importance. Prunes and cherries grow well in the Willamette Valley, although at rare intervals the greater rains of this valley may cause the prunes to burst upon the trees, and the cherries to rot before they are picked. The prunes are dried in artificial evaporators, in which temperature, humidity and circulation of the air are controlled, thus insuring a uniform product. The cherries are usually canned — an industry of increasing importance.

Because of its cool, moist summer the Puget Sound-Willamette Valley leads the country in the production of loganberries, raspberries, blackberries, and other small fruits. The greatest American centers of production of these fruits are scattered from Eugene, Oregon, at the south to Vancouver, British Columbia, at the north. Many factories prepare jam, preserves, and fruit-juices, and from Oregon to British Columbia the industry is growing. At Salem, Oregon, and elsewhere, many of these factories are putting California labels on the produce, which is then sold through California marketing organizations — a tribute to California leadership in the fruit-industries.

Unfortunately for this northern valley, these small fruits for which it has a natural advantage are not great staples, like the raisin, the prune, the canned peach, or dried apricot. In the spring of 1922 the loganberry growers from British Columbia to central Oregon met in Portland to devise ways and means to find a market for the 14,000-ton crop they expected that year, and they formed a co-operative association after the California model.

### The Puget Sound Valley

North of the Columbia River seems to be another world, the land of the gutted forest. Here the slightly greater rainfall of summer and the slightly cooler weather enabled the forest to take much fuller possession of the valley floor and the farmer has conquered only a part of the land. From Portland to Seattle and on to Vancouver, the railroad is ever in sight of forest, often running through the forest for half a mile or a mile at a stretch. Everywhere the forest flaunts itself or is flaunted at you — at the stations, sawmills; in the Cowlitz River, logs floating down to mills; on the railroad sidings, cars loaded with great logs that have come down from the mountains to the sawmills in the valley towns; beside the track old, abandoned sawmills tumbling to decay; in the fields, stumps — big stumps of the primeval forest, small stumps of the second-growth forest, rotting logs of various sizes; and everywhere at some point on the horizon are the burnt snags left by the fire that has finished up the wreckage left by the lumberman who culled the valley first before he went to the mountains. The dampness is so great that fire is not final and the forest tries to grow again. One sees young forest of every size — knee-high, house-high and higher. Some of the second growth is big enough to be a saw-log back East, but on the Pacific Coast it is still a contemptible small cull stick, for the lumberman there can still mine the mountain forest accumulation of past centuries. What a contrasting view one gets in the forested regions of western Europe! There clean lumbering, reproducing forests, and full use of everything are the rule and a forest-fire is as rare as a city-fire.

### Agriculture

In the Washington valley the fields are often full of ferns and give the appearance of half-abandoned New England. The railroad runs for thirty miles north of the Columbia River before it passes a 200-acre tract of land cleared and well-farmed. There is not another such tract along the road for many miles. Stumps, ferny pastures and strangely unused stretches of land are the rule, although there are some fully developed areas not far from the railroad, with dairy-farms, poultry-farms and berry-farms of great excellence. Near Puget Sound there are a few areas of well-cultivated land, but this land is nearly all easily farmed, recent alluvium, the recent filling of the Sound and only a few feet above tidewater. Some of this extra-good rich land is even below tidewater and has been reclaimed by dikes. On this flat, rich alluvium is an intensive agriculture of berry-farms, fruit-farms, and dairy-farms for the supply of the Sound cities. But just above these lands, on the bluffs, stand the sickening, burnt snags of the original forest. Struggling among the snags is the up-shooting young forest-growth, often fire-wrecked in its beautiful youth, in this land of the standing dead, in this valley of the would-be forest.

Why is this Washington valley so little used? The state wanted an answer to that question. A state investigation in 1922 found that agriculture in west Washington was at a standstill, that only 1000 square miles of land was improved, and that people were moving into towns almost as though it were New England. This investigation was one of the four results of the Washington State Land Settlement Association, formed in 1918, when we had the war-fever back of the attempt to enlarge crop-production. In addition to the survey the other results of this Land Settlement Association were a new land-reclamation law, a law intended to aid agricultural settlement, especially by ex-soldiers, and a constitutional amendment permitting the use of eminent domain on private land for reclamation and settlement. This new legislation permitted people to get hold of land easily. This was all to the good, but it dug no stumps, it hauled no lime. It was characteristic of methods in our Republic — a survey and then some new laws, whether we need them or not. In the succeeding five years no real results were in sight, but the problem was more clearly understood. It may be briefly stated as stumps and leached land of relatively low fertility but great possibility of improvement.

## The Difficulty of Clearing Land

First of all is the conspicuous problem of changing land from forest to farm. When the forest is gone from western Washington the land is not cleared. A host of stumps remains. It is estimated that it costs $150.00 to $300.00 an acre to dig and blast the stumps out and fill up the holes. On Vancouver Island uncleared land has a sale value of $50.00 an acre, but cleared land brings $250.00. If a farmer should pay himself wages for clearing it would often cost him as much as $400.00 or $500.00 an acre. Therefore he does not clear much land, and he does that in odd times. Because it is so difficult and so expensive to clear land, settlers on Vancouver Island in the midst of the forest that stands on potentially good agricultural soil clear only a little land and at once turn to the intensive crops of cheese, butter and berries for the jam factory. These enable a man to support his family on little land, if only he works hard. As an evidence of this intensive agriculture, one of the most conspicuous successes in the Puget Sound Valley agriculture has been in poultry-farming, co-operative egg-selling, after the model of Petaluma, California. It will take time to conquer the Puget Sound Valley stump-lands, and the task will not be extensively undertaken except under the pressure of greater need and desire for land. The United States has not yet reached that point. When the time comes that we need land as the people of Europe need land, the Puget Sound Valley, like the Willamette Valley, can become a rich agricultural district — a very rich and very productive district.

There are yet other handicaps to agriculture in the Puget Sound sections of the Valley. The land has been subjected to heavy rain for ages. As a result, potash and lime are leached out,[2] and the nitrogen content is low. Much of the soil-surface was carried to it by glacial streams which spread gravel instead of fine soil. Then, too, many of the clays, which are potentially rich, need a great deal of care in handling.[3]

This expense and difficulty of starting the farm is in great contrast to the ease of starting on the spring-wheat plains of Minnesota and Alberta, the newly irrigated lands of California, or the Columbia Basin. But when once conditioned, the Puget Sound lands have great productivity. In 1915 a fifteen-acre field in Island County, Washington, yielded (the national record) 117 bushels of wheat per acre.

[2] See section on Cotton Belt for leaching of soils in lands of heavy rain.
[3] " Such soils are likely to prove of high and very permanent fertility if properly tilled, but are generally very difficult to cultivate. They require large amounts of humus to keep the fertility in available form, to make the clay able to absorb and hold moisture, and to prevent puddling when wet and baking when dry." (Washington Agricultural Experiment Station, Popular Bulletin No. 7.)

## The Climate and Example of England

This Puget Sound Valley (the climatic duplicate of England) should some day rival England in wheat-yield, and the English wheat-yield is more than double that of the United States. In this future day of full use, the large yields of wheat will be only one of the crop-series in a rich agriculture of the Northwest European type. Barley, oats, potatoes, vegetables, beets and other root-crops (which are the European counterparts for corn-silage and which are recommended for this valley), in addition to fruits, will thrive and will support a dense population. Pastures in the wetter sections now outyield any pasture-land in America, except alfalfa lands, and support a thriving dairy industry. The same is true of the Willamette Valley, which, however, resembles west France more than it does England. In summer and winter temperatures Seattle is almost the twin of London, and Portland of Paris. (See page 635.)

## Cities in the Puget Sound–Willamette Valley

Even if it attains a full agricultural development, this Puget Sound-Willamette Valley is to be primarily a land of cities rather than of rural population. Already it has as large a proportion of city people as the State of Connecticut, and the city population is increasing much more rapidly than the farm population. Few places in the world offer better opportunities for the development of cities. The Puget Sound, a drowned valley, reaches a hundred miles inland. It furnishes a wealth of deep and sheltered harbors on which there is already a city population of more than half a million.[4] Portland (pop. 258,000), not favored quite so much by nature, has of late improved the Columbia so that her harbor is a rival to the harbors of the Sound.

Puget Sound is the natural place for the Alaska steamers to meet the freight-cars of the American railways. There is much Alaska talk and trade in Seattle. There is also much Oriental talk and trade, for this harbor, from one to three days nearer to the Orient than San Francisco, has several important steamship-lines in the Asia trade. The route is shorter than more southerly routes because the spherical shape of the earth makes the northern great-circle routes shorter than the southern routes. (Fig. 331.) Silk goes from Yokohama to New York in fourteen days. Therefore Seattle imported $205,000,000 worth of silk in 1922.

In Seattle, more than in any other Pacific city, one can feel commerce. From the city, on a high hill, you can look down at the Sound which spreads out at your feet like a map. Vessels and ferryboats can be seen coming and going. The harbor is so deep that ships could not

---

[4] Seattle, 315,000; Vancouver, 117,000; Victoria, 38,000; Everett, 27,000; Bellingham, 25,000; Tacoma, 96,000. Total, 618,000.

anchor on the bottom and anchoring buoys had to be installed. Nature
has made it very easy for Seattle to enlarge her harbor. Miles of new
water-front have been added in the midst of the city by the simple
device of building a ship-canal from the Sound to Lake Washington, a
long, deep body of water around which the city has grown. This little
canal made available better harbor facilities than London and Liverpool
have succeeded in building. These European cities have spent scores of

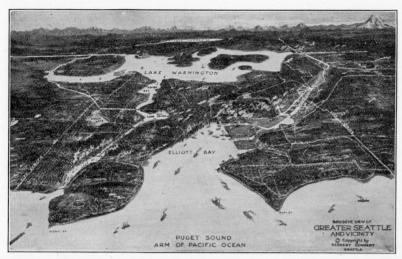

Fig. 328 — Lake Washington is a wonderful (almost) natural harbor. (Courtesy
Port of Seattle.)

millions of dollars in digging artificial harbors and in putting expensive
stone walls around them. Seattle is indeed fortunate.

Portland was for many years little more than a river port, because
the bars at the mouth of the Columbia prevented large ships from entering the river. During this time, Seattle took a long lead in ocean trade.
At last Portland became so desirous of being a seaport that she spent
$4,500,000 to deepen the river and build wing-dams to keep it deep,
while the United States Government spent $16,000,000 to build two
jetties at the mouth of the river. The jetties caused the Columbia to
dig a forty-foot channel through its bars.

The gap which the Columbia has cut in the Cascade Range makes
Portland the natural metropolis of the two agricultural regions of Oregon.
Portland is right in counting upon this gateway to the interior as the
factor which will give her a great trade — perhaps some day a trade
greater than that of Seattle, which is now her superior. A measure of
this advantage is shown by the proposal before the World War to dig a

tunnel under the Cascade Mountains near Seattle, to give Seattle better access to the Columbia Basin. The tunnel, which was to cost $50,000,-000.00 (pre-war estimate), was to be thirty miles long and to be used by all the railroads. This tunnel would save the Great Northern Railroad alone a haul of forty-eight miles and a climb of 2166 feet, and reduce the grade from 2.2% to 0.6%. As construction costs have nearly doubled since the estimate was made, it is plain that the Columbia Gorge used by the railways to Portland is worth at least as much as the cost of the tunnel — $100,000,000.00. Furthermore, boat traffic, cheaper than railroad traffic, can go far into the interior on the Columbia, but it must be said that the river, like most American rivers, is little used above Portland — an example of wasted resource because of unorganized transport. How long will we suffer such things?

FIG. 329 — The river harbor of Portland, Oregon, is becoming one of the great ports. (Courtesy Portland Chamber of Commerce.)

The significance of this Columbia gateway, particularly for future trade, is shown already by the appearance on the Portland docks of small quantities of phosphate rock from the great deposits of Utah and Wyoming.[5] It is easily possible that in decades to come millions of tons every year of this necessity of the land-wasteful modern agriculture will go out to the world through this natural gateway. Portland is the outlet for the Union Pacific system, through the Oregon Short Line. Seattle is the outlet for the Great Northern, Northern Pacific, and Chicago, Milwaukee and St. Paul. Vancouver, the second city of the Sound, is the outlet for the Canadian Pacific and, to some extent, the Canadian National. The Canadian trade will probably stay in Canadian territory, but now that Portland has good access to the sea there is no reason why the American trunk-lines should continue to spend millions to haul so much export freight over the Cascades, rather than down the Columbia Gorge to ocean-going ships at Portland.

[5] In June 1924, 2000 tons of copper was shipped from the vicinity of Salt Lake City to New York via Portland and Panama — a very significant episode.

It is unfortunate that this, like other parts of the United States, is a region of unbalanced sea-trade. The exports, lumber, grain, apples and wool, are bulky. The imports are few and light, silk being the largest single item. Thus, of the forty-eight ships that came from Britain to Portland in twelve months, only thirteen brought any cargo.

The commerce of Vancouver and Victoria is essentially like that of Seattle, Tacoma and Portland. In 1924, Vancouver had a feverish boom of grain-elevator building. Cheap ocean freights and higher railroad freights had caused the export via Vancouver of 22,000,000 bushels of Alberta and Saskatchewan wheat of the crop of 1922. Some of it went to England and Norway, and Vancouver is settling down to the idea that she will handle 100,000,000 bushels of wheat per year.

The city of Victoria, the capital of British Columbia, on the southern tip of Vancouver Island is said to be " less American than Vancouver, less Canadian than Winnipeg, less French than Montreal." It is also considered to be the most English city in Canada's " little bit of Old England on the Pacific Coast." Its climate is greatly like that of London (p. 635) and it is therefore easy to duplicate here the rich, green grass and beautiful gardens so characteristic of old England. The scenery among the islands of the Sound between Victoria and Vancouver is a vivid reminder of Scotch Loch Katrine and Loch Lomond, immortalized by Sir Walter Scott.

In one respect Victoria is American. As you approach the city by boat from Seattle you see columns of smoke and ask yourself if the city is on fire. Later you find that it is only a characteristic sign of the valley cities, the burners destroying the leavings of lumber-mills which endless belt-conveyors carry to these tall furnaces in endless streams.

City rivalries in this region are keen, as is usual between neighboring American cities. Seattle rejoiced because her ocean-tonnage reached the point where she surpassed San Francisco. Portland, now that she has her new harbor, hopes to rival Seattle. For decades Seattle and Tacoma boasted that each would outgrow the other, but the Tacoma slogan, " Watch Tacoma Grow," seems to have been meager in results. (See population figures.) For a long time these two cities had a ludicrous contest as to the name of an extinct volcano visible from both. In Tacoma it was called Mt. Tacoma. In Seattle it was called Mt. Rainier, and every properly careful person called it by those two names in the respective towns. A heartless board of geographic names ended this pretty quarrel and Seattle won, despite Tacoma's final bomb — a bill in Congress to name it Tacoma. Some one had found out that Rainier was a British officer who fought in our Revolutionary War. A mountain in *Washington* for *him? Sacrilege!* But the bill failed.

Seattle publicity interests revel in photographing the city so that Mt. Rainier, snow-capped, stands in the central background. Portland revels in having her picture taken with the cone of Mt. Hood in the background. Having been to both cities, I realize the importance of the photographs, because you can easily make a sojourn in both cities and see neither mountain. There is so much natural haze and cloud in winter and so much smoke from forest-fires in summer that both mountains are often invisible for weeks. It is, however, 'an interesting fact of human psychology that a thing seen occasionally is more appreciated than something seen constantly. These peaks give magnificent views, of the kind rarely seen from large cities.

## Manufacturing

As yet the manufactures of this region are mostly limited to industries supplying local needs — machine-shops, manufactures of local food-supplies, newspapers, wood-working establishments, and shipbuilding. The great importance of sawmills shows that manufacturing is in an early stage. The land is so new that manufacturing has not yet got to the more mature stage that would be indicated if the people were making chemicals, textiles or small machinery for export.

The simplicity of the industrial life of this region and the great dependence upon lumbering is shown by statistics of the leading occupations of Bellingham, one of the thriving smaller cities on the Sound: [6]

In this part of the United States the logs are so large, so much machinery is needed to handle them, that the larger mills are permanent, and often located on the sounds and harbors from which boats can carry away the export. The logs often come from the mountains by railroad and raft. The lumber-mill [7] on Puget Sound and other Pacific Coast lumber centers is a marvel of mechanical perfection. Logs six feet in diameter are whisked up into the mill by chains. Band-saws, running on

[6] Total number employed in manufacture .......... 3,373
Total number employed in trade and transportation .. 6,667
                                                       10,040

Total number of people employed in each of the leading industries:

| | | | |
|---|---|---|---|
| Manufacture of Lumber | 3,750 | Manufacture of Jellies and Jams | 200 |
| Fisheries | 500 | School Teachers (including Normal | |
| Coal Mining | 200 | School) | 448 |
| Manufacture of Cement | 230 | Street Railway | 150 |
| Woodworkers | 373 | City Employes | 154 |

[7] The scope of modern logging and lumbering enterprise is illustrated by the following. In January 1922, Mr. Long, a Kansas City lumberman, who had many mills in the South, and then in California, inspected a site at the junction of the Columbia and Cowlitz rivers. Twenty-two months later it had become the city of Longview, with 5000 inhabitants, daily newspaper, twenty-six stores, three modern hotels, paved streets, telephone exchange with capacity for 6000 phones. Work was nearly completed on the first unit of the lumber-mill, covering thirty-four acres. Also, work was nearly completed on the first unit, 1400 feet long, of the docks in the Columbia for sea-going ships. Work was in progress on the thirty-mile railroad from Longview to the company's 70,000 acres of timber. Full operation of the mill was expected to employ 4000 men in the city alone, giving it a population of 20,000 people. (Philadelphia *Public Ledger*, April 28, 1924.)

two wheels like a belt, rip off slabs and planks of any desired width or
thickness. These fall on rollers and glide away through the mill as
though floating on swift water. Suddenly they begin to move sidewise,
at right angles to their previous direction — they have been caught by
another set of rollers and are being carried off into one of the wings of
the mill. They are sawed and resawed. A single log makes many kinds
of lumber, according to the size of the pieces — beams, wide boards,

FIG. 330 — The accumulation of centuries making a roaring and fleeting prosperity. Nations would feel rich with the wood that goes up in smoke in
the big burner in the background, and so would the U. S. A. fifty years
hence. (Courtesy the Burlington Route.)

narrow boards, box-material, lath, shingles, little pieces to fasten bundles
of shingles together.

It is much like a Pittsburgh steel-mill in that men pull levers which
direct steam and electricity to do the work. For example, the man who
cuts boards into box-material sits on a raised platform, by a keyboard
something like that of a big typewriter. Each key controls a unit in a
battery of saws and rollers spread out in a row forty feet long in front
of him. Boards slide up onto the rollers. The operator touches a key,
and a circular saw, whirling on the end of a movable arm, drops on the
board and cuts off a worthless end as quickly as an axe would chop a
stick. At a touch of another key the cull-end whirls away down the
rolls toward the waste-chute. Another key is touched and a whole row
of saws falls upon the board, and changes it almost instantly into side-
pieces for a dozen boxes. The pieces slide away to their particular piling

place to be quickly followed by more and more and yet more as the man of quick eye and hand plays his keyboard, making the music of the saws.

## Forest Cremation

The lumber industry must continue its recent rapid development because the whole United States is increasingly dependent upon the Pacific Coast as its source of supply. Lumber, lumber, lumber — the great visible resource, the great pride and boast of Oregon and Washington. When I see their forests going up toward heaven in pillars of smoke, as every summer traveler sees them; when I see the land for a thousand miles shrouded in a pall of smoke, with every distant view shut out; when I am told by the Seattle Chamber of Commerce that Washington's lumber output doubled between 1908 and 1922, and that 65% of Washington's lumber is already gone, I can think only of the pirates in Stevenson's *Treasure Island,* who ate their breakfast and threw the remaining bacon into the fire, although they were without a ship on an uninhabited island. A leading Oregon banker seemed to regard forest-fires only as things which make the air hazy. He blandly remarked: "Burning helps it. The timber is as good at the end of three years burned as unburned, and easier to log. Dead cedar stands indefinitely. If fire follows lumbering immediately, the seed makes a good start after the fire; but if it waits two or three years, seeds start and the fire makes a clean kill."

A Puget Sound sawmill operator [8] whose plant I visited said, in discussing fires: "Oh, no! We only expect to get one crop. Ranchers come behind us and set fires to clear fields and their fires often get into the woods. It is all we can do to keep fires out of the green timber."

"Only expect to get one crop," and the fire that follows the lumberman burns up the good soil as well as the fine young trees that would make timber in twenty, forty, or sixty years! Thus the last lumber reserve of the United States is going; the next crop is being killed in infancy by those who take today's profits; and the East is just beginning to draw upon the West for its lumber. The price of lumber in the East has more than doubled in the first few years of the twentieth century. What will it do in the succeeding decades? We are now in a temporary period of exploitation, using lumber four times as fast as it grows.

Here we have a clear case where the individual sees and secures his

---

[8] Fortunately these men do not represent the general sentiment of the Northwest relative to forest-fires. We have here the contrast between the profit-taker and the wood-user. The State of Washington spends thousands every year for fire-prevention in forests. Educational campaigns for fire-prevention are conducted through posters and the public press; laws have been enacted regulating the use of fire in timbered areas by campers, tourists and others. Much has been done and much more will be done. It is needed — needed just as much by New York as by Seattle, for New York uses Seattle lumber.

dividends of this year so much more surely than the group (nation, state or city) can see and prepare for its future dividends. The whole world will soon suffer from this lumber destruction, but the valley cities that depend upon the industry will be the largest sufferers.

The climate that gave this region and its adjacent mountains the greatest forests in the world should give this region a permanent log-supply for the city industries, if man will take care of his forests.

### A Land of Cities

This region promises to become increasingly a land of cities because it has the resources of wood, water, commercial location, mechanical energy (power) and human energy (muscle and brain).

As for the wood, great mountain-areas can have no other rational use,

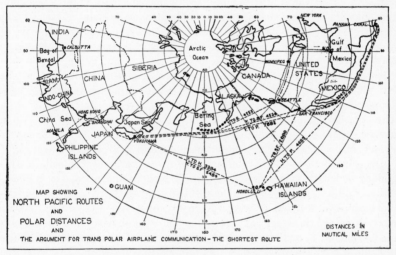

FIG. 331 — The map with the North Pole near its center shows surprising things about transpacific distances and the relation of land masses to each other.

and belong permanently in timber. As to water, there is no need for far-flung aqueducts such as that of Los Angeles. The Cascades and Coast Range, with snows, glaciers, glacial lakes, and a hundred inches of rain per year, produce within easy reach of the valley water-supply sufficient for many millions of city-dwellers.

The commercial location is not so good as that of England because the Willamette-Puget Sound Valley does not have an open road to populous hinterlands. Vast stretches of mountain and plain, or a long ocean route, lie between the Northwest and the populous East. However, the Orient with as many people as Europe has resources that are largely unused and ocean-freights are cheap, very cheap. The Panama

Canal makes it possible to bring pig-iron from Lake Erie or Pittsburgh by water at a cost which would make this distant source figure out finally at but a fraction of one per cent, in the cost of an automobile, machine-tool, or piece of cutlery.

As to mechanical energy, few realize the great riches in water-power within reach of this Valley. The Cascades and the Coast Range, along with the Rockies, which are now within commercial reach, give the cities between Portland and Vancouver access to many million horse-power [9] of hydro-electric energy. There is no location for power-resource in Europe or even in the Eastern United States to rival it.

## Human Energy

It takes brain and brawn, imagination and pushing power to build a city. In other words, it depends upon people, not only upon large numbers, but upon people having brains and energy. In the latter respect this region stands at the fore. The race is on between the two theories of energy, the cause of civilization. Professor Ellsworth Huntington, of Yale, astride his thermometer, says that civilization depends upon certain temperatures. Professor E. V. McCollum, of Johns Hopkins, astride his milk-bottle, says that civilization depends upon the amount of milk people drink. In either case the cities in this region are likely to win. The climate in this region is admirable for dairy products. If this region cannot supply enough it is but a short haul from the Columbia Basin or Fraser Basin, where farmers crave markets and land awaits irrigation.

Dr. Huntington's point about the climatic basis of civilization (explained at length in his epoch-making *Civilization and Climate*) is essentially as follows: A man feels more inclined to be active and he will do more physical work at a temperature of about 60° (55° to 70°) than when it is either colder or warmer. The second part of Huntington's theory is that a man's brain works best when the outdoor temperature is about 40°. This region has this temperature in winter. Look at the average temperatures for Seattle [10] and notice that in winter the temperature is right for the maximum of mental activity; in summer it is right for the maximum of physical activity. Dr. Huntington says also that man needs a moist as well as a cool climate. This climate is moist.

There is a third point to the Huntington findings; namely, man pro-

[9] *Water-power-Horse-power,* 1920

| | Developed | Undeveloped |
|---|---|---|
| Washington | 487,000 | 8,160,000 |
| Oregon | 295,000 | 6,318,000 |
| Idaho | 243,000 | 4,824,000 |
| Montana | 420,000 | 3,911,000 |
| British Columbia | 308,167 | 3,000,000 |
| | 1,753,167 | 26,213,000 |

(U. S. Geol. Surv. *World Atlas of Commercial Geology,* Part 11.)

[10] See table of temperatures on page 635.

duces energy best if there comes every few days a change in weather, either to warmer or cooler. Changes in temperature wake men up and make them want to do things. No one need suffer from monotonous weather in this region, because it is close to the path of the constantly moving cyclones which give it rainy or cloudy weather every few days, followed by clearing and cooler.

If Huntington's theory of climate ran contrary to the experiences of common men we might look at it askance, but everything that we know about history, including the industrial history of this and many other regions, confirms this theory. Shipbuilding offers an unusual opportunity to compare output in various parts of the United States. The whole nation strove to build ships with all possible speed during the World War. What did this effort show? At Philadelphia, the sun, shining upon the men and also upon the metal ships on which they worked, produced so much heat that the men had to stop work at times. The *Emergency Fleet News*, Sept. 19, 1918, devoted much space to accounts of sunstroke and heat-stroke in Eastern yards. Heat did not interrupt work on Puget Sound.[11]

In a winter number of the *Emergency Fleet News* there were articles about special quilted clothing for shipyard workers; the journal discussed the trouble Eastern yards had to keep their men from going to Southern and to Pacific Coast yards. Freezing weather is very rare at Portland, Seattle or Victoria. Snow-blockades, so bothersome from Chicago eastward, are unknown. Therefore, since shipbuilding is an out-of-doors industry, it seems but natural that this region should have won the shipbuilding records in competition with the rest of the United States, which it most emphatically did.[12]

I regard these Pacific Coast shipbuilding records as highly significant of a manufacturing future for the North Pacific Coast. It should be noticed that the Southern States and Southern California are not mentioned in these championship shipbuilding quotations. That too may be regarded as significant. The Puget Sound-Willamette Valley is undoubtedly less desirable than Southern California for fruit, recreation and rest; it is certainly less sought by the tourist and by those who have retired, and for good reasons. But it promises to be a work-center. The large and small cities that may be expected to arise along the water-fronts in the Puget Sound-Willamette Valley promise to be more important work centers than the smaller cool spots around San Francisco or the delightful region of Los Angeles.

[11] The evenness of the oceanic climate is shown by extreme temperatures. Seattle extremes are zero and less than 100° F. Over the mountains at Yakima they are —21° F. and 110° F.

[12] The yards of the Pacific Northwest took more pennants than those of any other section — in general shipbuilding (both steel and wood), in riveting, in welding, in framing wooden ships, in bolting. *Emergency Fleet News*, Jan. 1, 1919.

There is another man-and-climate theory that should be of interest to the people of this region. Dr. Charles E. Woodruff advances the thesis that the Teutonic blond complexion of English, Dutch, German and Scandinavian (as well as many of the qualities of this group) is due to the low percentage of sunshine in those countries. Since the section of the North Pacific slope central at Puget Sound has a Northwest European climate we may expect its people to approach rather than diverge from the Northwest European type. Dr. Woodruff puts it thus:

"There is one part of the United States which has almost the same dark, cold conditions as our original Aryan home near the Baltic — the northwest corner (of the United States) and southwestern Alaska. There are the cool to cold winters, short cool summers, plenty of rain, the sun appearing on the average of one day each week, some places having but fifty sunny days per year. According to popular theory the people here should be very badly off, but they are absurdly healthy, and as for the children they almost burst with rugged health. There is a remarkable similarity of this climate to that of Ireland, where blonds have flourished for thousands of years. The people are extremely comfortable in these fogs and rains, owing to the relief from the painful glare of the sun found in other parts of the United States. Indeed old residents often remark that they are not so comfortable on the bright sunny days as on the others. People who have made extended visits on business not infrequently go back for permanent residence, in the same manner and for the same reason that they return to the British Isles rather than stay in the United States.

"As an exception to the rule for the rest of the United States, there is an actual increased number of blonds in the cold, dark northwest part. The cities of Seattle, Tacoma and Portland are fairly bristling with them."

The facts of the weather, the theories about the weather and the facts of recent history all agree in pointing to Northwest Europe as the land which this region will tend to duplicate.

FIG. 332 — They grow for a thousand years and then in a single day they fall and go to the mill. Redwood logs. Humboldt Co., Calif., N. W. Coast (Courtesy U. S. Forest Service.)

## CHAPTER XXXIV

### NORTH PACIFIC COAST AND MOUNTAINS AND ICELAND

MOUNTAINS clothed with evergreen forest rise close to the seashore all the way from the Golden Gate northward to Prince William Sound at the head of the Gulf of Alaska. They often rise so sharply from the ocean that waves beat at the foot of a cliff, where there is not room for a road, or even for a man to stand on the shore. Everywhere these mountains are very often dripping with rain from the wet west winds. They are often wrapped in fog and cloud, and in the northern part are heavy with snow in winter. In the northern parts the mountain-tops are also heavy with snow in summer. In brief, this coast region might be called a long string of mountains, a long string of forest, a long string of fish and a long string of mines.

This North Pacific Coast has many surprises. The Japan Current, bringing warm water into the North Pacific, warms the air above it. The prevailing west winds blow this warm air over the land. Therefore, southern Alaska is warmer in winter than Washington, D. C., and at sea-level it has less snow. But the summer is quite different. To match the summer climate we must go to Scotland. (See table, p. 635.) Indeed, Kodiak Island, in the far northern Pacific, has a January temperature of 30°, the same as New York, and a summer temperature of 54°, only a few degrees cooler than the summer temperature on the west coast of Scotland.

There is much rain along the coast, sometimes as much as 80 to 100 inches a year. There are many rainy days. At low elevations are dripping forests; at high elevations the mountains are piled with snow, and snow covers much the greater part of the Pacific mountains in Alaska.[1] (Figs. 19, 107, 334.)

[1] Rainfall varies greatly even within this narrow region. One hundred sixty inches of rain fall each year at Ketchikan on the south coast, and also at Orca, at

The forest on the mountains of the Pacific Coast shows interesting adjustments to two of its enemies, cold and dryness. South of San Francisco Bay, the dry timber-line is ever ascending and the forests are pushed higher and ever higher up the sides of the mountains. From San Francisco Bay northward, the little rainfall permits forests at sea-level, but the cold of high altitudes makes the upper limit of the forest creep slowly down the mountain-sides. The ever-descending cold timber-line is 7000 feet in western Washington; 4000 feet at the south boundary of Alaska; 2500 feet at Cross Sound (latitude 58°); 300 feet at Prince William Sound, and a short distance farther to the west the cold timber-line reaches the ocean and the land is treeless at sea-level. Thence around all the rest of the coast of Alaska, the northern shores of British North America and down to Labrador, salt spray looks not up at the green trees.

## The Section with Agricultural Valleys

The warmer climate of the southern part permits agriculture in scattered mountain valleys. Agricultural valleys are chiefly in California and Oregon. By far the largest and most important valley of this region is the Puget Sound-Willamette Valley, which has already been described.

In California the Coast Range has many parallel ridges, with valleys between. Some of these valleys (Ukiah, Scott, Hay Fork, Trinity, etc.) widen out to considerable stretches of level land. These valleys have climates of great variety. If the mountains that stand between the valleys and the sea happen to be low there may be enough rain in the valleys for agriculture without irrigation. If the ridges are higher the valley floor needs irrigation, for which mountain streams will furnish the water. These little strips of agricultural land, usually from one to three miles long, are little islands of farm-land more completely isolated in a sea of mountains than islands are isolated in the sea. These isolated communities are chiefly busy with the Middle Western type of agriculture — grain and cattle. The valley farmers pasture their cattle in the near-by forests.

A number of these stretches of bottom-lands in all three states have rich pastures and a thriving dairy industry. As the small areas of level land are nearly all in use, it is fitting that extensions of agriculture here should be of the mountain type (see chapter on Appalachia). That mountain agriculture has begun is evidenced by a news item in 1921 to the effect " that the farmers of Humboldt County making European types of cheese had formed the North Coast Milk Goat Association and

the foot of the Chugach Mountains behind Prince William Sound. At Copper Center, in the Copper River Valley behind these same Chugach Mountains, the rainfall is but six inches, the lowest recorded anywhere in Alaska.

sent the secretary to Europe to buy pure-bred breeding stock." These
animals pasture on cut-over, burned-over hills, whose lumber is the chief
income of coast towns between San Francisco and the Strait of Juan
de Fuca.[2]

### Klamath Mountains

Between the Sacramento and the Willamette Valleys lie two hundred
miles of rugged territory called the Klamath Mountains.  This area is

FIG. 333 — The wood that remains after American lumbering would make the
Japanese or Belgians, or our own grandchildren, feel rich.  Fire has killed
a half-century of young growth which would have made a second crop.
Humboldt Co., Calif.  (Courtesy U. S. Forest Service.)

really an old plateau tipped up at an angle so that it is two thousand
feet high on the sea side and five thousand feet high at the base of the
Cascades.  The old plateau has been carved into a labyrinth of valleys
by three rivers, Klamath, Rogue and Umpqua, which drain it and flow

[2] " But there were men in these mountains, like lice on mammoths' hides, fighting them stubbornly, now with hydraulic 'monitors,' now with drill and dynamite,
boring into the vitals of them, or tearing away great yellow gravelly scars in the
flanks of them, sucking their blood, extracting gold.

" Here and there at long distances upon the cañon sides rise the headgear of a mine,
surrounded with its few unpainted houses, and topped by its never-failing feather of
black smoke.  On near approach one heard the prolonged thunder of the stamp-mill,
the crusher, the insatiable monster, gnashing the rocks to powder with its long iron
teeth, vomiting them out again in a thin stream of wet gray mud.  Its enormous
maw, fed night and day with the carboys' loads, gorged itself with gravel, and spat
out the gold, grinding the rocks between its jaws, glutted, as it were, with the very
entrails of the earth, and growling over its endless meal, like some savage animal,
some legendary dragon, some fabulous beast, symbol of inordinate and monstrous
gluttony." (*McTeague*, Frank Norris, Boni & Liveright, pp. 379–80.)

through impassable canyons, as they near the sea. In the lower courses of these rivers near their mouths are wide-open valleys containing thousands and sometimes tens of thousands of acres of arable land.

Much land in the upper valleys of these rivers is arable, but most of it needs irrigation. For this the water from mountain streams is near at hand. In the valley bottoms are many dairy farms. On the rolling slopes are wheat-fields and cattle-ranches. In the Rogue Valley an important fruit-center has been developed, with specialties of apples, pears and peaches. These valleys, at an elevation of 1000 feet or more, have a pleasantly cool summer climate. Medford, the center of the Rogue fruit district, has a July average of 53°.

### The Coast Range

The Coast Range in Oregon and Washington presents a bold front to the sea. In some places the cliffs rise from the beach. The west winds,

FIG. 334 — The deep snows of the Pacific mountains make one of the world's greatest water-power regions. Lane Peak, Tatoosh Range. (Courtesy Seattle Chamber of Commerce. Photo Asahel Curtis.)

blowing against these slopes, produce 138 inches of rain per year at 2000 feet. One hundred and fifty inches per year is estimated to fall higher up, although no observations have been recorded there.

Most of the rain falls on the Coast Range in winter, but some falls in summer also. The air is constantly damp, and the weather often cloudy. This wetness makes the forest almost impenetrable with undergrowth, and trees six, eight, ten, twelve and even fifteen feet in diameter stand thickly in the lower elevations where the higher temperatures prevail. Indeed, the Olympic Mountains, which raise snow-capped tops 9000 feet in elevation in plain sight of Seattle, are but partially explored, so thick is the forest, so damp the air, so drenching are the days. The same is true of Vancouver Island and the mainland north of it.

Little agricultural land is found near the shore except around Coos and Tillamook Bays, where the heavy rain and open winter make rich

FIG. 335 — "Rainier's Alpine Gardens are the most luxuriant and extravagantly beautiful I have ever beheld." — John Muir. (Courtesy Seattle Chamber of Commerce. Photo Asahel Curtis.)

pastures and important dairy centers. Such heavy rain is a handicap to agriculture, and it is therefore easy to see why agriculture has made small headway here. The lower lands at the west side of the Coast Range resemble western Brittany, Wales, Ireland and Scotland. These European pasture-lands, with less rainfall than western Washington, are almost without plow agriculture at the end of several thousand years of occupation by the white races.

## The Cascades

The Cascade Mountains, east of the Coast Range and north of the Sierra Nevada, extend from Feather River, near Mount Lassen, to the Fraser River in southern British Columbia. Like the Klamath Mountains, they are really a kind of wide plateau, seventy-five to ninety miles broad, in which many deep valleys have been worn. Unfortunately, the mountains give little water to the irrigation farmer, because most of the streams drain to the west where water is not needed. Very short streams with a sharp descent flow into the Great Basin and the Columbia Basin. Great is the climatic (rain) contrast between the east and the west sides of these mountains. On the west side there is a solid covering of the moisture-loving Douglas fir. On the east the dry timber-line is high and the forest above it is chiefly Western yellow pine, the tree of cool, dry land. The traveler can easily see this contrast at the Columbia Gorge, where, in the course of an afternoon's automobile drive, one passes from the western to the eastern slope of the Cascades. He sees thick forests of tall fir trees standing beside green fields on the western slope, but only brown mountains covered with low shrubs on the eastern slope, and no fields at all except a few which depend upon irrigation. I went through the Columbia Gorge on an August afternoon when the western mouth of the gorge w a s drenched by heavy rain, driven by the west wind. In the middle of the gorge there were showers, but the eastern end was dusty. The gorge is not wide enough to let much rain through. In winter, however, it lets enough cold come out of the interior to injure tender fruits for twenty miles around the western end.

FIG. 336 — " Sunset in the Canyon. An Oregon sun knows where to set, drenching all the pines with dragon-gold, tingeing to a still more mellow ivory the waving spikes of squaw grass, drawing the long cool shadows across the valley — and out there to the west somewhere the great Pacific has turned to a caldron of molten copper." (Courtesy Anthony Euwer, Portland, Ore.)

The people of Portland properly regard this gorge as a great treasure, both economic and scenic. It is indeed one of the earth's great sights, with its peaks, precipices, waterfalls, forested slopes, winding river, cloud effects and excellent automobile road.

Much of the Cascade surface is of volcanic dust, some of it so recent that in the territory around Mount Lassen dead forests stand buried in volcanic sand, while live, green trees grow in the top of the deposit. A string of extinct volcanoes several score in number reaches northward from the Sierras into Canada. Many of them are perfect cones, greatly beloved for their beauty, such as Mount Tacoma, 14,500 feet; Mount Hood, 11,200 feet; Mount Jefferson, 10,200 feet; Mount Adams, 10,500 feet.

One of these cones has performed an interesting geologic feat. Its top has collapsed, leaving a wide crater which is filled with melted-snow water, crystal-clear, and marvelously blue. This beautiful lake, called Crater Lake, is the gem of the Crater Lake National Park.

Equally beautiful but different in character is Lake Chelan on the eastern slope of the Cascades in Washington. There a great glacier dug out a valley-bottom to a depth below sea-level and then dammed up the lower end of it with gravel. Thus a lake much like the famous Italian Lakes filled the valley-bottom. One end is deep in mountain gorges and the other end is on the edge of the plain.

The Cascades and the Coast Range of Oregon and Washington are the homes of but few people, but they contain many lumber-camps where gangs of lumberjacks are slaughtering the mighty trees for the sawmills in the Valley towns. The logs are so big that many of them can be handled only by donkey-engines from which long cables are drawn out into the woods, so that the puffing little iron beast may drag the great log up to the side of the temporary railway upon which a single tree sometimes makes a train-load. The largest logs have to be split with dynamite because they are so large that no saws can saw them whole. When the crew moves on to another tract there is usually enough small timber left on the ground to make the thrifty Swiss or Japanese think that lumbering was about to begin. This small stuff is commonly licked up in the devastation of fire that usually follows the lumbering, killing the half-century or century accumulation of trees too small for saw-logs.

All of this mountain region should remain permanently in forest. It now contains over half of the rapidly vanishing saw-lumber reserves of the United States. Fortunately, thanks to the action of Presidents Cleveland and Roosevelt, and to a lesser extent of other presidents since 1890, much of the area has been set apart as national forests and parks. This indeed happened none too soon to save this region from destruction by fire. The State Forester of Oregon reports that in the year 1922 the 1800 forest-fires [3] outside the national forest burned over rather more

[3] Many of these fires are due to the careless tourist from other sections, often from the Eastern part of the country, who is careless with his camp-fires and cigarettes, or who has no conception of what devastation may result from such small beginnings. When fire-prevention is preached everywhere, so that it becomes a religion and is generally observed by the public, we shall have made great headway in reforestation.

than one-fiftieth of the total private forest-area of the State of Oregon.
When we appreciate the fact that a saw-log is from one to three hundred years old, a little figuring will show what this destruction means.
By letting her forests burn at the rate of 2% every year, Oregon will
have them all burned every fifty years — before they have had time to
produce a saw-log. Some areas may escape. Other sections may be repeatedly burned — one of the surest processes for making desert, the
green desert [4] (see chapter on Appalachia). It is indeed a pathetic fact
that even in an age of rapid settlement the forest-fire usually reaches the
forest of the frontier one or more generations before man needs to use

FIG. 337 — The wishes of the stock man have produced many a forest-fire.
Fire-killed " ghost trees " in a national forest on the Cascades. " Decades
ago the night sky was crimson with their light — burned enough to kill
but they did not fall. Year by year the bark flaked off and the gaunt
skeletons were left — the standing dead — unnumbered leagues of them
over the ranges everywhere." (Anthony Euwer, Portland, Ore.)

the forest products. Canada reports that nearly half of her total stand
of timber is in her section of the Pacific mountains and that the amount
thus far used for lumber is but one-seventeenth of the amount destroyed
in the same period by fires.

### Water-Power and Vacations

The heavy rainfall and the deep snow-fields give the mountains of
northern California, Oregon, Washington and southern British Columbia
the greatest amount of water-power produced by any similar area outside of the Congo Basin.

This water-resource of the mountains becomes the greatest material

[4] In dryer sections it is the red or brown desert of bare earth, witness many
sickening miles beside the Southern Pacific Railway in 1922 at the northern end of
the Great Valley of California.

asset of the near-by cities, not only for power but also for limitless supplies of good water.

These city populations also have riches of vacation-land in the mountains, where large areas are fortunately set aside as national forests.

### The Fiord Coast

From the north coast of Washington to the Gulf of Alaska the Pacific Coast is steep and broken. Instead of having agricultural valleys, the

Fig. 338 — Auto camping in the Coast Range near San Francisco.  (Courtesy Californians, Inc.)

coast is deeply indented by many long arms of the sea called fiords, a Norwegian word descriptive of the Norwegian coast, which is also a fiord coast.  These fiords were made by the gouging of glaciers and the sinking of the North Pacific coast.  Puget Sound, the first of these indentations, is just a valley into which the sea flowed after the land sank. Thus, the Coast Range of Washington, broken by the Strait of Juan de Fuca, reappears as Vancouver Island, and again in the Queen Charlotte Islands.  So much has the land sunk that some of these fiords are 2500 feet deep and have walls that rise steeply from the sea.  There are so many islands (the tops of sunken mountains) along this coast that the steamers bound from Seattle to south Alaska ports can take the sheltering route of an inside passage for almost the whole of the thousand miles.

This coast, with green forest below and snow-fields above, with cliffs from 2000 to 5000 feet high, fiords 100 or 200 miles long, is a rival in scenery of the famous fiord coast of Norway. It has even one thing the Norwegian fiords lack — glaciers.

The Pacific mountains, higher than the Norwegian mountains, have larger areas of snow-field, which pour vast ice-streams, millions of tons a year, down the mountain valleys and into the heads of some of the fiords, where they break off as icebergs. In some cases the ice-wall stands 300 feet above the water and ships cannot go too close for fear of being smashed or upset by the fall of a newborn iceberg. The greater ice-work

FIG. 339 — The location of Juneau, capital of Alaska, shows the scarcity of land on that deeply indented coast. (Courtesy Seattle Chamber of Commerce.)

of the glacial epoch is supposed to have helped to make the fiords, which are a feature of many coasts in this latitude.

Northwestward from Cross Sound, the Mount St. Elias Range, 50 to 100 miles wide, comes so close to the sea that streams from melting snows upon its slope plunge from the precipices and almost fall into the sea. When ships skirt the coast of this region one may stand on deck and look upon mountain walls that rise abruptly from the sea to a height of ten to twelve thousand feet. Such a coast is not to be found elsewhere in the world.

The fiord walls of southern Alaska are so steep, and level land is so scarce that even little towns of 3000 people, like Juneau, the capital, have difficulty in finding room for their houses. Prince Rupert, in British Columbia, just south of the Alaska boundary and now the terminus of a transcontinental railroad (the Grand Trunk), is experiencing great difficulty in finding room for grain elevators and railroad terminals.

It is even thought that some of the traffic may have to go to Vancouver, merely because there is not enough land level enough for a railway terminal and the necessary town.

### The Aleutian Islands and the Alaska Peninsula

The Aleutian Islands, the string of volcanoes which ends this Pacific mountain system, comprise the world's greatest volcanic laboratory. Unfortunately for those who wish to watch the processes, a mantle of fog hangs almost continuously over the scene. On one side of the islands is Bering Sea, whose waters are almost ice-cold, and on the other side is the Pacific, made warm by the Japanese Current. The contact of the warm and cold waters, similar to that off the Grand Banks of Newfoundland, wraps the Aleutian Islands in fog.[5] Ships may pass a certain island ten times and get only one good view of it. Some of the views are said to be marvelous, such as that of the Shushaldin Volcano, an almost perfect cone, snow-clad, standing 9000 feet out of the sea and brilliant in the rare sunlight.

It is said that the world's record for recent volcano activity is held by the eruption of Mount Katmai,[6] one of the many volcanoes which continue the Aleutian mountain range of the Alaska peninsula as the great arc of the Aleutian Islands.

### Fisheries

Before the white man came the Indians of the Alaska coast lived chiefly upon fish, in which the waters are rich. Smoked salmon from the annual run has been to them as much of a mainstay as corn to the Appalachian mountaineer. They even laid aside an annual supply of " butter," *i.e.*, the oil of a small fish, rich in fat. The Indians tried out the fat of the fish by putting them with hot stones into vessels of water. When the hot stones boiled the water the oil came to the surface.

The salmon is a remarkable fish. It has two habits that have made it an easy prey and a great resource to man. The first habit is that of being born in inland streams which have their sources in cold fresh water. The young fish remain here for only a few weeks; then they go out to sea where they stay until full-grown. The second habit which makes the salmon the easy prey of man is that of the adult fish, which returns to that same stream in which it was born to give birth to offspring and

---

[5] The life of the keeper of the lighthouse marking the Unimak Pass from the Pacific into Bering Sea at Cape Sarichef must require a remarkable psychology. He gets his supplies once a year by the supply-ship from headquarters at Ketchikan, 1300 miles away. Sometimes it is ten months between those spells of calm weather in which the mail-boats can drop his mail. Think what the radio may mean in such isolation.

[6] Fortunately, the absence of people prevented much or possibly any loss of life when millions, perhaps billions of tons of ash covered the area of townships. See *Valley of Ten Thousand Smokes*, National Geographic Society, Washington, D. C.

then to die.   For a long while there was a sharp controversy between fishermen and experts as to whether the salmon did or did not return to the same stream.   Careful experiments, made by marking the young salmon with tiny metal tags in their tails, have established the fact that the fish does return to the stream of its birth after having spent several years in places entirely unknown, during which time the salmon has grown from the size of a lead pencil to a huge fish, weighing ten, twenty, even fifty pounds.

Salmon affairs could not be better arranged to give man the opportunity of gathering a rich harvest of these treasures of the deep.   In returning to the streams of their birth s a l m o n come in great schools, and like a ship with an experienced pilot t h e y even follow a given course year after year in and out among the islands, deeps and shallows.   It is easy to catch these salmon, so easy that there is always danger of extermination. Salmon were once abundant in twenty-six rivers between New York and Canada.   Now they ascend only the Penobscot, and even there their numbers are few.   Alarming d e c l i n e  in numbers of salmon is now noticeable along the Pacific Coast.   The first commercial canning of salmon was undertaken in 1866.   The fish is so satisfactory in commerce that it was not many years before there were salmon canneries at the mouths of almost every river from California to Alaska.   Canned fish is one of the leading exports of this region.

FIG. 340 — Scooping up salmon, the cattle of the sea, near the mouth of an Oregon stream.   (Courtesy Portland Chamber of Commerce.)

A large cannery near the steep and almost landless mouth of a river in British Columbia or Alaska stands idle in the fall and winter.   In early summer a ship-load of cans and Chinese workmen arrives.   Then all is activity at this fishing-camp.   The fish are scooped out of the river with huge nets and put into tin-cans.   At the end of summer the ship returns, taking a cargo of canned salmon that goes to Seattle or San Francisco for distribution throughout the commercial world.

The temptation is the same as that of the mountaineer with the hens

(p. 233). Fish are so easy to catch and so good to eat. Why not can all of them? For practical purposes it has happened too nearly just that way, not only in the East but also in the West. On the Fraser River for many years the fishermen had, every fourth year, what they called the "big year." Enormous numbers of salmon came up the river in the big fourth year and laid their eggs. Enormous numbers of small fry swam to sea, to return again in four years to make another "big year." In 1913, the last big year, the pack in the Fraser River district, (partly American) was 2,392,000 cases. The next three lean years totaled but 805,000, or 35% as much. The "big year" averaged about $10,000,000.00 more output per year than a lean year.

It happened that railroad-builders blasted a big rock-slide into the Fraser, two hundred miles up the Fraser Canyon. The obstruction had such a form that the water rushed over and around it, making falls and eddies up which a salmon could not pass to the spawning-grounds. It was in 1917, the year of the "big run." Countless thousands of big salmon, having escaped the canning factories of the coast, swam up the Fraser River, pushed on by the cosmic urge that had carried their ancestors to the glacial lakes where they themselves had been born, where their ancestors had perished, and where they themselves were to procreate and die. The salmon swam until they reached the big rock-slide. They leaped up to get over the falls; they battered themselves against the rushing currents that coursed over the rock-slide, but all in vain. Countless thousands of salmon fell back, dead. The catch of 1917 was 559,000 cases; that of 1921 was 142,000. A few tons of dynamite would have cleared out the river. This was finally done, but not until the time of the big run was about over. This idiotic annihilation of the big year may well be called the greatest single calamity in the history of the fishing industry — the dashing away of an income of ten or fifteen million dollars. It was unworthy of the Turk or any savage race, yet we, the boastful Anglo-Saxons, did it.

Fortunately, Secretary Hoover (1922) placed some restrictions on the number of fish which Alaska salmon-canners may catch. The canners objected hotly, but it is certainly in the interest of public welfare that the restrictions should be made before the Pacific Coast salmon fisheries follow the fate of the Atlantic.[7]

[7] Dr. Barton W. Evermann, director of the Museum of the California Academy of Science, before the Pan-Pacific Commercial Conference at Honolulu, 1922, summarized the havoc that has been wrought along the Pacific coast of the United States as follows:

"Fur-seals — exterminated commercially from California coast between 1806 and 1820. Value of pelts taken, at prices today, $20,000,000 minimum. Alaska herd decreased from 2,000,000 in 1873 to 127,000 in 1911; now growing up under the protection of international convention. Southern sea-otter — exterminated commercially from California coast between 1812 and 1868. Value of pelts, at prices today, $200,000,000. Elephant-seal — exterminated commercially from California coast. Whales — extinction of between twenty-five and thirty species, once abundant the

The fishing industry affords one of the best examples of the appalling fact that we have skimmed the cream from this continent.  Fisheries, however, are much more hopeful than most cases of declining resources in that they can be restored if we give them a chance.  The sea is still there. We have not destroyed it, as we have destroyed the soil of corn-field, cotton-field and mountain-side.  Each female, laying thousands of eggs, has such powers of increase that it might be called super-geometric.

## The Seal Islands

From the Bering Sea part of this coast come nearly all of our fur-seal skins.  The home of these seals, the Pribilof Islands, affords a splendid example of the free resources of the sea, their use, their abuse, their possibilities.  In 1786, Gerasim Pribilof visited these islands (which were first sighted by Joan Synd in 1767) and discovered the fur-seal rookeries.

For ten months of the year these seals are at sea, sleeping on the waves and eating fish.  The breeding season approaches.  Male fur-seals crawl out upon the beach of the Pribilof Islands and begin to fight for beach-front space.  Finally it is settled among them by force of tusk and many wounds that each seal has a certain bit of beach-front.  In a day or two the females, heavy with young, begin to arrive.  The males meet them at the surf, grab them in their teeth, fling them over their shoulders to their own particular piece of beach.  This gives ownership to a harem.  In a few days the young, called pups, are born.  Then the females breed again.

For a number of weeks the young stay on the shore.  They are mammals.  The males do not eat during the breeding season, but the mother must feed to be able to produce milk.  She swims away into the sea to catch fish.  Sometimes she stays five days.  Owing to the three-mile limit in international law (which has made so much trouble with the Volstead Act), the United States Government was unable to protect the seals farther than three miles from the Pribilof Islands, so a ring of

---

length of the California coast.  Salmon — Sacramento, Columbia River, Puget Sound and Fraser River fisheries almost killed and still dwindling.  Alaska fisheries much diminished.  Halibut — Alaska fisheries now passing and must receive serious attention if to survive."  Here is what Dr. Evermann declares should be done if the sea life of the Pacific is to be saved:

" Extend the international convention of 1911, signed by the United States, Japan and Russia, to other maritime nations and modify the nature of the convention.  This for fur-seals, sea-otters and elephant-seals.  By international agreement declare a closed season on sea-lions, porpoises, whales and other species of sea-mammals pending a study of their habits by an international commission for investigating the national resources of the North Pacific, whose conclusions should form the basis for binding regulations.  Put into effect the regulations proposed by the International Fisheries Commission of 1908–09, to which Canada was ready to assent, but to which the United States objected.  If this were done the sockeye salmon fisheries could without doubt be restored to a condition equal to that of their best days." (*Public Ledger*, Philadelphia, Nov. 6, 1922.)

seal-ships surrounded the Islands, just as the rum-ships surround New
York Harbor.   Expert riflemen lay on their decks, shooting the mother
seals as they swam out to sea.   For every mother seal killed a pup
starved to death on the beach.   Of every six mother seals killed, five
had enough energy after the death-blow to dive, never to rise.   The
United States Government kept the seal islands as a monopoly, but the
Russian, Japanese and Canadian sealers reduced the number of seals
from 2,000,000 in 1873 to 127,000 in 1911 and threatened their extinction.   Then the United States Government made a treaty agreeing

Fig. 341 — Bull seals with their harems and pups on beach, Pribilof Islands.
Note the groupings. (Courtesy Seattle Chamber of Commerce.   Photo
Asahel Curtis.)

to divide proceeds with these nations if they would keep their subjects
away from the seal islands.   The treaty has been kept, with the result
that the seals are increasing[8] and giving a harvest of fur.   Seals are
polygamous; one male is sufficient for fifteen to fifty females (cows).
This ratio fits admirably into the needs of the fur-harvester.   The young
males or bachelors come back with their mothers and play around the
interior of the island during the breeding-season — tame as kittens, the
easiest possible prey.   Only these young males are killed and they are

[8] Their numbers doubled in less than five years.   In 1922, there were 604,000
seals on Pribilof Islands; 20,000 on Robben Islands (Japanese); 18,000 on Commander Islands (Russian).   In that year the United States Government took 31,000
pelts worth thirty dollars each.   Then sealskins went out of style, and Secretary
Hoover ordered a reduction in the kill.

killed before they have gashed up their pelts by fighting on the beach-
front.

There is an interesting by-product of the seal industry.  When the
seals are slaughtered for their skins the guards on the islands feed the
carcasses to blue foxes, and from the foxes a thousand or more pelts
are sold each year.  On one of the islands the foxes are so tame that
the housekeeper has to watch out lest they leap through the kitchen
window and carry off her dinner.

### Future Fisheries

Alaska waters are remote from large centers of population, and for
this reason the herring fisheries have been little developed, although it
is reported on good authority that the herring supplies rival in quantity
those which support the great fisheries of England, Scotland and Norway.  There are also important resources of clams, shrimps and other
fish.  Cod are reported to be abundant in many places, but they are
not caught to any great extent.

### Forests

Continuous dampness makes the coast of British Columbia and
Alaska thick with trees and still thicker with undergrowth — some of it
thorny, much of it yielding berries in great profusion, bush cranberries, wild raspberries, two or three varieties of huckleberries.  It is a misfortune that the forest-belt between the rocky shore and the snowy mountain is so narrow.  Yet the southern Alaska forests are estimated to have 100,000,-

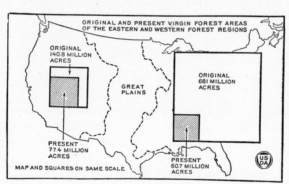

Fig. 342 — The wasteful old King Louis XV of France remarked, "After me the deluge."  It came.  What comes
after us?

000 cords of pulp-wood and to be able to supply permanently 2,000,000
cords a year, a third of the present paper-consumption of the United
States.  The wood-pulp product of British Columbia increased from 1000
tons in 1910 to 218,000 in 1922.  Nearly all of the southern Alaska forest
has been set aside as national forest.  One pulp-mill has already taken
a concession to work in it, and others will doubtless follow.  This North
Pacific forest has the great advantage of being almost unburnable because
of the humidity.

From Sitka southward into Oregon there is also some of the excellent Sitka spruce.   This wood, the chief timber of the Alaska coast, became suddenly valuable during the World War because its strength and light-ness caused its use for airplane construction.   Trees six to eight feet in diameter are sometimes found.

### Mining, Government Policy and the Alaska Railroad

In such country, almost without valleys or farm-land, usable resources must be those of the sea, the river, the forest and the mine.   As a source

Fig. 343 — Two thick seams of lignite.   Near Healy, 358 miles from the sea on the railroad to Fairbanks.   (Courtesy Healy Coal Co.)

of employment for man the mine has thus far been the chief rival of the fisheries.   The Klondike gold-rush of 1897–8 soon made the port of Skagway at the head of Lynn Canal the terminus of a railway which gave the shortest route to White Horse on the Upper Yukon.   The decline of the placer-gold output has caused a sad decline in the traffic to the boat-landing on the Upper Yukon, and Skagway is reported to be almost a deserted village.

Gold-mining in the coast district is on a more permanent basis.   Gold-bearing ore deposits have been found at eight places near the southern Alaska shores, and $8,000,000.00 of gold came out of them in 1922. Unfortunately, a great resource of gold was lost by the wrecking of the Treadwell Mine, across the sound from Juneau.   The yield of this enormous ore-body was less than $2.00 per ton of ore, but it was a profitable business and promised to yield for decades to come. The mine was being worked below the sea-level. Carelessness caused a break in the wall and in rushed the Pacific Ocean, with every appearance of permanent possession.

West of Mount St. Elias the Pacific mountain-region contains great riches of copper, gold and coal, the latter being estimated at sixty billion tons, a quantity equal to one hundred times the present annual product of the mines of the United States. In 1922, about half of the miners of Alaska were in the Coast and Mountain region. The coast mountains of British Columbia also have important mines of gold and copper.

The mineral resources of Alaska have caused bitter discussion. The question is, who should own them, and how. One party has claimed that the development of Alaska was being checked because the Government would not let people get at the resources. The other party maintained that giving the resources to individuals would result in trusts. The situation has doubtless been aggravated by our complicated government of Alaska, in which no less than thirty different bureaus have a hand. When Mr. Hoover became Secretary of Commerce in 1921, he found as an example of " red tape " that three different jurisdictions had to deal with Alaska bears.[9]

## Southwestern Alaska Grass-Lands and Brain-Lands

Perhaps Iceland, Norway, Sweden and Scotland furnish the best object-lessons for the ultimate future of the southern and southwestern coasts of Alaska. Recall for a moment Huntington's point that brain-energy is produced most abundantly at a temperature of about forty degrees. Mr. Vilhjalmur Stefansson, the Arctic explorer, who is of Icelandic stock, insists that Iceland is the supreme example of Huntington's

[9] The claim of Government interference with development of resources can scarcely be well supported when one considers the Alaska Government railroad. This railroad gives a sea outlet to Fairbanks, on navigable waters of the Yukon system in the heart of Alaska, a natural center for a possible future agricultural region. At present it is of much greater importance that this road passes through the copper, gold and coal section of the Copper River and Susitna valleys which lie in the Pacific mountains.

It would be an interesting story in the history of the Republic if one could know the full record of the lobbying and other political influences that resulted in the appropriation of $56,000,000.00 to build this railroad, which is 467 miles long. It was finished February 5, 1922. The Government has even built a hotel midway along its line, where passengers may stay overnight. The first full year's traffic operations brought in $718,000.00 and left a deficit of a million, to say nothing of interest on the investment. Perhaps enough big mines may be developed to make the railroad pay, but the usual history of mines is that they become worked out. Railroads have already been pulled up in the Colorado Rockies and elsewhere when mines were exhausted. To succeed, a road needs many people living along its line. Of this, the Alaska Railroad has small prospects for many years. The population of Alaska declined from 64,000 to 54,000 between 1910 and 1920. It may well be called a land of riches, but without people.

philosophy.   Reykjavik, capital of Iceland, has an average winter temperature of 32° and a summer temperature of 48°, never far from the average of 40°.   Dr. Stefansson says Iceland proves Huntington's theory because the Icelander leads the world in intellectual activity and productivity, as measured by, first, complete absence of illiteracy; second, the reading habits of the people; third, literary creations of the people;

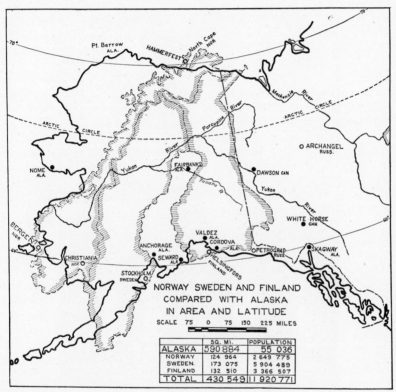

| | SQ. MI. | POPULATION |
|---|---|---|
| ALASKA | 590 884 | 55 036 |
| NORWAY | 124 964 | 2 649 775 |
| SWEDEN. | 173 075 | 5 904 489 |
| FINLAND | 132 510 | 3 366 507 |
| TOTAL | 430 549 | 11 920 771 |

NORWAY SWEDEN AND FINLAND
COMPARED WITH ALASKA
IN AREA AND LATITUDE
SCALE 75    0    75   150   225 MILES

FIG. 344 — The European countries are indicated by shaded boundaries and the European cities by open circles.

fourth, production of men of genius.   Enter an Icelandic farmer's home and you are quite likely to see books in Danish, German, English and French.   The farmer can read these books, though probably he cannot speak the languages in which they are written.   His choice of books seems to emphasize philosophy, history, science — material for thought, rather than light fiction which rarely provokes thought.

The thousand years of Iceland's history have given time enough for the good Norwegian stock to die out if the climate were poor.   Certainly Iceland's position in the world of intellect cannot be attributed to material riches. Six-sevenths of her total area of 40,000 square miles is bare lava-rock, almost uncrossable and utterly unproductive. The island is without forests, without coal. Peat is the fuel. The very cool summer temperature reduces agriculture to such a low figure that only 1.75% of the usable area is under cultivation — about three-fourths of an acre per capita, and that chiefly in hay, potatoes and a few turnips. There

Fig. 345 — Totem pole. Family tree of the Indians of the British Columbia coast, showing ancestry by carvings. It also shows *work* and *skill*. (Courtesy Seattle Chamber of Commerce. Photo Asahel Curtis.)

is not a field of grain, nor an orchard, for trees do not grow. The chief use of her land is for pasture. The people have about fourteen times as many sheep, about the same number of cattle, twice as many horses and twice as much hay per capita as the United States. Iceland's chief export is fish, which is three times as valuable as the sheep-product. Yet on this slim basis great mental activity is and has been maintained.

Southwestern Alaska (followed by Western Europe) has the nearest approach in all the world to this brain-energizing climate.[10]   The table of temperatures shows that the Alaska stations have lower summer temperatures than the European stations.   If any one is inclined to dismiss the Icelandic example as proof of climatic influence on brain-power, he has but to look at the temperature facts and the achievements of Norwegians, Swedes and Scots.   The influence of these people in the world, historic and present, is stupendous when compared to the influence of the same number of people in Egypt, and many other places that it might be invidious to mention.

TABLE SHOWING TEMPERATURES ON EAST COST OF NORTH PACIFIC AND EAST COAST OF NORTH ATLANTIC.   °F.

| | Jan. | July | | Jan. | July |
|---|---|---|---|---|---|
| San Diego | 54 | 63 | Lisbon | 49 | 66 |
| San Francisco | 49.5 | 57.3 | Bordeaux | 40 | 68 |
| Eureka, Calif. | 46 | 55 | London | 38.7 | 62 |
| Seattle | 39 | 63 | Paris | 36.5 | 65 |
| Astoria, N. Ore. | 40 | 60 | Edinburgh | 38.2 | 58 |
| Port Oxford, S. Ore. | 46 | 55 | Brussels | 34 | 63 |
| Portland, Ore. | 38 | 67 | West Scotland | 38 | 57 |
| Western Vanc. Is. | 39 | 55 | Bergen | 34 | 57.9 |
| Vancouver | 35 | 63 | Reykjavik | 32 | 48 |
| Sitka, Alaska | 33 | 53 | Stockholm | 26 | 62 |
| Kodiak I., Alaska | 30 | 53 | | | |
| Cordova, Alaska | 31 | 53 | | | |
| Valdez, Alaska | 21 | 52 | | | |

The Alaska stations having the closest resemblance to Iceland are Cordova, on the shore of Prince William Sound, and Kodiak on Kodiak Island.   The results of this temperature likeness are shown in the treelessness of the region beyond Prince William Sound, where wild grass six feet high [11] replaces the bushes and trees that clothe the coast from Prince William Sound to San Francisco Bay.   Cattle have run wild and thrived on Kodiak Island and also on Kenai Peninsula.   The United States Government has an agricultural experiment station at Kodiak Island.   It is working with some success at the problem of producing a good milk cow by crossing the fur-bearing (almost) Scotch Galloway breed with the heavy milk-producing Holstein-Friesian.   These animals are pastured for six months and in winter fed on grass silage.[12]   Good hay or grass silage can be made and potatoes, turnips, cabbage and other vegetables will ripen there.[11]   Apparently, the makings of another Ice-

[10] Alfred H. Brooks, Chief of the Alaska Division of the United States Geological Survey, states that the Indians of the South Alaska Coast were good workmen and had a well-organized social order.

[11] Bulletin No. 82, Bureau of Plant Industry, *Grass Lands of the South Alaska Coast*, C. V. Piper, 1905.

[12] In 1923 the Pacific Live Stock Company shipped from Seattle to Unimak Island, southwest Alaska, 2000 sheep of the Romney breed.   These sheep were of New Zealand ancestry, the breed having been developed in the Romney marshes in England.   Thence they spread to the wet, cool pastures of both hemispheres — New Zealand, Falkland, Alaska, etc.

land are complete, especially when one considers the good fishing resources of the region.

Manufacturing along the Alaska shore is possible if it should ultimately
prove desirable. The Alaska Railroad penetrates a coal field, and there
is much water-power in the mountains back of the coast of Alaska and
British Columbia. It is, therefore, possible that, as generations go by
and industries are more closely adjusted to natural resources, the North
Pacific Coast, along with Scotland, Iceland and Norway, may be a region
where industries that require the greatest amount of brain-power and
continuous thought will concentrate, just as other classes of industries
move toward cheap labor, or abundant fuel or some particular resource.

It must not be forgotten, however, that this land at the present time
is almost unpeopled, and that no such development as is here indicated
has yet made the first beginning. But resource is resource, and the
most important of all resources are those that make men. It is very
important in this age of science, machinery and changing society that
man should have plenty of brain-power. In a static society muscle
might be of much greater importance.

FIG. 346 — Good bunch-grass and spruce on Scottie Creek, longitude 141°, latitude 63° 55'. Land said to be not alluvial. (Courtesy Natural Resources Intelligence Service, Ottawa.)

## CHAPTER XXXV

### THE YUKON VALLEY — THE AMERICAN FINLAND?

THE great arc of the Yukon Valley, sometimes called the Yukon Plateau, is as long as the distance from Buffalo to Saint Paul, from New York to Chicago, from London to Venice. This vast area actually contains less people than are riding at any moment of the day in the subway cars of New York City.

Along the streams and lowlands and part way up the slopes the land nearly everywhere is tree-clad, but because it is so far north the trees lose heart as they climb the hills, and dwindle first to bushes and then to brush, and finally they give way entirely to grass and herbaceous plants of the Alpine type which often cover the slopes with red, blue and yellow flowers. There are thousands, tens of thousands of hilltops alternately snow-covered, grass-covered and flower-decked throughout this great area of 150,000 square miles. The rolling hills are interspersed with the lower valleys of the Yukon and its many branches. In some places these valleys widen out into large flat lands, some of which are several thousand square miles in extent. The largest, the Yukon Flats, is one hundred miles long and forty to one hundred miles wide.

In Europe similar lands in Sweden, Finland and North Russia are populous with farmers. Hence the name, the American Finland, given by those who hope for an agricultural future for the Yukon Valley. In Asia similar lands with fairly similar climate, as in Manchuria and Siberia, have been the seats of the settlement of the farmer and the stock-grower, but in America this Yukon has produced little but gold, and a very disproportionate crop of romances. (See Jack London, Rex Beach and many other writers of Alaska stories.) (Fig. 344.)

## Climate

The Pacific mountains shut the Yukon Valley away from the heat and moisture of Pacific winds, so the Yukon rainfall is light. The mountain barrier also makes the Yukon Valley a land with more heat in summer and more ice in winter than the Pacific shores, whose climate is tempered by the ocean. This region is so far north that the summer sun shines almost continuously. This cumulative sun-work has actually produced a temperature of 100° F. in the shade at Fort Yukon, at the mouth of the Porcupine River. That is a very high temperature for a place north of the Arctic Circle. The great heat helps to bring forth the summer crop of mosquitoes which make life in this region such a torment. The Arctic winter does not kill their pestiferous eggs. The record of a bear killed by Alaska mosquitoes seems to be fairly well authenticated, but it is explained, not by the size of the mosquitoes but by the fact that they stung the bear's eyelids until the eyes swelled shut with inflammation: the poor blinded creature had no chance to recover, escape, or eat, and the mosquitoes pestered the bear to death. (Fig. 18.)

The long day and the almost continuous sunlight of summer are balanced by the long nights and the almost continuous darkness of winter. In the Arctic winter the stored-up heat of the summer sun escapes from the earth, and since so little comes from the sky the thermometer goes down, down, and yet down. The lowest temperature observed on the continent was −86° F., at the mouth of the Pelly River, about 100 miles southwest of Dawson City. The popular belief that extreme cold causes correspondingly heavy snowfall is incorrect. Pennsylvania has more snow than the Yukon Valley, but it is a common occurrence for Alaska streams to freeze to the bottom. Then the watercourse bursts out through some weak place and flows along the top of the stream, freezing as it goes, and piling up great masses of ice. The stream, when choked with ice, ever seeks new courses, somewhat like a river building up a delta. Many a prospector while camping on the banks of a frozen river has received an icy surprise. He has pitched his camp high on the bank; and some night, when he has safely got his blankets all tucked in so that the 40° below zero bites him nowhere, he has suddenly received notice while asleep of a change in the course of the river. The wandering ice-water has flowed into his tent, soaked through his blankets, and struck his warm body with all the suddenness of a shot.

## Indians and Fur

Before the white man came, a few Indians occupied this country. They lived chiefly on the salmon which they caught in the streams and smoked at the season of the summer run. The Indians " cached " the smoked salmon high up on poles, where dogs and wolves could not reach it; then they went off in search of berries to dry for winter food and to hunt caribou and deer. The meat of these animals furnished food, and their skins were necessary for clothing.

The respect that these natives had for the property of others is an interesting social response to an environmental fact. The Alaskan native would starve to death beneath the " cache " of dried fish belonging to some other, but absent, native. He would die thus because he firmly believed that it would bring him the worst of bad luck to eat the fish. It should be noted that the whole structure of society would be destroyed if dried fish placed upon poles were not safe in the absence of the owner.

The Yukon River may be called the great heart of this region. Its waters shaped the hills, carved the valleys and washed them full of soil. The river brought the Indian his salmon, and salmon was more indispensable to him than bread is to us. When the white man invaded the region the river carried his steamboat, which is as important to him as salmon was to the Indian.

In the last decade of the nineteenth century an American trading-company ran steamboats up the Yukon; the boats brought out little gold but many furs — all there were to come. Apparently a miner or trader could buy furs from the Indians, carry the load on his back to the bank of a stream, put it in his canoe and paddle long distances. Perhaps he would go down the river with his furs or up the river and over the mountains to Skagway. The trading company with its freight monopoly effectively stopped other purchasers by the astonishing device of paying $5.00 for a muskrat skin that was worth $.25, and $100.00 for a mink or marten skin that was worth $5.00. The miner could offer no such fabulous prices for furs, and when he offered the Indian a fair price for pelts he received only scorn. But there was another side to the affair. When the Indian needed supplies he had to buy them from the trading company. The trading company put such big prices on everything — $.25 for a cartridge, $20.00 for a cap — that it soon got back from the Indian all the big money that it had paid him for skins. The Indian was at the mercy of the trading company because it had a freight monopoly with its boats. The canoeist could carry only money.

### Yukon Gold

The history of the Yukon country under American influence has two epochs, before the great gold-rush, and after. In 1896 and 1897 the discoveries of gold in large quantities on the Klondike and other creeks of the Yukon system near Dawson City created a close rival to the great California gold-rush of '49. Tens of thousands of men, knowing little or nothing of the country, rushed to Alaska by every route that they could find — up the river in boats, over the passes from Cook Inlet, Prince William Sound or Lynn Canal, up through British Columbia, across the Canadian plains from Calgary and Edmonton.

Most of these overland hikers could take no more supplies than they could carry. With unthinking recklessness they went into an unknown wilderness where there were no supplies, where the rivers freeze early and the winter is terribly cold. Many perished as they must in a country so devoid of supplies and with such a fierce winter.

The gold was stream-gold; to get it no company need be formed, but the solitary miner with his pick, shovel and pan could hunt where he chose.

Yukon mining ran a swift course. The stream-beds, easily visible, were soon cleaned out. Then placer mines worked the old stream-beds and gravel banks. Again the output declined, but still the prospectors, 1000 of them in 1922, wander up Alaska valleys and over Alaska hills, hoping to strike it rich. Does not every gambler expect the next deal of cards to bring him aces? The Alaska prospector leads a life whose labors would make it heroic if labor could do this. Staggering under a great burden of

Fig. 347 — Life, life with the gambler's tang, but for the miner with his pan there is no other. (Courtesy U. S. Geol. Surv.)

flour and bacon, beans and blankets, tent, axe, pick, frying-pan and rifle, the prospector toils on, hunting, digging, hunting, digging. As the days pass, the scanty food-supply diminishes and must be eked out with berries and game; then back he goes for more supplies and out again for more digging. Such is the life of the Alaska prospector, the man for whom the settled life of town, farm, wife, children, and home has little appeal. His average pay is less than that of bootblacks. He is sustained by the gambler's hope. He calls himself a " sourdough " after he has once seen the ice come and go on the Yukon. Before that he is merely a " chechahco," a tenderfoot.

If the miner strikes it rich he often takes his lucky thousands to Seattle or Chicago or New York and indulges in a swift round of reckless expenditure, then back he goes to Alaska to prowl once more in search of gold, a search which has become the whole of life, the only thing worth while to many. Tomorrow I may find it: Tomorrow! Tomorrow!

Mines, especially gold-mines, make, while they produce, an enormous per capita trade. With gold, fish and furs, Alaska has had the largest per capita trade of any region under statistical review. Most of the

FIG. 348 — The placer mine. Washing down gravel banks gave the Klondike gold output a slight reprieve in 1912 (Fig. 349). Courtesy Seattle Chamber of Commerce. Photo Asahel Curtis.)

people there produce but one thing and buy everything else, and they need much material for their industry, and much to live on in that land of cold winter.

Gold-mining is an industry that takes out and carries away, and save for the gutted forests wrecked by axe and forest fire it scarcely leaves a trace; for after the miner moves on, Yukon shrubbery and young spruce cover up the scarred bank and hide the mouth of the abandoned shaft. The population figures for the British territory of Yukon tell emphatically how poor is gold as the basis of community-building in the Arctic. If the Yukon maintains a large population for long periods it must depend upon the farm.

## Agriculture

The farmer builds up, and stays. Hence it is very natural that those departments of the United States government most interested in the development of Alaska should be filling the newspaper offices of the United States with copy about the agricultural resources of Alaska. They have given out a great deal too much glowing copy. They have not compared Alaska with its rivals. Therefore, they have perhaps pointed out as probabilities things that were only possibilities. It would be poetic justice (but too cruel) to make these boomers of Alaska live there as farmers.

Agricultural experiment-stations have been run for a number of years by the American and Canadian governments. This is good — good for their facts, but sometimes bad in the inferences that have been drawn from the facts.

The results at Rampart on the Yukon, and Fairbanks on the Tanana, have been very surprising to people who had thought of Alaska only as a land of snow and ice. The winter snow melts quickly in the long days of spring. Almost continuous sunshine makes plants jump. Peas grow with a rankness rarely found in the United States. Cabbages prosper, beets, radishes, carrots, parsnips, and the whole list of root-crops, including potatoes,[1] thrive exceedingly, and they become the chief dependence of the northern farmer. Wheat, barley, rye and oats have ripened grain of good quality.

The Canadian government experiment-station at Swede Creek, near Dawson, has produced wonders.[2]

If we may give credence to the estimate of the United States government for the Alaskan Yukon and to the Canadian government for the Canadian Yukon, the region has at least 100,000 square miles of land that is suitable for the plow or for the improved pasture-field. Government representatives of the United States, in attempting to appraise

[1] RELATION OF MEAN TEMPERATURE FOR JUNE, JULY AND AUGUST TO POTATO YIELD IN 1909 *

|  | June | July | August | Yield per acre (bu.) |
|---|---|---|---|---|
| New York | 65.° | 70.° | 67.° | 123 |
| Maine | 61.9 | 66.9 | 65. | 210 |
| Scotland | 55. | 58. | 58. | 350 |
| Sitka | 51.3 | 54.5 | 54.7 | |
| Dawson City | 57.9 | 59.7 | 54.8 | |

* (From " Potato-Growing in New York," E. V. Hardenburg, *The Cornell Reading Course for the Farm*, March 1919, p. 234.)

[2] It reported for 1921 that experimental plats of wheat planted May 4, harvested August 26, yielded fifty-four bushels per acre for one variety and forty-one for another. Two varieties of oats yielded 100 and seventy-two bushels; two of barley, thirty-three and forty-two. These were on bottom land. On the uplands it was too dry for grain. They have also had " good yields of potatoes of good quality " and " large yields of turnips." In 1919, at this station one variety of wheat yielded sixty bushels per acre and one of oats 105 bushels per acre.

Alaska, point out its re-
semblances to Finland.[3]

The United States Soil
Survey states that the
soils of the two regions
are similar. This may be
expected, as soil is de-
pendent upon climatic
conditions to an extent
not yet generally appre-
ciated. If the Yukon, with
100,000 square miles, or
with 64,000,000 acres, is
like Finland, it has unexpected possibilities as the
home of man. Finland
has only 7,000,000 acres
in cultivation or improved
meadow, but there are
100,000 farms of less than
7½ acres and 170,000
farms of larger size. The
total population is 3⅓

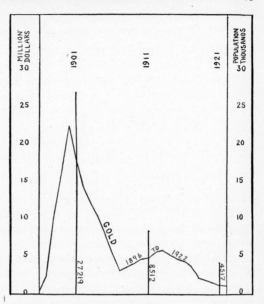

FIG. 349 — The intimate dependence of population
in the Yukon territory upon gold. Vertical
lines show population.

millions. The Finns are energetic, intelligent, progressive in science,
manufactures, education, government and athletics. Finland has many
surprises for the careful student. Her agricultural experiences may be
of great value in working out the newer problems of Alaska.

In considering Finland and Finnish agriculture it should be noted that
the live-stock is chiefly cows and the chief agricultural exports are
butter, cheese and milk.

It is probably true that a future development of agriculture in the
Yukon would be chiefly in dairy products, although seed-farming promises more immediate results. Yukon-grown seed would probably be
superior to seed that was grown elsewhere.

When the people who boost Alaska compare the Yukon Valley with
Finland they do not point out that Finland is a forest country. It has
more rain than the Yukon, and whereas dairy exports in 1912 were
$8,000,000.00, wood and articles manufactured from wood amounted to
$46,000,000.00. The fact is that the Finnish small farmer has two
jobs. He stays home in the summer and attends to his hay, oats,
potatoes, turnips and beets, and in winter he goes off to the woods or
factory while his wife and children feed and milk the cows.

What will the Yukon farmer do in the winter-time, that long cold

[3] See footnote at top of pages 644 and 645.

MEAN MONTHLY AND ANNUAL TEMPERATURES AT

| Station | Lat. | Long. | Jan. | Feb. | Mar. | Apr. | May |
|---|---|---|---|---|---|---|---|
| Uleaborg......... | 65 | 25.5 E | 14.4 | 12.6 | 18.9 | 32.9 | 45.0 |
| Kuopio........... | 63 | 27.5 E | 14.7 | 13.5 | 20.3 | 34.3 | 46.9 |
| Tammerfors....... | 61.5 | 24  E | 19.2 | 16.9 | 23.2 | 36.3 | 48.9 |
| Helsingfors........ | 60 | 25  E | 21.7 | 19.0 | 24.1 | 36.3 | 48.9 |
| Blagoveschensk.... | 50 | 127.5 E | − 16.6 | − 4.7 | 13.6 | 35.1 | 48.7 |
| Yakutsk .......... | 62 | 129.5 E | − 45.0 | − 35.1 | − 10.7 | 14.7 | 40.1 |
| Irkutsk........... | 52 | 104  E | − 4.9 | 2.1 | 16.9 | 36.3 | 48.6 |
| Dawson........... | 64 | 140  W | − 19.2 | − 11.2 | 3.5 | 28.9 | 45.8 |
| Carcross.......... | 60 | 134.5W | − 3.5 | 4.2 | 13.6 | 29.8 | 41.2 |
| Fort Yukon....... | 67.5 | 145  W | − 26.8 | − 15.0 | 1.1 | 20.3 | 41.9 |
| Tanana........... | 65 | 152  W | − 15.8 | − 4.5 | 6.0 | 23.9 | 44.1 |
| Fairbanks......... | 65 | 147.5W | − 15.3 | − 0.7 | 9.8 | 29.3 | 47.1 |

time when the sun gets up at nine or ten or eleven o'clock in the morning? That is the real rub in Alaska.

Fairbanks, Alaska, is the seat of an experiment station, and of the Alaska Agricultural College and School of Mines. It is the terminus of the main Alaska railway and one of the chief towns and chief home markets of Alaska. There had been 146 farm homestead entries (29,432 acres) there prior to June 30, 1923. Eleven of them had been abandoned, and at that date there were 398 acres in cereals, forty-six acres in potatoes and sixty-one acres in cultivated pasture.[4]

This small business had the advantage of temporary high prices and a starved home-market (see chapter on Rocky Mountains), where milk retails at $.25 per quart and local eggs bring $1.00 to $2.00 per dozen.[5]

A thousand acres were reported under cultivation at Fairbanks in 1914.[6] When one thinks of producing in Alaska for export in competition with other parts of the world it seems plain that for the present we should regard the Yukon as a reserve of low-quality farm-land, to be used by future generations when North America approaches Europe's present fullness of development of agricultural resources. Most of the Yukon may become a ranch for reindeer herds in a few years. Open-range pasture of reindeer is an easy and natural first step (see chapter on Arctic Pastures), and it promises to be a long wait before there is any other large land development.

### Government and Monopoly

So far as Alaska land is concerned, this generation of men has two tasks: (1) to prevent destruction, which means to keep out forest-fires and not to overpasture; (2) to prevent the development of monopoly.

[4] Letter from Henry Wallace, Secretary of Agriculture, September 26, 1923.
[5] Letter from G. W. Garner, Superintendent Alaska Experiment Station, Fairbanks, November 14, 1923.          [6] Bennett & Rice, United States Soil Survey.

FINLAND, SIBERIAN AND ALASKAN STATIONS.  °F.

| June | July | Aug. | Sept. | Oct. | Nov. | Dec. | Year |
|------|------|------|-------|------|------|------|------|
| 56.1 | 61.3 | 56.8 | 46.9 | 36.1 | 26.6 | 18.1 | 35.6 |
| 57.0 | 62.1 | 57.4 | 47.6 | 37.8 | 28.0 | 19.2 | 36.9 |
| 58.6 | 62.2 | 58.5 | 49.6 | 40.3 | 31.6 | 23.7 | 39.2 |
| 58.6 | 62.8 | 59.9 | 51.1 | 41.9 | 33.8 | 26.4 | 40.5 |
| 64.4 | 70.0 | 65.8 | 52.3 | 34.5 | 7.9 | − 11.7 | 29.8 |
| 56.2 | 65.8 | 58.0 | 42.1 | 15.6 | − 21.6 | − 40.9 | 11.8 |
| 58.5 | 65.8 | 61.2 | 49.1 | 33.8 | 12.9 | .7 | 31.8 |
| 56.0 | 59.3 | 53.6 | 42.4 | 24.8 | 0.6 | − 11.7 | 22.9 |
| 50.2 | 54.4 | 51.3 | 45.4 | 33.5 | 17.4 | 4.2 | 29.2 |
| 58.5 | 62.7 | 54.0 | 39.9 | 18.8 | − 10.8 | − 19.2 | 18.9 |
| 57.3 | 58.9 | 53.3 | 40.0 | 22.0 | − 1.9 | − 11.3 | 22.7 |
| 58.5 | 60.8 | 54.9 | 43.0 | 25.3 | 1.1 | − 7.1 | 25.7 |

Monopoly is out for water-power, forests, oil, coal, and other minerals and for ranch-lands. Monopoly is not discriminating. It takes the earth. The plan to monopolize is constant, insidious, bipartisan and far-seeing. The Plunderbund strives for monopoly now or in the future. It is a most unequal fight. The Plunderbund never sleeps, yet the citizens of the democracy are not sitting up at night as much as they should to keep waste and monopoly away from the resources in Alaska and elsewhere which they, their children and their children's children, will need.

Alaska, so far away, is a particularly easy mark of the Plunderbund, which strives through all the maneuvers known to politics to get into office its Bureau Chief who administers the law; into Congress its man who makes the law; into the Cabinet the proper boss who has such power over the resources in the care of the Government. And since government is the only way we have of doing an ever-increasing proportion of our economic work, the citizen has no escape from the necessity of eternal vigilance or the alternative of resource monopoly.

Fig. 350 — Winter round-up of reindeer on Golsova River, Alaska. (Courtesy U. S. Dept. Agr.)

## CHAPTER XXXVI

## THE TUNDRA OR ARCTIC PASTURES

### The Myth and the Fact

Northward beyond the tree-limit is the land of endless cold, of eternal snow and ice — at least according to popular belief, and some textbooks still in use. But this story of eternal ice is an interesting myth.[1] The facts of climate are quite different. The Arctic winter is indeed long, dark, cold and snowy, but the actual number of inches of snowfall is less than in northern Virginia, for example. The cold, therefore dry, air of Arctic regions cannot produce much rainfall; in many places it is only ten inches or even less. The rainfall being light, the snow does not get very deep. Believers in the snow-myth seem never to think of the intense heat of the Arctic summer, when the sun does double duty by shining also at night. At 60° north, the longest day has $18\frac{1}{2}$ hours of sunshine. At $66\frac{2}{3}°$ north, at the Arctic Circle, the longest day has twenty-four hours of sunshine. At 70° north there are seventy-three days with continuous sunshine, unbroken save by clouds. At the Pole, there are six months of continuous daylight. Several hundred thousand square miles of Arctic America have more than thirty days of continuous sun.

These long hours of sunshine soon melt the small accumulation of winter snow so that all Arctic America outside of Greenland and a few high mountains is as snowless in summer as the state of Maine.

In the weeks of endless Arctic sunshine the native does not know when to go to bed, save when he is sleepy, but the plants, since they

[1] For its origin see Smith, J. Russell, *Scottish Geographical Magazine*, March 1924.

do not sleep, get the full benefit of heat and light. Continuous sunshine seems to have a kind of cumulative effect upon vegetation. Experiments with the radish show that if it is given seven hours of sunshine per day it will extend its period of growth to a year. Give it twenty-two hours of sunshine per day, and it fairly leaps to maturity, ripening seed in a few days. Arctic plants, like those on the Alps and other high mountains, seize the fleeting opportunities for life by very rapid growth. Almost instantly after the snow melts they burst into leaf, bud, flower and seed. Some have stored up energy in bulbous roots for a rush of growth such as we have all witnessed in the crocuses, daffodils, bloodroot and other quick spring bloomers of lower latitudes. (Fig. 209.)

The wealth of plant-life on the sunny Arctic plain is indeed astonishing to those who have always believed the continuous-snow myth. Botanists report at least seven hundred varieties of flowering plants. The Arctic plains are gay in places with poppies, daisies, buttercups and many other showy flowers of bright color. The Arctic has three hundred lichens, two hundred mosses, and edible berries in great profusion.[2]

## The Caribou and Other Game

Wild animals are as much at home as the plants. The chief land-animal of economic interest to man is the caribou or wild reindeer.

The adjustment of the caribou to this land is one of the myriad responses of organism to environment. His skin has air-cells in it, which make it a remarkably warm leather for him and for us. A good coat of thick fur makes a blizzard slide off a caribou as water slides from a duck's back. He has long, sharp, flat hoofs that are excellent snow-shoes. When he comes to a snow-bank he can use his hoofs for snow shovels, and with them he can dig to the bottom of the snow-bank to get grass to eat. Sometimes only his tail shows above the top of the

---

[2] One of the industrial bulletins of the United States Government, the United States Department of Agriculture Bulletin 1083, *The Reindeer in Alaska,* thoroughly explodes the Arctic myth. It gives "A List of the Range Forage Plants, Observed and Collected on the Reindeer Ranches of Alaska" (in the Arctic tundra). That list consists of:

17 grasses (3 kinds of blue grass)
25 grasslike plants (many sedges)
215 herbaceous plants
30 browse-plants (woody — birch, willow, etc.)
9 ferns and fern allies
43 mosses
33 lichens
3 fungi
—
375 species of forage-plants

The vegetation list from a botanist's recent sojourn in Greenland is even more impressive. It included the famous blue grass of Kentucky, growing at Etah, West Greenland, seven hundred miles north of the Arctic Circle.

snow as he digs and eats. The caribou is not afraid to travel on ice, so when the Arctic Ocean freezes he goes from island to island of the Arctic Archipelago north of the Canadian mainland. He is a good swimmer and his waterproof coat keeps him warm and buoys him while he swims for two or three miles in the icy sea. Yukon steamers have had to stop while multitudes of caribou in migration swam across their course.

Herds of caribou congregate into migrating bands in numbers that would create an international sensation if they should appear on the Great Plains. Mr. Maxwell Graham, Chief of the Wild Life Division at Ottawa, tells me in a letter: "The greatest menace to reindeer ranching is the presence on the ground of millions of small wild American reindeer or caribou. One of the reasons for canceling the lease granted to the North American Reindeer Company some years ago was that the lease on the mainland of the Northwest Territories granted this concern was liable, any year, to be overrun by countless caribou who would sweep away in their midst the few hundreds or even thousands of domesticated or semi-domesticated European reindeer to be placed thereon." [3]

Mr. J. B. Haskin, Commissioner of Dominion Parks, thought (1919) that there might be twenty million or even fifty million caribou in Canada. It has been suggested that airplane hunting might make possible the corralling of the great herds and the annual removal of surplus males after the fashion of the old round-up of cattle on the range of the Great Plains.

Following the herds of caribou is the wolf. When old age or carelessness causes a caribou to fall behind the herd, the wolf pack eats. Almost as widely distributed as the caribou and the wolf is the rabbit, with a white coat in winter to hide him on the snow and a brown coat in summer to hide him on the ground. The rabbit is followed by his Nemesis, the Arctic fox.

Perhaps the muskox is the most remarkable animal in this astonishing land. He has a habit of defense that is excellent in combat with his natural enemies but fatal to the muskox when in combat with man. Muskoxen were early inventors of the famous military hollow square. When danger, namely the wolf or bear, appears, the muskox herd forms a circle, standing with heads out. Their sharp horns are a perfect defense. When man appears the herd forms for defense, standing there depending upon their horns. With his rifle man often kills the whole herd. The Eskimo or Indian can rarely resist such an opportunity for slaughter. Thus the muskox has been exterminated over large areas,

[3] Exact descriptions of great herds of caribou may be seen in a report, "Reindeer and Muskox," Department of Interior, Canada, pp. 30–31; also Minutes of Evidence, Senate of Canada, Report of Special Commission on Navigability and Fishery Resources of Hudson Bay and Straits; testimony of Captain J. E. Bernier; also V. Stefansson, before committee of Canadian Parliament, 1919.

but fortunately a few thousands remain — a precious seed for domestication. The muskox is a good beef animal; it has in addition an annual fleece of ten or fifteen pounds of wool. This wool has been tested and found to be good for making cloth. Mr. Stefansson, the chief literary protagonist of the utilization of the Arctic, prefers to call this animal ovibos because he thinks the market will not respond well to "muskox meat," because "musk" like "rat" does not appetize, although it tells nothing about the meat.

## Birds and Insects

The Arctic winter freezes the tundra to a great depth. The summer thaws it only a foot or two. Because of the underlying ice, the soil in summer is always moist. There are many little pools of water, and there are many lakes and streams, furnishing breeding-places for countless millions of mosquitoes. Water and mosquitoes make the tundra a popular summer-resort for water-fowl, ducks, geese and loons, which eat mosquitoes and other insects and water-plants, and raise their young in an almost uninhabited solitude. The summer haze of mosquitoes is to my mind an effective barrier to satisfactory life here, but it is true that man endures mosquitoes in many lands.[4]

## The Eskimo

The Eskimos have inhabited Arctic America for an unknown period. They live chiefly along the shores. The wild caribou has not made a satisfactory basis for life inland, because he is a rover. The fact that reindeer congregate in millions means that, for the time, large areas are without reindeer. Therefore they are uncertain for man's dependence. The sea is more dependable, with fish, seal, and the mighty walrus, whose

---

[4] "It is a wonderful place, this roof of Labrador. Ridge on ridge, some of it of considerable height, roll away seemingly to the world's end. In the valleys and cups of the hills lie thousands of nameless lakes. The winds, during the greater part of the year, rage over it. It is sheer desolation, abysmal and chaotic. Of dominant notes there are but two, the ivory-colored reindeer moss and the dark Laurentian stone. . . .

"While we were fishing the mosquitoes swarmed over us, nor as the sun rose higher did it bring relief from, but rather a reinforcement to, the hosts of Beelzebub, the Lord of Flies. We had grown used to them in the valley of the Fraser, and suffered as we then believed almost to the limit of endurance, but we had buoyed ourselves up with the hope that the wind and the chill of the high ground would rid us of the bloodthirsty battalions. Far from it. We soon discovered that the mosquitoes of the river valleys were but sluggish and incompetent as compared with the armies of these hardy mountaineers, whose vanguard stabbed us with red-hot needles sent well home. As to their numbers, I am hopeless of giving any idea of them. Suffice it to say that when Hardy put his military blanket out to air, phalanxes three or four deep settled upon it, until its color changed from brown to grey — a seething and loathsome mass of insects; and presently, as we moved about, above each of us rolled a pillar of mosquitoes, revolving and buzzing, and thousands strong. . . . The whole of the land-surface along the George River, near Indian House Lake, is seamed with the old trails of caribou that have pursued their age-long wanderings in this desolate region." (*Through Trackless Labrador*, by H. Hesketh Prichard, F.R.G.S.)

huge carcass furnishes hundreds of pounds of edible meat and a splendid thick skin.   The seal is to the Eskimo more than corn is to the Appalachian mountaineer, or the coconut-palm to the South Sea Islander. Its flesh, both lean and fat, is food.   In the cold winter a strip of seal blubber is a choice morsel to people who need much fat food.   Surplus fat serves as fuel in a little lamp or oil-stove.   Seal-skin makes clothing, tent, bucket; it serves to cover the framework of the kayak, or Eskimo boat, which is one of the triumphs of mankind.   The framework of the

FIG. 351 — The Eskimo A tlo hok looks interested while his wife and her friend split the walrus skin, 7 x 14 ft.   When done, it will cover a canoe, roof a house, or cover the sleeping-room floor.   (Courtesy U. S. Bureau of Education.)

boat is made of walrus and whale-bones, tied together with sinew.   Over the frame watertight seal-skin is sewed with sinews.   The boat carries one man.   He sits in the boat with the bottom of his outer shirt tied around the opening of the boat.   Thus, man and boat are bound together and both are water-tight.   If the boat upsets, it will right itself again and they can go on.   What other race has made such a boat, and what other race has made one of such inhospitable materials?

The seals also furnish food for the dog or Husky, which is the only domestic animal the Eskimo has.   The dog is assistant in hunting.   He is the draft-animal and pulls the sled on winter journeys, bringing in

the seal and walrus-meat from distant places. The Eskimo harnessing
is not in pairs, horse-fashion, as white men drive their dogs in the Yukon
and the Canadian forests. Instead, each dog has his own rope, and they
are spread out fan-like in front of the driver. The dogs are so attached to
the sled that in time of danger a single jerk of a thong releases every
dog.

The Eskimo snow-house has been exploited more than it is worth. Mr.
Stefansson says that not more than one-tenth of the Eskimos live in snow-
houses. They usually prefer the hut of stone, chinked with sods, but
the snow-house is a very efficient building, especially useful as a semi-
permanent dwelling when the family travels. Arctic snow is not loose
and fluffy, like that of middle latitudes. It is more like fine particles of
ice. It sticks together, and so it can be cut into chunks like bricks. The
Eskimo house-builder sets these chunks around on edge and leaning
against each other in arch-fashion. A little chinking with snow fills the
cracks. In a short time after a fire is made inside the interior begins to
melt, and the house promptly becomes a solid structure of ice. The igloo
becomes so strong after a little use that a man or even a bear can walk
right across the top of it without breaking through.

The igloo entrance is through a long tunnel, which, aided by a fur
curtain, keeps out cold, so that a small amount of fire, supplementing
the warmth of human bodies in the small space, makes the temperature
inside the igloo sometimes 80° or 90°. The people are naked to the
waist and sit perspiring, with a four-inch layer of ice between them and
forty degrees below zero.

In summer the Eskimo often takes a trip inland to hunt caribou and
to pick berries, which are dried for winter use. This is also the season
to catch water-fowl and hunt birds' eggs. Sometimes they keep the eggs
in ice for winter use.

When we consider our sensations on gloomy, cloudy days, especially on
the second day or third day when lights must be lit, we can begin to
imagine the feeling of the Eskimo as days with a half-hour of sunshine
pass into the days with no sunshine and those when there is no twilight,
and into the weeks when there is no twilight. How he welcomes the
returning sunshine! It is the signal for the greatest excitement and
celebration of the year, although it means a busy season of much work
after the vacation-time of loafing and visiting.

### Isolation of the Central Tundra

The Arctic Sea in and around the Arctic islands, north of the mainland of North America, is frozen or so full of floating ice as to be virtually impassable. One or two ships have worked their way through it
in the course of two or three years, but this achievement of a northwest
passage, which had been the object of mariners in the days of Columbus

and all through the era of exploration, was first accomplished by Amundsen, the Norwegian, in 1911. This shows the difficulty of access to much of this country, save by an overland journey. Thus the desire in Alaska to domesticate the muskox, found only in Greenland and the northern archipelagoes, brings up the very awkward problem of trans-

Fig. 352 — The isolation of the tundra is well shown by its one seaport, Nome, an open roadstead where ships are served by lighters and fly at approach of bad weather. (Courtesy Seattle Chamber of Commerce.)

portation, south to Atlantic ports, across America by transcontinental railway, north by Pacific steamships to Alaska.

## Greenland

When white men first reached Etah on the west coast of Greenland, latitude 78°, they found seven hundred Eskimos who called themselves "the people," and were greatly amazed to find there were any other human beings.

The terms "unexplored" or "unsettled" cannot be applied to southern Greenland. It is accessible. The harbors of its southern and southwestern coasts are open to ships each summer, and this interesting land must be counted as a part of Europeanized America. In the year 986 A.D., twenty-five ships set sail from Iceland to colonize Greenland. Fourteen of them landed on the southeastern coast. Other settlers followed and there were soon more than two hundred farms on the Greenland coast. For several centuries following there was active trade between Greenland, Iceland and Norway. Then European disturbances caused loss of interest in Greenland, and in the year 1410 the last ship sailed for Europe. The colony was all but forgotten, and when it was revisited by the explorers of the seventeenth century no trace of Norse settlers was found. The people seemed all to be Eskimos. There were legends of massacre, but our knowledge of eugenics gives good support to the theory that the Norse had disappeared by intermarriage. Cultural and legendary evidence supports this theory. In 1721 Greenland was effectively rediscovered by the arrival of a Danish missionary, and now these people are "civilized" and Christianized. There are some 300 Danes in residence and about 14,000 natives. One of the most famous and one of the most renowned scholars of Eskimo lore is the son of a Danish missionary and an Eskimo mother.

The trade of Greenland is a monopoly of the Danish crown, a friendly monopoly, whose effort is to keep alcohol and disease away from a native race. There are some sixty settlements (Colonis) or trading-stations along the coast of Greenland, but only one Coloni is on the colder eastern coast. Each of these Colonis has a superintendent responsible to the inspector for his district, for Greenland is divided into two districts for governmental purposes. There is also usually a clergyman in the Coloni and sometimes a doctor or teacher. There are gardens as far north as latitude 70°, where with care the cold-land farmers can grow good crops of broccoli, spinach, rhubarb, lettuce, carrots, and turnips. The natives live in the usual Eskimo house of stones and turf, although the more prosperous are now building houses of wood, which must be imported, since there is no tree in Greenland taller than the few rare dwarf willows, which are no higher than a man. There are some sheep.

## The Reindeer Industry

Greenland, like all the rest of the treeless Arctic, is ripe for the reindeer industry. It was a simple matter to let the cattle and sheep replace the buffalo and antelope of the Great Plains. It seems equally simple to let the domesticated reindeer replace his wild cousins in the Arctic grasslands and brush-lands.

When the destruction of game brought starvation to the Alaska natives, the United States Bureau of Education introduced reindeer from the old world, brought Siberians and Lapps to teach reindeer husbandry, established a system of apprenticeship among the Eskimos and gave them reindeer when they knew how to care for them.

Twelve hundred and eighty deer were imported. One hundred and sixty-seven came in 1892, the others shortly thereafter. In 1905 there were 10,000 deer; in 1915, 70,000; in 1922, 200,000, and the industry had arrived.[5] It is now thoroughly established in Alaska. The Eskimo, threatened with extinction thirty years ago, has not only been saved, but lifted from the life of a precarious hunter to that of a pastoral nomad who follows flocks and herds. This is an example, unfortunately

[5] See Bulletin 1089, United States Department of Agriculture.

a rare one, of benefit derived from the contact of a native people with the white man.

It is now well established that three Eskimos, aided by trained dogs, can relieve each other and keep constant watch over a band of a thousand or fifteen hundred reindeer. They can move their tents and follow their herd.

Upon the whole, reindeer seem to be about like other domestic animals in the care required on the range and in the corral.[6]

Capitalistic aspects of the industry are further shown by the establishment of a slaughter-house at Cape Nome and refrigerator-service to

Fig. 353 — The reindeer is beginning to replace the dog in winter transport.
(Courtesy U. S. Dept. Agr.)

Seattle and thence to New York, where the meat is regularly on sale in half a dozen hotels and much appreciated by the guests. The capitalistic stage of reindeer enterprise is still further indicated by the following episode: The Canadian Government has granted to Mr. Vilhjalmur Stefansson the pasture-rights on a part of Baffin Land, an area a little larger than England. Mr. Stefansson has allied himself with the Hudson's Bay Company, the most experienced of northern enterprisers, and they are starting the reindeer business at the northeast corner of North America.[7]

### The Ranches of the Future

It is apparently only a matter of time before the whole of Arctic America will be one great range fully occupied with meat-production like the great plains of western United States and southern Canada.

[6] For a fourteen-page history of the reindeer in America, see Smith, J. Russell, "The Reindeer Industry in America — a Study of a New Industry, and also of the Origins of Geographic Error." (*Scottish Geographical Magazine,* March 1924.)
[7] The Canadian Government has a small herd (about 130 in 1923) on Anticosti Island in the Gulf of St. Lawrence. This is the remnant of Dr. Grenfell's herd,

Owing to the fact that most of the Arctic tundra is underlaid by a body of perennial ice, the moisture-supply for those pastures is unique in its unfailing quality. Unless injured by over-grazing, the food-supply is therefore dependable. When one considers the desolating effects of irregular rainfall in dry-land pastures, it will be seen that here is an element of no mean importance for the even support of the industry. With the growth of the industry there will doubtless be a number of great slaughtering-plants located at points to which the animals can be driven, pasturing as they go, and convenient for export by rail and ship.[8]

FIG. 354 — Reindeer grazing on the tundra in August at Teller Station, Port Clarence, Alaska. (Courtesy Victoria Memorial Museum, Ottawa.)

If Alaska can support from three to four million reindeer, I estimate that British North America and Greenland will hold more than twice as many more; and, granting continuance of the present increase of $33\frac{1}{3}\%$ and an average dressed carcass of 250 pounds, we should therefore have an output of three or four million animals per year, 750 million to 1000 million pounds of meat and three to four million hides of wonderful quality for retaining heat and therefore excellent for making gloves and clothing. We may find out that these pastures can also be used — perhaps even better used — by the muskox. This animal equals the reindeer in picking a comfortable living in the northern archipelagoes, and has the added advantage of an annual fleece of excellent wool. Indeed, there is no reason to assume that the muskox is a poorer milk-

which did not do well in Labrador because of vicious dogs and the fact that the herd was too small to be easily handled. The reindeer is easily frightened and nervous unless he has a herd of many hundreds of companions to give the calm confidence needed for peaceful rumination.

    8 "It is estimated that grazing areas in Alaska will support from 3,000,000 to 4,000,000 head." (U. S. Dept. Agr. Bulletin 1089, p. 69.)

producing animal than was the original ancestor of the cow. Now that we know how to select and breed animals, perhaps the Alaska farmer a few generations hence may be tending muskoxen and selling their meat and wool, and possibly he may make cheese of muskox milk as the Laplander

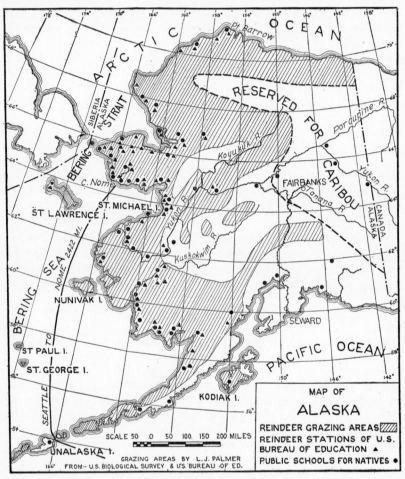

Fig. 355 — The land on the Kuskokwim is all right for the *reindeer*, but has too much brush and tree growth to permit satisfactory herding.

makes reindeer cheese. Surely man will have sufficient intelligence to domesticate rather than exterminate so wonderful an animal.

It is quite likely that the two animals, whose feeding habits are slightly different, may graze together, each eating his own particular kind of vegetation.

It is quite impossible at this time to predict the southern limits of the land of the reindeer. The wild caribou roams from Newfoundland through Quebec, Ontario, and at least the northern half of the forest region, and on into the Yukon and the Alaska peninsula. It is quite possible that a considerable area now called forest (really brush and scrub) will make its greatest return as a reindeer range. The Laplander sometimes takes his herds southward to spend the winter in the forests. The same thing may happen in America. The Yukon country is good reindeer-land. It may become like Montana and Wyoming with their herds of cattle and sheep.

This permanent ranch-industry can support only a scanty population, with only small trading-villages or trading-posts to supply commercial needs. Since it takes about thirty acres to feed one reindeer, and three nomadic families can tend 1500 deer, it figures out to three families to seventy-two square miles, or say one person to four square miles, plus the traders and carriers. This is not a large population. We may expect a rapid increase of the Eskimo population during the era of reindeer establishment followed by a static population at the ranch-maintenance level, just as the population is now static at the hunting-sustenance level.

### Minerals

The Arctic Tundra may become a land where there are cities, based not on reindeer-ranches, but upon minerals. Several hundred thousand square miles of old Archaean rocks may be expected to produce much metal some day, there is no telling when or what. The copper which the Indians find and use is, however, suggestive of one great need that may be supplied from this lone and little-known land. In 1924 Donald B. MacMillan reported finding seams of coal twenty-five feet thick in Ellesmere Land within nine degrees of the Pole.

# CHAPTER XXXVII

## THE ARCTIC SEA AND THE GREENLAND ICE–CAP

THE Arctic Sea is inhospitable. All winter it freezes, but every strong wind breaks up the ice and every change in the direction of the wind floats the ice away in a different direction. Thus the east wind may clear the western shore of an island, so that only blue sea is visible.

Fɪɢ. 356 — U. S. Coast Guard Cutter *Bear* in Arctic Ocean. A small pressure ridge is visible. After fifty years of heroic service in the lonely North, the boat, smashed beyond repair by Arctic ice, was retired in 1924. (Courtesy U. S. Coast Guard.)

Two days later the west wind may bring back enough of the floe ice to cover the sea for twenty miles in all directions with ice cakes two to four feet thick, a yard square, a rod square, a quarter of a mile square, as big as a farm. The hard wind will cause the ice-cakes to grind together with a roaring noise. A storm increases the noise to a deafening roar and jams the masses together so that they rise up into ridges, called pressure ridges. Sometimes these ridges are as high as a house, and most difficult to cross with a sledge and dogs. It was across such ice-fields that Peary with his dog-sleds reached the Pole. Crossing the pressure-ridges was one of his most difficult tasks. Another great obstacle to progress was the open spaces. Sometimes he would have to wait a day or two for fresh ice to form on open places between floes. At other times he would have to make detours of miles to get around the open sea.

### Life in the Arctic Sea

The Arctic seas are full of life. This fact is a surprise to the people of middle latitudes, even when they have accepted the fact that the tundra is full of life.  Is not the sea dotted with ice?  And is not the water always cold?  It is.  It is difficult to understand, but it is none the less true that cubic mile for cubic mile cold oceans contain more life than warm oceans, although not so many species.  This life is all based upon countless numbers of microscopic plants, floating in the ocean water, getting their sustenance from its limitless stores of salts in solution, the leachings of all the continents in all the ages.  These tiny plants are eaten by tiny animals, to be in turn eaten by larger and yet larger animals.  Thus, the codfish finds abundant food-supply, and the herring, on the Arctic coast of Alaska, can be scooped up in great quantities, while the seal, walrus and mighty whale find nourishment for their great warm bodies in the ice-cold water.  The seal's chief food is shrimp.  The whale, despite his great size, eats small fry, which he catches wholesale by taking hundreds of tons of water through his mouth, and spurting it out through the holes in the top of his head, after straining out the food between the closely set slats which enter commerce as whale-bone.

## The Bear-Seal Cycle

The seal and the polar bear make an interesting pair.  The seal, though he often lives in the open sea, was originally a land animal and must come to the surface to breathe.  Therefore, by much labor with his teeth, he maintains breathing-holes in the ice of the Arctic Sea.  From time to time he rises and, sticking his head through his hole, draws a good big breath which lasts him a long while.  By these air-holes his enemies wait for him, the Eskimo with his spear, and sometimes the polar bear.  But the seal, after he has fed, likes to take a nap in the sunshine, so he climbs out on the ice immediately beside his hole, turns and faces the entrance ready for an instant plunge, and takes a nap for about forty-five seconds.  Then he rouses himself and looks carefully around in all directions, seeking polar bears.  Then he takes another forty-five-second nap, and so on.  All the seals that slept heavily were eaten long ago by polar bears.  When a bear spies a seal napping, far away, he carefully goes to leeward, for the slightest whiff of polar bear is a sure end of a seal's nap.  Stealthily bear starts to crawl in seal's direction.  The moment seal's head moves, white polar bear, lying flat on the white snow, remains motionless.  When seal sleeps, bear again advances.  Sometimes a final rush nets him one seal, before the wary swimmer can plunge beneath the ice.  That is good hunting.

Since seal-meat seems to be a perfect ration for polar bear, and since seals live far and wide over the floe-covered sea, the bear, himself also an expert swimmer in ice water, travels freely from ice-floe to ice-floe, seeking seals.  Sometimes he makes the mistake of getting on a Greenland iceberg, which floats him down into the mid-Atlantic and melts beneath him.  Sometimes he takes an accidental ride from the east coast of Greenland to the Iceland shores, where he works sad havoc among sheep flocks. The Arctic, west of the northern archipelagos of Canada, is a safer place for bears, because there is no current there to carry the floes to warm waters, save a very small one through the narrow Prince of Wales Strait west of Alaska.

The polar bear has a satellite, or rather, a group of satellites. Wherever on the Arctic shores you find the track of polar bear, there are accompanying it almost certainly the tracks of from one to five or six Arctic foxes. Foxes are the scavengers, following the camp of the successful hunter of big game. The polar bear cannot eat all of a seal. Fifty or sixty pounds makes him a full meal. The seal weighs about 100 pounds and the bear does not save the leavings although the refrigerator is perfect. The foxes know this and they follow the bear. While he eats they sit at a respectful distance and most disrespectfully bark and scold and snarl. But they keep their distance for they know that the might of angry bear-paw can crush a fox. When bear has eaten his fill and gone upon his way the foxes feast upon the scraps from the rich man's table and then take up the trail and walk and wait.

### Mr. Stefansson Plays Bear

It remained for Vilhjalmur Stefansson to make use of this knowledge of the life habits of the Arctic Sea. He found that the Eskimos live for long periods of time on a meat diet and he learned to do so himself. Then he concluded that he and his dogs would play the game of polar bear and fox. Accordingly, to the horror of native and white man alike, he launched himself into the Arctic Ocean from the north coast of Alaska with one dog-sled, loaded with equipment, including tent, rifle, ammunition, clothes and cooking utensils. Like the polar bear, he stepped from ice-field to ice-field. Like the polar bear, when he saw a seal, he stealthily lay upon his stomach and wriggled toward the seal. At seventy-five yards he killed his seal with a 30-30 bullet. Then he and his dogs could eat. The remainder of the seal was put upon the sledge and man and dogs traveled across the ice-clad sea. The orthodox mournfully predicted his death and sorrowfully reported him dead, but he came back months later hale and hearty. He reports that he never missed a meal nor lost a dog. This was a great achievement in natural history, applied science and exploration. It has not yet resulted in any economic application but it is certainly an interesting and dramatic story.

### The Greenland Ice-Cap

Icebergs are great masses of ice that break off from glaciers that reach the sea. They are much larger than pieces of floe-ice. They are not common in the Arctic Ocean. There are none north of Alaska but there are many south of Greenland, because Greenland has a great store of glaciers to make icebergs. Greenland, excepting Australia, is the world's largest island. It is about 1650 miles long and 800 miles wide at its greatest width. Of the area, about 46,000 square miles belong in the region of Arctic pastures, and about 715,000 square miles are one huge glacier of the kind that once overrode northern North America. At its edges the ice slopes upward with an angle of about one degree. The slope becomes less and less until at the center it is horizontal. The elevation at the center is about 9000 or 10,000 feet, and the ice is supposed to be at least 6000 or 7000 feet deep, covering alike the mountains and valleys of inner Greenland. Only near the edges of the ice-cap do a few mountains, called by the natives Nunataks, stick up above this wide continent of ice with a snow-white top. In summer there are at times small lakes and streams upon its surface, but they soon plunge through cracks and flow beneath the ice.

The shores of Greenland have the longest and deepest fiords [1] known. Into the heads of these fiords flow tongues of ice as the great glacier relieves itself of the surplus by pouring out that host of icebergs which float down Baffin Bay and Denmark Strait, past the coasts of Labrador and Iceland, to be melted in the Atlantic by the warmer waters of the Gulf Stream drift.

In addition to its utter absence of utility, it is quite possible that the Greenland ice-cap is the coldest place in the world, because of high elevation, 9000 to 10,000 feet, combined with its high latitude and the reflection of nearly all heat from its white surface. The few explorers who have crossed it report that the storms upon its smooth snow surface are terrible indeed.

So far as one can see, this 700,000 square miles of ice (five times as large as the United Kingdom) has no present or prospective utility. No one wants to buy the ice. No one can get what is under it. I expect some day to get a prospectus inviting me to take stock in a reindeer company, but there can be no stock-selling scheme based upon the Greenland ice-cap unless some highly imaginative swindler conceives the notion of grafting the idea of a polar-bear farm on to the now growing idea of fur-farming.

The North Pole, crown of the Arctic, was found by Peary to be merely a piece of the deep sea across which floe-ice drifted back and forth. Greenland stops in latitude 83°, leaving nearly 500 miles of open sea across which it was necessary for Peary's sledges to travel for more than 500 miles. The Pole would have been much more easily reached had it been surrounded by land. There is now little reason why airships of one sort or another should not make a polar journey a simple and reasonably safe enterprise, almost any summer, granted the necessary funds, and persons who desired to go. But why go?

[1] The process of fiord-making is partly indicated by the fate of houses built 400 years ago in West Greenland and now under the sea.

# CHAPTER XXXVIII

## PEOPLES ON THE GULF AND CARIBBEAN

"Fifteen men on the dead man's chest —
Yo-ho-ho, and a bottle of rum!
Drink and the devil had done for the rest —
Yo-ho-ho, and a bottle of rum!"

By this verse in *Treasure Island*, Stevenson gives the atmosphere of the Caribbean in the eighteenth century, and indeed it still holds good in the twentieth century. The buccaneers of former centuries are now gone,

Fig. 357 — House and farm of the primitive agriculturist, he of the "*Verdammte Bedürfnislosigkeit.*" Long solid leaves, banana, and plantain; feathery leaves in foreground, royal palm; block of leaves, size of hand near front at right, cassava. Many other food plants unrecognizable in photo. Every leaf visible is the leaf of an economically useful plant.

thanks to better navies, but the solid forts built for protection against them still stand over many a harbor entrance. They remind us that even now the devil of piracy, the enemy of government, is not dead, but is only known by other names. At worst, he is a revolutionist, out with gun and cutlass to capture the custom-house, the presidential mansion, and the power to grant concessions. At best he is the political adventurer or concession hunter striving by diplomacy, persuasion and graft to achieve the pirate's goal — something for nothing, though others may perish.

Stevenson's verse is suggestive of certain aspects of contemporary Caribbean life, especially that of the white race there, and more particularly that of the North European stock. The Devil of Drink assisted by the Devil of Climate is still " doing for " them — busily taking the white men to their doom. Alone and unaided climate seems to be able to vanquish the white woman unless she be of Spanish stock. Witness the anemic women passengers returning from the Canal Zone at Panama and the pale American wives from the West Indies, who come back to the states for the vacation which they regard as so necessary for existence.

The Caribbean shores were settled early, often, even repeatedly, by the seed of many European nations, including Spanish, English, French, Dutch, and Danish. They all had colonies there through many generations of time. There is no doubt that these islands were colonized earlier and more thoroughly than the Atlantic shore of North America, but what do we find at the end of four centuries? We find that while in middle latitudes the white man throve and increased mightily and took possession of the earth, he has not made of the lands to the south a white man's land in any racial sense. Most countries on the Gulf and Caribbean are now chiefly Indian and mestizo, or negro and mulatto. In numbers the colored races are probably gaining on the white.

Indeed, the Caribbean might be called a land of racial annihilations. At the time of the first white settlements it was populous with Indians called Caribs. It is estimated that Haiti alone had 2,000,000 at that time. Now a Carib is a curiosity, so terrible have been the results of the white man's effort to enslave the race.

## Negro Slavery

When the white man found that the Carib could not be satisfactorily enslaved to work his plantations he brought in the negro.[1] While the

---

[1] It has been estimated that from 1680 to 1786 there was imported into the British West Indian Islands a total of 2,130,000 negroes. No one was too exalted or noble to refrain from profiting in this traffic. Shares of Guinea and West Indian stock were held by royalty, by ministers of the Gospel, as well as by ministers of State, alike by merchant princes and university professors. The widow invested her mite and the capitalist his surplus. An important result of this trade on its European side was that big business entered into alliance with government, was indeed often an integral part of government. The result in the West Indies was the rise of a class of capitalist planters, a class so influential that as early as the middle of the seventeenth century it broached the plan of sending representatives to the British Parliament." (" American Interest in the West Indies," Waldemar Westergaard, Ph.D., *History Teacher's Magazine*, October 1917.)

negro throve in the southern United States, and has given the white race close competition for numbers there, he has outnumbered the white man ten or even twenty to one in many West Indian islands. Only the Spanish in Cuba and Porto Rico and parts of Santo Domingo have maintained, through the generations, any substantial numbers of white or nearly white people. The superiority of the negro over the Indian and white races in the ability to live, labor and bring up children in the tropics has worked out its full fruition in these four hundred years. The native is exterminated, the white man is decimated in most of this area and driven back to live by his wits at superintendence as in slave days.

This failure of the white race to increase or even to remain numerically static in the West Indies may be put down to tropical influences. There are several elements in this influence, one of which is that of tropic diseases.

## Tropic Diseases

Yellow fever raged without ceasing for centuries in many tropic American localities. Dysentery was almost as destructive of life and malaria was nearly everywhere present on lowlands, and there were many other tropic diseases, all of which have kept down the numbers of the white race in the tropics. The discovery of the germ theory of disease, particularly the conquest of yellow fever, the hookworm, the partial conquest of malaria, opened new possibilities for developing the tropics but probably it is still true that the white man is maintaining his numbers in many localities only by constant replenishment from the lands of frost. It is startling to see how many of the important positions in tropic American business are filled by men born north of latitude 30°.

## Tropic Climate

Perhaps the most important factor of all is that of climate. Among other things tropic climate produces anemia. The high humidity of trade-wind shores prevents satisfactory perspiration, especially from the people of northern stock. Impurities in the blood-stream which should get out through the skin are thrown back on the lungs, intestines, and kidneys, and intestinal disorders often result. Water which should have been eliminated from the system through perspiration remains in the blood to thin it. The blood-count for red corpuscles becomes low. The blood as a stream of nutrition is inefficient. It therefore fails to build up the body as fast as would a supply of good red blood. As a result the white man finds, after a few months in the tropics, that he runs down in energy, becomes pale, loses weight, becomes anemic. His horse-power is reduced, he cannot do what he did in the North, and if he spurs himself to action and works hard he breaks down and illness may follow.

There is a saying in Porto Rico, where many Americans have been, that the first year the American woman is there she loses her good looks, and the second year she loses health, for in addition to the previously mentioned troubles the even temperature and damp air often produce a relaxation of tissues which causes abnormal loss of blood through increased menstrual flow, which is often prolonged and sometimes increased in frequency. As a result of these particular hardships on women, the English people in the West Indies regard it as a family calamity if a girl cannot be in England for two or three years during which she passes puberty. There is also a widely held belief, which I share, that the white people do not give themselves a fair chance. They are not willing to make the necessary adjustment of food, clothes and habits to keep themselves fit. Keeping fit is a task at best. For example, the West Indian heat makes physical exercise unpleasant except when taken very early or very late in the day. As a consequence the average well-to-do white woman from the North gets almost no exercise.

The West Indian climate is often called the Trade-Wind Climate. The wind blows nearly all the time and nearly always it blows from the east or northeast. The air is warm, almost always warm. It lacks the bracing coolness that comes in the United States with the passing cyclones and anticyclones. People who wish to praise this region point to the fact that New York and Chicago get hotter than Havana, San Juan or Kingston. This is true, so far as thermometers are concerned, but if I may trust my own skin I note a difference. In the swelter of New York I feel that my skin is hot but that under it I have energy to push myself along. In the West Indian port I feel that my whole flesh is hot and that I must sit down for lack of energy. Perhaps this explains the boast about there being so little sunstroke in the tropics. A man sits down, instead of pushing on. Thus the sit-stroke prevents the heat-stroke.

The monotony of this climate, particularly to the man of the North, accustomed to the bracing changes of weather, makes him long for a stimulant such as climatic changes bring in the North. Climate refuses to bring this stimulant, but the gasping Northerner may temper the trade-wind monotony by a drink of alcohol. So he takes a drink — often after years of abstinence in the land of frost.

There is another reason why the Northerner often spends the entire evening drinking with a group of friends. He says there is nothing else to do in a strange land. So drink is slaying the white man in the tropics more than it is in the North and more than it slays the tropic natives. "Yo-ho-ho, and a bottle of rum!" W. S. Whitford, Professor of Tropic Forestry at Yale University, says that according to his observation covering many years alcohol is killing more Northern men in the tropics than die from all the tropic diseases combined. My much smaller observations concur.

As a result of these climatic influences, direct and indirect, the white race has not increased in proportion with the negro. The negro is, of course, a native of the tropic climate, but his increase of numbers is probably due as much to superior birth-rate as to superior ability to withstand the climate. The high birth-rate is due partly to the large family and partly to the plurality of families which is very common throughout the West Indies.

### Ease of Living and the Tropic Garden

It is easy to provide for a family in the Caribbean countries, especially where the rainfall is regular. In these sections there still prevails in many localities a very slight modification of the primitive and world-wide tropic agriculture. I will describe the home unit. It begins with making a clearing in the woods, and this is sometimes done with a single implement, the long knife or machete. As an American in Santo Domingo put it, these people can take a butcher knife and raise as good a crop of corn as you can in Illinois, but not so much of it. With the big knife and an axe the small trees of the forest are cut down and burned in the season of least rain. Larger trees if not cut down may be killed by fire or girdled, and a patch of ground, often not more than a fraction of an acre, is ready for planting. The loose, grainy soil of the forest floor is filled with humus. It has no sod upon it and it does not need to be plowed. Only a sharp stick or possibly a hoe is required for planting the little clearing with shoots of the banana to be eaten raw, and shoots of the plantain, a big banana to be eaten cooked, and with sugar-cane for home-made sticks of candy. There will also be sweet potatoes, yams, corn, many beans, pumpkin and manioc, or cassava (often called yucca in the West Indies). The plant of the manioc grows five or six feet high, and its roots are as big as one's forearm. From the standpoint of nutrition cassava has about the same value as a potato, and it is a great staple food of the moist tropics.

The great stand-bys of these gardens are bananas, plantains and beans, and a few tobacco plants will produce that solace without cost and at a minimum of effort. Many of these people rarely eat meat, since their live-stock is often limited to a family or two of chickens and perhaps a goat or two. Occasionally they may catch some game or buy a little meat. If they are planning a long stay, lime, orange and coffee trees may be planted, and in any case such royal palm trees as grow there are likely to be carefully saved for their fruit and roof material.

There is no order about the tropic garden. The plants are not set in rows, but helter-skelter, in a way that looks crazy to us of the land of plows and straight rows. Pumpkins and sweet potatoes are on the ground, and growing above them in free and apparently aimless sociability are corn, sugar-cane, cassava and bananas.[2] No plow comes through this garden. It is cultivated by the machete, which the native slips along through the ground just below the surface to cut off weeds and shoots. One hand wields the machete while the other hand gathers the weeds. The garden thus gets a kind of clean shave. It is astonishing to observe the rapidity with which the native makes his simple tool do its work. Perhaps the agriculturist of the machine-using North will be inclined to belittle such inefficiency of equipment, but after having seen many of these little machete-kept gardens I am bound to confess that there were more weeds in my own American garden, well equipped with varied tools, than I saw in forty of the little West Indian *conucos,* cleaned with the machete.

## The Native House and Furniture

The native house is as home-grown as the food. Poles are stuck into the earth and cross poles are tied to them with palm fiber. Rafters and braces are tied to the cross poles with more palm fiber, and poles to serve as laths are tied to the rafters with palm fiber. The framework is now ready for the roof, which is commonly of palm leaves.[3] The wall may be made of palm leaves (tied on) or of the great boardlike sheaths that grow at the base of the leaf of the royal palm. These sheaths, almost like boards, are from three to six feet long and from two to four feet wide, and like the roof of leaves will last for many years.

If the dirt floor is not considered sufficient, a floor will be made of the outer surface of the trunk of the royal palm. This is sometimes used as weather-boarding in more pretentious houses. The gourd tree furnishes buckets, bowls, and other containers, unless the people choose to make such things of wood. Palm fiber, an ever-present tropic help, is used for making hats, baskets, rope and hammock. It is said that the hammock is a West Indian invention. Thus far in the creation of field, food supply and house, no foreign implements save the machete and possibly the axe have been used. It is therefore not surprising that a disappointed German, seeking trade, coined the term *verdammte Bedürfnislosigkeit* (damned wantlessness) to describe the economic completeness of these people who supplied their own wants without buying the wares of the disappointed trader.

[2] Mr. A. B. Ross, of Narberth, Pa., an experimenter of unusual originality, has worked out a system of hand-gardening by which he plants two or three crops on the same ground at the same time. In his garden the first peas have young corn beneath them. The first corn has a second crop of corn at its knees. Beans and tomatoes on poles and corn set far apart can stand over beets and cabbage and other low-growing plants and thus divide up the light which Mr. Ross says is the deciding factor. Altogether he claimed to make between four and five crops per year in Pennsylvania on each square foot of his garden. The point of peculiar interest is the close relationship that his great discovery bears to the age-old practice in the forest-garden of the so-called African " savage." *Big Crops from Little Gardens.*

[3] The palm leaf is not the soft leaf stuff of our Northern trees, as the examination of a palm-leaf fan will prove.

Just a pot in which to boil the cassava or sweet potatoes and a skillet in which to fry the plantain are the necessary cooking utensils. Many do not sit down at a table but eat out of hand, and therefore dishes are not necessary.

Clothing an entire family costs but little. Children often run naked in their earlier years even in the streets of the town. Blue overalls and factory shirts and home-made cotton dresses partially cover the older people. Shoes are not often necessary and usually are absent. Thus the cash income needed by the family is small indeed. If they live near the town a few loads (woman, donkey, or perhaps man-loads) of produce sold in the market will supply it. So will a few days' work on some plantation. Sometimes a part of the ground planted to coffee, cacao or tobacco will yield a few hundredweights to bring in the needed funds.

### The Simple Life and the Population Problem

This simplicity of existence has a profound influence on the population question. A woman can support the family if she has to, and the family solidarity that is so necessary to send children through high school and college in the United States and Europe is not needed; hence a different concept of family life has arisen or, perhaps one had better say, survived. The husband is not a necessity save for his company's sake, and that is often about all that the uneducated West Indian wife ever gets from her husband except for short periods. She supports the family, and if she wants to exchange husbands, why not? And if sometimes, in this process of swapping, the man gets two or three wives, it is merely an incident in the system. The more generous he is with his earnings the more wives he can collect.[4] A big negro stevedore who climbed upon a steamer at Turks Island, a most orderly and well-governed British possession, said he had fourteen children by his proper wife and fourteen others by three other wives. He was scarcely a subject for criticism here, or indeed in any other West Indian island.

A Dominican woman who was being chidden for her third shift of mates answered, " Life is too short to live alone." An employer in Porto Rico complained that if a man of the working class gets more money it often results not in a rise in the standard of living for the family, but in a second wife. Consequently, the increase is in population instead of in the standard of living.[5]

---

[4] Story has it that a West Indian planter's wife was approached by a man servant who told her that his spouse had left him and gone to Bermuda. " Oh, my! " said the lady. " Whatever am I going to do for a washerwoman now? " " Don't worry, ma'am," he replied, " I'm courtin' ag'in and I courts rapid."

[5] " What does a countryman do if he gets some money? " a gentleman in the interior of Santo Domingo was asked. " He buys a bright-colored sash that goes from shoulder to opposite hip, he buys a new machete, and he gets another wife " — a statement that is slightly figurative but strongly savors of truth.

There is a rather famous case of a cocoa planter in Santo Domingo. Large cocoa plantations are rare, but this planter had a very large one because of his system of management. Every time he got a new piece of cocoa plantation started he built a house in it and installed another wife. She looked after his interests in that part of the plantation. I heard of him three times, and each time the number of his wives varied. Some said he had eight, others nineteen, and yet others twenty-nine. When the American marines took possession of the island in 1916, one of their first acts was to disarm the natives; but the cocoa planter of many wives sent a friend down to the capital to plead for the return of his gun on the ground that he really needed it. To this the officer in charge is reported to have answered, " Yes, I think he ought to have a machine-gun."

The man of wealth and power also often succumbs to the ancient temptation of many wives (which figures so largely in the stories of the Old Testament). This is particularly true of the dictators. Zelaya, who ruled Nicaragua for nearly a score of years, admitted the paternity of fifty children. Gomez, the unmarried dictator of Venezuela in 1924, acknowledges seventy-eight children. Some say eighty, but perhaps that · is merely the love of round numbers. All of the males of this Solomonic brood are said to be in government " employ." It probably meant that they had good incomes for which they rendered no service.

In 1923 a story was current to the effect that Gomez, then getting old, desired to enhance his respectability by legally marrying the favorite of his common-law spouses. As this would have given a favored position to her children, other sons conveyed the word to Gomez that the day of his marriage would be his last upon earth. He did not marry. It is often true that these military dictators who have absolute power (life and death and confiscation) over everything within reach will throw a man in prison and add his wife or daughter to their harems.

When I was in Porto Rico in 1923 the estate of a wealthy native of the Spanish stock was being settled. The gentleman had left money to each of sixty children and had given them his name. The incident did not seem to be considered extraordinary. On the other hand, he was praised for his honorable action in thus setting these young people square with the world.

The results of this more or less informal polygamy are two — first, the rapid increase and great density of population in many localities; and, second, the increase of the ablest element. This more rapid increase of the able may account for the good looks of the people. A Chicago woman, a graduate of the University of Wisconsin, living in Porto Plata, Santo Domingo, averred that she did not know there were so many Othellos alive as can be seen in the streets of that town. And I can personally testify to the good looks of the women.

### Varieties of Peoples and Their Condition

There are wide areas in the United States where all the people are very much alike. Compared to these the region of the Gulf and Caribbean seems like a veritable museum of people and peoples.

The Caribbean mixture of races is amazing. The English classification used in the *Statesman's Year Book* for Jamaica admirably describes that particular island — white, colored, negro, East Indian. For Central America it should be white, Indian, mestizo (mixed white and Indian), negro, mulatto, zambo (mixed Indian and negro). Some islands, like the American Virgin Islands, are almost pure negro, while parts of Porto Rico and Costa Rica are pure white. Others, like Nicaragua, are almost completely of mestizo. A few thousand Chinese have straggled in, and then, as if to add to the variety, the British Government has permitted planters to import thousands of East Indian coolies to work the plantations of Jamaica and Trinidad.

Accessibility and inaccessibility have a marked influence on man, affecting alike the race and its condition.

Islands may be counted as accessible when ships are a part of their environment. Ships connect the inhabitants of these overcrowded islands with other lands and other men.

Where ships come there are jobs or at least the chance to go and get jobs. Out from a black mass of deck-hands or stevedores on a West Indian steamship, jabbering a mongrel French and Spanish, comes a surprising note, the good English of a native of St. Thomas or a British island. An unexpected and really unwarranted feeling of relationship rises within you for an instant. Hundreds and thousands of these men have worked abroad — as sailors, as laborers on the Panama Canal, on banana plantations in Central America, as elevator boys, waiters and domestic servants in New York City, the great Mecca whither so many ships go, and where there are so many jobs.

The inaccessibility of parts of Mexico and Central America profoundly affects the lives and condition of its people. There are native tribes living in the deep forest, many days' journey from steamship, railroad, wagon road or city. They have almost no dealings with white men and show no discernible cultural influences of white man's existence save that they have knives and cotton goods and a few other results of barter.

The mixed peoples of the Caribbean and the Gulf have lived under very different types of government, giving great variation in opportunities for individuals. The great masses in Mexico and Central America are untutored Indians many of whom speak only the native dialect. They have no chance of schooling of any sort outside the native instruction of children by parents. In contrast to this, the British have long conducted free schools on all their islands, with the result that many shiny black negroes speak with a perfection of grammar which would be an unintentional reproof to the generation of college students whom I teach, and which by the very elegance of its diction exceeds that of any faculty in which I have ever sat.

Directly across the straits from this Jamaica of free schools and negro education is Haiti, with a great mass of uneducated negroes who, since they threw off their French masters in the Napoleonic period, have unquestionably degenerated in what we call civilization. Rumors of cannibalism persist in coming out of Haiti.[6]

A chunky-looking young negro in prison was shown to my friend, Lieutenant Gebhard, as the survivor of four who had made soup of an American aviator who had been forced to land. " Fat soup it was," he told Gebhard.

An engineer of my acquaintance who has worked for months among the Haitians firmly believes that children are eaten. Being a lover of children, he got acquainted with all the youngsters of the little village and used to play games with them. Then one night there was a great beating of drums in the forest and nearly everybody was away. In the morning five children were missing. He was greatly excited by this. Parents only shrugged their shoulders. He tried to get up a posse to hunt them. People only grinned and took no interest. Several times this happened; drums were beating in the forest all night and children were missing in the morning — a religious festival.

The white people of the Gulf and Caribbean are almost as varied as are the other races. It is the cosmopolitan financiers of New York, Chicago, Paris, London, Edinburgh, Amsterdam and Hamburg who keep the wheels of commerce moving. The wheels of machinery in the oil fields are kept moving by a remarkable collection of gamblers, ex-revolutionists, ex-convicts, fugitives from justice, " down and outs," half down and outs, along with a certain number of expert geologists, engineers, and administrators and a goodly mixture of the lovers of adventure and victims of wanderlust.

The great plantations have their experts in technique and administration, for he who ventures largely into tropic agriculture must be among the intelligent of the earth. (See account of sugar plantation in chapters on Cuba and Santo Domingo.) The saying that it takes all kinds to make a world is herein exemplified.

The Spanish stock of Cuba, Porto Rico and Santo Domingo ranges from the simplest peasant to the noble and royal stock descended from Spanish governors and generals. Chance meetings with a man in an Apennine village, with another in a date garden of the Sahara, and with

---

[6] In 1921 the American government of Haiti had in prison at Port au Prince an old woman whose offense was reported as " eating three children."

others in West Indian towns have convinced me that a real gentleman is not to be hidden by mere difference in complexion, language, culture or costume. The stock of Spanish nobility is here.

In this region there is a clash of cultures — that of the abrupt, hustling and businesslike Yankee and that of the suave, polite, leisurely and chivalrous Spaniard. Spain's past has produced a culture in which the gentleman must be a man of leisure, engaged in the law, medicine, literature, or government service — above all an army officer. This Spaniard uses much form to communicate an idea, especially an unpleasant idea. You come to him for something he cannot grant and he says, " Come tomorrow " (*mañana*), and yet again *mañana*. If you push him for an answer he will say " No," but it is not his nature to do it that way.

An educated Porto Rican, addressing a conference of educators in Washington, said: " How I wish my fellow-countrymen could see you, so that they might know that there were Americans other than those who come to rule us or to sell us something! "

Upon the whole, the American in Caribbean countries is quite thoroughly hated and quite properly hated by the intelligent natives. They see our power, the advance of our empire, our financial domination, our insulting foreign policy. They remark that we have three-fifths of the area of Mexico, all of Porto Rico, Haiti, Santo Domingo, Cuba, Nicaragua, etc. Our manners are quite the opposite of the manners of the Spaniard. We are most frank, most outspoken. We are sure that we come from " God's country," from the land of " progress." We are sure that all that differs from our things and our ways is inferior, and we let the fact be freely known.

And then there is the dark skin! Sometimes we even go so far as to use the epithet " nigger " to people of pure Caucasian blood.

If Americans traveling and sojourning in the Caribbean lands should adhere to rigid rules of common politeness, and at the same time make a consistent attempt to understand the point of view of these people, many desirable things might easily come to pass. It seems that a great human opportunity is being overlooked in our contact with these tropic peoples. And on the other side there is no gain whatever.

Fig. 358 — Capitalism, science, and medievalism make a dangerous mixture. Mexican troops going to war. What for war? (Courtesy G. F. Weeks, Mexican News Bureau, Washington, D. C.)

## CHAPTER XXXIX

### GOVERNMENT ON THE GULF AND CARIBBEAN

THE countries of the American trade-wind lands are as much a museum of types of government as they are of races of men. They are indeed a rich laboratory in which almost every kind of government can be observed, save one — a good independent government. Climate has a big part in this. It has kept the white man down and made the man of color predominant — a fact of profound import.

Furthermore, fatigue is now known as the mother of irascibility and bad temper. Tropic lassitude is, therefore, a destroyer of that judicial calm so necessary for good government. It is an axiom of the tropic oil-fields that the American is abusive as he approaches a nervous breakdown, and the resort to violence is much more natural than it would be in the good bracing climate of England.

It is well known that in the United States a period of business depression usually throws out the party in power. The droughts and irregularities of tropic rainfall repeatedly produce disturbing hard times and the tendency is to blame the party in power.

Government is one of the most difficult problems faced by mankind. The objects of government — the attainment of the " inalienable " rights of " life, liberty and the pursuit of happiness " — are strangely elusive. Like every other nation upon earth, we are prone to think of ourselves as a model of good government, but any one who has intelligently read our newspapers for a few years can make an appalling list of the lapses of government in the United States from its ideals, even the ideal of form, decision by the will of the people expressed by the orderly casting of ballots and the arrest of offenders by the representatives of the law and their prompt and fair trial [1] by honorable courts.

[1] "Administration of Justice in the United States is not improving but is in a period of decline which began before the World War and was accelerated greatly by it." United States Attorney General Stone before American Bar Association, July 8, 1924.

The ancient institution of graft is still in our midst; elections are sometimes carried by the improper use of money; the forces that control some of our legislation would be an amazement to the honest voter. It is often disquieting to contemplate the men who are elected to office and much more disquieting to see who can be re-elected, especially in our cities.

A recognition of the difficulties and shortcomings of government in our own country should make it easy for us to sympathize with and understand the greater problems and difficulties that beset government in the countries to the south of us.

Between the Rio Grande and South America variety in independent government is exemplified by more than half a dozen racial complexes, calling themselves nations, and for about a century ruling themselves — namely, Mexico, Guatemala, Salvador, Honduras, Nicaragua, Costa Rica, Haiti and the Dominican Republic. In contrast to these self-governing groups there have been the colonial establishments of British Honduras and the British, French, and Dutch West Indies, and through most of the time the Danish and Spanish West Indies. Since 1898, the United States West Indies have been added to the list, and Spain is gone.

### Bryce's Conditions for Democracy

Failure, failure even to keep the peace at home, is the outstanding fact of government in Mexico and the other independent countries. Nor are the reasons far to seek. The sympathetic Viscount Bryce in his book, *South America* (Chapter XV), states the conditions under which democracy can be effective or indeed even exist.

First, democracy must have racial unity. This is completely lacking in every independent country and every large West Indian island.

Second, there must be a middle class of small property-owners, like the middle class of England, who have something to gain by good government and much to lose by bad government. No country in the Gulf and Caribbean has such a middle class.

Third, the country must have such geographical conditions that there is easy communication of persons and ideas from one part to another so that public opinion may have the means of becoming focused. This, too, has been absent in every independent country, save possibly Salvador. Salvador is larger than Maryland and has 213 miles of narrow-gauge railway.

Fourth, as Bryce points out, the Latin Americans lacked the experience in self-government which the people of the United States had had as colonists. When the Constitution of the United States was written it was mostly composed from selections of the experiments in government which had been tried in the colonies and found to have worked. As most of the new things in the Constitution had not been tried they did not work as expected, notably our electoral college, which has been from the very first a complete and lamentable caricature, of about as much value as the vermiform appendix. In contrast with the independence of action in the British colonies, every Spanish colony had a colonial history devoid of experience in self-government. The Spanish viceroy ruled. He made laws, administered them and judged the offender. The people obeyed, or endured the tyrannous consequences.

Fifth, at the beginning of independent government the people of the American states were, because of their experience, in a position to discuss principles and to have political parties. A political party with principles is a late refinement and the result of order and intelligent discussion. The Spanish American had not reached that degree of experience in order and stability. The newly emancipated colonies of Spain, from Chile to Mexico, had only military leaders. The newly emancipated Latin American voter had known governors, but he knew nothing of government. Therefore he was for General This or General That. When the general wanted office he called upon his followers, who took up arms and fought for him. Having conquered, the general could reward his friends.

Bryce might with propriety have laid more emphasis on education as a necessity for democracy. Democracy has little chance with a mass of people as unlettered and as strange to political knowledge as those of the countries between the Rio Grande and Panama.

The newly emancipated colonies of Spain in America copied as far as they could the one shining example of an independent democracy. To make their governments like ours they took our Constitution, saying that it was theirs. An Australian Bushman might just as well put on a Prince Albert coat and silk hat and say he was a member of Parliament, competent to make laws for the British Empire. The Constitution of the United States is a terrible misfit for an illiterate populace.

### Latin American Civil Wars — The Monroe Doctrine

In a short time the civil wars between General This and General That began. European rights were ruthlessly violated, but at the first sign of restoration of European rule there appeared Monroe's pronouncement, in 1823, that any advance of the political systems of Europe in this hemisphere was (is) " dangerous to our peace and safety," and " unfriendly." This amounted to a threat of war by the United States. But for this Monroe Doctrine there would not now be one square foot of independent soil remaining upon the American continent, south of the United States. Of this I am as sure as of anything that cannot be subjected to definite demonstration, although predictions of what might have been are by their very nature most risky. The fate of Asia and of Africa is suggestive. So is the history of the American continent. No sooner had the United States become engrossed in civil war than the French Napoleon III set up a satellite empire in Mexico, under Maximilian, an Austrian prince. It failed after French support was withdrawn, and French support was withdrawn only after strong diplomatic presentations from Washington, and after General Philip Sheridan was sent to Texas at the close of the Civil War with an army, the most experienced then on this globe. At that moment the United States also had the only fleet of iron-clad war vessels. At the same time Spain had retaken possession of Chile and of Santo Domingo. One of the constant cares of the American government for many decades has been to prevent the landing of troops from foreign war vessels in Caribbean waters or to get the forces to re-embark after landing had been made.

The Monroe Doctrine has kept Europe away from America; therefore the countries of South America, Central America and Mexico have been free to do the best they could about government. In Central America and Mexico there have been dictatorships which have usually, however, used the forms of a constitution, although the methods of constitutional amendment show that constitutions are literally scraps of paper. I cannot make that point more clear than by citing recent occurrences in Venezuela. It is true this book is not dealing with South America, but the Venezuelan case is typical and also it has the advantage of being current. The present President of Venezuela (1924), Gomez, was President in 1916, and the time for a new election had come. The leading afternoon daily of Caracas kept remarking that this was the year of the presidential election and it was about time for the candidates to appear. This was repeated several times. Then one day the President issued a manifesto reannouncing the freedom of the press in the picturesque and resounding eloquence of which the Latin American is so fond; whereupon the next afternoon this Caracas daily announced that its candidate for the presidency was Señor So-and-So. In the United States this support would have been an honor to make any citizen feel proud for months to come, and it would be mentioned by his children and grandchildren. In Venezuela it struck terror to the heart of the man named. He feared for his life, and under cover of the early tropic darkness he fled to the sea, chartered a launch, and before the sun rose was out of Venezuelan jurisdiction and safe in Curaçao, the Dutch island to which so many Venezuelans are glad to escape.

The fate of this presidential possibility was better than that of the editor of a paper in Maricaibo, Venezuela. One day in the summer of 1923, he stated in his paper that the Venezuelan minister to the United States had protested to the American government against the continuance in the United States of propaganda against the Gomez government in Venezuela. For this the paper was suppressed and the editor thrown into the dreaded San Carlos prison in the Lake of Maricaibo.

Six weeks later the paper was still suppressed and the editor was still in prison.

It should be noted that this Gomez, for many years dictator of Venezuela, retires at the constitutional end of his administrations and has a provisional president appointed for a time, but no one is uncertain as to who rules. It is Gomez. Venezuela has been a classic bad example, but Central America and the West Indies have furnished plenty of duplicates.

### Government in Mexico

For thirty years Mexico was an example of good government among Latin-American countries. This was due solely to the work of one man, Porfirio Diaz. From 1823–1876, before his time, Mexico had had an almost unending series of civil wars. Often two or three generals were in the field at once and rarely was there a period of more than three years of peace. This ferment was stopped in 1876 by the successful revolution of Diaz, who was able to retain his power. He was called President of the Mexican Republic. In fact this man, whose face showed his Indian blood, was an emperor, and belongs in the class of Caesar. The two rulers were alike in their ruthlessness, their exercise of individual authority and the maintenance of the forms of a democracy, although Caesar had the more democratic forms.[2] Caesar and Diaz were also alike in the centralization of their governments.

Diaz killed freely and out of hand. One of my students, an American, returning from years in Mexico, told me of some riots in a mining town — a little drunken disorder and some shooting and threats against property. Thirty-two men were arrested, put into a box-car, taken a few stations down the railroad, taken out into the bushes beside the track and shot by the Rurales (police). There was no pretense of trial. This episode explains how Diaz stayed on top in Mexico.

Diaz was an exploiter of resources and of men. The resources of the nation were given by the government (Diaz) to Mexican friends and foreign capitalists in princely units. The foreign investment and investor were protected. Foreign capital flowed into Mexico by the hundreds of millions of dollars. In a few years the citizens of the United States alone invested 500 million dollars, largely in mining property. Mexican industries and trade grew, and her material prosperity was the talk of the financial papers in every financial center in Europe and America.

Diaz was an exploiter of men because his system of taxation bore upon the poor and skipped the rich, and because of the compulsory labor he forced upon the people. Did the foreign mine operator want some

---

[2] The Romans of Caesar's day thought they had a republic. A widely told jest had it that in the palmy days of Diaz there had been an election in Mexico and seven votes were cast. Two of them were against Diaz, resulting in much search for the two men who voted against the government.

natives to work his mine? The *jefe* or local magistrate, if properly bribed, would often arrest a few harmless Indian farmers and fine them. Being unable to pay their fines they were thrown into jail, but the mine-owner could pay their fines and get them out. Then they were in debt to the mine-owner. Here the system of peonage appears. The debtor cannot stop working for the lender until his debt is paid. The lender then falsifies the accounts, so that the worker appears to be always in debt. An American once told me, as though it were smart, that on his Mexican plantation he kept the accounts of individual men. The system was amazing in its simplicity and also in its other qualities. At the top of each column in each page he had written out 1899, that being the year of the accounts. On every page he added up the driblets of money that had been given the men, plus eighteen dollars and ninety-nine cents. Every time the employer turned a page he stole $18.99, so there was no difficulty in keeping the poor devil constantly in debt, chained to his job. There has been much complaint about the inefficiency of the Mexican laborer, but why should he work hard? He cannot get away. Hundreds of thousands, perhaps millions, were and are thus chained. They cannot get away; they cannot get ahead.

As Diaz grew old a high-minded Mexican named Madero commenced to talk of reform. He promised land to the landless, and war began. Diaz fled to Spain, but Madero found it was easier to promise land than to give it. Riddled with bullets, Madero soon joined the other Mexican ex-Presidents [3] in the cemetery. Mexico had a rapid succession of conspicuous figures, all at the head of armies, Diaz, Madero (the younger), Huerta, Villa, Zapata, Carranza and Obregon.

Conditions in Mexican oil-fields near the end of Carranza's rule were instructive. Carranza was President. His official army of occupation of the oil-fields was ragged and unpaid and living on the country. In the same locality was the army of Villa, the so-called rebel leader. This army was much better supplied with arms and money than Carranza's, but neither group had uniforms and the difference between them and undisguised bandits was sometimes quite impossible to discern. Either party would ride into the camp of a mining company any time of day or night and call for food and get it. An officer of Carranza's army would walk up to the commissariat of the mining company and call for cans of milk, rolls of roofing, sacks of oats, saying that the goods were "requisitioned," and he would get them. No one had any idea that they would be paid for, nor were they. Upon the completion of a bungalow for the oil company's foremen, the "General" "requisi-

---

[3] Iturbide, her first ruler after her independence, was executed, and Carranza, the last, was shot under conditions that were much more than half murder, and it is fairly safe to predict that if the present ruler, Obregon, succeeds in dying comfortably in bed it will probably be in a foreign land after a successful get-away like that of the long-mighty Diaz, who fled by night to Vera Cruz and Europe.

tioned " it for some of his officers.  On Saturday afternoons the soldiers would go riding into towns, firing revolvers in the air as cowboys do in fiction.  Then would follow drunken orgies, with details much too bad to paint here.

The paymaster of a particular oil company had orders not to fraternize with nor to be in any way chummy with the " generals " of either "army."  One of the American oil-company officials had tried this by accepting a present of a horse from a Mexican " general."  Of course, this present required a return.  An account was kept and it was found that the " general " made it very clear that he expected certain presents, and he got them to the value of $2,000.00, about forty times the value of the horse.  Thereafter the Americans " handed out " when necessary, but with a dignified reserve that did not claim friendship.

These two rival armies in the Tampico oil-field fought occasionally, always from ambush.  The sight of a dead man hanging from the roadside as a warning was not unusual.

These difficulties occurred in one little corner, and were merely the harmless echo of the disturbances which had destroyed millions of dollars' worth of property and hundreds of thousands of lives in Mexico after the fall of Diaz.  Mine buildings were burned, the mules driven away and the men forced into the armies.  Trains were robbed, derailed and burnt.  Tunnels and bridges were dynamited and herds of cattle and sheep were driven away from the ranches.  Even magnificent churches, centuries old, were dynamited.  Killing was fairly free; scores of Americans were shot, and it was stated that some Mexican states lost half their people.  All this upheaval shut off the production of hundreds of millions of dollars of exports, crippled national resources until Mexican bonds had almost ceased to have value and the country relapsed, almost to the condition where it was before Diaz enforced order for a time.

A large part of the troubles in the Latin American countries arise from the fact that the age has forced upon a medieval people a capitalistic system.  The two do not mix to the advantage of the average man.  The system makes easy opportunities for concentrated wealth and power, while the people, in ignorant medievalism, are powerless to control their own destinies.

### Government in Haiti

While Mexico was the " good " example, Haiti has been a classic bad example.  Revolution in Haiti was a business: you captured the custom house, then you collected the tariff.  There is a report of an importer who paid tariff one evening on a shipment but failed to take it away.  The next morning a revolution had placed another party in power and he had to pay another tariff on the same shipment.

The United States took possession of Haiti in 1915 after peculiar acts of violence.  A deposed President fled to the French embassy.  By international law he was in French territory. This is a common expedient in Latin America. The deposed ruler, not having time to reach the boundary, flees to an embassy or a consulate. His enemies camp outside to wait for him. Sometimes they camp for months, but legally he is in a foreign land. When he steps in the street he is back in the country of his enemies; therefore he delays stepping into the street until chances for his get-away look good. In this case, however, the enemies of the deposed President would not wait, nor be gainsaid.[4] They entered the French embassy and took out the deposed President. They threw his Excellency over the fence to the crowd, and the mob cut him into pieces and carried the pieces through the streets. In all international decency France would have been compelled to deal with Haiti or get off the diplomatic earth. We dealt with Haiti instead, by taking charge of the country. We have governed it ever since and there is small prospect of our withdrawal.

### Foreign Trouble-Makers

We should not blame the Latin American peoples alone for the hundreds of armed uprisings and successful revolutions in the various Latin American countries. Foreigners, including Americans, have often started, financed, or carried on the revolutions. For example, I am credibly informed that a certain American, head of an important American enterprise in a Central American country, was the right-hand man in a would-be revolution. He went to an American port and secured the arms. He shipped the arms into the country. The enterprise was a failure. The leader was killed; the American barely escaped with his life. If the revolution had been successful, the American was to be Commander-in-chief of the army at $75,000.00 a year. Was he fundamentally different from Captain Kidd, except that Kidd succeeded? In 1856 an American, William Walker, desired to duplicate the operation by which Americans went into the Mexican territory of Texas, settled, revolted, and then joined the United States. Walker raised an armed force, usurped power in Nicaragua and in 1860 invaded Honduras. There he was captured and executed. It is often asserted that foreign financial

---

[4] The particular offense was grievous. One T. Simon Sam, a big negro, President by right of revolution, was looked down upon by the better elements of Port au Prince as a rough-neck and a cut-throat. An uprising against his rule was in progress and was being maneuvered by the better people of the city. To stop them Sam arrested 170 of the young men and women of the best families in the city, put them into the prison, and announced that he would kill them if the revolution did not subside. The palace was surrounded. Sam sent word to the commander of the jail to carry out the order for execution, and 168 young men and women were butchered. The city rose in a fury, but Sam succeeded in getting to the French embassy, where the American consul and other foreigners had taken refuge. The American consul got word to an American war vessel thirty hours away, and as it steamed into the harbor the populace, realizing that they had to move quickly to get Sam if they got him at all, stormed the embassy.

interests furnish the money for revolution [5] and get their reward in concessions, and there are many men in whom the zest for adventure is so strong that they will gladly help in such enterprises.[6]

It has been repeatedly stated and commonly believed that the administration of the United States, chiefly indeed President Roosevelt, was the active force back of the revolution by which Panama became independent of Colombia. A New York lawyer of renown is credited with actually having engineered the uprising. The provocation was that the government at Bogota was very unreasonable if not impossible to deal with, and before the Panama Canal could be built some negotiation was imperative. In short, Colombia was holding up the world by demanding a huge sum of money, before she would permit the enterprise which greatly benefited her. The new government of Panama, which was recognized within twenty-four hours by the United States government, promptly made a treaty which gave us possession of everything we wanted on the Isthmus, and for reasonable terms, though the terms to Panama were also most liberal. Latin America was naturally scandalized, the Colombian people were embittered, and the $25,000,000.00 finally paid to Colombia by treaty nearly twenty years later was commonly talked of as amends for our having fomented a revolution which caused her loss of territory — but there was also an oil concession involved.

## The Typical Revolution

The Panama revolution was very unusual in the breadth of its influence because of the close relation of the United States government. The usual revolution has been much more nearly a personal or small-group matter.[7] Usually there have been real grievances to encourage

[5] I once heard an American of national reputation jocularly refer to a certain very well-known firm as having "financed half the governments and all the revolutions in South America."

[6] The newspaper account of the career of General Lee Christmas, a native of Louisiana, is suggestive. "The entrance of Christmas into the upheavals of Central America was incident to a revolution in Honduras in 1897. At that time he was a locomotive engineer in Honduras and on one of his trips ran into a revolutionist stronghold. The revolutionists piled aboard his train and ordered him to run it to a point where the federal forces were concentrated. When the fighting began, Christmas was obliged in self-defense to take a rifle and pitch in. The battle was won by the revolutionists, who made him a captain on the spot. From that time until 1911, when he assisted in overthrowing the government of President Davila in Honduras and reinstating that of General Bonilla, Christmas spent the greater part of his time fighting or planning to fight. Nicaragua, Salvador, Honduras and Guatemala were the scenes of most of his fighting and, in a large measure, he was instrumental in placing five presidents in office by revolutionary tactics. Christmas was the original of the character 'Clay,' hero of Richard Harding Davis's novel, *Soldiers of Fortune*, and he and the novelist were fast friends until the death of Davis." (From the *North American*, Philadelphia, January 22, 1924.)

[7] One of the pet pieces of bombast from the badly governed parts of Latin America is the statement, backed up by statute, that education is free and compulsory. The only drawback is that there are no schools. To see the real farce

the revolutionists, but rarely indeed have grievances been righted after they have with much rhetoric and eloquence been made the pretext of uprising. The revolution has seldom been an affair of justice. In many cases it would be more accurate to say that piracy and banditry have chosen the mask of government and the forms of taxation because it was safer and more profitable than exploitation on a smaller and less respectable scale. Sometimes a more or less benevolent despot like Diaz would provide a period of brilliant rule, with many good aspects of government, like that of the Medician rule in Florence.

The revolution business has caused much trouble for the American State Department because, by the Monroe Doctrine, we are in a sense standing back of these Latin American countries. Innumerable offenses have been committed against the property and persons of European citizens living in the Caribbean countries. For many of these offenses, if committed in Africa or Asia, the policy of the home governments would have been to take amends in the form of occupation of ports and annexation of territory. But foreign governments have been forced to remember that behind affairs in Mexico, or Haiti, or Guatemala was the Monroe Doctrine and the great power of the American government. It was partly to prevent such landings for the purpose of settling property claims that we stepped into Santo Domingo in 1907 and took financial control of the country. By this arrangement the United States government collects the Dominican customs and turns over 51% of the revenue to a New York bank, to be distributed to foreign creditors. As a result of this receivership Europe ceased to push its claims and we had a new semi-colonial venture on our hands. It will be many a day before the end of the American receivership of customs in Santo Domingo.

## The Question of Imperialism

This whole question of the Monroe Doctrine and the action of independent countries in Latin America brings forcibly to our consideration the fundamental question upon which people seem born to differ, " Is it better for a country to have order and force by outside authority or to remain independent and in a state of chronic disorder? " Aside from countries protected by the Monroe Doctrine, or other " big brother " influences, this question seems to be largely theoretical. The weaker peoples have not been allowed to remain in their maze of confusion. The way of the world has been conquest, if conquest is not too difficult. Thus the white man in America has taken the lands of the Indian and Europe has taken almost all of Africa and most of Asia. This is not

---

we should observe the way that General So-and-So promulgates a constitution, abolishes a constitution, declares martial law, combines twenty-seven states into nine provinces, separates them again, grants concessions and builds government railroads to his own town or his own land.

only modern practice, it is as old as history. Egyptians, Medes, Persians, Chinese and many others had conquered empires for themselves before the time of Christ. Modern land-grabbing is not exclusively a European and Caucasian game. The Japanese in the last forty years have gone out, like Europe, rough-handed and red-handed, to grasp and build an empire, for which they have greater need than any other power. But for the Monroe Doctrine all Latin America would long ago have been covered with European flags, which would have maintained a far higher degree of order and fostered a vastly greater business, commercial and educational development than now exists.

## American Imperialism

The United States has been in a peculiar position, in that we would neither let Europe rule Latin America nor go there ourselves.[8] Our reluctance to interfere or rule is due partly to our faith in the democratic ideal and partly to the fact that we had protested against European influence or possession. But despite all our protestations we took more possessions between 1898 and 1918 than any other nation.[9] During that time no empire grew so fast as the possessions of the United States. We have annexed Hawaii, Guam and the Philippines, and have advanced into the Caribbean like a glacier. All presidents and parties have the same policy. We have annexed Porto Rico, put a protectorate over Cuba, taken military possession of Haiti, Santo Domingo and Nicaragua.[10]

If we compare Porto Rico at the end of eighteen years of American rule with her sister island, Santo Domingo, we observe a striking contrast between the effects of good outside colonial rule and poor independent rule. In 1916, when we took Santo Domingo, Porto Rico had a universal system of free schools; Santo Domingo had a very much smaller number of schools. One island had good roads and much prosperity; the other had mule trails and little prosperity. One had

[8] Of one thing we can rest assured, whatever the Monroe Doctrine has done in deciding who shall rule or who shall be free, it has brought us no Latin American love. In a statement given to the Buenos Aires Nacion, Dr. José Leon Suarez, an Argentine authority on international law, says that " with the course of time the Monroe Doctrine has become an elastic theory protecting exclusively the interests of the United States, and it is subject to such arbitrary interpretations and applications as circumstances may warrant whenever the Washington administration sees fit to make use of Monroe's name."
  The peoples who are independent by grace of the Monroe Doctrine see our power, our political aggression, our personal bad manners, our diplomatic insults. The students in a college in Montevideo have had to learn by heart " the twenty-seven great insults of the United States to Latin America."
[9] This does not consider the " mandates " created by the Treaty of Versailles.
[10] As an evidence of our active imperialism I cite the statement (see Literary Digest, December 29, 1923) for the press issued by the United States Navy Department concerning General S. D. Butler of the Marine Corps. This one man has served in China (Boxer Uprising), Cuba, Nicaragua, Panama, Honduras, Mexico, Haiti, Santo Domingo and France.

considerable sanitation. The other had almost none at all. The external evidence looks favorable for outside rule, but it does not prove that the Porto Ricans or the Dominicans prefer outside rule. To Europeans all this seems merely a copy of her own economic imperialism and deceptive diplomacy. In an article on "Dollar Diplomacy," in *La Revue Universelle*, Paris, September 15, 1923, Pierre Arthuys says: "The American trusts, the pathfinders of Yankee Imperialism, march ahead of the Great Republic; they bribe, they buy, they seize. Usually the American government remains in the background for a time, until a convenient occasion comes to indorse their operations — even though these have been scrupulously ignored and even disavowed previously. . . . In Central America, 'civilizing capital' has practically monopolized the natural resources of the little republics, making the local governments its tools."

### The West Indian Colonial Governments

The West Indies afford a great variety of types of colonial government. Let us look at a British example. As one sails to Haiti, Caicos Island appears, white lime and sand shining through a thin cover of light green bush. No tree, no house for miles. Then on an eminence of thirty feet a two-story frame house, shadeless, but with lighthouse and flagpole beside it — the seat of government, residence of the commissioner. We drop anchor, a boat full of black deck-laborers starts out from the island and then turns back. It must wait for government. Government, British government, appears in a rowboat with a crew of three black oarsmen. The captain of this blue denim crew shows his superiority by wearing a pair of old canvas shoes. The shoes are out at the heel and without laces, but none the less he is the captain of a barefoot crew of two oarsmen. Government itself is represented by two persons, one a handsome mulatto of forty-five — a customs consul — with cap and blue uniform, and the air and tone of authority. Beside him in the rowboat is his chief, the customs officer, an unobtrusive young white man with a thoroughly English accent. He wears a white suit, white shoes, white helmet, white collar, neat tie, and is unobtrusive, with little show of authority.

"All well?" he asks, in a low tone, looking at us. "All well," answers the purser. The people may now mingle without danger of contagion and the boat-load of negroes again approaches the steamer. A rope is thrown over and one after another twenty-seven men and boys, clad in shirts, overalls and straw hats, climb hand over hand up the rope, walking with bare feet up the side of the steamer which they proceed to help unload.

On the wharf, faultlessly dressed and receiving his mail, is the ruler of the settlement, the commissioner or governor, as we would call him. It is evident that here is a man of ability, ruler of six hundred blacks and forty whites on Caicos, a coral strand with salt works and sponge fisheries.

Caicos and Grand Turk are dependencies of Jamaica, governed from Jamaica, where most of the laws for these islands are made, though some are made by the council which sits at Grand Turk, twenty-five miles from Caicos. This Council is composed of three officials appointed by the governor of Jamaica and three *appointed* residents of the island. The natives consider it a great honor to sit on the Council and to write J. P. or M. L. C. (commonly) after their names, yet one of them told me that they pass only the laws that they are told to pass and receive no pay for the doing of it. It is plain that the government of Caicos and Grand Turk comes like the rain, from above, and is no concern to the people themselves. It is one of the best of colonial governments in that it weighs lightly upon the people, affords them a reasonable degree of justice, and gives them enough education to meet their needs. Disturbances of the peace are few, and the memory of man runneth not to the time when there was murder in the islands.

This government from above (and a good government it is) may be considered an example of the British West Indian type of government. The Jamaican organization shows its essence admirably. The Governor, appointed by the Foreign Office in London, is assisted by a Council of twenty-nine members. Of these five are ex-officio members by virtue of being (appointed) members of the Governor's cabinet. Ten are appointed, theoretically, by the King of England, really by the Governor, or the Foreign Office in case of a contest. In addition to these *fifteen* appointees there are *fourteen* members of the Council elected by the people of Jamaica on restricted suffrage. The Council therefore has access to the opinion and knowledge of the natives of Jamaica in regard to local affairs. But while the native members may bring information of local needs, their relative number shows where the final power lies. On an actual show-down the elected natives have fourteen votes, the appointing power has fifteen votes and the chairman, and England rules. Is there any dispute about the vote? Will the natives rise in rebellion? In the harbor lies a warship, and in other not very far distant harbors lie other warships, so a military insurrection can be crushed almost as quickly as if it happened in one of the counties of England. Thus Jamaica has had centuries of peace and order and a government which maintained a relatively good system of schools. It also maintains courts wherein justice is quite as sure as in the courts of the United States, and furthermore it is quicker, cheaper and freer from entangling technicalities.

The government of Porto Rico also has the essential element of the Jamaican government — outside control. Only the machinery differs. The Governor and the judiciary are appointed by the President of the

United States. The Porto Ricans elect members to their own Senate and their House of Representatives, but the laws passed by the Porto Rican Congress can be vetoed by the United States Congress.

The French and Dutch colonies are governed in much the same way, except that in the Dutch colonies all the members of the Council are appointed.

Another type of government rules in the island of Haiti. This government has offered us one of the ironies of history, only matched by the irony of that historic occasion when Thomas Jefferson, sitting in a cool summer-house near Philadelphia, wrote the famous passage about the inalienable rights to life, liberty, and the pursuit of happiness, while at the very moment his hundred slaves toiled for him in the hot Virginia sun. The Haitian irony was afforded by Woodrow Wilson, who, as the German imperial power tottered in the fall of 1918, caused the pulses of hundreds of millions of people to beat more quickly, and their brains to seethe, by enunciating the doctrine of the self-determination of peoples. At that very moment, as commander of the armies and navies of the United States, he held military possession of the so-called Republic of Haiti and the so-called Republic of Santo Domingo. He had taken them without even the official knowledge and consent of the American Congress. A stubborn Haitian Congress which refused to approve a treaty we had drawn up was driven out of the legislative chamber by United States marines with drawn bayonets. The marines are said to have given more or less assistance in the election of a new Congress that was willing to sign a treaty giving us the right to keep order in Haiti (a vast authority) and granting other powers which virtually established an American protectorate. In Santo Domingo we were even less careful of form. On the ground that the interests of foreigners were in jeopardy, we landed marines in 1916, took physical possession of the country and set aside the President and Legislature, only leaving the courts alone. For seven years the island had a military government administered by officers of the United States Army and Navy. The theory of the occupation is that it is temporary, but well-informed persons do not expect it to be so. We may " withdraw " but I think we will return.

The Cuban government is yet another type, in theory the best of all, because it keeps open the door of hope. Jamaica and Porto Rico have good governments sustained by foreigners. When will foreign rule end? In theory, probably, never. Cuba is independent, save for an amendment to her constitution, embodied in a treaty with the United States, called the Platt Amendment, which lets the United States take charge of Cuba's foreign affairs and gives us the right to intervene in periods of disorder. In 1906 the United States did intervene; it established military government for a time, put Cuba on her feet, and then withdrew to let her take care of herself. This is an admirable theory, if we accept its basic assumption, that Cuba has or can develop the power of governing herself in a way that is satisfactory to civilization.

In 1922 the United States intervened in Cuba again — a remarkable kind of intervention.  One man in white duck clothing went to Cuba — General Enoch H. Crowder, of the American Army, the special representative of the President of the United States.  All that he did was to confer with the Cuban administration.  He made no pronouncements, he led no army, but everybody in Cuba knew that behind this single white-clad figure was the power of the United States of America.  Cuban politicians made a great clamor, for to them General Crowder was a most unwelcome visitor.  They had four men in office where one was needed. The savings to Cuban revenue which General Crowder made by eliminating offices were splendid for the Cuban taxpayer but appalling to the Cuban political ring, which loved office as dearly as any other political ring, and was proceeding rapidly to ruin Cuba, by the same process that caused seven Brazilian admirals to be drowned when one small Brazilian warship sank some years ago.

### Reform by Outside Force

This problem of giving good government to our neighbors who do not want us to do it presents itself most seriously to the American mind in Mexico.  What about Mexico?  Mexico is a vast storehouse of riches, especially mineral riches, but millions of its people have been hopelessly unprosperous for years at a time because of political and military disturbances.  Shall these times of chaos be allowed to recur?  There is much reason to think they will if Mexico is let alone.[11]  Then, shall she be let alone?  "No."  Who shall clean up Mexico?  "We shall," say millions of typical Americans.  Why?  "Because we think it ought to be done and we think we ought to do it."

This is, of course, in violation of the whole spirit of Anglo-Saxon government.  Since a band of indignant Englishmen caught King John at Runnymede in 1215 and made him sign Magna Charta, the development of British liberty has by almost continuous struggle been brought to the point where judge, jury, and executioner are three men, or groups of men, not one.

If the United States decides that Mexico needs to be cleaned up and sets out to do it, we become judge, jury and executioner.  By so doing we will violate Mexican patriotism and find Mexicans united to the last man, putting up a good fight.  In 1916, we sent General Pershing into Mexico with an armed force to catch Villa.  We did not catch Villa and

[11] We have devised a new way of interfering in Mexico exemplified very clearly in 1924 when de la Huerta, the reactionary, tried to overthrow Obregon.  The United States government sold arms to Obregon and prohibited the private shipment of arms to the rebel leaders.  These are acts whose ultimate significance is hard to guess.  What will they produce in fifty years if kept up?

military experts said it would take a quarter of a million men three years to bring order in Mexico and that the cost would be hundreds of millions of dollars. The Mexicans, like every other nation, believe in themselves and in their own kind of government. They fear us because of our power; they hate us because of our offensive manners. The North American and Latin American have far different cultures. Each believes that his own form is best. Here is the stuff of which wars are made, especially when we consider the aggravating effects of North American capital and North American bad manners in Latin American countries.

America has a grievance against Mexico. Our citizens have lost hundreds of millions of dollars, and a great many of them have been killed because of Mexican disorder. We are likely to have fresh grievances of this sort unless we come to rule through Mexicans like Obregon, whom we support on the throne. If we do "clean up" Mexico, we shall be acting as judge, jury, and executioner. Suppose we acted instead as an individual acts in a civilized community. If I go down the street and see a man beating his children I do not go in and club him. I may in an emergency stop him until the policeman comes. The policeman takes the man to court. Witnesses are called and testimony taken. The third party, the court, hands the children over to the Society for the Prevention of Cruelty to Children and the evil has been rectified. Suppose the aggrieved Americans, instead of persuading the American government to invade Mexico, persuaded the American government to complain about Mexico as a bad neighbor to a third party, some group of nations, acting in concert. Suppose the international association should investigate Mexico. Instead of Mexico being invaded by an army of the hated Gringoes (Americans), she would be visited by a delegation wearing long-tailed coats and silk hats, learned and honorable men of experience and renown in their own country — Portuguese from Portugal and Brazil, Spanish from Spain, from Argentina and from Chile, men speaking English, French, Italian, Japanese, Swedish. The gentlemen bear no arms. They come to seek facts. They travel over Mexico. Some of them go incognito; they seek information by all means within their reach. Some send special and trusted agents to places where they cannot go. They go back to some foreign city and confer. At the end of two months they make a pronouncement. They tell Mexico she must do thus and so, or they will appoint a guardian. They appoint a committee to see that Mexico does do thus and so.

After a lapse of time it is deemed that Mexico has not complied. The Commission on Mexico solemnly reports the fact to the group of nations. The group decides to take charge of Mexico. That means force. But note the effect upon the Mexican morale. If a quarter of a million Americans invade Mexico every Mexican who can raise a gun has his patriotism stirred to resist because he knows the Americans are wrong. But if the group of nations, after sending a commission of many nationalities, including several Spanish-speaking countries, takes months or years to the matter and solemnly tells Mexico she won't do, consider what a blow it is to morale. Mexico's enemy is not the hated Gringo. It is England, Spain, Argentina, Chile, sister Latin American countries, the mother country, disinterested Switzerland, disinterested Japan. The Mexicans wonder if after all they may be wrong, since all the world has condemned them even to the point of being ready to use force on them. It is to be expected that at this point the resistance of any nation would lose its main strength, morale.

A small blockade, cutting off all trade, could then bring Mexico to the point where she would have to submit to government by some group organized by the group of nations. She would then be in the same position that Cuba was in 1922 when General Crowder went there with suggestions, but with one difference. She would lose most of her power to hate the invader because the invader would be judicial rather than national — an organized world of many nations — rather than just one nation.

Such a solution, appealing to the wisdom of disinterested third parties, is too sensible to remain indefinitely unemployed because of national greed, and the pride that formerly resorted to duels as the means by which gentlemen settled their differences. If this kind of government ever comes to Mexico, the group of nations might create it by sending one resident commissioner or adviser who would be assisted by a body of experts gathered as other bodies of experts are gathered for service in some distant place.

FIG. 359 — The cane field best symbolizes West Indian commercial history since Columbus introduced the cane. Note stripped stalks in foreground and litter of leaves. (Courtesy National City Co.)

## CHAPTER XL

## THE WEST INDIES — TRADE–WIND ISLES

### A. TRADE-WIND CLIMATE

THE West Indies stand in a warm sea, and the trade-winds, warmed and moistened by this sea, blow across all of them. These are the two great primary geographic facts about this group of islands whose area is but little larger than that of Great Britain.

These trade-winds, always warm, but nevertheless refreshing sea-breezes, blow mostly from the east or northeast. Thus, one side of every island is windward and the other side is leeward. The third great geographical fact about these islands is that most of them are mountainous, giving to the windward sides much more rain than the leeward sides receive. This makes great differences in climate within short distances, a thing quite unknown in the eastern half of the United States, where our whirling cyclonic winds blow in quick succession from all directions upon every spot of territory. Thus both sides of the Appalachian Mountains are nearly alike in their rainfall, forest growth and productive possibilities. On the contrary the West Indian (trade-wind) mountains have different worlds on their opposite slopes. The eastern or windward side, cloud-bathed and eternally showered upon, is damp and dripping. There are jungles with velvety green ferns, and forests with huge trees. The rainbow is a prominent feature of the landscape. On the windward side one receives a striking impression of lush vegetation. On the leeward side of the very same ridge and only a few miles distant there is another kind of world, the world of scanty rainfall, with all its devastating consequences. (Figs. 20, 360.)

On the Jamaica mountains, 6000 feet in height, the rainfall contrast ranges from 200 inches on the windward side to fifteen inches on the leeward plains. Porto Rico mountains are only 3000 feet high, but the rainfall ranges from 120 inches to less than forty. Often there is a ring of cloud around a trade-wind mountain. This cloud is formed by the cooling that results from the moist trade-wind being forced upward in

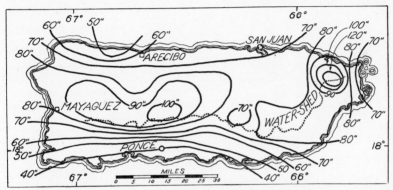

Fig. 360 — This map of annual average rainfall should be examined in comparison with Fig. 362. This can be taken as a trade-wind type. If the mountains were higher, the contrasts would be greater. (From Dr. O. L. Fassig's manuscript map.)

crossing the mountain. The cloud cap is almost as much a part of the elevated trade-wind isle as is the forest itself. It streams away to leeward from the crest like a flag. As the cloud mass floats from the land it becomes smaller and less dense and finally fades entirely by evaporation.

In the summer months the greater heat of the sun makes the larger islands somewhat hotter than the adjacent sea. This causes the air over the islands to become heated and therefore to expand and rise, and air rushes in from the sea to fill its place. The rising air cools and condenses the moisture, which falls to earth in the tropic shower. Often the rain is accompanied by thunder and lightning and usually it comes in the afternoon or early hours of the night. This type of rain (convection rain) comes to all sides of the islands.

Most trade-wind lands have, broadly speaking, a rainy season and a dry season. On the windward side the dry season is not really dry at all, it is merely less wet (see rainfall graph for San Juan); but on the leeward side (see rainfall graph for Ponce), there is the pronounced dry season. This is characteristic of the south shores of Jamaica and Porto

Rico, and of most of the area of Cuba and Haiti, and the interior and leeward areas of Central America and tropic Mexico (Fig. 19).

One more thing, a deadly thing, must be told about this climate. For reasons not fully understood, trade-wind rainfall is less regular than the cyclonic rainfall of the eastern United States. Therefore the tropic isles are subject to drought and all the hardship that drought brings.

At intervals, fortunately rather rare, the heavy tropic cyclones, called hurricanes, sweep through the West Indies.[1] These hurricanes are like the cyclones of the United States, but stronger. They sometimes smash down banana plantations, uproot trees and destroy buildings and ships.

These variants of the West Indian rainfall — rainy and dry seasons; differences in altitude affecting the amount of rainfall; the stubborn fact

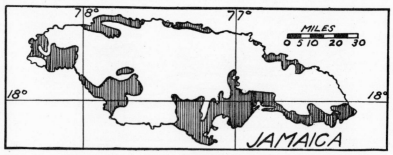

FIG. 361 — These maps (see Fig. 362) made to the same scale show the resemblance of Porto Rico and Jamaica in size, shape, position, direction, latitude, and proportion of alluvial plains. Vertical shading, alluvial plains; solid black area (Porto Rico only), above 1000 feet.

of occasional drought — all combine to make corresponding variations in forest growth. The heavy, continuous rains of the windward slope make the *rain forest*.[2] This is the forest of tall, large trees, through which one can pass readily because the high foliage is so thick that the undergrowth is smothered. In other places where rain is less abundant and where there is a dry season we see the real jungle — a forest of small trees all tied together with creepers and vines, and often so matted as to be impassable until a path is chopped. Where the rainy season is short and the dry season is long, there are scattered trees and thickets of scrub, which give way to the savanna — grassland with occasional trees — as rainfall becomes scantier and the dry season more pronounced. Where the rainy season lasts only a few weeks, the hard life conditions

[1] For a description, see Salisbury's *Physiography* or any text on Meteorology. For emotional description, see *Typhoon,* by Joseph Conrad, master painter of the tropics.

[2] The edge of a tract of rain forest is impenetrable. When it is cut the impassable jungle springs up to fill its place. If left alone long enough the process of growing and smothering again restores the open rain forest.

produce only cactus, grass, and scattered bushes, many of them thorny.
Considerable areas of such land are to be found in southwestern Santo
Domingo and adjacent parts of Haiti, where three mountain ranges
running northeast and southwest cut off the trade-winds from the interior
and southern plains.

The influence of the mountain in making rain is most marked, as any
rainfall map (Fig. 360) will show. One day in July 1923, I climbed
halfway up the mountain at the east end of Porto Rico, where the rainfall is more than 100 inches per year. San Juan, at sea level, had been
suffering for many months from drought, and on the day of my journey
the city lay under bright sunshine. Twenty miles away, at an elevation
of about 1000 feet, which I reached at eleven o'clock, there was a succession of clouds driven by the northeast wind. The clouds became

FIG. 362 — (See Fig. 361.)

larger and thicker, and in two hours' time I had passed through seven
showers, none of which was heavy. The rain would fall for a minute
or two and instantly the sun would shine, if indeed it did not happen
to be shining while the rain fell from some particularly small cloud.
The native manager of the estate to which I was going met me dripping
wet. He did not take the trouble to change his clothes as he went into
the forest with me. There was a reason why he should not, for in half
an hour the sky, alternating sunshine and cloud, seemed to open and
pour water down upon that mountain-side for perhaps fifteen minutes.
But the return journey showed that it had not rained at all two miles
away and a few hundred feet lower down. The rain that fell above the
1000-foot level might be called mountain-made.

B.  PORTO RICO — TYPICAL MOUNTAINOUS TRADE-WIND ISLAND

A mountain trade-wind island like Porto Rico shows clearly the many
contrasting influences of elevation on the windward and leeward sides.
The eastern plain of Porto Rico is so wet that the sugar planters have
to make expensive artificial drainage ditches, putting in tile drains and
ridging up the fields so the cane may have enough dry earth to stand in

and not be drowned out. On the south shore, quite to the contrary, great efforts are expended to get water to the cane-field, for irrigation is there necessary. For this purpose some of the water is brought from the too-abundant supply of the windward side. The people have gone so far as to make reservoirs near the summit of the mountains on the rainy northeast; then they dig tunnels under the mountain backbone of the island to carry water to the more arid southwest. Thus in three places this fairly common trade-wind-isle device of making the rainy windward section supply water for the drier south side is utilized in Porto Rico.[3]

On the south side of the island one sees rivers on the map. But at the end of the dry season the automobile swings down through the gravelly stream beds, bone-dry. The road is dusty. There are but few trees. The country creates a shadeless impression. The villages look hot and unhomelike, resembling Spain, whence the people came.

There are wide expanses of silver-green sugar-cane where there is water for irrigation, but beyond the last irrigation ditch is the brown and empty land, much like Southern California's summer landscapes above the irrigation line. The forest fire I saw in the scanty open forest above heightened the resemblance to California, which is also maintained by the large areas of pasture land, with a cactus here and there, where the big herds of Porto Rican oxen were resting after the arduous harvest.

Going from Ponce up the south side of the mountains affords a great contrast to the green journey up from San Juan. The first three miles of plain and low hills are almost treeless, with close-cropped grass. Where there is forest the trees stand apart and one can see well between them, as in the foothill forest of Southern California or Majorca. The few houses along the dry stream-bed look hot and desolate. There are no cottages on the hills, only pasture, but as one looks up the valley into the higher zone of greater rain, toward the backbone of the mountain, each headland projecting into the valley is greener than the one below it, and the final distance is very green. The road climbs steadily, and six miles from Ponce the northeast (moister) side of a hill has a patch of very thin corn and some banana plants, so small that they almost resemble corn. As the automobile sped along, the corn patches quickly became greener and the banana plants larger and more numerous. At eight miles it was raining a little, the mountain forest was thicker, plantain leaves overhung the road, the road itself was strewn with ripe mangoes, and big pumpkin vines climbed down the banks from the gardens above. At twelve miles ferns hung over the bank by the roadside and the rain came down in

---

[3] This method, very common in Hawaii, was used in Madeira more than two centuries ago, and the masonry conduits built by the slaves of that day to carry northeast streams to southwest slopes are still in good working order.

torrents. At eighteen miles, just before we crossed the divide at 2000 feet, wild caladiums and wild canna grew beside the road in a riot of wet tropical greenness.

As we entered the banana belt, houses began to line the roadside and the neighboring ravine, but there were not so many of them as there were on the north side of the island. The north slopes, from bottom to top, are almost everywhere dotted with the thatched houses standing in the midst of t h e little machete-made farm described i n t h e chapter on Peoples. Steepness seemed no barrier. Even after seeing the terraces of the Apennines and the shores of Lake Garda I had not dreamed that men could live and grow crops (other than tree crops) on such steep lands. Transportation by w a g o n is unthinkable; even by donkey it is most difficult. T h e footpath and the man-pack are the common types.

Porto Rico has r i c h soils. The backbone of the mountain is of volcanic origin a n d w a s pushed up out of the sea with much limestone on its slopes. That is a rich combination. Its name means rich port.

Fig. 363 — While I was focusing my camera in the back yard of a house in a north-coast Porto Rican village, the heir apparent of the family entered the scene and thoughtfully paused to contemplate and suck his thumb. It should be observed that he did not put his hands in his pockets, as careless boys in America so often do.

Picture taken to show how Porto Rico supports so many people. It is evident that shoes and clothing are not a heavy expense. The house and yard were bowered with trees, with an undergrowth of shrubbery and a carpet of creeping things — all edible, every plant of them — coconuts, plantain, banana, coffee, cane, beans, greens, and flavorings. (Photo J. Russell Smith.)

## Tropic Abundance

This land which has always the warm trade-winds, twelve months of rain, the palm tree, and rich soil, naturally gives the impression of tropic abundance. But the oft-made statement that the tropics will grow everything is quite misleading. Perhaps they *might,* but practically they will not, as the newly arrived Yankees promptly discovered. The newcomer plants a garden of New Jersey vegetable seed bought from a New York seedsman. The ants eat up most of the seed. The next time he plants his seeds in boxes, and transplants the young seedlings, only to find shortly that the beetles have cut off most of his plants at the top of the ground.

Tropic abundance applies to the enemies of plants as well as to the speed of plant growth. When it comes down to practical edible plants now available and capable of surviving, their variety in the tropic garden is smaller than the variety in a Northern garden. If I want a good and varied garden I will go to the United States, not to the middle of the West Indies. After scanning many West Indian markets in midsummer I found that my own United States garden was richer in variety, and there is a plethora in the American city market as compared with those of San Juan and Ponce. What is worse, most of the tropic stuff is flat and insipid in flavor in comparison with our own. These handicaps, in combination with the tropic inhibitions on labor, cause the diet to be very restricted and monotonous. Rice and beans are the great staples of Porto Rican diet for all classes of people who live by the proceeds of trade rather than from the produce of their own gardens. With the Americans I met who had been there as long as a month and were eating at Porto Rican tables, I found it difficult to keep the conversation away from food, so vociferous was their state of rebellion against rice and beans. Both rice and beans are imported, although there is still much unused land in the island.

### American Rule

When the Americans took possession of Porto Rico in 1898 it was a populous island. Under the Spanish dominion it had been chiefly valued for the sugar plantations of the plains, which were then producing about 50,000 tons a year. Coffee was the rival product, produced by the machete farmers of the plateau and brought down mountain paths on man-back and mule-back to the ports. Spain did nothing to encourage the coffee but it was the only thing the natives could grow in the hills and have to sell.

The government of Porto Rico by the United States since 1898 has brought two great changes into the economic life of the island. These are free trade in sugar and a system of roads. We opened the best gold mine the Porto Ricans ever saw by giving them free trade in sugar to the American market, thus presenting many millions of dollars to the Porto Rican sugar-growers each year.

As for the roads, they required so much work and money and offered so good an opportunity for graft, that the Spanish colonial government did not bother with them. In four centuries Spain had made 275 kilometers of good road in Porto Rico. In eight years the United States had made 800 kilometers. There is now a good system of roads, going around the island and crossing it several times and connecting all the main points. The roads are much better than any similar mileage that can be found in a similar area of the United States outside a few of our most populated sections. Roads are perhaps more necessary in the West Indies than in the United States. The rainy season, with its daily soaking, often makes the clayey land impassable for wagon, beast, or man. When the Americans took possession it was common to say it cost more to get coffee twenty miles down to the port than from the port to Europe. Twelve oxen have been known to be stuck in the mud, with nothing but an empty, two-wheeled cart attached to them.

The opening of the American market to Porto Rican produce without tariff charges has caused the trade of the island to increase from $8,500,-000.00 exports in 1901 to $49,000,000.00 in 1915 and to $72,000,000.00 in 1922. Tobacco increased nine-fold in value; sugar-export increased from 50,000 tons in Spanish days to 300,000 or 400,000 tons now. Coffee has not increased. Its chief market had been in Spain, and Spain raised a tariff against coffee as soon as we took the island. The excellent quality of this " mild " coffee has not yet become generally known to us in our recently opened market, and it is considered expensive in comparison with the cheaper Brazilian coffee. It is a slow process to create a new market for coffee.

These three products — sugar, tobacco and coffee — keep the leadership in the exports of the island, although the American influence has resulted in the export, to some extent, of oranges and grapefruit, though this is still a minor industry and shows no great signs of growth.

### Sugar

It is in sugar that the influence of the Yankee occupation has made itself most felt. The tariff advantage of a cent or two a pound is an enormous incentive. New areas of semi-arid land are now becoming available for cane culture under the newly established irrigation systems in the southern half of the island. The crop is not expensive to raise and a planting will last ten years. One may simply grow cane and sell it to the nearest " central." To establish a " central " or modern sugar-mill is quite another matter. The industry, with its huge mills, is capitalistic, and therefore tempts the men of Wall Street to organize it. The Porto Rico sugar-lands are passing more and more into their hands. As a result, extensive investment in sugar-mills and sugar estates has been made, and because of the high price of sugar much hilly land that was in forest or in coffee plantations in the days of Spanish rule has been cleared and put to cane (and gully washing).

Sugar makes much commerce. Most of the new mills are made of structural steel covered with corrugated iron. Mules are sent from Kentucky and Tennessee, hundreds of them, and plows, harness and wagons must be supplied from the United States. Even coal must be sent, for the little tram trains that run about the plantation on miniature railroads. The sugar industry employs more than 60,000 laborers in the fields, and there are many others working at the mills, on the tram-roads, and driving ox-carts.

The common method of growing cane is still by hand labor. The process is somewhat as follows: The ground is plowed and harrowed with ox-teams. The shoots of cane are planted and men with hoes keep down the weeds, some of which they pull by hand. In a day, eight or ten men will clean an acre of young cane. This is done two or three times before the cane-plants are large enough to shade the earth completely and keep down the rival growth. After this, the cane is let alone for several months until it is ripe. Then the great labor of the sugar harvest begins. The cane is hauled to the mills by ox-teams and temporary railroads and the field is left littered with cane leaves. After the cane is once established, it is allowed to grow up for second, third, or even fourth cuttings; or sometimes even more. The leaves that remain after cutting are piled between the alternate rows. They cover the ground so effectively that only one row needs to be cultivated after the first planting.

The predominance of hand labor is shown by the fact that in a morning's journey 175 field laborers were seen, while only five oxen were drawing cultivators, and most of these had a boy leading them as well as a man guiding the cultivator.

The sugar worker is nearly always a landless man, often living in the villages on company land, without gardens, and depending upon the store for his food supply. In such a store the most conspicuous things were a row of open boxes of rice, dried peas, dried beans in two varieties, dried chick-peas, a box of salted pigs' feet, and pigs' ears at $.08 a pound, and a box of dried codfish, all standing out in the open, exposed to flies and the humidity, but keeping perfectly because they were salted or dried.

## Tobacco

Tobacco is grown chiefly in the mountain valleys and slopes of the northward-draining interior where it is the staple crop. It is commonly planted in November and harvested in February and March. After the tobacco harvest the ground is planted to what are called minor crops — corn, with beans in the corn, and sweet potatoes, for the local food supply. After harvest in May and June the ground is plowed in July, and through July, August, September and October it is limed and harrowed repeatedly to make it fine, mellow and rich for the great event of the year, the planting of tobacco in November.  If the rainfall were a little more regular, a crop might be grown in the time between the minor crops and tobacco.  The farmers, however, do not take the risk of drought, though it would perhaps pay to do so under a greater pressure of man upon the land.

Much of the Porto Rican tobacco is grown under cotton cover which keeps away beetles and wind, and increases the humidity, and the fineness of the leaf, thus making it more valuable for cigar wrappers.  These ghostly-looking, white-covered fields are very expensive to operate.  The cloth can be used only four times and this phase of tobacco-growing is

FIG. 364 — Shade-grown tobacco under cheesecloth, and tobacco houses on the hills of central Porto Rico near Cayey.  Characteristic hill landscape. (Courtesy Robert S. Platt, University of Chicago.)

only practised by corporations, mostly with American capital.  The tobacco barns are striking in appearance, with their huge bulk spread thickly over the landscape.  Tobacco lands in the neighborhood of Caguas, one of the important tobacco districts, are worth $500.00 an acre on the flats and $300.00 on the slopes which are less fertile and of course harder to cultivate.

### Coffee

Coffee is grown on the higher, steeper, wetter mountain slopes between 400 and 2500 feet in elevation.  Here there is mile upon mile of steep hillside which appears from a distance to be forest.  A nearer view reveals the feathery tops of a leguminous tree universally used to shade the coffee tree and also to fertilize the coffee-tree with the nitrogen from its roots. Beneath this open-topped shade are coffee-bushes, ten or twelve feet high, and often sticking out from among them are the great spear-like tops of the plantain. Coffee-picking is something in which an entire family can engage. After the coffee-season is over the cane-season begins, and many of the laborers migrate from the hills where coffee is raised to the cane-fields below. Coffee-berries are picked by hand as we pick cherries or currants. They are dried to get rid of the pulpy skin and then put through various machines for sorting and sizing. A wide pavement and a dry season of sunny days are important in coffee-curing.

In open spaces by the roadside and in the villages in the mountain valleys the coffee-drying yard, with its cement floor, is the symbol of this industry, just as the tobacco-curing house is a sign of the tobacco industry and the tall smokestack and red roofs of the sugar-mill are of the sugar industry. (Fig. 378.)

The coffee-grower is quite different from the sugar-worker in his relative dependence upon trade and upon the garden. Coffee is the crop of the independent mountaineer. Unlike the landless sugar-laborer a coffee-grower back in the hills usually has his *conuco* with plantains, corn, beans, sweet potatoes, and often the caladium. A man with two acres can have half an acre of coffee and keep his garden and goat roving around over the remaining one and a half acres. These gardens are often planted out, allowed to grow for two or three years and then abandoned, giving the country a cut-over appearance and causing a great scarcity of wood. It is fortunate that the gardens are abandoned, for otherwise their almost unbelievable steepness would cause them to be washed away. I climbed through a coffee-grower's garden that had been so recently abandoned that old corn stalks were still standing and a few sweet potato plants were yet alive, but the stumps of the previously cut bushes were still there, and the wild growth was again holding the soil in place. The slope was so steep that I could climb down only with difficulty but not in a straight line. Going back I was glad to avail myself of stumps and bushes to help me up the slope. The near-by coffee plantation was on land a little less steep. Holes had been dug in the hillside to stop the wash. There were often six or eight to the square rod. Some of the holes would contain a barrel of water. When they were washed full of leaves and sediment a coffee-bush was planted in this accumulation of fertility and a fresh hole was dug. This combination of fertilizing and erosion-control called Ahojado de Mino (hole of the mine) is said to be common in Porto Rican and Central American plantations. It is the best thing I saw as an aid for the continued presence of man on those slopes. The principle is capable of wide application.

### The Population Problem

The utilization of such steep land is one of the characteristic results of a population of nearly 400 people to the square mile (about ten times that of Iowa) supporting themselves by agriculture in a land three-fourths of which is mountainous.

Nearly every Porto Rican family, if able to afford the luxury, has a goat or two. The milk is used for children and for cheese and the flesh is sold in the markets. Cows are not common. They eat too much.

The American rule of Porto Rico has produced great increase of trade, but the accompanying rapid increase in population is creating a grave problem. Under the last twenty years of the Spanish régime, the population increased 1.3% per year. Under the last sixteen years of American rule it has increased 1.6% per year. In the year 1915 the registration

FIG. 365 — Panorama of Cayey, Porto Rico, one of the larger interior towns. Tobacco-curing houses on distant hills.

of births and deaths showed an increase of 2%. In other words, the increased trade of the island has merely accelerated the birth-rate and increased the number of people with little or no increase in the standard of living. Porto Rico is crowded. The cities are crowded. Governor Yager said: [4]

" But, owing to their inherited improvidence, their racial characteristics, and perhaps to the tropical climate, those checks upon population which in colder climates seem adequate to keep the increase of people well within the limits of subsistence seem to be lacking among them. The birth-rate seems to bear no relation whatever to the conditions of industry and the opportunities for employment."

Intelligent Porto Ricans are naturally concerned.[5] They see that the landless are increasing; there are now more than 800,000 of them. They also know that hundreds of thousands of these people are absolutely

[4] *Geographical Review,* March 1916, p. 212.
[5] Judge Rodriguez-Sorra, of the district courts of Porto Rico, says: " There is danger, too, in educating the people before there is work in Porto Rico for educated people to do. Education serves no purpose among a poor and ragged population except to increase discontent."

dependent upon the continuance of the American tariff. If that pref-
erential advantage should be swept away from Porto Rico, she would have
to grow sugar in competition with Cuba and other tropical areas where
the natural resources are better; and it could not be done. This would
create almost as much of a calamity as a great earthquake, for the
standard of living is now low, and if the income of the people were cut
down a third, many of them would face starvation. Even now they are
living on rice and beans, or bananas and beans, or sweet potatoes and
beans, with a little dried codfish, and meat once or twice a week.

The Porto Rican may be poor but he is proud. One sees more beggars
on Fifth Avenue in an hour than in San Juan in a week.

One of their population problems is the Jibaro. The word means
"one escaped from civilization." When the Spaniards began to enslave
the natives some of them ran away to the interior. When the Spaniards
brought negro slaves some of these also ran away to the interior. When
they deported petty offenders to Porto Rico nearly all of them went
to the interior. There the three runaway strains have mingled, producing a care-free dweller in a thatched hut, but a man ill-fitted by temperament to face the rigors of a steady job. As the struggle for existence
becomes more industrial, extinction may be the fate of the Jibaro.

The dense population of Porto Rico is almost exclusively rural and
agricultural. The proportion of the city population is about the same
as in the Dakotas. San Juan, the capital (71,000 population), has a
location that was better for the days of pirates than it is for the present.
It is on the tip of a narrow peninsula. Motor busses flock up and down
this peninsula, now a mass of growing suburbs. These busses are named
like ships and the names bespeak the mingled forces of the new Porto
Rico — Popularidad, La Gloria, Perla de Caribe, Paris, La Joya del
Hogar (home), Baby Smile, Jack Dempsey, Eversharp, and Goodyear
Cord. These last reflect the discovery that certain firms will paint a bus
if they can name it.

We see another sign of dense population in the Porto Rican needlework industry. This kind of household industry is an ill-paid source of
income for women in many densely peopled lands. The skill of the
women and girls is marked in making lace and drawn-work. This artistic
craft-work of Porto Rico is superior to that of Mexico, and a future
development and organization of the industry is to be expected. In 1923
a New York firm opened a large factory in Ponce to make clothing for
the United States market.

The Porto Rican straw hats that are sold in the American markets are
made in the eastern end of the island. There the moisture-laden air
encourages the palm to flourish, but even so there are not enough palm-
leaves to supply the demand for these popular hats and quantities of
prepared leaves are imported from the Dominican Republic.

The hand weaving of straw hats is a household industry. Sometimes the old men help the women and girls. Traveling traders buy
the hats and sell them to dealers either for export or for local wear.

There is a discussion of Porto Rico's future in the concluding chapter.

## C. JAMAICA

Jamaica, with an area of 4207 square miles, is a close physical twin
of its neighbor, Porto Rico. The two islands are alike not only in shape
but in character. Jamaica, like Porto Rico, is mountainous. Its high
mountain backbone runs from east to west, with valleys cutting into it

FIG. 366 — This picture from the windward side of Martinique might typify
Jamaica or almost any other West Indian island. Tree fern at left.
(Courtesy Robert S. Platt, University of Chicago.)

on all sides. Much of this area is, in the English sense at least, unculti-
vable. The stretches of coastal plain, though they comprise only one-
sixth of the area, are excellent for sugar and bananas. The Jamaican
uplands are not volcanic and therefore not so fertile as those of Porto
Rico, but like Porto Rico the island has much limestone on its lower
parts. Jamaica has many caves with interesting prehistoric remains.

The climates of the two islands are essentially alike. The population of
Jamaica is only half as dense as the population of Porto Rico. Jamaica
has had better government, especially during the nineteenth century, than
Porto Rico. For two hundred and fifty years it has had the great colonial
blessing of British rule. Through most of the time the island was of
interest to the mother country through its products of sugar, molasses
and rum. Its long possession by the orderly and capitalistic British
means that it is a well-equipped island. Although it is only thirty-five
by 140 miles in extent, it has 200 miles of well-equipped standard-gauge

railway, government-owned. Ninety miles of steam and electric tramway run around the island, twenty-five miles of mule tramway, and 1144 miles of excellent stone road, reaching all parts of the island and everywhere wide enough for automobiles to pass. There are 2000 miles of telegraph and telephone lines. (Fig. 361.)

The city of Kingston, which has one of the finest harbors in the world, serves twenty steamship lines. Its location, almost at the gate of the Panama Canal, places it on one of the world's greatest commercial highways. Local lines circumnavigate the island, which has many small outports. Proportionally the United States cannot rival these facilities.

### Diversified Industry

Despite all these advantages, the island is far less prosperous than Porto Rico, and has a much smaller development of trade. This is partly because the negro population can emigrate and do tropic field-labor much more easily than the Porto Rican whites. Another important reason is that Jamaica has had no boon like the American tariff which hands over to the people of Porto Rico ten or twelve millions of dollars a year that they would not otherwise get. As a consequence the Jamaica sugar industry lingers along as did that of Porto Rico before American possession, exporting 30,000 or 40,000 tons a year. It boomed tremendously in the sugar famine of 1919 and 1920 and slumped so dreadfully immediately thereafter that the island government had to loan $2,000,000.00 to the sugar planters. There

FIG. 367 — I saw a West Indian saddler stop work one morning to eat breakfast — a chunk of bread and an avocado. This fruit, 20 to 30% fat, the product of a beautiful tree, is one of Nature's rich gifts to the tropics. The seaman's name " midshipman's butter " is descriptive of nutritive function. If we could learn to can, dry or otherwise preserve it, and then like it, a great new food supply would become available. (Courtesy U. S. Bureau of Plant Industry.)

are many " ruinate " sugar estates dating back to the days of slave prosperity. The industry is carelessly prosecuted and there is unused land which might be productive if it were fertilized, but the expense would be considerable, and at the present time it cannot compete with the fertile and all but virgin cane-fields of the neighboring island of Cuba.

Jamaica has a number of establishments for the manufacture of dried banana products — pieces of dried banana called " banana figs," whole dried bananas called " fig bananas," and cooking bananas dried so thoroughly as to be hard. These are broken into pieces to form banana chips and ground into meal. One of the companies has its own factory in London to grind the chips into flour; for while banana flour does not keep long, it is excellent for breakfast food, porridge, puddings and other dishes, and is recommended for people of weak digestion. The possibility of substituting this tropic carbohydrate for the cereal or potato of the temperate zone is a question of relative cost and food habit — and food habits change slowly.

The only important industrial change that has happened to Jamaica in the last fifty years has been the development of the banana business. Ten to fourteen million bunches a year are now exported, bringing in about $10,000,000.00 revenue. This development is due almost entirely to American enterprise, to the United Fruit Company of Boston, which has put on the fast steamship lines and guaranteed to take all the bananas of the island. The ruin of the crop by hurricanes for six-month periods three years in succession, 1915–17, shows some of the trade-wind-island difficulties.

Because its trade is smaller than that of Porto Rico, less than half as much per capita, Jamaica must depend more upon home supplies. The produce of the garden patch around the palm hut is spoken of in Jamaican statistics as " ground provisions." Thus the yam, in nutrition like the potato or bread, is a staple article of the Jamaican workman's diet.

The lack of any great all-absorbing staple like the sugar of Porto Rico has caused the development in Jamaica of many minor industries. Three or four thousand tons of cacao beans are exported each year from the wetter areas on the north side. Most of the world's supply of allspice, or pimento, some 11,000,000 pounds, is gathered from the low, rounded trees that stand in Jamaican pastures. Often small boys climb the trees to gather the clusters of fruit while it is still immature. Or the clusters may be cut off with knives fastened to the end of poles. When dried in the sun, or in dryers, the fruit — then called spice — is ready for shipment. Most of the work in this industry is prosecuted by the women, for whom it is admirably suited.

There are small shipments of lime juice, rum, coconuts, logwood for dyestuffs, beeswax and honey gathered from the blooms of logwood and lignum vitae trees in the forest. Sometimes the bee products are worth as much as a dollar per capita for everybody on the island. There is also a growing industry in preserving fruit, especially guava, for which there is a demand in England. One of the best known products of Jamaica is ginger. The underground stem of the plant is dried and is of such superior quality that it brings double price.

FIG. 368 — A sea of sugar cane in central Cuba. It is divided by lanes into
The white buildings of village and sugar-central appear in the distance.

Hand-made hats called " panamas " are manufactured. They are made
out of the leaf-stalk fibers of a palm called jippi-jappa, named from the
canton in the province of Manabi on the coast of Ecuador where the
finest of these hats are made. Those made in Jamaica commonly pass as
a lower grade of the genuine article. It takes two or three days to make
a hat of ordinary quality and ten or fifteen days to make a really fine
one. It is worthy of note that this industry requires no equipment but
skillful fingers and it can be carried on in any hut. The results of a
year's labor can be carried away under your arm.

### Population

The situation and prospects of Jamaica are best shown, however, by
an analysis of her population. The blessings of two and a half centuries
of British rule have produced an island with nearly a million people, of
whom the ruling, owning, controlling 2% are white. About 2% are
Hindus recently imported as contract laborers for the plantations. There
is a sprinkling of Chinese, who carry on nearly all the small merchandise
business. Then there are increasing hordes of negroes, field laborers,
about half illiterate, despite the many free schools maintained by the
British government. The attitude toward education is well indicated by
the complaint of a country school teacher in Jamaica over the loss of
time of the pupils in connection with the washing of their clothes. She
said it took one day to wash, one day to dry the garment, and one day
to iron it. When one considers the limited wardrobe required for this
climate the humor of the situation appears. This novel service of a piece
of cheap cotton would doubtless appeal to the schoolboys of many lands.
It is interesting to see the people as they work around their thatched
huts or wend their way to the town market-place with bunches of
bananas or baskets of yams or vegetables on the female head, but not
for a moment on the masculine head. The traveler is at times startled
by the apparently awful quarrels that he overhears. The deluge of
dangerous words leads him to anticipate imminent murder, but nothing

squares to aid in fighting fire that sometimes runs through the dead leaves.
(Courtesy West Indian Sugar Finance Corporation and National City Co.)

happens. The words of the childlike West Indian have a lighter specific gravity than those of New England or of Scotland.

The chief export of Jamaica might well be said to be young negroes tempted by greater wages in lands of greater resources. In a few years before 1920 it is estimated that 200,000 left the island, going mostly to the cane fields of Cuba, the banana plantations of Central America, and to the United States. A decade earlier it was these Jamaica negroes who did most of the manual labor in building the Panama Canal. We boasted not unjustly of this achievement and the average reader might have thought that we North Americans actually did the digging. It is the West Indian negro who mans the banana plantations of the United Fruit Company on the Caribbean shores of Central America. Nearly every freight steamer that enters the West Indies picks up at Jamacia or some other island of first call an extra crew of deck laborers who load and unload the vessel while in West Indian waters and leave the boat when she sails away. I have even found records of the Jamaica negro building railroads in Paraguay and Southern Brazil. A recent census showed that 20% of them are infected with hookworm, but the Rockefeller Institute has come to the rescue with clinics to rid the population of this disease. As the new knowledge of scientific medicine and prevention of disease is applied to the peoples of the tropical countries it will tend to accelerate an increase of population and cause us to wonder where the surplus will go. Has not the time come for science to form some new concept with regard to human quality? Thus far it has done wonders to increase the *quantity* of humanity. The Rockefeller Foundation with its war on tropic diseases might well be called the greatest negro breeder of all history.

### D.  CUBA [6]

#### Sugar

Cuba is queen of the sugar-cane world as well as queen of the Antilles. Its area is 44,128 square miles, while all the other West Indies together

[6] For an excellent article on Cuba see Whitbeck, *Geographical Review*, April 1922.

have but 45,882. Not only is Cuba large but its soils are rich and its surface is good for machine agriculture. Most of its surface is a rolling plain, like that of Kansas or Iowa, admirable for agriculture, especially for growing sugar cane. On 80% of her area, Cuba has limestone soil, the richest there is except the lavas. Some of her lands have been under cultivation for 400 years, and even yet but little fertilizer is used. Once sugar-cane is planted it is allowed to give eight, ten or even twelve harvests before replanting, and two tons of sugar per acre is a common yield.

Cuba's location, close to the United States, the world's greatest sugar-market, makes her delivery costs on sugar only $.00$\frac{1}{4}$ a pound. To cap the list of advantages, the climate is approximately perfect for the production of sugar-cane, the great commercial dependence of Cuba. No other independent country has so great a dependence on one crop or one industry. For minor industries she has the world-renowned tobacco lands of Western Cuba, ranches and frontier on the eastern plain, and lumber and mines in the mountains at the extreme east, but the characteristic Cuban landscape is a rolling plain, light green with sugar-cane. The cane fields are sprinkled with the white trunks and dark green tops of the royal palm, with here and there in the distance the smokestacks and red roofs of the sugar-mills.

This island lacks the high central mountain range found in the other three large islands. The central water parting can scarcely be noticed. It is followed by the trunk-line railroad of the island. This open plain has therefore fairly uniform rainfall. The amount is almost ideal for sugar, forty-five to sixty inches per year, with the rainy season in summer, when cane needs to grow, and the dry season in winter, when it is necessary to put sugar content into the cane. While the weather is wet the sugar content of the cane-juice is low. As the dry season comes the cane seems to pump the water out of the earth and exhale it into the dry air and concentrate sugar into itself. Then comes the harvest, for which a dry season is so desirable to keep the cane-field from becoming a sea of mud.[7]

Cuba is a land of commerce rather than of the *conuco*. We should really think of it commercially as an extension of the one-crop area of our own South, this crop being sugar instead of cotton, and the people living from the store and trade as do the people of the Cotton Belt. For this reason the commerce of Cuba is five times as great as that of all the rest of the West Indies together, although she has less than half the people of the Archipelago.

The sugar harvest in Cuba is a great national exertion. At the opening of the season chemists, engineers, and other experts arrive from the United States. Thousands of negro laborers come from Haiti, Jamaica

[7] Cane sugar production was also discussed in the section on Porto Rico.

and other islands. On hundreds of plantations tens of thousands of men are busy cutting cane, loading it into ox-carts and into little freight cars on plantation railroads, where toylike but very genuine locomotives carry it away, perhaps many miles [8] to the great central where engines of large factory size run heavy crushers and a surprising array of machinery which turns out each day its hundreds and even thousands of sacks of crude brown sugar. Cuba has a good system of railways running from end to end of the island, and many short railways connect the plantations with the numerous outports where ships await the cargo. There are so many excellent harbors that it is said that Cuba's exports leave by a hundred gates. The sunken coast has many fine harbors.

### Trade

It is difficult for our imaginations to grasp the meaning of great numbers, for example, the size of this Cuban sugar industry. The exports of sugar to the United States amount to ten freight trains, each with twenty cars of fifty tons each, or 10,000 tons per day for every day in the year. This is two ship-loads for every day in the year. Actually there are several ships loaded with Cuban sugar en route to the United States every minute of the year and sometimes a veritable fleet of them.[9]

On the return trip the steamers carry almost every conceivable article of commerce, from Ford cars, blue overalls and plows to grand pianos, silk stockings and movie films from Los Angeles.

All this trade calls for cities. The twelve largest cities (population in thousands: Havana, 363; Cienfuegos, 95; Camagüey, 98; Santiago de Cuba, 70; Guantánamo, 68; Matanzas, 62; Santa Clara, 63; Manzanillo, 56; Pinar del Rio, 47; Sancti-Spiritus, 58; Trinidad, 40; Cárdenas, 32) contain 37% of the population of the island, which on the whole has a distinctly larger proportion of its population in cities than the state of Maine or Kansas.

### American Political Influence

Most of this commercial development has happened since 1898, when Cuba was blessed by emancipation from Spanish rule. Since that time

[8] One plantation has 200 miles of railroad and twenty-five engines. There are 4000 miles of private plantation railways on the island. The 2800 miles of public railway give Cuba a railroad density equal to that of California. The tropic climate and the temptations of graft have been too much for the country roads. They are reported to be in execrable condition.

[9] It is perhaps worth pointing out that this greatest import of the United States, this staple which now makes up 20% of the calories of our diet, is quite an infant in the world's industry, and not at all a necessity of diet. With only the sugar produced by the bee, the human race produced Confucius, Moses, Aristotle and Plato, Caesar and Charlemagne, and the dietitians are wondering if we can keep on eating it as we do and keep on having health and good teeth.

Cuba has had the support and aid of the American government and an opportunity to make the best of herself. This American aid is one of the brightest spots in one of the darkest chapters of human history. That dark chapter is the foreign policy of nations, including our own. In this field man still often feels at liberty to be a savage and a devil and he acts the parts. It was the fame of Cuba's good fortune (and that of the Philippines) that brought flocking to Mr. Wilson's hotel in Paris in 1918–19 the representatives of the Armenians, the Azerbaijanese, the Poles, the Hungarians, and the other downtrodden peoples in such variety that it puzzled the best geographers in the world to locate them all on the map.

Since 1898 Cuba has shared the prosperity of Porto Rico, on a much richer economic basis. She has a scanty population of but sixty-five people to the square mile. Her lands are largely arable rather than mountainous and really she is a new agricultural frontier. This agricultural frontier awaited only the coming of capital and this followed the American guarantee of peace and reasonable order.[10] The great fact of Cuban economic life is the investment of more than one billion dollars of American money in sugar plantations since the exit of the Spanish rulers. Some estimates place these holdings of cane-land at 4,000,000 acres, about one-seventh of the island. Companies own nearly all of the 200 sugar-mills (centrals) although much of the cane is grown by tenants and small owners.

Under these conditions the 3,000,000 people of Cuba are producing 4,000,000 tons of sugar, which cost in 1922 $.0215 per pound sacked up at the Cuban mill (United States Tariff Commission). In 1916 the cost was estimated at $.015, and before the World War the Tariff Commission estimated that it cost $.017 per pound to make raw sugar in Cuba, $.028 in Porto Rico, and $.041 in Louisiana.

### The World War and Cuban Commerce

In the high-price orgy of 1919 and 1920, raw sugar rose to $.15 a pound. The income that year from a single acre of good cane-land was a thousand dollars. The prosperity of Cuba knew no bounds. It was almost an intoxication. Speculation ran its course. Sugar plantations were sold and resold, doubling and trebling in value. The high price was capitalized as though it would last forever. On the north shore, near Havana, the newly rich sugar planters started to build their palaces, each trying to outdo his neighbor. One hundred thousand dollars, $200,000.00, $300,000.00, $400,000.00, half a million, three-quarters of a million, a million dollars they cost, but before some of these structures were finished the sugar bubble burst, and for years thereafter the trade-wind blew through the walls of unfinished palaces.

[10] We have a great naval base at Guantánamo Harbor on the east coast facing Haiti.

Cuban commerce rises and falls with the price of sugar. In the gala days of 1920 the foreign trade of the island was three times as great as that of Spain. In that year she imported 50,000,000 pounds of condensed milk. Two years later it was only 19,000,000 pounds, while imports of 4,700,000 pounds of pickled pork dropped to 1,300,000 pounds. In that year Cuba regained her normal life.

In twelve months before November 1922, Cuba's foreign trade was $956,000,000.00; during the next twelve months it was $466,000,000.00. In this slump imports declined from $562,000,000.00 to $183,000,000.00. Imperialists find themselves vindicated in the manner in which the Cubans handled this prosperity. In the closing months of 1922 at the end of a period of prosperity such as the world had almost never seen, Cuba had to borrow $50,000,000.00 to pay the running expenses of the government in time of peace, when she had not been at war. It was then that General C r o w d e r went to Cuba (see chapter on Governments). The political gang in control had had a l o v e l y time. Almost everybody held office and the pay

Fig. 369 — Here is the record of the causal factor in the unprecedented prosperity that wrecked Cuban finance.

was good. Much of the borrowed money went to pay arrears in salary (for which there had been little or no service), and the school system was reported to have broken down for want of funds.

Cuba's sugar industry shows that the island is still an agricultural frontier while Jamaica and Porto Rico buy fertilizer for old land. Cuba's sugar industry is moving eastward through the island to fresh lands exactly as the wheat industry of the United States and Canada has moved westward and northwestward for fresh lands. There is still plenty of land available in tracts from 1000 to 60,000 acres, for Cuban land, after a fashion in Spanish countries, was given out in large grants, the popular grant in Cuba being all the land included in a six-mile radius from a central point.

## Cuban Tobacco

Cuba is famed the world over for the aromatic quality of its cigars. The tobacco is all produced in a small territory ninety miles by ten called the Vuelta Abajo in Western Cuba. The peculiar limestone soil imparts a flavor which cannot be explained, denied or duplicated. Here the rich owner grows his acres under cheesecloth and produces the high-priced cigar-wrapper, while the dweller in the thatched hut grows a little patch of cheap filler, under the open sky, exposed to all the irregularities, insects and weather.

The Vuelta Abajo tobacco-growers are almost exclusively white and are largely natives of the Canary Islands. So intensive, so perfect, so expensive is the cultivation and fertilization that two acres require the full time of a man. The land is worth $1000.00 an acre and a *good* crop is often worth that much, sometimes twice as much. It takes two years of curing in sheds to develop the fine flavor of the best Havana tobacco. The manufacture of cigars, an industry requiring a small table, a sharp knife and nimble fingers, is the leading manufacturing industry of Havana. The cigar-workers have the wise habit of entertaining themselves by hiring a professional reader. This melodious-voiced individual sits on a platform above his audience. The day starts with the daily papers, then come the comic weeklies, of which Havana has a good supply, and finally, to finish out the day, hair-raising fiction.

As is so often the custom once an industry is started and a reputation established, Cuba is now importing considerable quantities of tobacco for the manufacture of " Havana " cigars.

## Fruit and Vegetables

Since the American occupation there has been a slow development of the grapefruit and vegetable industries. These are located near Havana, close to the ships, and in the Isle of Pines, south of Cuba. This isle was colonized by several hundred Americans under the erroneous impression that it would belong to the United States. Grapefruit of the Isle of Pines reach the American market in August and September before those from Florida are ripe. The industry was larger in 1910 than in 1920. Distance, tariffs and rival foods are against it. In the season of 1922–23 a quarter of a million boxes were sent, also many peppers and eggplants. The vegetable shipments from the Isle of Pines alone were 20,000 crates in 1921, 25,000 crates in 1922, 75,000 crates in 1923.

## Iron-Ore

Like America, Cuba has mountains of iron-ore. Near Santiago, hematite is scooped up by steam shovel of the Bethlehem Steel Company as the copper-ores of Utah and iron-ores in the better mines of the Superior district are scooped up. It is but a short distance to the port of Santiago, where ore steamers load for Baltimore and other United States ports.

## Population and Prospects

For the next few generations, Cuba has an entirely different outlook from either Jamaica or Porto Rico. If Porto Rico can support 375 people to the square mile, Cuba can easily support twice as many, or 750, whereas she has only sixty-five. The tobacco output can increase, the sugar output can increase, and the production of vegetables and grapefruit is for decades to come limited solely by the demand. As a measure of the undeveloped resources of Cuba it should be pointed out that her 4,000,000-ton crop of sugar is being produced on 5% of her area, that 80% of her land is excellent for the use of agricultural machinery, while 10% or 15% more is good for the *conuco*, or mountain garden farm. If she had the labor and the market Cuba could grow all the sugar the world now uses. The location of her eastern and western mountain ranges, with their ends toward the trade-winds, gives her almost no land to the leeward of mountain ranges and therefore too dry for good food production. There is no such other island.

Population is rushing forward to fill the void made by Cuba's empty lands. Between 1910 and 1919 the *Statesman's Year Book* reports an increase of 34.8% — far ahead of Porto Rico, and in the class with the United States in its early decades.[11] In the year 1921, under the influence of the sugar boom, 148,000 immigrants reached Cuba. This was at the rate of 5% of her total population, corresponding to five or six million immigrants for the United States. Our rate has rarely reached 1% per year. Fortunately one-half of these people were from Spain. Unfortunately, 30,000 were Haitians and 27,000 Jamaicans, negro field hands. In the year 1922, after the slump in sugar, only 20,000 immigrants arrived. The Haitians dropped from 30,000 to 300, the Jamaicans from 27,000 to 3000.

One-tenth of the population are foreign-born white, mostly Spaniards. Six-tenths claim to be native white,[12] and three-tenths are classed as colored. The towns are thoroughly Latin. The country is negro and mulatto with people living in the ever-present palm-thatched house. The Cuban may live in the palm-thatched house but he spends no effort to ornament it. Often he has no garden, so great is his dependence upon the country store. He prefers to work for wages rather than to grow his own food.

---

[11] Increases in the United States were:

| | |
|---|---|
| 1790–1800, 35% | 1830–1840, 32.6% |
| 1820–1830, 33% | 1910–1920, 15% |

[12] It is perhaps ominous for Cuba's future that when a Cuban gets rich he often claims to be a Spaniard.

All colored races are lovers of games of chance; nor is the Spaniard averse to them. In Cuba the lottery ticket is everywhere thrust in your face with the joint appeal to your own gambling instinct and your pity to buy from this little girl who needs money, this old woman who needs the money, or this lame beggar who can eat if you buy. There is a cock-pit in every town, and the ever-present sportsman with a rooster under his arm, the rooster yearning to fight, the man yearning to watch and bet. If you wish to test your Spanish, follow the betting of the cock-fight, as the odds change with every lightning thrust of the alert contestants. If you can do this you have indeed achieved the language.

Havana, with a population of 363,000, nearly as large as that of New Orleans, is much the largest city of the West Indies. It shows the marks of a national capital. It is the commercial and financial center of the island as well as the legislative and administrative center of a centralized government. It has a terminal railroad station costing $3,000,000.00 with mosaic floors, the interior finish of Italian marble. Almost unrestricted gambling and alcoholic drinks add (for some) to its natural winter charm. Cuba is a Mecca for American winter tourists.

The predominance of the English language in the business of the island is causing some of the schools to begin to teach English. Indeed the Americanization of the island has already gone so far that it is a much less interesting place to visit than most of the other West Indian islands. Aside from the American operation of the island, American store clothes, Ford cars, and the great trade with America, perhaps the best evidence of Americanization (but not necessarily of benefit) is furnished by the welcome to a returned Cuban baseball player.[13]

## E. THE ISLAND OF HAITI

### Santo Domingo ("San Domingo")

Shining shoes is the chief industry of Santo Domingo. At least that is the impression I got from the number of times I was invited to have a shine, whether I needed it or not, in the towns of that country. I also resolved while there to buy some white duck suits, so that I

---

[13] "No conquering hero returning to his native land could have received a more hearty welcome than did Adolfo Luque, the premier pitcher of the National League, when he arrived in Havana late today. Long before the steamer, *Governor Cobb*, came to her pier the wharves and near-by streets were jammed with thousands of admirers. The army, navy and city, and the professional, semi-professional and amateur baseball leagues were represented in the parade that escorted the Cincinnati twirler up to the office of ' El Diario de la Marina ' where toasts were drunk to his health. Several bands were in the procession, and the people brought out every conceivable noise-making instrument to add to the din raised by the shouts of 'Viva Luque.' At times the baseball enthusiasts almost mobbed their idol's automobile in trying to reach it and pat Luque on the back or receive a handshake from him. Luque's face was wreathed in smiles as he responded to the welcome. He was showered with flowers along the route from the pier to the newspaper office." (By the Associated Press, Havana, October 2, 1923.)

might appear as well dressed as the pleasant and polite young mulattoes who carried my baggage and served me with good food in this land of the well-dressed cavalier.

## People

There has been much inaccuracy in speaking of Haiti as a negro island. Haiti, the nation occupying the western and more populous third of the island, is a negro land, but the population of Santo Domingo, the eastern two-thirds of the island, is very far from black. It is true that the official figures, giving 25% white, 50% mulatto, and 25% negro, lean quite too strongly to the Caucasian side, but the proportion of the population that has no strain of negro blood is very difficult to establish without the study of genealogy. Granted a moderate amount of sunburn the chances of distinguishing between an octoroon and a white person are not good. Often, indeed, it is impossible to make the distinction, and with the smaller fractions the difficulty increases, although occasionally a child is born who is much darker than the rest of the children and there is revealed an unexpected negro strain.

Some, perhaps harshly critical, claim that there are only a few of the great families of Santo Domingo entirely clear of any negro strain. Observation of the people leads me to the belief that they have, on the average, more Caucasian blood than negro blood and the absence of a social color-line certainly makes the island a haven for the mulatto. If I were one I should certainly emigrate to that land. There is, however, a natural social grouping of complexions, so that the pure white and the pure black rarely meet in the same social gathering.

In the summer of 1923 I attended a dance in Santo Domingo in company with a handful of Europeans. It was ten miles out in the country from the city of Santiago, whither a half dozen of us rattled in a Ford jitney. The host, a well-to-do landowner, had a frame bungalow lighted with acetylene gas. Careful scrutiny of the guests convinced me that some were pure Caucasian, that many others would have passed as such in New York, while some showed unquestionable signs of African blood. But none appeared to be more than one-eighth negro and I estimated the average blood of the audience to be at least 96% Caucasian. A girl of much darker skin entered the room, but it was only for a moment. She was a servant taking a child to bed. There were no shooting affrays, no knives were drawn. There was no quarreling. A little warm beer was served but it produced no hilarity — indeed, the first half of the dance proceeded from 10.30 to 1.30 with a perfection of propriety that could not have given the smallest possible offense to the most puritanical matrons of New England. I was told that the last half was equally proper. The hair, dress and clothes were of New England, the dance of New England; indeed, this standardization of the world promises to make it a very drab and monotonous place.

Only the music had the slightest sparkle of local color. It had a tang and jingle of the jungle, for the orchestra of ten pieces averaged at least 56% black. The combination of African and Spanish produces a much better appreciation of music than the Anglo-Saxon has. Every town in Santo Domingo, almost every town in the West Indies, has a fine public square, with music every Sunday evening, and perhaps every evening in the week, good music at that.[14] On the square there is usually a fine church, often a cathedral, and during the hour of music the populace gathers to promenade in good clothes.

It will not do to dismiss the Dominicans as being either black or wholly uneducated. It is true that 70% of the adults are illiterate, whereas in Italy the proportion is only 30%, but the wealthier Dominicans have long made a point of sending their sons and sometimes even their daughters abroad for education, often to the United States. " I am a graduate of Cornell," replied the Adonis whose beautiful English, as he served me in a store, caused me to inquire where he had learned it. And at every turn throughout the island I met men educated in the United States or Europe.

### Government

This island of Haiti was the favorite land of Columbus. He called it Hispaniola (little Spain). He founded Santo Domingo City promptly after the discovery and the ceiba tree to which his boats were said to have been tied is still pointed out on the bank of the river there. In the cathedral lie his bones. Yet this island is today less changed by man than any other in the West Indies. Seventy-five per cent of its area is still in forest. For forty years this was the center of Spain's empire in America, and the ruins of the palace fortress built by Diego, son of Christopher Columbus, still stand. Through its archways passed Cortez to the conquest of Mexico, Pizarro to the conquest of Peru, Balboa to the discovery of the Pacific, and various others of the terrible conquistadors and hardy explorers.

The native population, estimated (probably too highly) at 2,000,000, promptly melted away under the Spanish enslavement and other cruelties and the diseases of the conquerors. A few survived in the mountains of the interior but they are a negligible factor in the population. Then came the slave-ship with the tougher population from Africa, able to endure labor and contact with the Spaniard. Thus at the end of four centuries we find the so-called republic of Haiti, with most of its people black, very black; while most of those of Santo Domingo are mulatto or white, many of them with thin lips and fine features, and some even

---

[14] This appreciation of music, in combination with the scarcity of news, is shown by the double-column announcement of the coming of the Italian opera singer, Titta Ruffo. For a week daily leading columns appeared about him in the papers of Santo Domingo city.

with blond hair. The chief explanation of this difference lies in the terrible massacre and expulsion of the whites from Haiti at the hand of the negroes at the time of the French Revolution.

Fig. 370 — Christopher Columbus was a great man. One might almost say that he *were* a great man, for he appears to have left three sets of bones. Here in this shrine in the Cathedral of Santo Domingo city are his best bones. His Spanish official bones are at Seville (Spain), and his native son bones are at Genoa, Italy. (Courtesy Pan-American Union.)

From the time of the French Revolution to 1844 the whole island was under the rule of the Haitians — a sad chapter of civil war, cruelty and massacre. In 1844 Santo Domingo succeeded in establishing its independence from Haiti and began a career of revolution on its own account. It is said that between that time and 1916, when the United States took

control, only four presidents either died in office or finished their term.
The others passed out by violence. The rule was largely by bands or
armed gangs. The foreigner who wished to run a sugar plantation made
his peace with some particular band which he financially subsidized. They
in a measure policed his property, fought off would-be revolutionists, and
perhaps did a little private killing upon request. It was an easy way to
get land. During this era the common way of financing a revolution was
for the organizer to borrow money from some man of means, the " general " giving in return an order remitting tariff duties to that amount
after he had come into possession of the government. This remission of
tariffs often became a kind of vested right by which many a fortune was
built up. Thus a few big families, often of the finest Spanish blood,
fomented revolution after revolution, and operated the country for several
generations. The loser in one of these civil wars usually fled to some
other West Indian island, to South America, the United States or Europe,
always planning and striving during the interval to get back. New York
and New Orleans are today sprinkled with such colonies from Latin
American countries — hoping to win a revolution.

The public debts created by these fly-by-night governments resulted
in the " receivership " by the United States described in the chapter on
Governments. This was done by treaty, one of the conditions of which
was that until the Dominican government paid all of its debts no more
public debt should be created without the consent of the United States
government. In 1916 an admiral of the United States issued a proclama-
tion announcing that the treaty had been violated and that the country
was under the military occupation of the United States.[15] So far as can
be gathered by unofficial inquiry, it is generally believed that the real
reason was the fear that Germany or some other European power would
take possession of the Bay of Samana at the east end of the island, a
harbor with a narrow and easily defended entrance, and with enough deep
and sheltered water to hold the navies of all the world.

### American Intervention

From 1916 to 1923 the country had its greatest period of peace and
order — order enforced by the United States marines with government
by the naval officers.

There was one result of the occupation which, all parties agree,
was good. It was the complete disarming of everybody, save for the
possession of the machete, the universal tool of agriculture. With the
American zeal for reform we bowled over most of the existing government, including the school system, which was an unusually good one
when we consider the condition of the country. In 1886 a Dominican
patriot succeeded in setting apart a fixed revenue for education, the tax

[15] The only violation was unpaid salaries to government employees.

arising from the licensing of stores. This school fund of $200,000.00 a year had been respected through all revolutions. The Americans did away with it saying they would make a larger appropriation. They did. The first year it was $1,300,000.00. The next year, and for three years thereafter nothing; and that was the condition in 1924, at which time there was a fine agricultural building that had never had a pupil and was then being used for police drills.

The greatest physical achievement of the early years of the American occupation was the building of roads. For four centuries the northern and southern sides of the island had been separated by a horseback journey of several days through the forests, or a sea journey (three days

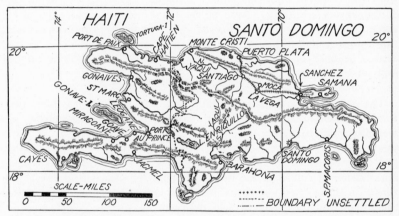

Fig. 371 — This map of Haiti shows the general location of the leading mountains and rivers, but no one should attempt to explore by it. Cartography in this island is still at a low ebb.

by steamer) around the east end of the island. There were two short railroads in the northern settlements but it was then as it is indeed today, the land of the men on horseback, for a few hundred miles of highway still leave most of the area untouched. Therefore the young gallant canters about the streets and through the woodland path and grassland trail on a steed, presenting a most neat and martial appearance.

The government of occupation, that is to say the American Navy Department, began to build a national system of roads. In four years' time they had completed a line from the capital city at the south across the island to Santiago and on to Monte Cristi on the north coast. Branches were partly built, connecting most of the cities south and west as well as north and east with the ends of this trunk-line. Great enthusiasm for roads prevailed. In some towns everybody turned out with pick and shovel to help, but most of the work was done by Haitians, negroes, quite black, imported for the purpose. They built themselves palm-roofed villages and made gardens in the forest along the road, where they worked for sixty cents a day.

The question is, will these roads last? The experience of many parts of the United States is not reassuring. We have found it easier to build a solid road than to maintain it. This is probably more true in a trade-wind island, where a season of drought lets roads crumble to pieces, and a season of torrential rains helps to wash them away. Parts of the Dominican highway through the wet forest could only be supported by putting logs into the miry clay beneath the stones. When the logs rot the future of the road seems to be assured — quagmire.

In any case the roads can touch only a small portion of the total area. They can help no lumbering enterprise of the modern variety and most of the forests are as they were before the Americans came, difficult of access. It is not uncommon for mahogany, rosewood, and other tropic woods to be cut into pieces 24 × 18 × 9 inches, two of which are slung across the back of a mule or donkey and carried for miles to port or railroad.

### The Northern Ridge and Valley

The island of Haiti comprises four mountain ranges, with three intervening valleys. The northernmost range is often close to the sea. As seen from Puerto Plata, the northern slope exposed to the trade-winds shows the tangled jungle of a moist slope, sprinkled with the clearings and the palm huts of the primitive agriculturist. Fortunately for the preservation of soil upon the mountain-sides, the clearings of the roving agriculturist are often abandoned while the logs of the forest still lie upon the ground and its roots still hold the earth.

The south side of the range in the so-called "rain-shadow" of the mountain has the open forest and cactus indicative of its light rain.

The first long valley, running from Monte Cristi in the arid west to Samana in the humid east, gives a vivid example of the variation of tropic climates within short distances. The eastern end of the valley is wet all the year because the trade-wind blows into it. Here most of Santo Domingo's yearly harvest of 20,000 tons of cacao beans is produced. Nearly all of it is grown by the small farmer, an acre or two along with the varied products of the *conuco,* which can here keep the same ground for generations because the land in this alluvial valley is as flat as Illinois, and as black and as rich. Here also is grown much of the tobacco export, some of the coffee being grown on the hills. The merchants in the towns who buy these products from the small farmer told me they could not buy land, hire men to grow tobacco, and make any money, because the peasant proprietor does not count his time, and really works as his own boss, for a very small wage, smaller than he would accept as an employee. This is manifest in the prices — three cents or four cents a pound for leaf tobacco, the sum paid in 1923 by the merchant after the grower had hauled it many miles on muleback to the market town. Eighty per cent of these growers had borrowed money from the merchant while they were growing the crop, much after the fashion of the Southern cotton-grower. This eastern valley is famed throughout the West Indies as one of the garden spots of the American Mediterranean.[16] It was named by Columbus La Vega Real (the royal meadow) and is so known to this day.

In one of the most prosperous towns I called upon the local representative of the Department of Agriculture. He told me that about four acres was the average holding of these farmers, that to most of them the plow was unknown, and that their whole agriculture was performed with the axe and the machete; that he was trying to establish the great reform of having them use the mattock instead, and if I had come along half an hour earlier I would have seen a peon in his garden

Fig. 372 — Tobacco going to market in Santiago in the ever present palm fiber carriers. (Photo J. Russell Smith.)

using his mattock. I had in fact seen the said reformed peon. I should like to know how many weeks it would have taken him to dig up an acre of soft level dark earth at the rate I saw him working that hot July day.

The agricultural official told me that most of these people did not own even a donkey. When the local merchant bought from the people he sent out donkeys to bring back the tobacco, cacao and coffee. They lived almost exclusively on boiled plantain, perhaps buying a bit of meat once or twice a week when they came to town.

A near-by garden showed the fecundity of the land. Within a space not over twenty-five yards square were a mango tree, a lime tree, an orange tree, a breadfruit tree, a cacao tree, a coconut tree. Corn, with sweet potatoes running through it, was planted beneath all these trees. In the back of the garden was a pig-pen. My guide pointed out a new house with a young palm-tree by it, saying, " He has planted palms and in a year or two he will have enough to roof all the outbuildings he wants." It is the rule of that country that a roof 5 × 10 yards in area can be built from twenty " horses " of palm-leaves, a " horse " being two packages, twenty-five each, costing ten cents per " horse " delivered. Five

[16] " Among the most impressively fertile districts of the world." Vaughan and others of U. S. Geological Survey.

men make the roof in half a day. It lasts for twenty years, and makes a very pleasing roof to look at from within, with the regular rows of knots where the palm-fiber bindings fasten the long leaves to the poles.

### Sharp Contrasts of Tropic Climate

The part of the valley draining east is a land of the banana; the part draining west is the thorn forest. Yet there is no mountain range in the middle of this valley, although a mountain range walls it in from the sea along its north side. The water parting, altitude 209 meters, near Santiago, altitude 195 meters, is so gentle that the captain of the marines who kindly took me to ride in his automobile was quite sure that there was no water parting there. Yet the mere change of slope and a few feet of fall causes the country east of Santiago to be one of pasture. Eighteen miles east of Santiago and only 57 meters lower than the water parting there were wide expanses of scrub, heavily sprinkled with cactus ten feet high, while at the end of the valley near Monte Cristi conditions are virtually desert,[17] with a rainfall of less than twenty inches per year, falling in torrents, much of which runs away. In the center of the valley near Santiago one passes in ten miles over a gentle incline from pastures into a country where every foot is occupied with little farms covered with corn, bananas, plantains, then cacao and coconuts, until at a distance not more than twenty miles from the Santiago cactus, one is in the full luxuriance of equatorial agriculture. Forty miles farther east, at Sanchez, where winds blow into this valley from the sea, the humidity is so great that it is common for people to put corn into their shoes at night to prevent their molding before morning.

In the west end of this valley, toward Monte Cristi, in the dry land, the houses had walls of basket-work or mere small poles, sometimes plastered, but more often not. The bleating of goats was a common sound, and goat-skins are the chief product for sale.

The lower part of this valley appears to be one of the rich, unused agricultural opportunities of the world. There are tens of thousands of acres of alluvial soil, lying well for irrigation, not many feet above the river, fed by continuous rains in the high mountains at the center of the island. An enterprising Belgian engineer had a very prosperous rice-plantation, proving the adaptability of the land for this produce, while its suitability for sugar is manifest and it is probably excellent also for alfalfa. Why it remains unused in this capitalistic epoch I have difficulty in understanding.

[17] " The resemblance of this region to the arid plains of Lower California is very striking. The same dry soil covered with a scanty carpet of grass; the same low, straggling-limbed open-foliage acacia-trees; the same tall columnar cactus, with its undergrowth of *opuntias;* even the same cloudless sky made the likeness complete." (W. M. Gabb: " On the Topography and Geology of Santo Domingo," *Trans. Amer. Philosophical Soc.*, Vol. 15 (N. S.), 1872-80, pp. 49-259.)

## The Pine Forests

The second ridge in from the sea is covered for seventy-five or one hundred miles with pine forests. It is the opinion of botanists and foresters (*Geographical Review*, Vol. 12, p. 217) that the pine forest is purely the work of the *conuquero*, who by repeatedly cutting, burning, cropping, and returning nothing has reduced the fertility to the point where pine, noted for its ability to live on little, takes possession of the land.

I had the fortune to meet two Alabama lumbermen who had just cruised this pine area thoroughly. They reported five billion feet of splendid pine, with tall trees that carried their size well. But because of the broken nature of the country, there was no known means of getting it out at a profit and they were going home sorrowing. Throughout the forest area they reported coming to *conucos*, where they were hospitably received and well fed. The pine-forest was sprinkled with mangoes, enough, they declared, to have made them millionaires if they could have sold them for a cent apiece in New York.

Most of the interior of Santo Domingo can be classed as almost unsettled. Here and there is a village in the tropic woodland or grassland, far removed from transportation.

## The South Coast

The south coast, with its rainy and dry season, to which Columbus brought sugar-cane, is the chief seat of the sugar industry. There are large areas of level soil, underlaid by coral limestone, which weathers into a soil of great fertility. There is enough rain to turn it into jungle, tightly tied together with myriad vines. This makes difficult clearing, but I saw considerable areas of it being cut down and burnt and put into sugar-cane. One company engaged in clearing the forest and planting employed 8000 men for many months. To carry cane from the fields across the river to the mill, a bridge costing $1,000,000.00 was built. The hand-culture of the cane was proved by large logs which were lying in all directions among the growing cane. An American company with 100,000 acres in this region expects to clear, plant, and abandon the region in about six or seven years. " But isn't this wasteful in the long run? " someone asked the manager. " Oh, well," he replied, " we won't be here then." These Dominican sugar operations are good types of financial internationalism. Capital is mostly American, management is mostly American, often with European assistant managers and technical experts. Much of the cane field-labor is done by Haitians. There is usually a marked darkening of the complexion as one goes from coffee, cacao, or tobacco lands to the cane-fields. The smaller superintendents, such as gang-foremen, timekeepers, weighers, bookkeepers and other clerical workers about the field and factory, are often Porto Ricans who have been educated in the public schools and come over to work for the sugar-grinding season and then return. These superior positions of the Porto Ricans naturally produce jealousy, so that there is a saying in Santo Domingo that the only good Porto Ricans are the ones who walk over.

### The Arid Southwest

The southwestern part of Santo Domingo is a land of marked aridity, as is evidenced by the salt lake Enriquillo, which has dried up to such an extent that its surface is at present one hundred and forty-four feet below sea-level. It lies in a plain with salt-encrusted areas sometimes square miles in extent and little vegetation but cactus and thorn. Springs at the foot of the mountains on each side give a belt of tree-growth at the foot of the hills, which are themselves in turn bare or bush-covered on the lower slopes. With increasing elevation increasing rain permits the growth of coffee, which is the chief export.

Save for the new sugar enterprise recently started near the port of Barahona, this corner of Santo Domingo is a very primitive region, as much Haitian as Dominican.[18] It might produce much henequin but it awaits the enterprise as well as the laborer.

Across this arid plain flows the second large river of the island, the Yaqui del Sur. On an alluvial plain near its mouth, not far from the port of Barahona, is one of the largest of the West Indian sugar enterprises, which had to add to all of the other labors the great task of making irrigation and drainage ditches. The drainage ditches were necessary to carry off the salt, which otherwise would come to the surface and kill the cane. Indeed the first crop of cane was ruined because of the high percentage of salt that it carried along with the sugar. The next crop, however, was good, and the company expects a great future. It has a great resource in virgin alluvial land and irrigation water and location close to the port, Barahona. Any such opportunities in Jamaica and Porto Rico were used centuries ago.

### Future

What is the future of Santo Domingo? The first fact to keep in mind is its great undeveloped agricultural resources. It has a much larger percentage of level land than Porto Rico, so that its population of forty-five to the square mile is not more than one-tenth of what it

[18] A European engineer who worked for months in this region says: " Dominicans and Haitians have in general from one to six, eight or ten wives. In general they buy their wives from their fathers. Funerals are the occasion of big parties during which women drink sweet liquors, men drink strong ones, and dance and sing. Haitians are afraid of devils. There is a Roman Catholic priest in ———. I do not think his influence is very great. My strong impression is that the Haitians are losing the civilization they reached under the French control. But I know that in the republic of Haiti there are still some very well-educated negro families."

might be if its resources were as heavily pressed as those of Porto Rico. With such a small population in such an Eden, it is not surprising that the people should not be keen to seek regular jobs laboring on the plantations of foreign capitalists. Hence the description given of them by an American official (see Special Agents Series, No. 141, *The West Indies as an Export Field,* Department of Commerce, Washington, 1917, p. 165):

" As a rule, judged by Northern standards, the labor is not very satis-factory. In the country and in the vicinity of the towns, the men live upon their little patches of land with perhaps one-tenth of the exertion required in making a living in the United States. The small farmer plants his sugar-cane and has nothing to do in that connection for the next twenty-five years except gather the crop. He plants a hundred or so banana or plantain sprouts, and he has food in abundance indefinitely. He plants his papaya trees and there is plenty of fruit. Squashes and melons come up where the seeds fall. The wild trees of the near-by woods give him coconuts, mangoes, nisperos, anóns, guanábanas, and other fruits. Wild bees give him honey. Sweet potatoes, once planted, keep on producing, while the yucca or ' yamie ' (cassava) grows wild and is a good substitute for potatoes. It requires little exertion to raise chickens, goats, cattle, or a few razorback hogs. Thus there is no necessity for sustained endeavor and the average Dominican is not ac-customed to it. He is not trained to obey orders and to work to the satisfaction of some one else. Not feeling necessities keenly, and not caring much for dress and the non-essentials of existence, he does not see any pressing reason for continued and strenuous application to a task." That statement is a bit strong in spots, but it savors largely of the truth. An American exporter writing about a long-promised shipment of mahogany said, " The man has promised to deliver your lumber very soon, but that means nothing here."

The greatest problem facing the Dominicans is the problem of social organization. Will they enter the age of regular work, science, sanita-tion, and education? The investigators of the Rockefeller Foundation report one-half the population to be suffering from hookworm, and in rural districts the percentage is sometimes higher than that. One need go no further to explain the lack of desire to work. If they are left to themselves the social and industrial change will be slow. If they are properly aided by America the change may be rapid. The prospect of continued American rule is excellent. In 1924 the country was in a peculiar and sinister deadlock. The American State Department was definitely and actively trying to get out of Santo Domingo, but the gov-ernment of Santo Domingo was in the hands of the Navy Department, with 2500 marines in charge. The attitude of the marines is well char-acterized by their frequent statement that " it is a hell of a job to run

this damned country." But they were very free with their predictions
that they were never going to get out. Meanwhile the official American
plan was to re-establish the government and sail away. As a step toward
this re-establishment and exit the Navy Department had relinquished its
military government, in large part, early in 1923, had persuaded the
Dominican political parties to unite in establishing a provisional government which was to hold office until an election could be held and the
permanent government organized under the newly elected president and
congress. Meanwhile the election was postponed from month to month
because one of the leading political parties refused to enter the field
with candidates and prepare for an election. This party was bitterly
upbraided by the other parties for its refusal to co-operate and thus help
Santo Domingo to escape from the hands of the foreign rulers.

This episode reflects the governmental weakness of the Spanish
temperament, the lack of the larger loyalty which often expresses itself
in treachery and is here seen causing a party to take the position that
they would rather have the Yankees continue to rule the country than
have the government pass into the hands of the other party of their
own countrymen.[19]

These Dominican incidents, together with the recurring troubles in
Cuba and the collapse of her educational system, are unfortunate
precedents for the contemplation of one who looks for the early complete
independence or even the complete home rule of any West Indian island.

Perhaps the most hopeful element in the Dominican situation in 1924
was the strong desire of a Board of Christian Work formed by the
*united action of several Protestant churches* to launch and carry on an
educational scheme with other organizations. Several day schools had
North American teachers. These schools were to serve as practice schools
for teacher-training and as feeders for a central boarding school which
would further train teachers for the country schools. Incidentally, also,
such an organization would be a wholesome source of information and
tend to check the unreasonable exercise of arbitrary power which must
lie in the hands of any foreign ruler.

Late in 1924 a president was elected and there was much talk of " with-
drawing " of marines. I do not expect it to last long.[20]

### Haiti

So far as mountains, valleys, soils and climates are concerned, Haiti
is merely the extension of Santo Domingo. The boundary cuts from the

[19] This, in its philosophy, is the same as the axiom of American politics, that it
is better to dominate a defeated political organization than to be beaten by the
other wing of your own party. Example, the Republican party in the Presidential
campaign in 1912.
[20] See " Caribbean Policy of the United States," William R. Shepherd, *Jour.
International Relations*, vol. 11, no. 1, July 1920.

north shore to the south shore right across the mountains and valleys of the almost uninhabited center of the island.

## The Historic Background

Haitian history from the end of the French dominion, 1791, to the beginning of the American occupation, 1915, may well be cited as a period of reversion to nature. In 1791 Haiti was one of the shining glories of slavery, if slavery may be said to have shining glories — luxurious palaces of the French owners of large estates, hundreds of thousands of slaves laboring under the taskmasters and by their labors making great commercial prosperity. Then came the French Revolution. Its spirit of Liberty fired the slaves to rebellion under the genius of Toussaint, who is undoubtedly to be reckoned as one of the great men of his century. There followed terrible massacres of the French, and the flight to Cuba of three thousand of the other leaders of the people. For more than a century since this purging Haiti has very properly been called the land of the negro. Any one who is inclined to call the people " niggers " should have some one make an impartial appraisal of manners. An American government report describes them thus: " The Haitians are generally of an amiable disposition, polite and courteous to a degree, considerate of others, possessed of good manners; this is especially true of those who have had the advantages of ' instruction.' "

These people had an unfortunate start for their century of independence. They had been stolen from their own homes in Africa. Their own native culture and social organization were destroyed, and the only chance to absorb European civilization had been the contact with the oppressor who used them as work animals and concubines. Very properly it may be said that they started with no culture save a sprinkling of French that remained after the furious expulsion of their rulers. Add to this complete independence the possession of firearms, and we have the beginnings of a century of civil war, oppression, rapine, revolution.

It is said that in April 1922, two Haitian presidents met on friendly terms for the first time in history. Every previous president is said to have died by violence or to have sought safety in flight. It should at once be mentioned that these two peaceful presidents were the first to have no real authority. Behind them stood ranks of American marines. One was the first dummy president going out of office, the other the second dummy president going into office under the American administration.

In 1791, the last year of French control, 88,000 tons of sugar worth $24,000,000.00 were exported. In 1915 just seventeen tons were shipped, but none was reported for 1914, the last year of Haitian rule. The figures for cotton were respectively 38,000 tons worth $3,500,000.00

at the beginning, and 1600 tons at the end of the period. Coffee fared much better, having shrunk only from 48,000 tons to 38,000 tons, and there was a new factor, namely, 3000 tons of cacao.

### Sugar, Coffee and Peace

Why did sugar disappear so completely and coffee hold its own so well? The answer is the relative fitness of these two industries to political chaos and primitive agriculture. The mansions of the old French sugar planters were vine-clad ruins; their old sugar-mills were buried in new forest; the jungle had long since reclaimed their cane-fields and there was not a modern sugar-mill in the whole island, for the sugar-mill is an expensive, scientific, capitalistic enterprise, as has been fully explained, and political chaos is as fatal to it as it is to higher education.[21]

Coffee, on the other hand, is a bush that grows on almost any humid tropic hillside, and indeed it thrives so well in the damp West Indies that it grows wild over large areas in the interior of Haiti and eastern Santo Domingo. The natives go out and pick up the berries from the ground, so that the Haitian coffee, the chief export of the country, sometimes comes to market mixed with pebbles.

The small shipments of cotton were gathered from wild plants, for cotton here lives from year to year, not being killed by frost as in the United States. The native's mode of life varies little from that of his distant cousin in Africa. The palm hut, surrounded by plantains, yams and cassava (cassava is a great staple); a few goats, picking up their living as they can, furnish milk and skins to sell, and a few chickens, also picking up their living, furnish some eggs and a bit of meat. Such has been the life in the Haitian forest. For decades the traveler in Haiti has been meeting men and women, especially women, walking to market ten, twenty, fifty miles, carrying a sack of coffee, or a bundle of logwood roots or a logwood stump. The more fortunate might be leading a donkey or two with added burdens, but the majority bore their burdens on their heads, trading at the towns for the barest necessities that such meager commerce could yield. So primitive was this life that two different foreigners who have traveled much on business in the interior of Haiti have told me that in recent years they have seen grown women as naked as birds' eggs and as unabashed as Eve before the episode of the apple.

### The Haitians and Their Capital City

The capital city, Port au Prince, is beautiful to behold as one approaches it from the sea, with its long, curved white beach, the blue

[21] The collapse of Haiti is typical of the collapse that may come to any country of high organization when the destructive bonehead rules in the place of the creative brainhead — Babylon, Nineveh, Tyre, Carthage and many more.

mountains in the background and the whitewashed buildings nestling in the palms. After one arrived, in the native days, the sense of beauty was quickly lost in the stench that overpowered all the other impressions of the traveler who entered the city. One hundred thousand people with no sewage system whatever were crowded into a city on a flat, hot, humid, often breezeless tropic plain. The streets were littered with dirt, garbage, excrement and every kind of waste. The experience was a shock to all peoples from lands where sanitation is a science.

When the Americans landed in 1915 there were four automobiles in the capital and most of the business of the city was in the hands of Syrians, comparative newcomers.

In a land where the soldier rules and the general was the top of the frequently changing heap, military pomp was naturally a conspicuous part of life.[22]

It should not be forgotten that there has always been in Haiti a small minority of intelligent, cultured, traveled people, educated in Europe, chiefly in France. The French drama has never ceased to flourish in Port au Prince. There have always been Haitian families whose inherent and cultivated qualities really fitted them to mingle in any society. Their political acumen has been high. Despite the century of disorder, the black and military rulers of Haiti should receive credit for their skill in keeping clear of foreign entanglements. For more than a century they succeeded in avoiding the entanglements of foreign debt much better than the statesmen of most Spanish-American countries.

## The American Occupation

The coming of the American occupation merely brought one more revolution to Haiti, the first since 1791 that caused an actual revolution

---

[22] This was picturesquely described as follows by Mr. Dawson, an American traveler, about the time of the American occupation:

"Military service in Haiti is compulsory. The pay for the soldier trickles down through military channels, colonel to major to captain, in a gradually diminishing column, and disappears altogether long before it reaches the common soldier. It is not an uncommon sight to see the soldiers begging and soliciting money in the streets, and when one visits the President's palace the entire bodyguard lines up with hands outstretched begging for coppers.

"The Generals of Haiti are worthy of a chapter to themselves. 'General' among them is a title conferred for any sort of service to the state or to a political party at the moment in power, and does not necessarily mean that the bearer of this title has had any military experiences whatever. However, as soon as some big black politician receives his title he immediately buys himself a uniform of whatever color and style his fancy may dictate, to which he adds a collection of all sorts and kinds of medals. Thus arrayed, he mounts himself on one of the diminutive ponies of the island, and rides around in great pomp and splendor. The General shows to the best advantage in the military reviews which happen often in Port au Prince. Here he gallops around the parade ground and shouts orders to the soldiers, to his fellow generals, to the band, and to the admiring spectators, burying himself with dust and glory."

in conditions. It was not a diplomatic enterprise. The treaty which we forced the Haitians to sign provided that "the Government of the United States will by its good offices aid the Haitian Government in the proper and efficient development of its agricultural, mineral, and commercial resources and in the establishment of the finances of Haiti on a firm and solid basis." It went on to say that a military adviser would be appointed to organize the army and police system, and that a sanitary officer would be appointed, with authority to clean things up. The cleaning up began promptly. Water supplies were established. Irrigation works were built. Roads, bridges, railroads, telephones, telegraphs, hospitals, and free dispensaries were opened. General vaccination took place. American marines in small groups took charge of squads of fifty or a hundred natives and trained them to become the local police force (gendarmerie). The members of this force received free grammar-school instruction. In the prison, the death rate, which had been 65% per year, dropped to less than 2%, and the prisoners were taught trades.

There are no such uncertainties in regard to the American occupation of Haiti as there are in the case of Santo Domingo. We have virtually established a protectorate and it is to be hoped that we will hand over to the Haitians all of the administration which they can conduct.

The key-words of the opening paragraph of the treaty, "development," "agricultural," "mineral," "commercial," "finances," are suggestive. There is every reason to expect great economic development in Haiti. The resources are there. Columbus described the island to the Queen of Spain by crumpling up a piece of paper and throwing it on the table to indicate its mountainous surface. These mountains cause a great variety in climate, surface and resources.[23] Among the mountains are many valleys with rich alluvial soil, and the more than 2,000,000 negroes afford a very considerable labor supply that now finds partial employment in other lands. They were glad to go to work in 1916 for $.20 gold each day, and went over to Santo Domingo to build roads for $.50 per day. Haitian valleys can produce hundreds of thousands of tons of sugar per year. Four large central plants were constructed within the first three or four years of the occupation. Many of the damp and sheltered valleys are also excellent for cacao. The hills can produce much more coffee than they are now producing, while much of the arid land to the southwest is well suited to henequin, of which the natives have long grown small quantities for the manufacture of cordage for local use.

---

[23] "There is hardly any country presenting a greater diversity of soil and climate, with all the varieties in such close proximity and each so nearly approaching perfection of its kind. There is need only for communication to make these natural advantages available and assured markets for the abundant produce that will then be brought forth." (*West Indies as an Export Field*, U. S. Dept. Commerce.)

F.  THE LESSER ANTILLES

From the east end of Porto Rico to the coast of Venezuela is a great
curve of islands 800 miles long.  They are the Lesser Antilles.  All save

FIG. 373.

two, Barbados and Trinidad, are the tops of old volcanoes.  Many of
them rise sheer from the sea.  Some are surrounded by coral reefs.  A
few have small areas of low plain built up by streams washing down

their steep sides, but most of their area is upland, much of it steep and mountainous.

All are swept by the trade-winds which make the surf beat hard and cut the cliffs to windward, while gentle sandy beaches sometimes form on lee shores. Differences in elevation, slope and soil combine with this master climatic fact of the trade-wind to cause a great variety in landscape and life conditions. Some of the islands are low, and because elevation is necessary to wring water from the trade-wind on a small island these low islands are dry and treeless. In contrast to this is

FIG. 374 — This picture on a highway in Martinique is typical of many islands so far as transport, costume, race, and scene are concerned. (Courtesy Robert S. Platt, University of Chicago.)

Martinique, a volcano (380 square miles) with its peaks generally hidden in clouds, drenched by the frequent passing trade-wind showers and looking at a distance like soft green velvet. A nearer view shows these velvet slopes to be a covering of tree-ferns pierced with the spears of wild banana leaves.

Some of the islands have solid soil and many streams. Dominica boasts a stream for every day in the year. Other islands are of cracked tufa, or porous volcanic ash, or of coral limestone, full of cave passages. These islands are streamless. In some a well cannot even reach water and the people depend upon catching rain-water and storing it in cisterns. In times of drought they must bring water in ships from some more favored isle. In such islands the pump at the well or cistern is as great a center of social life as it was in Biblical times, but alas, the five-gallon kerosene can from the American refinery has completely replaced the shapely earthen water-jar of the Orient. But the human form beneath the head-borne burden is still stately.

As for the past, these isles are full of history. As for the present and presumably for the future, they are full of negroes.

In the buccaneer-colonizing period, the sixteenth, seventeenth, and eighteenth centuries, the Lesser Antilles had a great attraction for European land-grabbers in search of sugar colonies. Here is the trail of every naval colonizing power of that period. At the end of every war they usually swapped a few islands. The almost unbelievable esteem in which these islands were held is shown by the difficulty that Benjamin Franklin had in persuading the British to take Canada instead of Guadeloupe in 1763 at the end of the Seven Years' War.[24] The high prestige of the Lesser Antilles in this period may be partially explained by the fact that *some* tropic land was greatly desired as a source of a great desideratum by each of the sexes — sugar and rum. In that day of uncontrolled fevers no other tropic lands were so healthy as these small wind-swept islands. Their ill-watered condition carried with it relative immunity from mosquitoes, now known to be the foster-mother of much tropic death. The small island was easy to control and it gave at least potential command of other shores. Thus the shore of the now useless English Harbor on the coast of Antigua still shows great harbor-works that have come down from the last half of the eighteenth century, when Britain spent 125 million dollars fitting it up and fortifying it as a great naval base for the careening and fitting and sheltering of ships for the command of the coasts of the Americas. Beet sugar, the emancipation of the negroes, and the opening of other tropic lands have greatly diminished the importance of the Lesser Antilles in the eyes of colonizing powers.

### Variety of Conditions

Travel in the Lesser Antilles gives one a sense of variety in humanity as well as in landscape. A Sunday in Martinique opened with a busy sunrise of buying and selling in the public market. Then came mass in the solid old Roman Catholic Cathedral. As the sun was now getting warm, the next event was a cock-fight in a cool but crowded little amphitheatre on a breezy hill-crest. The event was marked by universal joy. The birds fought with unbelievable enthusiasm. They were unhappy only when separated and sprang to their deaths with avidity; they were painted the color of blood, so that there would be no impression of gore to disturb the feelings of the audience. The betting in mongrel French was astonishing in its speed and fury. The stakes gave to the staid North American mind a new sense of the financial importance of the poultry industry.

[24] See Stefansson, V., *Northward Course of Empire,* where this champion of the North gives a choice collection of similar misappreciations of Northern lands.

At one o'clock came the great art-event of this continental-negro-trade-wind Sunday. The Latin and African cultures mingled in the production of the opera *Carmen*, sung in French in the open-air theatre by a negro cast. Thus did art and religion, sport and economics give variety to the week-end in the monotonous trade-wind climate.

Since emancipation removed the spur of slavery in the first third of the nineteenth century, the Lesser Antilles, like other West Indian Islands, have produced more leisure and less exports (goods). Like the larger islands some of them have many economic as well as historic ruins in the remains of fine old mansions, mills and distilleries of the sugar-planters.

Sugar, along with its children, molasses and rum, still remains the chief commercial product, but the varied conditions help to make a varied export. The island of St. Vincent grows about 2000 acres of sea island cotton, which the growers claim to be the best of its kind in the world.

In the humid valleys of Grenada a few hundred tons of nutmegs and cacao are grown for export. In Guadeloupe the vales of reeking humidity add vanilla beans to the cacao. On the forested hills of Dominica, the lime grows wild and the fruit is gathered by the natives for export and for the manufacture of lime-juice. In St. Lucia, British capitalists are growing bananas for the British market and they are also extending the coconut plantations.

Limitations of space prevent any detailed discussion of these islands, save three parts — the Virgin Islands of the United States, Barbados, and Trinidad — which are of especial interest.

### The Virgin Islands of the United States

The Virgin Islands command the chief gateway to the Caribbean and the Panama Canal. Hence, they are a kind of Gibraltar, a kind of Singapore, a point of strategy coveted by the imperial mind as it contemplates middle America.

In 1865, the United States negotiated a treaty providing for the payment of seven and one half millions for these islands. We were just out of the Civil War, during which period both Spain and France had made much headway in nullifying the Monroe Doctrine by establishing their military power in Mexico, Santo Domingo, and Chile. Denmark ratified the treaty but our Senate did not. In 1902, after we had taken Porto Rico and while we were planning to begin the Panama Canal, we offered Denmark five million dollars, but this time Denmark refused to ratify, owing, it is said,[25] to German influence in the Danish Parliament. Prices had risen by 1917 when we paid twenty-five millions because we were afraid that Germany would buy the islands. It was a

[25] *Geog. Review*, Nov. 1917.

very high price to pay for a bay-rum factory, some critics said, but it was not a transaction in the economic sphere. It was partly a disinfecting process — getting rid of European bases or possible bases in the middle of America, and especially beside a much-used ship passage.

On the islands, much was expected to result from the American occupation, but, on the contrary, little but disappointment has followed. There has been little economic rehabilitation. The government has been left in the hands of the Navy Department and the natives complain that its form is as undemocratic as any European establishment in the West Indies. One man has acted at the same time in the varied and conflicting rôles of attorney for the government, magistrate, chief of police and member of the Board of Paroles and Pardons. Perhaps the terrors of this combination of powers are somewhat shown by the fact that the jail at the capital is so comfortable that it is sometimes necessary to drive prisoners away to get rid of them when their term is out. The food is better than at home.

In Charlotte Amalie, the town of 8000 on the beautiful harbor of St. Thomas, one hears much of the golden age of shipping which is past. This golden age had two epochs. The first epoch was in the days of the large sailing vessels, which unloaded many cargoes of goods a year at St. Thomas. The goods were distributed by small sailing vessels throughout the West Indies. This made much stevedoring and other business which died down when steamships began to carry freight direct to many islands.

The second golden age was the bunker business. Being in the pathway of commerce, they furnished bunker coal to dozens of steamers each month. While this lasted, there was prosperity because of the pay-roll for long lines of men and women carrying baskets of coal from dock to ship. But the oil-burner and the rerouting of steamships have almost ended this business and the new government brought nothing in its place, so the native sighs for the good old days, and observers wonder how he lives. He tills the ground but little, and indeed, his island with its droughts is not encouraging to tillage. The hills of St. Thomas are almost as bare as Arizona; drinking water is scarce, and the gardener often grows his lettuce in tin cans to make the watering more effective.

The 900 people on the Island of St. John derive their chief income from the distillation of the essential oil in the leaf of the bay-tree. The leaves are crushed and soaked in distilled water. A gallon of this oil turns a hundred gallons of common rum into bay rum.

St. Croix has more rain and hence depends upon sugar plantations.

In 1923, there were about equal numbers of men and women in the fields, getting forty and thirty cents a day respectively, plus a house and a patch of ground which they rarely cultivated. On government works favored men were getting sixty cents per day, but the naval officers in charge said the *cost* was as great as in the United States. The men looked big and strong, but when it came to lifting heavy things, they were much weaker than Americans. A newly arrived officer usually began with feverish efforts trying to make his gang hustle, but they wouldn't hustle, and in about two days the officer was tuckered out and things went on as they had gone before he came — slowly.

The Virgin Islands negro speaks English because he came from British islands. He is a very religious and much bechurched man. St. Croix alone has the old Danish state church, Lutheran; Roman Catholic; a very high Anglican church with confessional robes and incense, called

Fig. 375 — Virgin Islanders dramatizing the scriptural episode of David and Goliath. Goliath wears the high headpiece. David, whose face photographed poorly, is directly below the gigantic club held by the second man on Goliath's right. (Courtesy John C. Gebhard.)

"apist" by the Catholics; Seventh-Day Adventists; "Christian Mission" (faith healer); Salvation Army, and much free and unorganized exhortation on the public square. With these gullible people any eloquent native returning from abroad can start almost anything he pleases.

To these people the church seems to be matinée, concert, movie, radio and baseball combined.

On holidays little troupes of plantation hands come into town from the estates and render scriptural scenes in the streets, an interesting survival of the miracle play, the earliest form of dramatics in Western Europe. Sometimes there will be half a dozen troupes in town at one time. They fashion their own costumes with laces, gay-colored cloth, paper and the tin of gasoline cans. They adapt their speaking parts from the Bible, even to "thee" and "thou." The episode of David and Goliath is the great favorite in this drama. A goatskin head-dress two feet high makes Goliath look big. After an appropriate dialogue, enriched by dramatic license, a small boy hits Goliath with a rubber ball and all is over but the passing of the hat. And into the hat a very poor populace puts a surprisingly large contribution. On the next holiday, which soon comes, it is all gone over again with unfailing delight.

### Barbados, an Example of Full Population

The Island of Barbados has an interest far beyond that of its area, 166 square miles, or its population, 156,000, mostly black. Its great interest lies in the fact that so many people live on that little bit of land, furnishing an example of two things rarely met — a permanent agriculture and a fully populated land. Barbados should be of especial interest to persons who have swallowed Professor East's statement [26] that the rapid increase of tropic population will shut off tropic food export because the tropic denizen will eat it all. There is no sign of this in Barbados, Mr. East's best but neglected example of full population. The facts of population surpass anything of like nature in the western world:

| Year | Population | Density per sq. mile |
|---|---|---|
| 1861 | 152,275 | 917 |
| 1871 | 161,594 | 973 |
| 1881 | 171,152 | 1030 |
| 1891 | 182,306 | 1096 |
| 1901 | No census taken | |
| 1911 | 171,983 | 1034 |
| 1921 | 156,512 | 940 |

The decline seems to have come about as the natural result of population pressure expressing itself in a declining birth-rate, combined with emigration caused by greater economic opportunity elsewhere. The white man, being able to pay the fare, has fled until his proportion is said to be 7%, but that figure doubtless includes many who are not of pure Caucasian blood. The tropic development that has followed the conquest of yellow fever has created jobs for many Barbadians in Panama, the Central American banana plantations, and the Cuban fields. Many, also, have found work in the United States.

The heavy population has a small element of support in the increasing foreign travel, in the business of coaling ships, in the handling of an entrepôt trade that is half as great as the domestic trade. Another factor that should not be overlooked is the high degree of arability and the high fertility of Barbadian land. Out of a total area of 106,470 acres, about 74,000 are devoted to large-scale sugar production. Of the remaining 32,000, about 10,000 are in pasture, about 3000 are bare rock and sand dune, and the rest are devoted to food-production —

[26] *Mankind at the Cross-Roads.*

13,000 holdings have less than five acres each. A 200-acre sugar estate is considered large and most of the work is done by the owners of the small plots, often not over a half-acre in extent.

A factor that should be emphasized is the absence of manufacture. Less than one-tenth of the people live in towns, and cottages are scattered over the countryside so thickly that it is hard to say where villages end.

The island itself has been pushed up from the sea by a series of geologic lifts and rests. During the rest a coral reef was built. After the next upheaval the coral reef became a ring of limestone cliffs supporting a great terrace. The island is now a series of terraces held in by the limestone cliffs, reaching up to an elevation of 1100 feet.

The surface is level. The whole rests on porous coral limestone. Over most of the surface there is no erosion, a point of profound importance, and the water finds its way to the sea through openings in the limestone and underground streams. These streams are tapped by pipes that deliver good water at every roadside hamlet. These facts of drainage and good water, combined with the clean trade-wind breeze, make Barbados a health resort for the Caribbean and for the Brazilian coast. They also help to explain the early development of the island. More than a hundred years ago it was famed for its dense population which made necessary the scientific saving of every weed. George Washington marveled at it in 1752 and described it well.

The level surface, the absence of erosion, the fertility of limestone soil, plus careful fertilizing, have kept up the productivity of the soil to a high degree. This affords a great contrast with the wasteful exploitation still going on in all the Greater Antilles. One travels over Barbados on good roads, past neat cottages through a waving sea of sugar-cane, enlivened by glimpses of the ocean. And when one has gone one wants to return.

Nearly every plantation laborer has his patch of land planted to "ground provisions," yams, cassava, bananas, plantain, breadfruit, beans, onions and squashes. The trade-wind climate lets him grow food the year round, unless there is an unusual drought, which causes crop failure and increases the theft and death-rate. With the money earned in the cane-field or sugar-mill, he buys fish, a little meat, flour, if he can afford it, and clothing, chiefly cottons. Many others, poorer people, eat little but what they grow. This one-crop commercial agriculture produces a per capita foreign trade of about $125.00 per year, greater than that of the United States. This trade is made up on the export end of sugar, molasses and rum. A scientific [27] and very skillful department of agri-

---

[27] The way of science in agriculture is not always smooth. The English imported the mongoose (see Rikki Tikki Tavi in Kipling's *Jungle Book*) to eat snakes. He also ate lizards. The lizards therefore ceased to eat froghoppers and the froghoppers increased greatly and made a pest of themselves by eating sugar-cane.

culture (English-operated) has made many experiments in the attempt to escape this dependence on sugar, but the success has been small. There have been shipments of mangoes, cassava, yams, bananas, vegetables, and winter melons, but sugar still holds the limestone battlements, where with every planting of the cane the negro's spade, digging in the last crop of cane-leaves, often turns over the whole of the soil mass which is commonly only from sixteen to twenty-four inches deep. The absence of erosion is a vital factor in this permanence of agriculture.

A rich field of investigation awaits the sociologist who will hasten to study the Haitian negro before American control controls him too much and compare him with his Barbadian brother, who considers himself the aristocrat of the West Indies. He boasts of the fact that Barbados has never been anything but a British possession. He is proud of his neat home and his perfectly cultivated bit of earth. Two-thirds of his children between the ages of five and fifteen are in school.

## Trinidad

Trinidad, with 1862 square miles of rolling land, is more than ten times as large as Barbados and its population is only one-fifth as dense. Climate and surface may explain the difference. It is not so wholesome as Barbados, nor so marvelously tillable. With an English government to protect and encourage and carry on scientific work, and English capital available for development, the agriculture of the island may be expected to develop as demand increases. At present sugar, cacao and coconuts are the chief agricultural exports, with the prospect of an extensive development of the banana industry. It is a practice here to plant coconuts in the cane-fields and keep on growing cane for five years.

The asphalt lake of Trinidad, first described by Sir Walter Raleigh in 1595, is well known and just at present its probable parent, an oil deposit, is furnishing the chief export of the island.

One-third of the population is East Indian, brought over to work the plantations. Aside from this, the population is made up much like that of Barbados. I regret that life has no such importance in store for many of us as that which seems to have descended upon the large and handsome negroes, towers of self-esteem, who stand in the streets of Port of Spain (the capital) and tell the populace where to walk and how. These officers of the law are clad in spotless white and adorned with much gold lace. There is one white man on this police force — the chief — but he does not look particularly important.

FIG. 376 — The thickness of the henequin leaf shows the material with which transportation and decortication have to deal. As the plant gets older the stalk gets taller. (Courtesy National Railways of Mexico.)

## CHAPTER XLI

### YUCATAN AND THE BAHAMAS — SEMI–ARID TROPIC AND SUBTROPIC LIMESTONE PLAINS

A SHORT time ago, as the geologist counts time, the northwestern part of Yucatan, the Florida Keys and the Bahama Islands were coral reefs slightly below sea-level. Then the reefs were raised a few feet or at most a few score feet and became limestone plains. This slight elevation does not cause much rain to fall from the trade-wind. The limestone plain of Yucatan suffers a further handicap in regard to rainfall by being on the leeward side of the land mass. (Fig. 377.)

The rainfall of Yucatan is thirty to forty inches, falling chiefly in a rainy season. As in Barbados the surface water on this limestone land goes at once into the openings in the limestone. Rotted from this very leaky rock, the soil is so scanty as to furnish no home for luxuriant sugar-cane. As on the edge of our own Great Plains, there is just enough effective rainfall to produce a sustenance crop of corn. The Maya Indian of Yucatan scratches around among the stones with hand tools and plants a hill of corn here and there in a hatful of soil and there is just enough rain to enable him to get enough of a crop to keep soul and body together for a time. This sounds like slim pickings, and so it is. But mark! Even this has proved better for man than the riotous forest that crowds the swampy Gulf and Caribbean coasts on both sides of this limestone plain. On three sides of this area the rainfall increases, the forest increases, and man decreases. This point is strikingly shown by completely uninhabited forest areas of Quintana Roo, into which one may walk from Yucatan unimpeded by anything save jungle. On the plain of

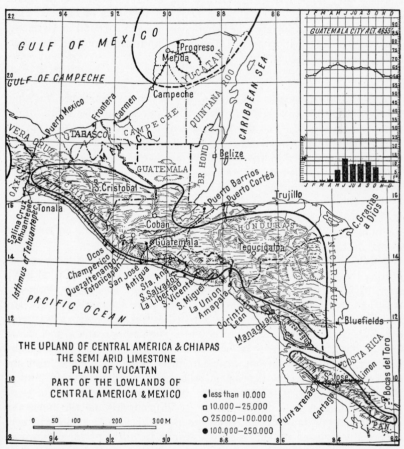

Fig. 377 — The climate graph in upper right shows the seasonal rain of tropic land away from trade-wind shores and the cool temperature of the upland of low latitude where fire feels good.

Yucatan, where nature produces only scanty forest scrub and savannas, there are few mosquitoes. Therefore many centuries ago, man and not the mosquito became the dominant animal. He could always pick the zone that best suited his corn crop, for the flat peninsula is a transition area with rainfall grading from heavy on the east to light on the west.

The gradation of vegetation from scrub to rain forest is complete. For centuries the plain has (for its resources) been peopled, heavily peopled, by the men (and their descendants) who reared the Maya civilization — a civilization which the more astounds us the more we learn of it.[1]

These people and their neighbors in Guatemala had palaces, temples, statuary and large cities. They had an alphabet — one of the great mental achievements — and a calendar as good as ours or better. They had an astronomical society when there was none in England or Germany. The chapters of their wonders fill volumes and create one of the interesting puzzles of history.[2]

## Henequin

The limestone areas of Yucatan turned from sustenance farming, chiefly corn, to capitalistic commercial production as the result of an American invention. The self-binding reaper caused a new demand for cheap string about 1880. This article of commerce was obtained from the long, tough fiber in the thick heavy leaves of the henequin plant, which grows wild over nearly all parts of this dry limestone plain. In a few decades Yucatan has become the commercial slave of henequin just as Barbados is of sugar or Mississippi once was of cotton. Henequin fiber, called sisal, is not so good as manila hemp, but it is good enough for binder-twine. The price of sisal is therefore dependent on the price of manila hemp.

This one product makes up 95% to 98% of the export of Yucatan. During the World War, when there were no ships to bring the rival hemp from Manila, the henequin dealers and the State Government formed a trust and reaped a golden harvest by getting more than war profits. The State and Federal governments participated by taking heavy export taxes, over four cents American gold per pound. The post-war slump was shown by exports of 930,000 bales in 1920, 560,000 bales in 1921, 460,000 bales in 1922.[3] This means that henequin fields were abandoned, and the people who had come to depend on wages were no longer able to buy at the store and now found themselves hungry and in want. The four sugar plantations of Yucatan supply only one-fourth of the home demand, and while most of the corn needed for bread is home-grown there is normally a cereal import. The depression caused the people of Yucatan to start a vigorous policy of henequin utilization, and in a little while they were making nearly a hundred articles, including hats, neckties, belts, slippers and baskets.

Henequin growing on a commercial scale is a capitalistic enterprise.

[1] See Huntington, Ellsworth, *Civilization and Climate.*

[2] Huntington, Ellsworth, *Proceedings of the American Philosophical Society,* vol. 52, no. 211. For fuller account see Morley, Sylvanus, *The Inscriptions at Copan.*

[3] Part of this was due to curtailment of production by the trust to enable the demand to catch up with the supply.

There is a wait of four or five years while the two-year-old suckers take root and grow to maturity. That wait requires capitalistic psychology. The young plants are expensive. They are set out three by ten feet apart in hand-made holes in the unplowed and usually unplowable rocky soil. This is the labor of the Maya laborer of the henequin plantation. His machete keeps down the rival vegetation until the plants are grown. After this they yield ten to fifteen leaves every six months for ten to twenty years. Tramways are needed to carry the thick and heavy leaves to the engine-driven machines that tear out the 3% (by weight) of fiber. This equipment calls for heavy expenditure of cash and capital again. In its capital and organization, even down to the plantation tramway, the henequin industry bears more resemblance to sugar than to coffee.

Henequin prosperity has given Yucatan a good system of railroads with a station in Merida, the capital (65,000 population), which is said to resemble the Union Station in St. Louis. In the cities are many residences, handsome within and without, but the whole rests on the basis of a Maya population exploited by the peonage system (see Index).

### Florida Keys and Bahamas

The Florida Keys and the Bahamas, in about the same latitude as Yucatan, bathed by the same warm ocean currents, built by the same corals, differ from Yucatan in having a thinner soil covering and an Anglo-Saxon government. Their chief export arises from their service as a home-place for sponge-divers who go out in open boats, and dive and tear sponges from the still submerged coral reefs in the shallows that surround these islands. Next to sponges, the second official export of the Bahamas is sisal, an industry which the inhabitants copied from Yucatan, whence the plants were introduced.

It is probable that for some years after 1920 the chief export was bootleg liquor, largely of European manufacture, smuggled across to Florida. Between 1914 and 1921 the Bahamas' imports jumped from £376,000 to £1,096,000, but the official exports only increased from £223,000 to £378,-000. What became of the difference is perhaps covered by the following joke from a Florida newspaper: "Temperance Speaker: 'I'd move heaven and earth to enforce the prohibition law.' Voice from Audience: 'Try something simpler. Move the Bahamas.'"

It is but forty miles across quiet waters from the Bahamas to the coast of Florida, with its many lagoons and many violators of the Eighteenth Amendment.

The Bahamas have some traffic in pineapples which can grow in their thin and rocky soil, and there is some export of winter tomatoes to the United States.

The economic value of dependable human qualities was well shown by the experience of an American promoter with abundant capital and business experience who went to the Bahamas to consider going into the tomato-export business. Plenty of people offered to grow tomatoes on contract, but production was the small end of this business. To reach market the tomatoes would have had to be taken in schooners to a Florida port, and thence by boat to New York. Careful grading and packing were vital. Could the Bahama workers, mostly negroes, be depended upon to observe the proper rules of sorting and packing? The Yankee entrepreneur was afraid to risk it. He gave up the idea of raising tropic tomatoes, and he went back to the Great Lakes where, though the thermometer reached zero in winter, he could depend upon the workmen of Northern European stock to do as they were told in shipping northern produce.

The Bahamas contain the islands first discovered by Columbus, and after all this time their population of 53,000 bespeaks the poverty of their 4400 square miles of rocky land. The islands have a warm and even climate, but there is no hope of irrigation, or any important soil or mineral resource. They are not a land of promise.

### The Salt Industry

Turks Islands and Caicos, to the southeast of the Bahamas, are even more inhospitable. The rainfall is but twenty-two inches at Cockburn Harbor, and irregular at that. On this treeless and forsaken waste, the people say that when they want to get into the shade they put on a bigger hat. Their chief income is from the sale of salt, obtained by the evaporation of sea-water, which can be made to yield 5000 bushels of salt per acre of salt-pans (drying vats) per year, if the season is not too rainy. In some places the water can be caught at high tide. In other places it must be pumped into the pans. For this service the trade-wind and a homemade windmill often suffice. The first concentration kills the vegetable matter, which is precipitated and thrown away. Further concentration causes the precipitation of chloride of lime which is also thrown away. The water is then pumped or run into the salt-pans. These are filled several times until a fine thick crust of salt has settled. Then the remaining liquor is returned to the sea before its other contents are precipitated and the salt thereby spoiled. It is not surprising that the Turks Islander leaves his reef of sand and limestone, where everything (even sometimes water) must be bought. These people go to widely scattered places.

### Key West

Key West (pop. 19,000) is the largest city in the Bahama-Florida-Keys area, and it is an interesting exotic. The whim of a Standard Oil multimillionaire gave it a railroad built for many miles on concrete arches over the shallow coral sea. No hope of profits lay behind this enterprise which has made Key West, the one frostless city of the United States, a railroad terminus for car-ferries to Cuba. The whim of legislation, which put a high tariff on cigars, caused Cuban cigar-makers to move to Key West (and also to Tampa) by hundreds. Between Greek sponge-divers and Spanish-speaking cigar-makers, Key West seems like a foreign town.

FIG. 378 — Cement coffee-drying yard near San José, Costa Rica, typical of tropic American uplands from Mexico to Bolivia and Brazil. The servant holds the richly saddled steed. (Courtesy Pan-American Union.)

## CHAPTER XLII

## THE UPLANDS OF CENTRAL AMERICA AND OF CHIAPAS, OAXACA, AND GUERRERO IN MEXICO

### Resemblance to the West Indies

CENTRAL AMERICA and Lower Mexico, the lands between the Cordilleras of Mexico and the mainlands of South America, are trade-wind lands — a long mainland rather than a string of islands, as in the West Indies. Their climate comprises the same elements and factors — easterly winds bearing moisture and rain to easterly slopes; wet, forested eastern plains, made wetter by flooding rivers fed by heavy rain on eastern mountains; dry places on the western sides of mountain ranges and behind the mountains; southwestern coasts that are dry like the southern coasts of Haiti and Porto Rico; central uplands like those of Porto Rico and Jamaica, differing only in being higher and wider. (Fig. 377.)

The highland backbone of the region between the Isthmus of Tehuantepec and the Isthmus of Panama divides it into three regions: the wet, forested, and unhealthy east coast, where there are few people; the less wet but also unhealthy west coast, where there are also few people; and the volcanic uplands in the interior, where most of the people live.[1]

[1] " It seems a curious reversal of what we are wont to call normal conditions, when one sees rich, fertile plains along the coast almost uninhabited, then finds the

Few places in the world offer less excuse for the economic discussion of the political units as such, rather than as economic regions.

## The Surface of the Highlands

This upland region is one of Nature's late works. Most of its surface has been poured out and blown out by many volcanoes. Guatemala alone has thirty, two of which are still active.

This upland interior has not only been volcanic in its formation but also volcanic in its history.

## A Troubled History

Central America is a storm-center of history. In its present state of organization or disorganization, it includes seven political divisions, one of them a colony: British Honduras, Guatemala, Honduras, Salvador, Nicaragua, Costa Rica and Panama, all save British Honduras falsely masquerading under the names of republics.[2]

Since most of the people of Central America live in the upland, it is the upland that has dominated the history of these countries. Central America ended the brutal period of Spanish rule by beginning an equally brutal or even more brutal period. It was really a period of private wars dignified by the names of rebellions and revolutions. The five Latin countries north of Panama were originally five subdivisions of a Spanish province. Shortly after they became independent they were annexed for a year or two to the empire of Mexico. Next they tried independence for a couple of years and promptly fell to warring among themselves and split into five pieces. Then from time to time they have been combined in twos, threes, fours and fives, but never for very long at a time. In 1921 a new union of three of the subdivisions into a Federation was announced, but it too perished within its first year, another example of the infant mortality of states. The history

---

population fairly dense on steeply sloping, stony mountain-sides at altitudes of three to five thousand feet, and finally on the hilly plateau at 8000 feet see little thatched houses clustering thickly everywhere, and every available bit of land almost as carefully and industriously cultivated as in China." — From " Guatemala and the Highest Native American Civilization," by Ellsworth Huntington. *Proceedings of the American Philosophical Society*, vol. 52, no. 211, Sept.-Oct., 1913.

[2] AREAS AND POPULATION OF CENTRAL AMERICA

| Country | Area | Pop. | Pop. per sq. mi. |
|---|---|---|---|
| Panama | 32,380 | 434,208 | 13 |
| Costa Rica | 23,000 | 468,373 | 20 |
| Nicaragua | 51,660 | 638,119 | 12 |
| Salvador | 13,176 | 1,526,000 | 115 |
| Honduras | 44,275 | 662,422 | 14 |
| Guatemala | 48,290 | 2,004,900 | 41 |
| British Honduras | 8,592 | 45,317 | 5 |
| Total | 221,373 | 5,779,339 | |

of these countries is something that has not yet reached our imagination. It is too difficult to believe — witness this passage from the *Encyclopaedia Britannica* (vol. 19, p. 645, Eleventh Edition), quoting F. Boyle: " Of its [Nicaragua's] five earliest rulers, ' the first had been a murderer; the second a murderer and rebel; the third murdered the second; the fourth was a forger; the fifth a murderer and rebel.' Then came the hopeless revolts of the Indians against intolerable oppression."

To continue the quotation: " In 1823 Nicaragua joined the Federal Union of the five Central American states, which was dissolved in 1839. While it lasted Nicaragua was the scene of continual bloodshed, caused partly by its attempts to secede from the confederacy, partly by its wars with Costa Rica for the possession of the disputed territory of Guanacaste, between the great lake and the Gulf of Nicoya, partly also by the bitter rivalries of the Liberal and Conservative parties. During the brief existence of the Federal Union no fewer than 396 persons exercised the supreme power of the republic and the different states."

Nor is all this chaos a matter of the past. In Honduras, politically the worst of all the states, there were thirty-three revolutionary outbreaks[3] between February 1, 1920, and August 1923. On these occasions, martial law was declared and machine-guns swept the streets of the capital. Then the people held an election, but they could not elect because the winner must have a majority. After this came real civil war and a dictator. As a result Honduras early in February found itself without laws, either statutory or constitutional, and with its commerce paralyzed, its industries stopped, its telegraph lines cut, all printing suspended, and life and property endangered. To obtain revenue the dictatorship resorted to the imposition of forced loans on natives and foreigners alike — and in the case of the latter in violation of treaties with foreign countries.[4] Much can be said against the advance of American rule in the trade-wind lands,[5] but the provocation has been great. The policy of the United States government, first announced by Mr. Wilson and maintained by Harding and Coolidge, not to recognize governments won by revolution and unsanctioned by ballot, may bear great results. In November 1923, Chief Justice Taft upheld this policy

[3] *Review of Reviews,* April 1924. Associated Press dispatch by courier from Tegucigalpa, March 1, 1924 (Philadelphia *North American*), said that in a month a civil war had cost 1500 lives, a number proportionally twice as great as the American losses in the World War. " Notwithstanding statements by the Washington government that Uncle Sam would not permit any more revolution in Central America; notwithstanding the treaties signed at Washington in February 1923, and on board the United States steamship *Tacoma* between the presidents of Salvador, Honduras and Nicaragua and the three American ministers to these countries; notwithstanding all these activities meant to insure peace in Central America, Honduras has been in civil war since early in February."

[4] *Reviews of Reviews,* April 1924.

[5] See New York *Nation,* almost any issue.

in an arbitration case. He refused to recognize certain Costa Rican oil concessions, because they had been paid for in cash, given to an unrecognized dictator in the face of armed revolt just before he fled the country — with the cash.

## People and Production

Since Central America has had so much war, it is easy to see why it should have poorly developed transportation and primitive industry, and

FIG. 379 — This primeval method of grinding corn (it makes wholesome breadstuff) still baffles the vendors of machinery in some parts of Central America. (Courtesy Pan-American Union.)

why, like the uplands of Haiti and Porto Rico, it should depend so largely on the valuable and easily transported coffee. Coffee is far and away the chief export of the uplands; it is here what cotton was to the South.

This highland extends from western Panama to the Isthmus of Tehuantepec, with only one short break at Lake Nicaragua. It has the great advantage of tropic uplands — coolness, moderate rain, and no mosquitoes. The soil produced by volcanic dust is very rich and enduring, so that these highlands were populous with natives when discovered by the white man. The conquering Spanish promptly and wisely made their settlements on the cool plateau, where, to this day, every capital city is located.

The upland region includes parts of many countries but life is much the same in all. The greatest point of difference is in the racial make-up. In Central America the Spaniards did not exterminate the Indian. Over most of the area, the Indian makes up the great bulk of the population. He lives by the primitive agriculture of machete and hoe described in the chapter on Peoples and in the section dealing with Porto Rico. The traveler on the plateau trails is quite likely to meet a string of Indians with sacks of coffee on their backs, trudging toward the railroad station. The Indians wear home-made shirts and trousers of the cheapest undyed cotton cloth and a home-made hat of palm-leaf fiber. They live in native villages of thatched houses and often own land in common.

The little fields are set almost exclusively to corn, black beans and squashes. The squash is much prized for making a stew which is sometimes enlivened by a bit of meat. Around the village there may be trees of mangoes and alligator pears. The banana does not thrive because of the dry season which lasts from November till April — the season for harvesting and drying the coffee. As the land is mostly steep and the population often is too dense for roving agriculture, the Indian farmers sometimes ridge the hillsides into little terraces to keep the soil from washing away.

The few white people of the coffee zone live exclusively in the towns. If a man has capital and wishes to start a coffee plantation he is quite likely to buy from the president a large tract of land, including an Indian village or two. By this process the villagers become the vassals of the white owner. By the laws of the country, the Indian cannot run away from his village and the land-owner has the right to conscript, for a certain number of days' work per year, the poor wretch who has inherited this land from ancestors who may have held it for centuries. These are the people who are seen along the roadsides bearing sacks of coffee on their heads. There is a saying that " God made the mule to give the Indian a rest."

If the plantation owner does not get enough labor supply by this vassalage, he may have some half-breeds in peonage, and. at the end of a week's work he distributes to a family a ration of corn, beans and salt. Anything else they get they must grow in their gardens. The owner also distributes weekly an allowance of about $.25 in American gold in cash, which furnishes the family's money and affords the basis of the great luxury of the Central American Indian and half-breed — a weekly drunk — when he can forget his peonage.

Central America traded by way of the Pacific for 300 years. There were good reasons for this. The Central American plateau is much nearer to the Pacific shore than to the Caribbean, and travel was so very difficult across the wet eastern plain in the pre-railroad days that it was easier to sail around Cape Horn and climb up from a Pacific port. Every country has a Pacific port, but for 300 years the journey from the seaport in the plain to the capital on the plateau was most laborious, being accomplished by mule and sometimes by ox-cart over trails and gutted roads. The first railroads were on the shorter Pacific routes, bringing out the trade of Guatemala, Salvador and Nicaragua. Only Costa Rica had its first railroad to the Atlantic. To this day the chief centers of population of Honduras depend upon cart and automobile to connect the capital, Tegucigalpa, with ships at the port of Amapala on the Gulf of Fonseca, a beautiful arm of the Pacific. Nicaragua is still hoping to build a railroad to the Atlantic, and Salvador has no need of one.

The coffee-plantations extend in an almost continuous strip along the plateau from the Mexican state of Chiapas (where there is room for considerable extension of coffee-growing), and through the uplands of Guatemala, Salvador, and Honduras and the small upland section of Nicaragua between Lake Nicaragua and the Honduran boundary. South of Lake Nicaragua, Costa Rica has the same dependence upon coffee, which is the chief claim upon the produce of foreign lands.

Salvador is the smallest and most populous of the Central American countries, but it is no more populous than parts of Costa Rica or Guatemala. The point is that nearly all of its land is in the plateau region of coffee, beans and corn.

The Costa Rica plateau is unique in that most of its population is largely white, many of the natives being pure white of Spanish stock, generally recognized by travelers as of better caliber than other people of Central America. They are better clothed and better shod, although they have the same agriculture and the same economic dependence upon the coffee export. In the very best parts of this undulating upland the small farms, with their stone-fenced fields of corn and potatoes, resemble New England. The houses have plastered walls and tiled roofs.[6] The capital city, San José, a beautiful white town, is very distinctly a center of European culture, but the isolation of the region is well shown by the fact that the thirty-five miles of motor-road connecting it with some of the neighboring towns comprise the motor-roads of the whole country, which is as large as New Hampshire and Vermont combined and has a population one-third larger than that of Vermont.

Eastward from the high plateau of the volcanic ranges there is in central Guatemala an upland section of many mountain ridges called Alta Verapaz. This is high enough to be healthful. It receives more rain than the plateau, and here not only coffee but the banana is at home. In this locality the Indian houses are surrounded by banana plantations

---

[6] An interesting series of articles by Robert S. Platt, on Central America and the West Indies, appeared in *Journal of Geog.*, 1923.

which provide fruit for home use.  As the population is scanty the people practice the primitive roving tropic agriculture, cutting down the forest for a crop or two of bananas and corn, and letting it grow up while they clear another piece of ground.  Their money-crop is coffee, which can reach the railroad only by being carried for two or three weeks on man- or mule-back.

On the eastern slopes of these uplands, forest, much of it pine, claims the land at about 2000 feet elevation, and soon gives way to the tropic

FIG. 380 — The plow of Pharaoh and the work-beast of poverty still do service in many an upland field if perchance it is not tilled by hand.  (Courtesy L. A. Bauer, Carnegie Institution, Washington, D. C.)

jungle, at lower altitudes.  On the western slopes, which have less rain, the coffee, corn and bean zone runs down to about 1000 feet elevation. In these intermediate forest slopes between the coffee-zone and the lowland there are scattered cattle ranches, furnishing an export of hides and local produce of meat for the more densely peopled coffee country just above them.

The Guatemalan and Costa Rican uplands go up to 7000 feet, a height where frost is common.  Everywhere above 6000 feet wheat, barley, and potatoes are grown.  The ground is prepared for wheat with a hoe; the crop is cut with a sickle, tramped out by feet of animals, winnowed by the wind, and ground by hand, and it may be added that the resulting bread is much more wholesome than that from the finished flour that is made by the boasted mills of Minneapolis, for it has in it all the mineral salts and vitamines, as well as the very important roughage.

## Mining

The boom literature of Latin America makes much talk of Central American mines, but the recent record of output is not impressive. True, the Spaniards in the early days worked thousands of natives to death in gold-mines. There is still some gold produced in Guatemala and manganese in Costa Rica. There is much talk of silver, lead and zinc, but there are no important mining industries and until they are proved it is better not to count on them. Those that exist are almost exclusively under foreign management, chiefly American but in some cases English and German. Hand mining can be carried on almost anywhere, but scientific and efficient mining usually requires much heavy machinery. This calls for roads and transport which Central America lacks. Think of the difficulty of operating a mine at the far end of a 150-mile ox-cart road and mule trail. It is small wonder that Honduras is reported to be strewn with the wrecks of machinery and men.

## Future

The best lands in all this plateau have been taken. While there is much unused land it is like the used land, hilly. Therefore it offers no possibility of an easy use of machinery and scientific mechanical prosecution of agriculture. At the present time some of the native fields have the almost unbelievable slope of forty-five degrees, which is much steeper than the common house-roof. It is therefore difficult to see how this region can be expected to more than double or treble its present production, and if it does it will be along very much the present lines, with one or two products for export, presumably coffee, perhaps tobacco, possibly fruit. All the other produce will be eaten by the local population, which can double or treble quite as fast as products can, provided peace and sanitation give the present high birth-rate a chance to function normally by producing grown-ups rather than infant funerals.

The great problem of the southern countries of North America again arises — political security. This has come to Nicaragua in the form of the American protectorate, with the American marines keeping order without the shadow of treaty right.

Central America has also another problem of no mean proportions, a plague of earthquakes — a not uncommon accompaniment of volcanoes. For generations cities have been shaken into ruins all over Central America and the coming of the age of science has nothing to stop them or even tell when they will come. In December 1917, and January 1918, San Salvador, capital of Salvador, was destroyed, and Guatemala City, a city of 100,000 people, was almost completely demolished. These same earthquakes destroyed the Costa Rican city of Cartago, and by an interesting irony of history destroyed the Palace of Peace that had been built by Mr. Andrew Carnegie to celebrate and perpetuate one of the frequent unions of the warring Central American states. Further irony was furnished by the government of the United States. One of the first decisions of the Court of International Justice which sat in this palace at Cartago was violated by the United States, because it interfered with our strong-hand Caribbean policy (see chapter on Government).

### The Mexican Uplands of Chiapas and Oaxaca and Guerrero

Chiapas is to Guatemala what New Brunswick is to Maine — an extension of the same thing, with an imaginary line dividing lands,

FIG. 381 — When we think of the future of this region it is well to remember that the ancestors of the present natives built cities with ornaments like this — and history has done much running in cycles. (Courtesy Pan-American Union.)

peoples, cultures and industries while in reality there is but little difference. The uplands of Chiapas show a continuation of the Guatemalan corn, beans and coffee-plantations, the same uneducated Indian farmers who have been there for centuries and the same lordly Spanish and mestizo rulers.

The chief export is some 4000 or 5000 tons of coffee from the district of Soconusco on the Pacific slope. It is sent to market by way of Salina Cruz. Chiapas has much unused coffee land and savannas with good pasture.

Westward from Chiapas is the highland of Oaxaca, and Guerrero, cut off from Chiapas by the lowlands of the Isthmus of Tehuantepec and cut off from the main highlands of Mexico by the deep Valley of the River Balsas. This plateau is not so high as the Central Plateau of Mexico. It resembles more the uplands of Chiapas but there are two differences — rainfall and surface.

The uplands of Oaxaca and Guerrero have not been covered over recently with volcanic ash and lava to level up and enrich them. They are, on the contrary, an old land where the streams have had time to cut the terrain into a myriad of valleys leaving little level upland at the top and making but little level valley land at the bottom. In these two respects they resemble the Allegheny Plateau.

As a further handicap, the rainfall is light and so variable as to make agriculture uncertain save in a few favored valleys that are wider than the rest and offer room for irrigation. Long ago these became the seats of crowded Indian populations and in one of them is today the present state capital, Oaxaca, surrounded by a cluster of villages. This region has been but little frequented by Americans because it offers so few resources for investment or inducements to travelers.

Fig. 382 — This picture of a rubber plantation (with some bananas in the fore-ground) is a typical east-coast forest scene save for the absence of creepers and gloom. Labor, oriental labor, shifted the industry to southern Asia. (Courtesy National Railways of Mexico.)

## CHAPTER XLIII

### THE MOIST EASTERN LOWLANDS OF CENTRAL AMERICA AND MEXICO

#### Tropic Heat

By comparing this region with the neighboring plateau one has a fine opportunity to see how a few geographic factors dominate a region and man's use of it. The plateau is populous, the eastern plain below is not populous. Why? The plateau is cool, the plain is hot. The plateau has moderate rain with a dry season; the plain has much rain and no dry season, the one locally called the dry season being merely less wet than the rest. In eastern Guatemala the natives say it rains thirteen months in the year. The plateau is well drained; the plain is swampy. The atmosphere on the plain is so damp that at Colon it is a common practice to put shoes and clothes into " a dry closet " where a burning lamp keeps them from molding.

We of the North often have an exaggerated idea of tropic heat. At Puerto Barrios, on the Caribbean coast of Guatemala, May, the hottest month, has an average temperature of 81° (St. Louis has 79.1°), and a January temperature of 74°. Many parts of the middle United States are hotter, if you ask the thermometer, but the trade-wind heat and humidity are continuous, day in, day out, month in, month out. Note the difference between the hottest and coldest month, only seven degrees. There is more difference between day and night than between winter and summer. This is true of all shores against which the trade-wind blows.

### Jungle

The thick forest, often with much undergrowth, all tied together with creepers, is the result of this continuous heat and moisture. The jungle is not necessarily a sign of fertility. It is a sign of heat and moisture. The northerner, seeing the palms and the thick vegetation, is prone to overestimate tropic fertility. Aside from fresh volcanic and limestone soils and alluvial lands the soils of rainy tropic lands are prone to be poor. The heavy rain has leached them, often to a low grade of fertility. They get no respite by a winter protection of freezing, as is the case in the North. Plant roots are ceaselessly sucking out fertility.

This east coast of Central America starts at the seaside with sandy beaches, often a long sand-bar, like that on the New Jersey coast. Behind it are salt lagoons sometimes called lakes; then come swamps and large areas of sand interspersed with areas of good soil. The plateau soils, mostly volcanic, are on the whole much richer than the coast-plain soils. Between the seacoast and two thousand feet elevation is the natural home of the mahogany, logwood, coconut, rubber tree, chicle tree, monkeys, parrots, jaguars, wild pigs, alligators and turtles, and in addition the dominant animal, not man, but the mosquito — buzz! buzz! buzz! bite, bite!

### Lack of Development Explained

All these difficulties explain why the east coast has remained almost unsettled and even in parts unexplored by white men, why it is still in the undisturbed possession of the few native Indians who manage to exist there.[1]

Until the coming of the railroads the east coast was as far away from the people on the plateau, and almost as little known, as the Pacific coast was to the rest of the United States at the time of the Mexican War.

If any one is inclined to say that the lack of development of the eastern plain is due to Spanish misgovernment let him consider the facts and figures for Belize, or British Honduras. At the end of genera-

[1] " For day after day, however, the traveler finds no inhabitants, and place after place which appears on the map as a village proves to have only two or three houses or to be merely an abandoned hut. Roads and even trails are almost non-existent, and in most places the machete must constantly be used to open up a pathway." " Guatemala and the Highest Native American Civilization," Ellsworth Huntington, *Proceedings American Philosophical Society,* vol. 52, no. 211.

tions of British rule the population is nine per square mile, mostly black, and the chief exports are mahogany and chicle. Belize is the world metropolis for chicle, a gum used for the base of chewing gum and gathered as rubber is gathered, by tapping the tree in the dry season. Much of it is brought over the land boundaries of British Honduras from the back country by negroes and Indians who have ranged the unsettled forests as hunters seek furs in the north woods. Note that British rule and British capital have brought Belize only to the lowest stage of extractive or exploitation industry — gathering the free products of nature.

Hard woods of the forest have been the main attraction of all this coast to the trading man. In 1798 Jamaica wood-cutters landed on the coast of Belize and started to cut logwood. The Spanish attacked them and the wood-cutters drove them out and hoisted the British flag. It still waves, but to this day this British colony is almost unpeopled save for wood-cutters.

The man who gets mahogany is called a mahogany-hunter, a name which by implication tells much about the tropic forest. Rarely does this forest have solid stands of good timber, as do the forests of the temperate zone. The mahogany-hunter climbs a tall tree from which he can look over an expanse of thick forest. In the distance he sees other mahogany trees towering above the level. He gets the location of one or two, climbs down the tree, and may have to take his machete and laboriously cut a path toward the located tree. If it is near a stream or a land that will be overflowed, all is well, very well. The tree can be cut down and wait there until the next rainy season, when he returns to the place and the log is floating; but often the thicket will not let it float away. Laboriously, with machete and axe, the man, wading, splashing, canoeing, riding on the log, chops a pathway by which the logs can be floated through the forest to some stream and, down the stream, to some port. If the tree happens to stand on land that is not overflowed land, a roadway must be cleared through the forest for a heavy-wheeled cart to take the logs to some point where water can do the rest. Those who have seen mahogany logs on American wharves have noticed that they have been nearly always squared with axes. This is done in the woods to reduce the labor of handling under such adverse circumstances.

This land of forests with an export of mahogany and logwood has such expensive logging costs that its ordinary supply of pine-wood is imported from the United States.[2]

[2] It was reported in 1923 Commerce Report that American lumbermen have bought 10,000,000 feet of pine stumpage on uplands of British Honduras, and that they are going to install American machinery and get out lumber in the American way for the Caribbean market. Will they? Commerce Reports will tell.

### The Rubber Epoch

The Castilla rubber-tree grows in much of this forest country and for a few decades there was a lively business in gathering the rubber from the wild trees, which were usually killed in the process; for who would leave a rubber-tree alive for some one else to kill, when by killing it himself he could get rubber he would never otherwise see? The rubber product has disappeared for two good reasons: one the almost complete extermination of available rubber-trees, and the other the cheap supply of plantation rubber in the far East, where the abundant coolie labor in Ceylon and Malaysia produces at a cost that a Central American Indian can rarely afford to match.

The coconut grows wild along these shores as it does on nearly all other tropic shores, and since it thrives well on sandy sea-beaches it is very accessible to the boatmen on the lagoons. It is of rising importance and value, being one of the chief exports of Honduras.

### The Panama Canal and Tropic Sanitation

Panama has long been a center of Isthmian transit, first by mule-trail, then by wagon-road, then by railroad, and finally by canal. The Panama Canal is the greatest thing that has happened in Central America since its settlement by the white man. It dominates not only economics but politics, for the creation of the Republic of Panama is generally recognized as an episode in the construction of the canal. Panama is only a shadow state, a dependency of the United States, which conducts its foreign affairs and largely supports it through the quarter of a million dollars annually paid for the privilege of building a canal and holding in perpetuity a zone ten miles wide for the construction, operation and defense of the canal.

The early works in this region, namely the Panama Railway, built in 1849–52, led to frightful loss of life because of the deadly climate, especially the yellow fever. It was finished only by the aid of Chinese, and it was often said, figuratively, of course, but with a sad basis in fact, that there was a dead Chinese for every tie in the forty-nine miles of railroad. Later the French, under de Lesseps, flushed with their success in building the Suez Canal through the desert, started to build the Panama Canal through swamp and jungle. They failed, partly because of graft but much more because of yellow fever and other diseases. I have talked with men who worked on this enterprise, and I know that the work was undertaken only by men in financial desperation, tempted by double or even quadruple salaries, and that they lived in haunting fear of early death. And the way that Europeans and Americans died on those works gave them abundant reason to fear for their lives.

In the short period of less than twenty years that intervened between the collapse of the French enterprise and the beginning of the American work on the Panama Canal, the world had entered a new epoch, so far as the tropics were concerned. This new epoch was introduced by the advance of the germ theory of the disease to the point where yellow fever was no longer a mystery. It was known to be carried from one man to the next by the female of one particular genus of mosquito, the Stegomyia. Malaria also was found to be mosquito-borne. These discoveries made a profound difference in the reputation of Panama under the two canal enterprises. Since the mosquito was the enemy he was systematically fought. At the source of every stream near the canal-works a barrel of crude petroleum was emptied, going in drop by drop to furnish a continuous skim of oil, which is fatal to the young mosquito as he thrusts his head above the water to breathe. Every marsh was drained or oil-coated. Trees were cut down and even tall grass was cut down, so that the wind, blowing from the sea, could comb the mosquitoes out and drive them back into the forests. Panama, which had had one of the highest death-rates in the world, soon had one of the lowest.

This was no democracy where the Board of Health had to be elected or appointed by an elected mayor, and where the political pull of the owner decided what would be done about a nuisance. Sanitation was carried out by the United States army. The sanitary policeman walked down the back street. Was there a hole in the mosquito netting? If so, a fine fell upon the unlucky owner, for he might have yellow fever, or malaria, and a mosquito might go through that hole, bite him and become infected and go and bite someone else. Was there a tomato can in the back yard? If so, a fine fell upon the careless owner, for a tomato can would be filled by the frequent rains and raise a few dozen mosquitoes. Thus by stringent measures the death-rate became almost unbelievably low. A new member has been added to the sanitary force, a small, easily domesticated fish, the Gambusia or top minnow. He will live in the rain-barrel or cistern and eat the mosquito larvae. His great trouble is prosperity, which sometimes gets him into the frying-pan when he ought to be on his beat.

## The Banana Industry, a Type of Organization

The knowledge of tropic diseases and tropic sanitation worked out and demonstrated at Panama has since been applied with striking success to the production of bananas. In 1922 we imported 20,000,000 bunches of bananas at New Orleans, 11,500,000 at New York, and 3,500,000 at Philadelphia, all of them from the Caribbean shores, most of them from Central America. It is one of the most highly organized industries of the world.

First good land, thousands of acres of it, must be obtained. It must have access to a harbor. Into the harbor sails a ship with a manager, various clerks and timekeepers, accountants, engineers and hundreds of negro laborers. One force builds a store, a hospital, and rows of houses with wooden walls and corrugated steel roofs. Another force builds a railway line back into the banana land, which needs seventy-five inches or more of rain, well distributed throughout the year. Ditches are cut to drain off the surplus rain-water. With machete and axe the undergrowth is cut away so that only the big trees remain, making a park-like forest. The planting now occurs. Stakes are set about eighteen by

FIG. 383 — Unloading bananas beside a plantation railway. Unlike rubber, the banana cannot be carried from oriental coolie fields. (Courtesy United Fruit Co.)

twenty-four feet. At each stake a twelve-inch hole is dug and the bud or underground shoot from a banana stalk is carefully planted. Before this begins to grow the great trees are cut down, acres of them, and left as they fall. They give the appearance of devastation, as though unbelievable tornadoes had leveled the forest. This is the time of danger. If this mass catches fire the plantation is ruined. If a flood comes the young shoots decay in the ground. If, however, all goes well they grow, perfectly protected by the mulch of forest tree-tops. In three or four months the first cleaning begins. Men with machete and axes cut their way through the mass, chopping down the shoots of young trees, chopping away enough branches to be sure that the sunshine reaches every young banana shoot. This process is repeated every three or four months as long as there is a banana plantation. No plow is used, nothing but the machete to subdue rival vegetation. In the continuous humidity fungi riot, processes of decay are speedy, and the wood-eating white ant sometimes takes a hand. In a short time nothing remains but the big logs, and sometimes they are gone in a year.

If for any reason the work stops, the jungle promptly reclaims its own; therefore the cleaning must be continuous. The ditches need frequently to be reopened, and many little bridges by which the tramways cross them must be renewed. Occasional floods may wash out half of them.

At the end of fifteen months the banana plants are twenty to forty feet high and the first bunches are ready. In the meantime tram-lines have been laid all through the plantation, often only a few hundred yards apart. The land is too soft and mucky for a wagon, but a mule may trot along and pull a little tram-car through the plantation. The use of this draft-animal also makes it necessary to provide clearings for pasture-land.

The harvesting crew includes a cutter who has a knife on a long pole with which he makes a cut in the side of the banana stem so that the bunch bends over and can be cut off. The backer takes it on his back, and trudges away to the tram-car, where the mule-driver waits to take it to the railway, which in turn takes it to the wharf.

When a banana stalk has produced one bunch, it dies, but in the meantime several new shoots have grown up around it. These are thinned out to the proper number, and a few months after the first harvest the banana plantation is in continuous production and must be cut every week or even twice a week.

The plantation receives a wireless that a steamer from New York, Philadelphia, Boston or New Orleans will arrive at its wharf at a certain hour. Instructions go to the division superintendents who start work at daylight and plan the work in such a way that there will be a continuous supply of bananas going by endless belt conveyors into the hold of a ship, which loads 75,000 bunches in twelve or fifteen hours. In the hold of the ship the bunches are kept in place by board partitions, much like farm-gates, and the hold of the ship is packed full, save for necessary passageways. Refrigerator coils promptly reduce the temperature to prevent speedy ripening, and in three or four days' time the cargo will have passed from Honduras to New Orleans, or in a week from Costa Rica to Boston. There endless belt conveyors are lowered into the hold, whence the bananas are lifted to the wharf, where continuous rows of stevedores or long traveling belts take them to freight-cars waiting alongside. The freight-car is iced in summer and warmed in winter, for the banana ripens too fast in hot weather and promptly turns black when exposed to a temperature less than forty-five degrees.

All this process requires an almost endless amount of inspection: Inspection in the plantation to see that ripe bananas are picked. Inspection on the tram-car to see that they are not bruised. Inspection at the wharf to see that they are not too ripe. Inspection in the hold of the ship every six hours to see that they are keeping properly. Inspection at the wharf in unloading. Inspection in transit, and again inspection at unloading, so that soft and imperfect bananas do not get to market.

It is natural that such speedy handling of a perishable product requiring so much special equipment should demand thorough organization. The banana importers began by owning ships but they found they could not depend on regular supplies for their ships, so they began to own plantations, which now produce a large proportion of the supply, although some are still privately produced. Owning ships and plantations, the importers had to own wharves and plantation railroads, also to control piers at American ports, and then to develop special staffs to attend to speedy dispatch and proper cooling and heating of bananas, and special companies to sell them quickly before they spoiled.

With all this equipment and all these ships, the next step was to use the deck-space for passenger cabins. This did not interfere with bananas in the hold. But passengers must be made comfortable in good hotels. Therefore the fruit company was driven to the next device, that of building fine hotels in the tropics. I doubt if the world affords another example of industrial organization so far-reaching in its elements. As a kind of side-line the banana companies run sugar plantations, lots of them, just like other sugar plantations. Sugar is now the second export of this region.

It is probably in the realm of government that the most interesting work of this company is done. If the full truth could be told about their experiences with Latin American governments, I suspect it would make the *Arabian Nights* look pale. But then the real inside story of American politics, which we also never hear, would be about as interesting. Indeed, an American fruit company is often accused playfully, though perhaps not entirely in jest, of operating governments and running elections and even revolutions. If, as has so often been said, American business corporations have been able to control year after year the councils of American cities and the legislatures of American states, why should not an equally great American corporation control so weak and often venal a thing as many a Central American government? When one considers the close approach that some of these governments bear to plain banditry, the question arises, what would happen to a business enterprise that was not in some kind of well-established relations with the government? The draft, to raise an army, is one of the commonest of their devices, but it would mean devastation to the banana-crop if the draft got its labor force.

The American fruit company that does most of the banana business in the Caribbean is often called a monopoly, and indeed its control of the business does give it that power. It is, however, a monopoly of organization, almost identical to that of the Ford Motor Company, which in a world where all the elements are free to all comers, has developed an organization so thorough and so great that it can have no rival.

Five of the six short railways of Honduras belong to the United Fruit Company and the sixth belongs to the government and hauls bananas. Nearly all the railroads on the east coast of Central America are American-built, American-owned banana-roads.

This banana industry of the Caribbean shores does not arise from the superiority of this region as a banana-producer. It arises as a kind of natural monopoly of location. This is the best place of the tropics near enough to send fresh bananas to the large American market. We see the true relationship of Central America to tropic industry in rubber and coconut oil, which are non-perishable articles of fairly high value, and can afford the freight charges of the long journeys. Central America is a natural place for both industries, but the heavy population and resulting abundant labor supply of the Far East and of the Pacific Islands make these latter regions the center of rubber and coconut-oil production, while Central America and the West Indies send to the American markets the fresh coconuts, which also have a certain element of monopoly.

With all its organization and its absence of rivals the fruit company has its troubles. A cyclone often beats the banana plantations of a whole district to shreds. In May and June 1923, winds did one and a quarter million dollars' worth of damage to the plantations on the coast of Honduras. Then since the small amount that escaped would not fill a ship the service had to be discontinued until full production had been restored. This is frequently happening somewhere along the Caribbean.

### Unused Land and the Future — a Problem in Sanitation and Organization

The banana companies, like everything else in America, have begun with the cream. They have taken the best locations. Unfortunately, most of the Central American low plain is not good banana land. Bananas need rich soil and the planters have thus far limited themselves largely to the alluvial fans and plains which the mountain streams have spread out toward the sea. The alluvial fan, of which Costa Rica has many, is indeed a prime banana-patch. So are the flood-plains of the Guatemalan rivers. Already railroads have been built, seventy-five miles long, to reach these few choice spots.

Disease is beginning to ravage the banana-plantations. This is the usual accompaniment of the crowding of plants under conditions of domestication. A fungus, the banana wilt, has made it necessary to abandon certain locations, and this may work more damage.

When a banana-plantation is used up by semi-exhaustion of the soil or abandoned because of the wilt it becomes apparent that no permanent settlement has been established. The company pulls up the railroad tracks; the managers, clerks and Jamaica negroes go to the next plantation, and the jungle returns to its own.  Notice that all this is nothing but African jungle-farming (described in the chapter on Peoples) on a gigantic scale.  There is no new technique save transport and export.

What is the future of this jungle?  Perhaps it is to remain a jungle. If it is to be permanently reclaimed the attack upon it must be serious and the government will have to be the strong, despotic government that comes from some cool land, where the vigorous energetic white man can enforce sanitary measures akin to those of Panama, akin to the management of a banana plantation.  This aspect is discussed in the following quotation from " Guatemala and the Highest Native American Civilization," Ellsworth Huntington, *Proceedings American Philosophical Society,* vol. 52, no. 211:

" Only some powerful stimulus, like the demand of the United States for fruit, could cause such plantations to arise.  The strictest supervision is necessary in order that the bushes may be cut every three months, for in a year the native vegetation grows ten feet or so, and if left to itself would soon choke the banana plants.  Still more unremitting vigilance is necessary to keep both the white men and the natives in health.  From the wages of every employee, whether he receives fifty cents or fifty dollars per day, the company takes 2% to pay for sanitary measures.  Every plantation has its doctor and dispensary, and natives and foreigners are continually dosed with quinine.  Yet even so, at certain seasons of the year, a single train may carry a score of staggering fever patients, the present hospitals are wholly inadequate, and in 1913 the company was erecting a new hospital at a cost of $125,000.00.  Mr. Victor M. Cutter, manager of the Guatemala division of the United Fruit Company, states that about 90% of the people in his district, both natives and whites, suffer from malaria and its *sequelæ.*  In spite of all precautions about 20% have the fever in a serious form."

The great eastern province of Petén, west of British Honduras, making up about one-third of Guatemala, has about 5000 people, and 4000 live in one town.  In the rainy season Petén is dotted with lakes.  In all seasons it is plagued with malaria.  About 1920, certain incursions of Mexican bandits caused the Guatemalan government to send into Petén contingents of men from the near-by highlands of Coban.  In a few months so many of them were dead that when men of Coban were ordered to go to Petén they ran away, anywhere, even at the risk of their lives.  The task of eliminating malaria from such a tropic plain is something that has not yet been attempted.  Panama is but a spot.

The commercial banana plantations have chosen only the large blocks of land.  It must be so.  Aside from this, most of the plain of eastern

Central America and the lower slopes of the uplands seems to be unsuited to commercial banana-growing as we now know it.

In Porto Rico much hill-country subject to heavy rains, like that of eastern Central America, is densely peopled and the banana is an important crop for the local food supply and the home market of near-by cities. There is no reason why similar developments might not occur on the eastern slopes coming up from the lowlands along the Caribbean. It becomes evident at once, that this is a second-class location. Getting this fruit to the American market would be much more expensive than the present system above described. We have not yet been compelled to pay that much for bananas. In future decades outside control of Central America may give the population a chance to increase to the point where the labor supply will be sufficient to turn much of its lowlands into plantations of sugar, coconut palms, oil palms,[3] bananas and other tropic produce, while the hills might become populous like the hills of Porto Rico.

The prospective exhaus-

Fig. 384 — " A neglected source of delicious food. The raceme of seedless pejibayes which Don José Zeledón is holding at the base of the palm which bore them, weighs about twenty-five pounds. Four or five such racemes are produced by the palm each year. When it is recalled that these fruits contain as much nourishment as avocados, and far more than bananas, the relative oblivion in which the pejibaye has been allowed to remain during the four centuries which have passed since it was first noticed by Europeans, seems unpardonable." (Wilson Popenoe, plant explorer, U. S. Dept. Agr., *Journal of Heredity*, vol. 12, no. 4, 1921.)

The tree is grown from Lake Nicaragua to Ecuador, and like the date is almost the sole sustenance of peoples. It has been cultivated for unknown centuries, suggestive of the possibilities of tropic agriculture if scientifically prosecuted. The tree grows from sea level to 5000 feet.

[3] The *Scientific American* reports (1922) that thousands of tons of cohune nuts waste annually in northern Guatemala. They have an oil content of 65%, as compared to 42% for African nuts of great commercial value.

tion of gasoline and the possibility of the use of alcohol instead may entirely change the basis of tropic agriculture. It is now limited to food products and valuable raw materials. If alcohol can be made from some cheap, quick-growing plant, fields of alcohol material may quickly spread over tropic lands that are now receiving from the white race only the occasional visit of the botanist and the zoologist, making collections for his museum, or the prospector in the endless quest for gold, or that scientific prospector, the geologist, looking for the mysterious traces of oil.

### The Lowlands of Eastern Mexico

The east coast of Mexico is an arc, wet in the middle and dryer at the ends where it merges into the Yucatan plain and the lower Rio Grande region. In most of its length it is but a duplication of the east coast of Central America, sandy beaches, lagoons, meandering watercourses, swamps, in places dense forests, and the ever-present mosquito and malaria. These are the reasons why Vera Cruz was for centuries known as the hotbed of yellow fever, dysentery and other tropic diseases and was called by the people of Mexico the " City of the Dead." If it had a climate like that of France it would be a great city, for it would contain all those to whom it is advantageous to live in a good seaport. Actually, after the fashion of trade-wind shore ports, it contains only those who *have* to be there. Thus Vera Cruz has but 36,000 people, although it began as the first Spanish settlement in Mexico and is today the chief port of that country. In West Europe or California it would have a million people if it had such a country as Mexico behind it.

It was the base for the Spaniards during their conquest of the Aztecs, and also for General Scott, Commander-in-chief of the American Army, conquering the same places. The city was many times attacked and several times sacked by pirates, hence the great fortress, San Juan de Ulloa, on an island in the mouth of the harbor. The harbor is, naturally, but a shallow lagoon, but jetties have been built, and the current, thus narrowed, has cut out an excellent entrance to a good harbor.

The plain itself is only a dozen miles wide at Tampico, but at the most southern point it widens out, so that the Grijalva River, draining Chiapas, is navigable for 270 miles, and the Usumacinta, which drains part of Guatemala, is navigable for ninety-three miles.

The rainfall in the Isthmus of Tehuantepec is nearly 200 inches per year; at Progreso it is only thirty because the peninsula of Yucatan cuts off the trade-wind. The rainfall declines so rapidly east of Tehuantepec that there is some land along the bay of Campeche having a savanna landscape. Behind this, in the mountains, the rainfall is greater, the forests are dense, and logwood (the word Campeche means logwood) has long been the chief export of Campeche. Here chicle is also gathered by Indians of the forest.

In the Tehuantepec region the forest is almost unclearable, but this, of course, makes prime banana-land. There was little export to the United States before the period of wars beginning in 1911. In 1923, the industry was starting again.[4] One company was planning to export bananas to Los Angeles by way of the Tehuantepec railroad, a fact which speaks significantly of the lack of good banana-land on the Pacific coast.

The hothouse climate of the dampest part of the Tehuantepec district is the ideal home of the vanilla-bean vine and there is a consider-

FIG. 385 — Sugar cane on a plantation in the lower lands of the state of Orizaba. (Courtesy National Railways of Mexico. Photo Hugo Brehme.)

able production of these beans. Farther north near Vera Cruz declining rainfall makes good conditions for sugar-plantations, and a production of 70,000 tons in 1922 was more than half the commercial crop of Mexico and about equal to one-fifth that of Porto Rico.

### Petroleum

The low plain of Mexico is almost as important in the world of oil as the low plain of Central America is in the world of bananas. The Tampico oil-fields have furnished the world's greatest gushers. In 1910 a column of oil spurted 600 feet in the air. The changing breezes blew it for miles in all directions, wetting everything and creating the greatest possible risk for a flash of flame that might have been the nearest approach to the Old Testament Day of Judgment ever seen upon the earth. At the end of nine days the oil workers, at terrible risk of instant cremation, succeeded in harnessing the well, which gave a meas-

[4] The local growers, seeing the success of the Sisal Trust in Yucatan, combined to raise the price, but they did not realize their helplessness until the ships ceased to call for the fruit. There were other bananas.

ured flow of 261,000 barrels in twenty-four hours. This is the world's sprint oil record, but this Tampico oil region also holds the world's long-distance record. The Casiano well No. 7 yielded 63,000,000 barrels of oil in seven years, and the famous Potrero del Llano yielded 94,000,000 barrels in eight years after its opening in 1910. Think of the continuous spurt of fortune as day and night, for weeks, months, and years, this steel pipe continued to spurt out its daily competence of more than 100,000 barrels of oil. No wonder the term " striking oil " has become synonymous with sudden wealth.

## Oil and Politics

Consider also the possibilities for international embroilment and civil war, with a source of wealth like this in a semi-bandit country such as Mexico has been at times. If any

source of wealth has ever tempted men to fight it is surely these oil-wells. The whole output of Mexico comes from about 800,000 acres of land, an area only equal to that of one concession of land rich in oil-seeps that has been granted for a term of forty years by the Mexican government to an American corporation. Suppose you knew of such another tract of land. Suppose a tottering Mexi-

FIG. 386 — Referring to the Mexican civil war of 1924, a French cartoonist conceiving the whole affair in oil colors, thus portrays the " Enemy Brothers " in his " History Without Words."

can government would not grant it to you as a concession. Suppose you had a few million dollars of extra money. You could buy a few thousand rifles, a few dozen machine-guns, a few million cartridges for the rival general, and he would probably promise you almost anything in the line of laws or concessions after he got into power. It is openly alleged that such things happen. Certainly someone, often a foreigner, finances civil wars and revolutions in Mexico and other countries, and the ins and outs and financial backings of the various Mexican military enterprises since 1910 would make interesting reading — if one knew them and dared print them.

## The Wells, the Oil, the Shipment

These Mexican oil-wells have such a prodigious flow because of the peculiar rock-formation. Most wells flow from porous sands and one well drains only a small area. Mexican oils are in caves of old, hollowed limestone, really great underground tanks, where they can flow freely rather than by slowly filtering through the usual sand or sandstone.

Most American oils are driven out by the pressure of gas on top of the oil. The Mexican oils are on top of artesian water, salt water at that, so they have an enormous and steady pressure, averaging 300 to 800 pounds per square inch, with a record of more than 1000 pounds. Thus they flow from first to last, whereas most American wells must be pumped after the gush of gas is over, and the last of a Mexican oil-well is the rising of salt water. Thus Potrero del Llano was running its usual 100,000 barrels of oil per day at midnight, when the shifts of

FIG. 387 — Building the pipe line on the beach at Tuxpan, a town on a harborless barrier beach. (Courtesy Atlantic Refining Co.)

watchers changed, and at 2.30 A.M. it flowed salt sea-water, and the golden day for that pipe was over with no gentle tapering off.

Mexican oil comes hot, sometimes as hot as 180° F., which is very fortunate, for the oil is so heavy and thick that when cold it does not flow well. Some of it cannot be sent through pipe-lines except for short distances under much pressure. Much of it is sent to sea in barges, for which the location could not be better because the chief oil-field is on both sides of the Panuco River, down which barges can carry it to Tampico, which is a deep, safe river harbor.

Forty miles south, the southern field, behind the port of Tuxpan, has a different method of shipment. The oil can be made to flow short distances through pipe-lines, which are carried a mile or so to sea, where vessels lying off the beach load from the end of a great rubber hose. These shipping pipes are scattered for twenty-five miles up and down the coast, opposite an oil-field one mile wide, forty miles long, a few miles inland.

This Tampico oil-field is an unwholesome place, unwholesome physiologically owing to malaria, unwholesome morally owing to its crowd of gamblers, with its free flow of drink, with its renegades from America and many other countries, with its colony of Mexican grafters, gamblers and the usual flock of prostitutes. Then there are two other human types, the honest lover of adventure who likes to be in such a place where life is in the raw, and the experts — geologists, accountants, chemists, superintendents — who for the most part remain sober.

American interests are said to own 57% of the oil-lands of Mexico, so far as known; and in 1922 we took 136,000,000 barrels of a total of 185,000,000 barrels shipped from the Tampico district. Mexico took only 7,000,000 and the rest was scattered to the ends of the world from Chile to China.

## The Future of the Oil-Field

Dr. G. O. Smith, Chief of the Geological Survey, estimated in 1920 that Mexican oil-reserves were about 6,000,000,000 barrels, or forty-five

Fig. 388 — Razing the tropic forest, building roads, dragging in machinery and pipe, digging wells, all combine to make a tropic oil-field a scene of mighty labors. (Courtesy Atlantic Refining Co.)

times the export of the year 1920. Such estimates are, of course, uncertain and, owing to the present tendency of oil estimates to under-run, let us hope this will be the case in Mexico; for it is a very important source of supply to the consumers of the United States as well as the financial and commercial interests.

The Americans are the best oil-well drillers and operators in the world; witness the personnel of most foreign fields. It is said that every well in Mexico was drilled by an American. With oil-lands leased to American companies, the wells operated by Americans, the business managed by Americans, the supplies coming from America, the oil going largely to America, with all these things in Tampico, it is no wonder that the Mexicans call it "Gringolandia," Gringo being Mexican for American, somewhat as "Greaser" is applied by Americans to the Mexican.

In twenty years Tampico has grown from a squalid little town without sewers to a modernized, well-lighted city of 100,000 people, where seven- and eight-story steel and concrete office buildings stand beside ancient Mexican stone structures. It is the first oil-port in the world. It has a tonnage of shipping, entering and clearing, greater than that of any Atlantic port save New York. For miles at sea the surface is often covered with petroleum, spilled overboard in the course of the day's work of loading the tank-steamers which come from every important country.

The American invasion of the Tampico district is so complete that American farmers there are growing tomatoes and onions for shipment by refrigerator-cars to the American market in December.

Oil-wells are fleeting. When its oil is gone, Tampico, naturally only a port for the northern interior, will have hundreds of houses for bat-roosts, and this time may not be many decades away. It is possible, perhaps even probable, that other oil-fields will be found in the eastern plain between Tampico and Panama.

Fig. 389 — The Honduran port of Amapala on the beautiful Gulf of Fonseca. In this gulf the United States has a naval station. Note the trees growing only in the ravines on almost naked mountains. (Courtesy Pan-American Union.)

# CHAPTER XLIV

## THE PACIFIC COAST OF CENTRAL AMERICA AND SOUTHERN MEXICO

### The Leeward Side of a Trade-Wind Land

FROM Panama to latitude 21° on the west coast of Mexico is one long, long monotony. Save where mountains reach the sea in the Mexican state of Oaxaca and Costa Rica there is only the white surf of the Pacific beating upon an almost unbroken white sandy beach. Behind this there is often a fringe of coconut trees growing wild, and often a lagoon; and behind the lagoon is a flat bushy plain, sometimes swampy and always malarious.

Behind the swamp is a belt of grass-land, often with clumps of trees and thickets of thorn forest. Jungle begins at 500 to 1000 feet, and ascending the slopes it changes into a real tropical forest at 2000 to 3000 feet. Here grow mahogany and tree-ferns. Farther up the mountains the growth changes to cool forests of pine. In some places, especially in Panama, where the continental divide is lower, the forest comes down to the sea.

### Rainy Season — Dry Season — Grassland

This is the lee side of a trade-wind land. While the east or windward side has rain most of the year, the leeward side has a rainy season and a dry season, hence grass and bush rather than forest. Only in summer does the land become warm enough to make the temperature-contrast with the sea which causes air to rise from the land and the sea-winds to blow in and bring moist air to this lee side. Then the great white cumulus clouds form in the afternoon, rise, cool to the point of condensation, and with a crash of thunder and lightning down comes the shower of rain. Next day it rains again, and the next, and the next, and the next.

At that season the streams, almost or quite dry a few weeks before, become rushing torrents; much of the flat land is flooded; in the hot humidity everything becomes green with rank, rapid growth. The grass shoots up knee-high, waist-high, or even head-high. In the dry season

Fig. 390 — The water supply for a town on the west coast of Mexico. (Courtesy Southern Pacific R. R. Co. of Mexico.)

the heat is great, the grass turns yellow, and the trees often shed their leaves, giving the appearance of a northern snowless winter, but this does not prevent the region from being cursed by malaria.

This is naturally the land for the cattle ranch, and much of the narrow coast-plain is used for pasture, but this calls for a very sparse population, for these ranchers are not tillers of the soil, builders of hay-stacks or fillers of silos. They merely drive cattle from one grass tract to another. Most of these rancheros are mestizos or Indians, ever astride the high-horned cowboy saddle on the back of a stunted pony of Spanish-Arabian descent, throwing their lariats over the long horns of mongrel cattle of neglected breeding and Spanish descent. The rancher's house commonly has a thatch roof, but his cattle-pens often pay tribute to the steel mills of Pittsburgh, being built of barbed wire, which makes the cheapest fence.

### An Undeveloped Land

In a few places mountain streams are diverted to irrigate sugar plantations. In the Mexican states of Colima and Guerrero there is some irrigation of rice, but the areas of these cultivated lands are small.

This is also the land where men gather the wild coconuts, which are important in some localities, especially in the Mexican section. Millions of them rot at many places along the shore, which has a very sparse population. There is no development of towns here save for the few unpleasant and unhealthy and often unsightly ports which handle the trade of the adjacent highlands. Harbors are few and far between, so that most of the trade is carried in open boats to ships that lie offshore. The Gulf of Fonseca, beautiful with mountainous shores and wooded isles, affords a wonderful harbor. Here the United States government has the concession for a naval base, a part of the treaty by which we assumed a virtual protectorate over Nicaragua. Acapulco, on the best harbor on the Pacific coast of Mexico, is the largest city on all this coast (pop. 5000). It is an unhealthy place, the outlet for the uplands of Guerrero, and perhaps for Mexico City if a projected railroad is ever completed.

As to the future of this west coast, the elimination of malaria and the coming of better government (two things hard to obtain) might easily result in a doubling of the population through the more intensive prosecution of the cattle industry. This could be brought about by using the plow in the production of forage-crops, which would have several times the food-value of the present wild grasses.

Many of the dryer sections are admirably suited to the production of sisal. A few plantations have been started in Honduras and Salvador and there is room for many more. Coconuts might be grown on an extensive scale.

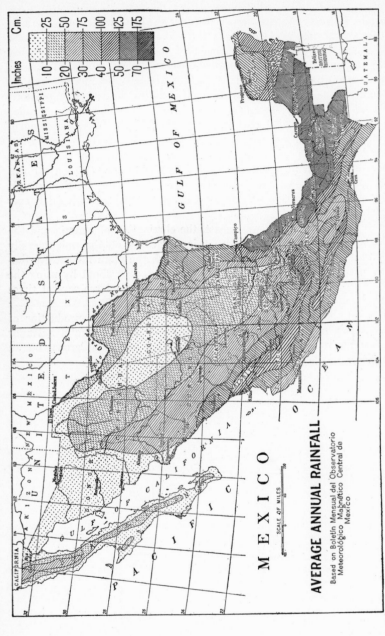

Fig. 391 — See how this map shows up the desert and semi-desert areas. (From McBride, *Land Systems in Mexico*, American Geographical Society, New York.)

## CHAPTER XLV

### CENTRAL PLATEAU, MEXICO

THE spider's solid body is held up in the center of a far-reaching circle of thin legs. Similarly the central plateau of Mexico, heavy with people, the center of population and government, looks out in all directions to thinly peopled corners of the country — empty Quintana Roo, scanty Chiapas, desert Sonora, and Lower California, unexplored western Sierras, dusty Chihuahua and Tamaulipas with its chaparral.

This part of Mexico, so small in area, is so large in its population [1] because its plateau-climate is cool enough to be healthful, its rainfall is small enough to keep most of the area free of swamps and large enough, though barely (twenty to thirty inches), to permit the growth of food. Here again as in Yucatan we see the advantage of meager rather than abundant vegetation. The northern boundary of this region is the northern limit where crops will grow without irrigation.

The soil is rich and the long growing-season permits two crops a year.

FIG. 392 — Idealized cross-section of Mexican Plateau. *AA,* sea level. Shaded area, old mountain masses. Dotted area, alluvial and volcanic filling. Black, lava cap.

This favored region is also studded with rich mines to furnish jobs for city workers and a product for export.

The plateau-dweller has two industrial worries: will there be enough rain to make a good harvest, and will the price of silver, lead, and copper keep the mines going?

### *Formation of the Plateau*

Once this land consisted of low mountains and wide valleys. Then it was lifted up several thousand feet and became the plateau. The entire plateau was pierced through with scores of volcanic cones which proceeded to cover most of the surface with lava or volcanic ash. Therefore, it is a rich land, like the Columbia Basin. This volcanic outpouring dammed up most of the streams and made the valleys into vast lakes.

---

[1] Of fifty-two cities having a population of more than 10,000, thirty-four are above the elevation of 3280 feet. These thirty-four cities have approximately 1,750,-000 people, while the other eighteen cities have but 350,000 people. (*Bull. Am. Geog. Soc.*, vol. 46, p. 132.)

Here mud mixed itself with volcanic ash which made wide expanses of the choicest kind of soil when the rivers had cut outlets and drained the lakes. The formation resembles that of the Red River Valley of Dakota, Minnesota, and Manitoba, but this northern valley had no volcanic ash to enrich the soil. The basin in which the City of Mexico stands, unlike

FIG. 393 — This view of the city of Guanajuato is a splendid portrayal — cactus, peon with big straw hat, the woman in black, the glaring landscape of flat-roofed houses and bald hills from which the city digs its living. (Courtesy Pan-American Union.)

the Valleys of Puebla, Tlaxcala, Guanajuato, Queretaro and Jalisco, has no outlet. As a result seasons of heavy rain caused flood-waters to back up in the city and remain. It took a long time for the water to evaporate, and a most unwholesome situation arose, which has been remedied at great cost by the digging of long tunnels to make an artificial outlet to this rich and otherwise favored tract of land.

These old lake-beds, like the flood-plains of the Nile and Euphrates, made farmers many centuries ago of the men who lived there. The climate helped to settle man down and encouraged him to till the soil.

### Climate

This central plateau is as remarkable in its climate as in its soil. The maps show it to be within the tropic latitude, but because of the elevation it does not have a tropic climate. The winter is cool, with occasional frosts and rare snow. The average January temperature of Mexico City is 54°, the same as that of Yuma, Arizona. Its hottest month, May, before the beginning of the summer rains, has an average temperature of 65°, the same as Quebec, one degree cooler than Salem, Oregon, in the Willamette Valley, four degrees cooler than Montreal. Summer temperatures of 88° and 90° are rare. It is hot in the sun by day, but, as is the case in all arid lands, surprisingly cool in the shade, so that the sojourner needs a sunny room even in July. The nights are always so cool that one sleeps under blankets, and the summer traveler is advised to carry overcoat and wraps. Indeed, some Americans say this part of Mexico is destined to be a center of summer travel, so comfortable are the temperatures in an interesting land.

This climate is so different from the tropics that the natives of the plateau perish in the hot and humid plains of lowland Mexico as quickly as, or even more quickly than would the people of North Europe or the Northern United States. In the Diaz régime the banishment of offenders to the tropic forests was a common punishment dreaded by the people but little less than a direct sentence of death before the firing-squad, which has been the fate of so many thousands of Mexicans, from presidents to peons.

The rainfall of the City of Mexico, typical of the plateau, twenty-three inches per year, is ideally distributed for growing crops. One-tenth of it falls in the winter, when the frost might injure crops. It rises in effective crescendo throughout the summer months (Fig. 246): May, 1.9 inches; June, 3.9 inches; July, 4.1 inches; August, 4.7 inches; September, 4.1 inches; October, 1.8 inches.

This rainfall, with the hot sunshine, makes the plateau a land of wheat, barley, corn and beans, especially corn and beans, the great staple foods of the Mexican populace. Mountain streams bring water which can be used for irrigation.

### People and Civilizations

Here Cortez found the rich Aztec Empire [2] with a complex social organization and the unheard-of collections of precious metals which

[2] *The Literary Digest,* July 12, 1924, reports the discovery near the City of Mexico of a library with books of carved stone estimated to be 7000 years old,

astounded Europe and roused the brutal Conquistadors of Spain to an orgy of crime that should make the Caucasian race blush for the next thousand years.

At that time the Indian farmers had this plateau in a high state of cultivation. For centuries they had been using mountain streams for irrigation and their physical achievements, as shown by the ruins of palaces and pyramids, entitle them to much more respect than they have

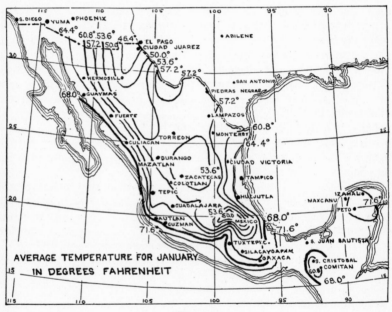

Fig. 394.

received. The Spanish conquerors took their empire and made their capital city the capital of the Spanish province which was rich in human material. Here in 1524 was the first European school in the new world, in 1536 the first printing-press in America, in 1693 the first newspaper of the New World. Today the City of Mexico is larger than any city south of Chicago and Philadelphia and north of Rio de Janeiro.

There is no negro population here. There has never been room for negroes. The Indian was accustomed to labor. Therefore he has survived Spanish tyranny and abuse. He is still on the land and his land-

---

perhaps 10,000 years old. They are the product of a "Mongoloid civilization," buried like Pompeii in volcanic ash. This ash, in connection with lava flow, does much to aid in estimating the age. Many of the books deal with the stars.

If all these things are true, the philosophic historian has more mysteries for contemplation and solution.

hunger is the stuff of which revolutions are made. The system of peonage previously described has been in full force here. The Spanish conqueror took the land, regarded the natives as work-animals, and treated them accordingly.

There was no social problem, no land problem until toward the end of the reign of Diaz. Then came Madero promising land to the landless. The organized labor-movement, with 800,000 members in 1923,

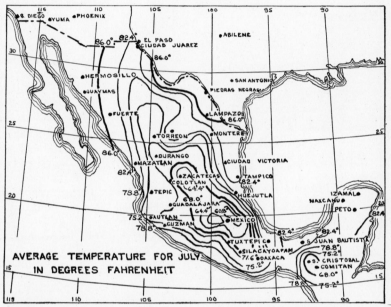

Fig. 395 — Examine this July map and see that the bulk of the Mexican people do not live in any tropic climate. Particularly instructive is the comparison of Mexico City with New Mexico.

was the first step in Mexico away from mere personal loyalty to a leader. It made common cause with the landless peon. Obregon regarded himself as Madero's successor. In the early months of his rule it was said in Mexico City: "We have got to satisfy the Indians' land-hunger or there will be another revolution. The Indians have destroyed four governments in ten years." Hundreds of big estates were divided up [3] and the land given to the Indians who as peons or proprietors had been on it for many centuries.

[3] The Supplement to U. S. Commerce Report, p. 16, No. 42, Review of 1922, puts it gravely thus: The government pursues the agrarian policy relentlessly in spite of the severe criticism of the press and protests of landed interests, assuming this to be a serious obligation under revolutionary promises.

## The Land Question and Education

Then followed in 1923 a national campaign for education in a land of illiteracy. A million primers were printed. Five hundred public libraries were opened. Money was scarce, so people gave up their jobs to help. It was a kind of crusade. Volunteer teachers turned out by the thousand to teach night schools bearing signs: "Entrance free. Learn how to read tonight." There was no entrance fee, no registration. The thirsty simply entered and drank at the fountain. Frank Tannenbaum found a school sixty miles from Mexico City where there was no book, paper, pencil or

FIG. 396 — These figures taken from ruins of buildings built in Mexico centuries ago indicate that we have much yet to learn about American history. (Courtesy National Railways of Mexico. Photo Hugo Brehme.)

desk, but there was a teacher with a black cloth and three pieces of chalk, and there were eager learners.

Few in Mexico believe that the government can keep its promise to

FIG. 397 — This ruined Pyramid of the Sun at San Juan Teotihuacan, near Mexico City, ranks well with any ruin in sheer bulk and weight of labor. (Courtesy National Railways of Mexico.)

pay for these confiscated estates, especially in view of the objections raised by the proposed tax of one-tenth of one per cent on land which Obregon proposed but was afraid to try to collect. Then, too, Mexico owes the *foreigner.*

It has been pointed out that the land-owner whose land has not been taken cannot borrow to produce because of his fear that his estate will go.

It is also true that the peon, now that he owns the land, has often gone back to subsistence-farming rather than to commercial production and trade has fallen off. This seems to vindicate the West Indian observation that the man in the *conuco* is better off than when he goes to the plantation. The *conuco* makes ease. The plantation makes trade.

Mexico now has two parties, and perhaps it is fair to say that she has made the first step away from the sixteenth - century medievalism that has too long survived upon such large areas of the American continent.

If the modern epoch is starting, it starts under great handicaps. The people of Spanish stock have the Castilian prejudice against work. In their social code it is degrading. Most of the people are Indians or mestizos, poor beyond belief and accustomed to the lowest possible standard of life. When railroads were first built in

FIG. 398 — The peon and his patch of irrigated corn, also his row of peppers. (Courtesy Southern Pacific R. R. Co. of Mexico.)

Mexico one of the troubles was that the people would set up housekeeping under the freight-cars and get run over.

The common diet of the masses is corn-cake and beans, " tortillas " and " frijoles "; soul and body cannot be kept together with less. With a frying-pan and an open fire the kitchen is equipped, so that the freight-car to keep off the rain and a blanket to wrap up in really do complete the necessities. In the morning, wrap up in the blanket, pick up the frying-pan and the moving is complete. This is, of course, extreme, but it is real. It is this low diet of the peon that enables the Central Plateau to support so many people and send corn, barley and beans to other parts of Mexico.

### Crops and Local Markets

Large fields of corn and beans are conspicuous in many parts of the Central Plateau, especially in the lower lands. Some mountain, often a volcanic cone, is nearly always in sight, and the lower slopes, where it is too dry for corn or beans, may be covered with maguey, of which there are often wide expanses.  It is from the juice of the maguey that the national drink, pulque, is made.  Since it will keep only forty-eight hours, trains of pulque run into Mexico City as milk trains do to the cities of other lands.  Compare the influence of the two on death rate.

On the higher mountains are forests, provided the forests have not been cut away.  As this land has no coal and has been populous for many centuries, there has been a heavy drain upon the forests, and one of the sights of the roadside is the barefooted Indian charcoal merchant with his stock upon his donkey, coming from some distant charcoal burners' camp, and making his way toward the town along with farmers and their donkeys loaded with farm-produce.  They all sit about the ever-present public market square with goods spread out on the ground for the city-dweller's inspection.  Dickering for a sale is one of the events of life for them.

### Mining and the Foreign Capitalist

Metals are the money-crop of this region.  The volcanoes did not cover all of the surface of this plateau.  A flat and fertile plain of volcanic ash will end abruptly against the rocks of an old mountain deeply cut by gulch and canyon, millions of years older than the soft showers of ashes that have partly buried it.  In the old rocks are the metals dug by the men whom the farmers feed with crops grown on the new volcanic ash.  Scores of towns and small cities cluster with their houses of adobe or stone around mines of silver, lead, copper, zinc, many of which date back to the Spanish conquest.

Fig. 399 — Hauling hand-made " doby " bricks, the well-nigh universal building material, on donkeys is a degree of efficiency that often prevails where the Mexican makes the plans. It also explains the great possibility when machinery is used. (Courtesy G. F. Weeks, Mexican News Bureau, Washington, D. C.)

Most of these mines have succumbed to the later conqueror — the foreign capitalist.  It takes money to equip a modern mine, lots of money.  When a Mexican gets enough money to equip a mine, he sees Paris instead, sees it grandly.  Thus the mines gravitate to the hands that can hold money.  Nothing is more natural than that the Rocky Mountain mining-promoter should have gone on over to Mexico, especially when a man like Diaz, wanting industries, gave concessions freely to those who would come and work them.

Toward the end of the reign of Diaz the American consul at Chihuahua estimated the wealth of Mexico at $2,434,000,000.00, of which Americans owned $1,058,000,000.00; English owned $321,000,000.00; French owned $143,000,000.00; Mexicans owned $729,000,000.00. Mr. Frank Carpenter (in his book, *Mexico*) estimates that the Americans own $500,000,000.00 worth of Mexican mines, while the Mexicans own but $20,000,000.00 worth. In ranches, the Mexicans still have five times as much as the Americans, but these too are going. These figures are only estimates, but it is universally recognized that American capital dominates nearly all the important large industry of Mexico. And it is of course a truism that the Mexicans want Mexico for the Mexicans. Here is a situation full of possibilities of trouble in the decades to come.

### The Cities

The outstanding human fact of this plateau is the City of Mexico. The census of 1910 credited it with 1,080,000 people. The next rival city, Guadalajara, had but 118,000, and there were in all Mexico but five cities above 50,000. It is difficult to see why this city towers so far above all the rest and how it can be supported, but there it stands, sumptuous, like Paris, with many fine buildings, with a cathedral which is the largest and most highly ornamented church in America. There are schools, colleges, eighty baseball teams, and a museum of antiquities

FIG. 400 — The booth of the small tradesman. (Courtesy National Railways of Mexico. Photo Hugo Brehme.)

that is an archeologist's heaven. How is this city supported? In this, too, it resembles Paris in being the capital of a country with a highly centralized government. Thus many employees of government naturally belong in the capital. Then, too, graft, the weakness of Spanish-American government, unduly enlarges the number of persons living on government. The Spanish-American love of city life means that every Mexican who can possibly afford it has a home in the City of Mexico for most of the year.

There are commercial reasons also. It is a very considerable railroad center and point of distribution for the farming country around, and for the mining camps. On the industrial side, it has factories, especially for woolens and cottons, with machinery, mostly European, and run by electric power brought from the eastern slopes of the mountains. The factories, however, are not the most characteristic aspect of industry. The handicrafts still support many thousands at pottery-making, leather work, clothing manufacture[4]—jobs that are done in factories in the United States. Political disturbance works in favor of the hand-worker as against the factory.

One more fact needs to be emphasized to explain the large population of this city. That fact is poverty. While it has the sumptuousness of Paris, it has all the beggardom of Naples, and little suffices for the Mexican peon. Corn, beans and pepper, a bit of charcoal to fry and

Fig. 401 — Winnowing grain in the wind in the street of Amecameca, a village in the state of Mexico. It is on the basis of these people, now so conservative and tenacious, that Mexico has once or more than once been great. (Photo Hugo Brehme.)

bake, overalls, cotton shirt, blanket and adobe house made out of the clay of the ground, roofed with the fiber of the palm or the straw of the field or the tile from its clay—and thus five or ten Mexican families live on the dirt floor on the income of an American artisan.

The city of Puebla to the southeast of Mexico City is near the water-falls of the plateau's edge. Here many thousand cotton operators tend machinery run by hydro-electric power, and by engines fed with Tampico oil, and make "manta," the cheapest of cotton cloth.

[4] The Mexican women do beautiful needlework and Celaya is an especial center for drawn work. At the car window the picturesque vendors offer you drawn work, ropes, hats, shawls and pottery of exquisite workmanship, but unless the buyer knows the goods he is likely to discover later that he has bought something made in Connecticut or Germany rather than in Guadalajara (pottery) or Celaya (drawn work).

## Future

The future of this plateau region is primarily a political question. If the stability of Diaz could return and science and machinery could be applied to the agriculture as they are to the mining, this region might double its agricultural production. There is more water-power in the mountains to run factories; the mines within this territory still have unworked ores, while the mineral resources of other parts of Mexico seem to be almost untouched. A peaceful and prosperous Mexico might easily see the population of the Central Plateau doubled, provided there is no great change in standards of living; another alternative would be a more expensive standard of living and smaller increase of population. Whether it will be increase of numbers or increase of standards is an interesting question in social psychology. The odds are in favor of numbers.

It should not be forgotten that the people of Mexico are predominantly of Indian blood, that many of the rulers have been of Indian blood and that these people once had a civilization that compared very favorably with that of many parts of Europe at the same time. The Mexican Indian is distinctly artistic and very musical. His future is hard to predict if he really has a chance.

# CHAPTER XLVI

## THE MEXICAN CORDILLERA REGIONS

THE Mexican Plateaus are completely cut off from the Mexican shore-lands by the eastern, western and southern cordilleras. These mountains, which lie somewhat in the form of the letter " u," usually rise two or three thousand feet on the plateau side with many peaks standing higher, and go down eight or ten thousand feet on the seaward side. The outer, or seaward slopes of the Sierra give a fine example of the three zones so often mentioned by the Mexicans in describing their country: *tierra caliente* (hot land), elevations up to 3000 feet; *tierra templado* (temperate land), with its best development at 5000 feet; the *tierra frio*, or cold zone, above 7000 feet. These zones, coming close to each other on the steep eastern slope, help to make this region a botanist's delight because of the great variety of plants to be seen growing close together. The seaward slope of the western Sierra runs out into the desert, but the seaward slope of the eastern Sierra runs down into a wide tropic plain where jungle covers much of the land. Above this coast jungle comes a wealth of orchids, and then of evergreen oaks, deciduous oaks, pine, spruce and fir, which spreads out into fine forests between 9000 and 10,000 feet on the slopes of the volcanoes. The forest does not disappear until 13,000 feet, above which come the Alpine grasses and flowers, which are distributed throughout the world with strange uniformity in certain temperatures, whether they be at sea-level in Alaska, at 10,000 feet in Colorado, or at 14,000 feet in Mexico or yet higher on the Andes.

The continuity of these mountain walls has done much to prohibit travel from the sea to the interior of Mexico, especially on the west, where there is no break, no railroad, no used trail even, between the American boundary in latitude 33°, and the canyon of the Rio Grande de Santiago in latitude 21°.

The southern mountains are a string of high volcanoes, but they make less of a barrier than the eastern and western ranges. It was here that the first and for a long time the only railroad entered the Plateau from a Mexican port — the line from Vera Cruz, a difficult and expensive piece of engineering, late in its inception and long in building.

The greater part of the Sierra region has few people. One section, however, is populous. That locality is the outer slopes of the Sierra at the southeastern tip of the plateau and especially the part near the giant cone of Orizaba, eternally snow-capped and three and a half miles high. The mountain slopes here are made of volcanic ash. The trade-wind brings them more rain than comes to any other part of the Sierras. The melting snows of Orizaba furnish water that may be used for irrigation in a dozen valleys that gash its slope.

### Vera Cruz to Orizaba

The journey from Vera Cruz to Orizaba displays the life-zones of this area. As one goes up the scene changes rapidly. The narrow plain behind Vera Cruz is grass-land because of the long dry season. The cattle-ranches show few signs of human activity. Immediately as the road enters the mountain signs of more continuous rain appear. The valley floor is silver-green with sugar-cane or darker green with corn. Everywhere the mountain-sides are dotted with palm-thatched houses of the primitive agriculturists with their bananas, plantains, corn and other vegetables immediately around the house. Steepness is no barrier. There seems to be a hut in every little pocket where one can be perched — where man can climb he can use the machete and the banana-plant can stand. The land is populous, like the windward slopes of Porto Rico. The porous soils of volcanic ash do not wash as much as other soils. I doubt if the world affords a steeper agriculture. After climbing a few hundred feet the railroad enters the coffee-zone with its three layers of vegetation — close to the ground the dark green shrubbery of the coffee-tree, and here and there among the coffee the more lofty banana-plants, and standing above everything else thin-topped shade-trees. Thatched houses are everywhere.

At 4000 feet in one of these valleys in the midst of fertility and climatic delight is the city of Orizaba, the largest city of all the Sierras. Neither mosquitoes nor malaria are found at this altitude, and Orizaba, built on the site of an ancient Aztec town, is a summer resort for Cubans, and a winter resort for the City of Mexico. The region is warm enough to grow sugar as well as corn, coffee, bananas, tobacco, and a great variety of produce, as well as many beautiful orchids and ferns. Not only is Orizaba a resort, it is a manufacturing city too, where there are thousands of cotton operatives. In this Manchester of Mexico the machinery is driven by engines burning Tampico oil and by electric energy from near-by water-power plants fed by the trade-wind rains and melting snows, melting on the flanks of the volcano Orizaba, the second highest mountain in North America.

A half-hour beyond Orizaba, the railroad passes 5000 feet elevation and enters another world. It leaves the tropics. The sugar-cane, bananas and coffee give way to corn and beans. The scattered thatched houses give way to villages with houses of thick adobe walls and walled gardens behind them.

## Populous, Isolated Little Valleys

There are many of these fertile valleys cutting back into the mountains on the edge of the plateau and opening out to receive the trade-wind rains. They are the most densely peopled part of Mexico. In some places the land is terraced and the hoe agriculture resembles that of Japan in technique and in the density of population supported. These deep populous valleys, notched into the edge of the upland, are a striking feature of Mexican geography and Mexican life. Riding along on level land, you suddenly see over your mule's shoulder a ravine 3000 feet deep and full of Indian villages and tropic produce. While you look at the landscape a train of Indian men and women walk past guiding their donkeys loaded with bananas, yams, oranges, limes, and other warm-land produce that grows in their valley but will not grow in the plateau zone above them. They are carrying the produce of their warmer valleys to the city market of the next higher and therefore colder zone. Thus Guadalajara, Puebla, and other cities near the edge of the plateau have their markets enriched by the produce of two climates.

Much of the southern Sierra is cut into a labyrinth of deep and isolated valleys with little level land in their bottoms and none on the mountains. Travel must be by long, steep, difficult mule-trails. There is almost no trade. Large districts here have no white people at all and the Indian lives very much as he always did save for the influence of some trade-goods — cotton cloth, machete and rifle. The mountains of this southern Sierra reach the sea, and this part of the coast has one port, Manzanillo, having (1924) the only railroad from the plateau to the Pacific. The ripe fruits of political chaos are shown in the prohibitive interest-rate there of 10% per month (*United States Commerce Report*, March 5, 1923) and exports limited to turpentine — one of the primitive non-capitalistic extractive industries.

## Eastern Sierra

North of Vera Cruz, the eastern Sierra is narrow; it receives less rain than farther south and it has a scanty population.[1]

[1] Mrs. Clare Sheridan, the sculptress, seeking a vacation in the northern part of the eastern Sierra, praises the beauty of the region. "We made camp in a glen, with mountains towering above and cascades and rapids near the tents, . . . warm and sunny, full of flowers, butterflies and water falling, water rushing and water pools that trickle. I have loved spring days in England, with their mist of bluebells in the woods and brimstone butterflies, the color of primroses; but this seasonless country that has never known frost, this heaven of eternal sunshine and riot of beauty, is almost too wonderful to enjoy. It is as if one had picked all the best from every corner of the earth and put them here and made a composition picture. On one side of me were bamboo, palm trees and tall feathery reeds; and the moon caught the flat of the leaves and turned them to silver. I said good-by regretfully, lingeringly and tearfully, although I realized that if I lived in Mexico I would weary of the seasonal sameness."

Near the center of this eastern slope is Ciudad Victoria, the capital of the state of Tamaulipas and a health resort for the people of the near-by lowland. In a gateway in the northern Sierra made by the Santa Catarina River is Monterey, the Pittsburgh of Mexico, the rival of Orizaba for the leadership among Sierra cities. The coal-field at Sabinas is not a good coal-field, but it is the only one in Mexico. The iron ores of Durango, aided by a high tariff, enable Monterey to smelt some iron for use in the foundries and machine-shops of the city, which claims a population of 70,000. Sitting in a land of drought (twenty-two inches of rain), the surroundings of Monterey bear little resemblance to the tropic gardens of Orizaba.

## Western Sierra

It is the western Sierra which has the smallest population of the Sierras and the greatest prospect of industry, wealth, and opportunity

FIG. 402 — This concentrator, this huge plant sprawling down the Mexican mountain-side, and full of machinery, shows the necessity of capital, technical skill, and industrial organization in the mining industry. (Courtesy G. F. Weeks, Mexican News Bureau, Washington, D. C.)

for investment. In its present form the western cordillera is the work of volcanoes. An old mountain mass of quite unknown shape has been buried under many thousands of square miles of lava. This happened long ago, and since that ancient time the streams, cutting, cutting, cutting, at the eastern and western edges of the lava plateau, have notched valleys into all its edges and cut down into the old mountains beneath it, thus exposing to the prospector their mineral contents which the volcanic period helped to develop. On the east side these valleys are little but canyons, often a thousand feet deep, with here and there a little patch of valley land at some bend in the stream. The stream itself is usually lost soon after it emerges into the dry interior (basins).

The west slope is a succession of sharp valleys cut back into the plateau, and sharp spurs of mountain reaching out into the plain, getting nearer and nearer the ocean the farther south they go.

The high plateau top is often fairly level, covered with forests of pine, oak and cedar, standing over grassy, park-like floors much like the upland forests of Arizona and New Mexico, of which indeed they are almost a duplicate, almost a continuation, save for a break near the Mexican boundary. In winter they are deep with snow.

The sharp canyons, branching out into labyrinthine valleys, isolating tracts of high mesa, provide localities that are most difficult of access. In these isolated places it is more than likely that there are Indians who have never in their lives seen a full-blooded white man and who are carrying on a primitive life, almost uninfluenced by the white man.

It is not hard to see why this is a land of no trade routes. On both edges of the mountains the journey takes the traveler up boulder-strewn canyons which a distant downpour of rain may turn into a flood, carrying the possibilities of death by drowning, or of hours or even days spent perched on some ledge with a roaring flood in front and an impassable cliff or gulch behind. When the top is reached, much of it is rough lava, making bad going. Therefore the only rail-route from the coast of the Gulf of California to the interior is by way of Arizona, New Mexico and the railroads to the Central Plateau, which reach out several branches toward the western cordillera.

The good forests on the cool uplands are not likely to enter foreign trade, although along with the mountain streams they are a great godsend and source of supply for men who will dig the metal out of these western mountains which are thought to be very rich in metals, " the mineral storehouse of the world."

### A Mineral Storehouse

The cracking and raising of the old mountain rocks by the lava that finally covered them is the very best process for the collection of ores, which have been exposed along both edges by the streams that have cut valleys through to the old rocks. The heavy production in past centuries under primitive conditions can be considered as a sample, pointing the way to great future production when the deposits are worked by modern methods. Thus the Rosario mines and the Guadaloupe de los Reyes mines in the west slope, several days on horseback from the coast, sent $175,000,000.00 worth of silver by mules down to the Pacific port of Sinaloa before the year 1900. These and many other mines have been worked by the wasteful and expensive methods that must be used where machinery cannot be had. Often these ores have been lifted out by windlasses or carried out in sacks. There can be no good smelter in such a place, so the ancient *arrastre* is the substitute. By this process mules pull a heavy, stone roller over a stone floor and crush the ore. The richest pieces are then picked out by hand and hauled away on mule-back to be finally smelted at Jersey City or in Wales. It is well known that most ore deposits have a small proportion of their metal in ores that are rich enough to stand the cost of such processes. There is usually a larger quantity of lower-grade ores that can stand the cost of a plant equipped for large-scale production, provided there is good transportation. To develop these ores may cost hundreds of thousands or even tens of millions of dollars for a single mine.

When the trained geologist and the expert engineer have gleaned the last facts about the mineral wealth of these mountains, they will doubtless find generations of work for tens of thousands of men and scores of millions of capital. The great need of security for such highly capitalistic enterprise is shown by the details of a particular unit described in the *United States Commerce Report,* January 15, 1923. It was a projected hydro-electric enterprise near the boundary of the states of Sinaloa and Durango. All surveys were complete. They called for an eighty-foot concrete dam to store water to run a 25,000 horse-power plant to send power over 275 miles of transmission line to operate mines and furnish light and power in towns, while the water stored by the dam would be of service both as flood control and as source of supply for irrigation on the plains below. Many such enterprises are possible up and down this large and rich region. Engineers are available. Capital is available. Workers are available. Only political security is lacking. If these enterprises are built, the situation at the famous Cananea mines near the Arizona boundary will be repeated over and over again. These mines in 1922 had 160 Americans, chiefly in positions of skill and superintendence, and 2000 Mexicans, chiefly, of course, Indians and half-breeds, doing the rest of the work.

## The Mexican Workmen

The life and labor of these people is well told in the words of an American mine superintendent who had employed them. One day, while he was making an inspection, something went wrong and he started to fall to his death.

" My helper, a Mexican boy of twenty-two or -three, watching above, had seen the break, thrown himself on the loose end to counter-balance my weight, and been hoisted up into the pulley. He had risked losing a hand and perhaps his life, but he had saved mine.

" This chap was no model of virtue; he was an average Mexican.

You had to figure on his being drunk at least one working day in the week. We were measuring contractors' work and you knew perfectly well that when you came to his brother-in-law's stope, if he had anything to do with it, there would be an overpayment of at least ten tons. . . .

" There are fundamental points of variance. To begin with, the American is a worrier. The future is always bothering him; he has the success of any endeavor deeply at heart. It is physically impossible for a Mexican to worry. This same helper of mine had a small baby that died in one of the rare cold spells. He was rather moody the last two days and the morning the child died he did not work; but the next day he was back, quite cheerful. If some allusion to the affair came up he would burst into tears and be horribly depressed for an hour or more. But once it was out of his mind he was perfectly normal again. And the Saturday afterwards he was at the dance, as intoxicated as ever. His feeling was sincere enough but it just wasn't in him to worry.

FIG. 403 — Mexican soldiers, with their wives, traveling on and in box-cars. (Courtesy G. F. Weeks, Mexican News Bureau, Washington, D. C.)

" We measured contractors' work and calculated their pay once a week, but we had to advance them money every day. There is a Mexican law to that effect. If we were to pay them on Saturday, by Monday the company would have to support the entire community for the rest of the week. . . .

" I was in probably the best-run big mine in Mexico. Our wages were high out of all proportion to the country. A base rate of three pesos a day (about a dollar and a half) and any good contractor making ten. Yet about 5000 Mexicans live in the little one-room company houses, about twelve feet square, a family to a house, sometimes two and three if things aren't going well. And there is no race suicide in this part of the world. Six, eight, ten people sleep in this one room, tight bolted up, with built-in windows. They eat heavy, greasy, highly seasoned native concoctions and drink spirits which make an American bootlegger a dispenser of soft drinks. The men worked underground all day, the temperature of the average working place being around eighty degrees, and came up on top and went home in the same clothes, to be changed only on Sundays to the brilliant striped shirts with which they imitate

Northern culture. And yet foremen will go blind with rage at the Mexican ' mucker ' who will average only eight tons to the American's twelve!

" The American foreman, however, is not usually as bitter as those who are in less direct contact with the men. . . .

" The Mexicans are children. That is the idea that pops into your head the first time you have anything to do with them. It is a childish trait not to worry; it is childish to care little how one lives; it is childish to be cruel with one hand and kind with the other. And they are childish in their need of being understood thoroughly before anything can be done with them.

" But they are children playing with real tools. There was, in that camp, an average of about a murder every ten days. I think in 90% of the cases both individuals were drunk. The company carried 1200 men on the payroll to insure a production from a thousand — one man in five off drunk or recovering every day. . . .

" I hold no complete brief for the Mexican. I have worked with him enough and been too whole-heartedly angry with him for that. He is inclined to be lazy, without responsibility, thriftless and extremely dirty — though for this I blame no one but his employer. But I do hold that when treated justly he is very tractable; his very lack of worry makes him infinitely easier to handle than his American rival over the line. Like a child, he will repay trust with trust, understanding with understanding, and he is capable of great improvement." — " Mexicans on the Job," Ralph McAllister Ingersoll, *Our World*, August 1923.

Any reader of this should remember that the writer quoted above was speaking of day laborers, and that there is a class of educated, cultured, traveled Caucasian Mexicans, representatives of Spanish stock and culture.

# CHAPTER XLVII

## THE TRADE, PLACE AND FUTURE OF NORTH AMERICA

### Part I. The Interdependence of Regions

THE most striking things about the continent of North America as the Home of Man are (1) its riches and (2) the interdependence of the different regions that comprise it. Each region described in this book has a surplus of one or more commercial commodities [1] which could not possibly be consumed within the region by its present population. Each region has many, many commercial deficits, so it is scarcely an exaggeration to say that each region is dependent to some extent upon every other one (Fig. 272), and greatly dependent upon many.

This mutual interdependence gives rise to an enormous trade, and explains why the settlement of the greater part of the continent by white men awaited the coming of the railroad. Steam transportation permits an inland region with one salable product to enter the full commercial life of the western world. This one fact has settled vast frontiers in a few decades and given us an orgy of trade, and, as is so often the case with new things, the pendulum has swung too far. In agriculture, at

---

[1] The list of regions and their leading surplus commodities:

The Coasts of Newfoundland and Labrador — fish, sealskins, iron-ore.
The St. Lawrence Valley — lumber, wood-pulp, dairy produce, asbestos.
New England-Canadian Maritime Region — textiles, shoes, miscellaneous fine machinery, hardware, jewelry, and fish.
The Erie Canal Belt — clothing, heavy machinery, gloves, and cameras.
Northeastern Highlands — wood and fur, milk, granite, marble.
North Atlantic Coast Plain — truck.
The Northern Piedmont — milk, apples, horses.
The Appalachian Ridge and Valley Region — anthracite coal, silk goods, peaches and apples.
The Allegheny Plateau and the Carolina Mountains — soft coal, iron, steel, glass, petroleum, wood.
The Ozark-Ouachita Uplands — live-stock, wood, peaches, apples.
The Cotton Belt — raw cotton, cotton cloth, lumber, naval stores, iron.
Subtropic Coasts and the Florida Peninsula — rice, cane sugar, citrus fruits, winter vegetables, phosphate rock, sulphur.
The Corn Belt — corn, oats, wheat, beef, pork, horses, some machinery.
Ohio Valley — tobacco, iron and steel manufactures, live-stock.
North Central Dairy Region — butter, cheese, pork, zinc.
The Winter Wheat Belt — wheat, beef.
The Spring Wheat Region — wheat, rye, oats, butter, beef.
The Upper Lake Region — iron-ore, copper, lumber.
The Lower Lake Region — agricultural machinery, other iron and steel manu-factures, automobiles, packing-house products, apples, grapes.

least, we are swinging away a little from such complete commercial inter-dependence. In nearly all sections of the country the agencies promoting agriculture are trying to persuade the individual farmer as well as localities to grow a greater variety of crops, and therefore to become a little more independent. We have found this in the Cotton Belt, the tobacco sections of Virginia, the wheat belts of the United States and Canada, and elsewhere.

Three forces have promoted this slight revival of local self-sufficiency. One is the generally wise policy of not putting all your eggs into one basket, emphasized alike by drought, frost and war. Another is the rising freight-rates, which make it more difficult to import distant produce. For example, the Massachusetts farmer finds he is more or less compelled to shift from Minneapolis bran to home-grown soy beans. The third, and most fundamental of all the reasons, is in agricultural economics, the fact that diversification helps to maintain fertility.

### Interdependence in Manufacture

In manufactures the swing toward greater interdependence is still on. The movement toward the development of manufacturing regions with

---

The Great Northern Forest — pulp-wood, lumber, fur, silver and other metals.

The Great Plains — stock cattle, stock sheep, wool, sugar-beets, potatoes.

The Lower Rio Grande — wool, stock cattle, citrus fruits and winter vegetables.

The Rocky Mountains — gold, copper, silver, coal, phosphate rock, wood, wool, apples, peaches.

Arid Southwestern Intermountain Plateaus — wool, mohair, stock cattle, stock sheep, gold, silver, copper, water-power.

The Great American Desert — Egyptian cotton, cantaloupes, early vegetables, dates.

Western Interior Arid Plateaus — wheat, sugar-beets, potatoes, wool, cattle, sheep, gold, copper.

The Columbia-Fraser Basins — wheat, apples, wool, meat.

Valley and Coast of Southern California — moving-picture films, citrus fruits, winter vegetables, miscellaneous manufactures.

The Sierra Nevada — lumber, water-power, gold.

Central California — prunes, peaches, raisins, plums, oranges, lemons.

The Puget Sound-Willamette Valley — prunes, cherries, vegetables, small fruits, sawed lumber.

North Pacific Coast and Mountains and Iceland — wood, salmon, halibut, seal-skins, gold; (from Iceland) fish, sheep, wool, sheepskins, tallow.

The Yukon Valley — gold.

The Tundra or Arctic Pastures — reindeer meat and reindeer skins.

The Arctic Sea and the Greenland Ice-cap — whale products and sealskins.

The West Indies — Trade-Wind Islands — sugar, molasses, tobacco, winter vegetables, coconuts.

Yucatan and the Bahamas — sisal and sponges.

The Uplands of Central America and of Mexico — coffee, hides.

The Moist Eastern Lowlands of Central America and Mexico — bananas, mahogany, chicle, petroleum, vanilla.

The Pacific Coast of Central America and Southern Mexico — hides.

Central Plateau, Mexico — silver, gold, lead, zinc.

The Mexico Cordillera Regions — gold, silver, lead.

cities, and factory product, and separate regions of rural population and raw-material production is manifested by much evidence in recent years. In the period between 1910 and 1920 the United States gained in population 14.9%, but more than a thousand counties lost in total population, and many more in rural population.[2]  In this one decade the urban population of the United States increased from 45.8% to 51.4%, while the rural declined from 54.2% to 48.6%.  When one reduces these figures to percentages, urban increase of 25.7% and rural of 5.4%, the figures are startling, and manifestly their tendency cannot long continue. If it did, we should all be living in cities in a few decades.

This is more than a simple country-city shift.  The location of the

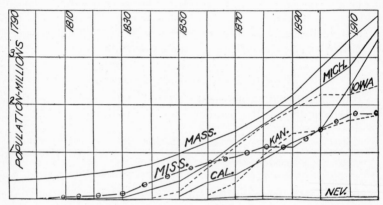

FIG. 404 — Manufacturing areas grew.  See Massachusetts and Michigan.  Raw-material areas grew much less.  See Kansas, Iowa, and Mississippi.

urban increase shows the separation of the manufacturing regions from the raw-material regions.  Most of the city growth occurred between Portland, Me., Minneapolis, Chicago and Washington, D. C., but the gains on the Pacific Coast have been striking in quantity and even more striking in character.  In the decade 1900–1910, the Pacific coast states increased in population 75%; in the decade 1910–1920, 33%.  Even this last was more than double the United States gain, and these states also exceed the average of the United States in proportion of city population.  They have about three city people to two country people.

This manufacturing centralization is in large part a matter of transportation — water transportation.  It pays for a factory to be near the sea or a water-route.  The wide-reaching advantages of the water-route rather than the rail-route are well shown by the statement (in a letter) of Mr. A. R. MacDonald, member of the Wisconsin Railroad Commission: " At the present time manufacturers of many Wisconsin products

---

[2] Rural population, according to the census, comprises all people living outside of incorporated places of 2500 inhabitants or more.  (Fig. 151.)

find it cheaper to ship to Eastern points, chiefly New York, then to ship by boat down the Atlantic coast, through the Panama Canal, to the Pacific coast. The saving by this method, as compared to direct freight shipment, is approximately $1.00 per hundred pounds."

This Eastern land of manufacturing regions is the focus toward which the producers of raw materials direct the vehicles loaded with their produce. From Florida and the South the coasting steamers and the freight-trains, rumbling endlessly, toil northward to city land with their cotton, rice and lumber, oranges, grapefruit, vegetables, rosin and turpentine. From the center of the continent there roll without ceasing the monthly thousands of carloads of wheat, flour, oats, corn and wool, and

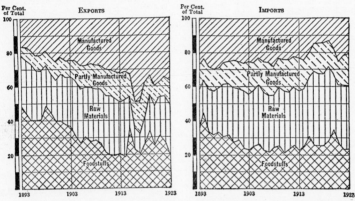

FIG. 405 —The increasing percentage of imports of raw material, and the increasing percentage of exports of manufactures show the increasing dependence of the United States on the prosperity of other countries. (Courtesy Guaranty Trust Co. of New York.)

the other thousands of ill-smelling cars of grunting, bawling, squealing animals to be sweetened, stilled and chilled at packing-plants before proceeding elsewhere in more close-packed refrigerator cars, cans or barrels. Across the Great Lakes proceeds the annual summer rush of crude raw material with its terrible weights described in another chapter.

Rushing over the high Rockies and the wide plains come the aristocrats of long-distance freight-traffic, the thousands of cars of California fruits and Washington lumber. The supreme haster of all is the millions of dollars' worth of raw silk that rushes from Japan to New York by way of Seattle, the quickest of all routes.

Outward from the factory area goes an almost equal value of manufactured goods — shoes, automobiles, clothing, phonographs, skates, rifles, bicycles, pins — this list as long as Montgomery Ward's catalogue. Most of these things go in carloads to Spokane, Atlanta, Denver, Dallas, Des Moines, Baltimore, Indianapolis and other jobbing centers where wholesale houses feed it out in small lots to the retail stores in hundreds of tributary small towns and villages — a wonderful world in which to live! A world of physical plenty and increasing monotony, witness the *Saturday Evening Post,* the mail-order catalogue, the clothing styles, the phonograph and the radio. Exit local color.

### A Reaction in Manufacture Also

Perhaps this regional specialization of manufacture, like the regional specialization of agriculture, has swung too far. There are signs that it has. We may yet have a revival of manufacture for local needs as we are already having of agriculture for local needs. Two comparatively new industrial factors make this possible. One is the widespread distribution of electric power in town, village and home. This is sweeping across the United States and Canada at the present time with great speed and apparently is but in its infancy. The second factor is standardization. These two factors may make it possible to manufacture many small things in small villages, possibly even the farm-home. *It may become easier to transport the man's raw materials and his produce than his food.*[3] This may

Fig. 406 — It takes three or four continents, if not indeed five, to produce the makings for a single telephone instrument, a daily necessity to the man who thinks we can keep out of international entanglements.

[3] Buried in this idea is the great gap between the cost of living (personal and social) in the big city and the small town or the farm.

shift some kinds of manufacture from Boston, Worcester, Detroit, or Chicago to farms and villages in food-producing sections of New York state, Michigan, Manitoba, Saskatchewan, or the Rocky Mountain valleys. Mr. Henry Ford is carrying on at the present time some very suggestive experiments in this line. He has, for example, in a little village on River Rouge a small factory with fourteen employees, who live in a country village and make a tiny valve. This little factory produces nothing but this valve, but it supplies all of these valves that are wanted in the Ford works. A truck comes out each morning from the main plant with raw material and makes a round of this and several similar factories, supplying raw materials and taking finished stuff back to the works. There is no economic reason why these things might not be made 400 miles away rather than a dozen miles away.

Standardization is the second factor that may help to decentralize industry. Standardization and automatic machinery have gone so far that there is no longer any mystery about knitting a sock, making a shirt or a small standardized piece for a complicated, assembled machine. The little pieces for the lawn-mower need no longer be made by men who live in the crowded homes of Philadelphia. The completed pieces could easily come by truck or train from some village nestled in the hills of the Piedmont, forty or 400 miles away. And that example might be duplicated ten or twenty thousand times over in an analysis of the machine manufactures in America. It is possible that we are at the beginning of an era of the partial redistribution of manufacturing men over the land where food production and climate and commercial access are good.[4]

There is no reason to expect such a development to limit the actual volume of trade (because of general increase in volume) or to eliminate regional interdependence, but it may reduce the proportion of a man's wants that are secured by inter-regional trade. Its chief result is likely to be the scattering of manufacturing into town, village and farm throughout the present manufacturing area, taking it away from large cities.

## PART II. THE INTERDEPENDENCE OF CONTINENTS

North America is rich both in proportion of the world's wealth[5] and in variety of economic goods, yet the make-up of that universal con-

---

[4] Mr. Henry Ford's idea about the restoration of the age-old two-job era (farm work-manufacturing work) for each man and how it can be done, and what it can do, is worth careful investigation by anyone interested in this point. It may be the greatest thing that has happened to us (in the realm of economics) since the Industrial Revolution piled us up in cities.

[5] The United States alone has 40% of the world's installed water-power, 35% of the railroad mileage, 57% of the telephone and telegraph, and over 80% of the automobiles. It produces 71% of the cotton, 50% of the coal, 64% of the petroleum, 52% of the timber, 60% of the zinc, 59% of the copper, 52% of the pig-iron, 48% of the lead — all of which totals up to a great moral responsibility, such a stewardship as the world never saw before.

venience, the telephone (Fig. 406), shows how dependent we are upon
other continents. The commercial family of America rises in the morning and dresses itself with the produce of all continents — wool from
Australia and Argentina, silk from China and Japan, buttons from
Ecuador, cotton from Carolina, but also from Egypt. If it is winter,
the furs are probably from Canada or Siberia. The shoes of the men
are of Argentine calf-skin, those of the women and children are probably
of goat-skin from India, Africa or Mexico. The rubber comes from
Malaysia. The felt or derby hat is of rabbit fur from Australia, France
or Belgium. The breakfast has tea (India, China or Japan), coffee
(Brazil) or cocoa (Africa, Ecuador or Brazil), cereal sweetened with
cane-sugar from Cuba, Porto Rico, Hawaii or the Philippines, bread of
flour blended with Canadian wheat, and perhaps an egg fried in vegetable
fat from the South Sea Islands or a Texas cottonseed-oil mill. So on
we might follow through this family's day and find its economic de-
pendences at every turn resting upon some of the five foreign continents.
Perhaps, and most unfortunately, the part that appears least dependent
upon foreign produce is the brain cavity, where the error still often remains that America is independent of the rest of the world.

### Interdependence and Bullet War

If the average American voter understood our inter-continental interdependence, our inter-regional interdependence and our international
interdependence to the point where he *felt* it, this world would promptly
become a better place in which to make a living and to live. The person
who thinks the United States or even North America is independent of
the other continents or can be prosperous without them or without
their prosperity should review what happened before the World War,
during, and immediately after it. Before the World War we had a
half-century of steady progression of industry and trade. This trade
depended on an increasing European population, increasing European
trade which promoted the steady increase of settlement, production and
export of agricultural produce from North America. Then came the
spasm of increased export at fabulous prices during the World War,
followed by reaction. The years 1921, 1922 or 1923 witnessed Russia
in chaos, Hungary in civil war, Austria standing in the international
bread-line, Czecho-Slovakia and Poland maintaining standing armies
proportionately as great as those of the United States at the height of
the War, Italy and Jugo-Slavia on the verge of hostilities over Fiume,
France and Germany in the White War of diplomacy and blockade which
continued the Red War of battles and blood. The results of this continental chaos cut off a great part of Europe's import trade and Great
Britain had millions of unemployed.

The results of Europe's trouble smote North America in her remotest corners. It was a trade blow. Our export trade fell off. Prices of farm produce slumped and dark depression trampled the plans, dashed the hopes and shrunk the estates of millions in central North America, all the way from the Atlantic to the Pacific and from the warm Gulf to the cool lakes north of Winnipeg.

Farmers in Kansas and Nebraska burned corn in 1921 while hundreds of thousands in Europe starved to death, but the farmer is no more to be blamed for burning corn than the people of New York for burning coal. Each was burning the most available fuel at the price and the place. The war and the resulting furies of price-change and trade-change had played havoc with the farmer's price-ratio. In 1913 the American farmer could purchase at Springfield, Illinois, a wagon, a corn-binder, a grain-binder and a gang-plow for 716 bushels of corn. In the high prices of 1920 he could get them for 583 bushels of corn. The next year, 1921, after the bottom had fallen out of the European trade, it required 2027 bushels of corn to buy the machinery and nearly all farm staples were in the same proportion — low, while all manufactures were high like the machinery and stayed so for several years.

This great key fact of cheap farm produce had a long series of consequences, of which I cite a few. In the United States lands prepared for irrigation were not irrigated. In 1924, acts of Congress provided for deferring of payments by farmers who owed the government money for the erection of irrigation equipment. At that time $25,000,000.00 of reclamation money due the government was classed as "deferred, doubtful or bad." In Canada (1922), 120 miles east of Calgary, I rode along irrigation ditches stretch-

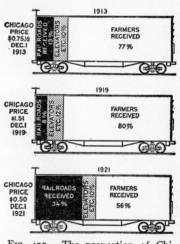

FIG. 407 — The proportion of Chicago price received by the farmer after paying 500 miles of freight on a bushel of corn from Sioux City, Iowa, to Chicago. The World War, juggling corn price and freight rate, played havoc with American agriculture. (Courtesy U. S. Dept. Agr.)

ing through the fertile plains. There was water in the ditches and there had been for a year or two, but there was not a farm in sight and settlers were not coming. There was no money in raising wheat, the great money-crop of the center of the continent, and good Canada grain-lands could be bought that year and the next year and the next year for a fraction of the assessed valuation. In 1924, the Dominion Government closed land offices it had maintained in Omaha and many other American cities for twenty-five years in its process of giving away quarter-sections of land to young American farmers who went to Canada. It still had some land, but the young Americans were not going to Canada. They were going to town. The price of manufactures still remained high.

For the first time in a century the frontier had ceased to show the signs of abundant resources (effective ones making industry), and we saw a peculiar reversal of a century long ratio of wages. In January 1923, when the average of farm wages was 30% above the 1913 level, it was only 15% above it in the West North-central States (Wheat Belt), whereas it was 56% above it in the North Atlantic States (where factory prosperity still continued).

In January 1924, the president of the Wheat Council was quoting a letter from President Coolidge showing approval of the attempt to cur-

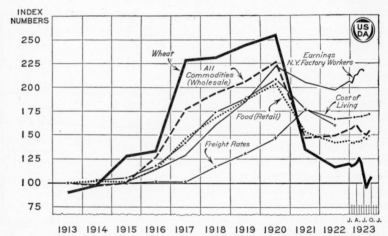

FIG. 408 — One of the indirect economic results of the World War. Using wheat as a type, we see here a measure of the crushing upset that the War gave to American agriculture.

tail production: " The effort in an organized and systematic way to establish such a measure of control over the wheat acreage as will measurably insure against over-production is altogether to be commended. Almost every important business except agriculture has trade organizations and associations through which it is possible to deal with such vitally important matters. Quite obviously the business of agricultural production would benefit by the same methodical approach to the underlying problems which it must always confront." (*The Public Ledger*, Philadelphia, December 31, 1923.) In the spring of 1924, the National Producers' Alliance was signing up farmers by the thousands

in Nebraska and elsewhere. in this effort to limit production. " The
' control-production ' idea in farming is rampant in Nebraska this spring.
Half a dozen or so separate organizations are busy among farmers in
Nebraska combining them into societies having for their object restriction and curtailment of production of wheat, corn and other farm
products. Each of these organizations reports farmers are anxious
to join." (Special to *Public Ledger,* Omaha, April 13, 1924.)

The price record of a particular Illinois farm is an index of the land-
value result of this trade demoralization. An 800-acre farm twenty
·miles east of Decatur, Ill., sold for $200.00 an acre in 1913. In 1919, it
would have brought $400.00 or more. In June, 1924, it sold at auction
for $145.00 an acre, although a hard road had been built within a mile
of it a short time before.

All these lost billions of land-value with the accompanying tens of
thousands of foreclosed mortgages, bankruptcies and blasted farm-
homes are but one of the minor results of a world war fought 4000 miles
away in Europe, which suffered a hundred-fold as much as did America.
Certainly the study of international trade is a great argument and great
goad to men to try out their brains and their good will in the matter of
sending organized war into the discard where the personal war of the
duel fortunately lies. Just suppose a Napoleon could mobilize the power
of this age.

### Interdependence and Trade War

We also need to see the end of those provocations to ill will, those inter-
ferences with the full use of the earth's surface that arise from tariff
wars and legislative wars. The man-made boundary is of increasing
uselessness, and the harder it is for freight to cross the greater is its
interference with the welfare of mankind. The increasing uselessness of
political boundaries that interfere with trade is suggested in the words
of Mr. W. S. Murray, Chairman of the Super-Power Survey of the
United States Geological Survey, when he declared in a public address:
" I believe he (the Secretary of Commerce) will agree with me when I
say, let us, in putting super-power on the map in copper, concrete and
steel, forget state boundaries. Let us not try to make one state bigger
than the nation. Let us rather make the nation what we have called it,
these United States, united through their governors and their public
service commissions." Perhaps Mr. Murray would agree that his conception needs to go one bit further and apply to international boundaries
as well, for it is true that his first super-power map had on it dotted
lines indicating the ultimate need for the continuous transfer of power
across the boundary from Canada into the United States.

That is merely one of the many ways in which we should be better off
if we could forget in all economic things the United States-Canadian

boundary, across which at different seasons flows the foreign trade of Canada through the United States and of the United States through Canada, and across which there is the continuous satisfaction of reciprocal need — our coal for their wood, etc. Why interfere with it? Is it good or bad, and what of the future?

The widened reach of the commerce that supports the common man, due to regional interdependence, is the greatest single change that characterized the past 100 years. Its big result — the population of the world nearly doubled in this time — flowed naturally from the increased

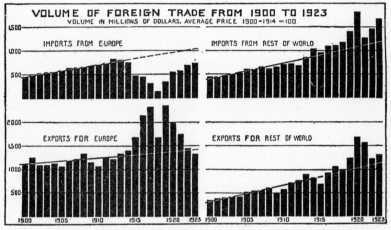

VOLUME OF FOREIGN TRADE FROM 1900 TO 1923
VOLUME IN MILLIONS OF DOLLARS. AVERAGE PRICE 1900-1914 = 100

IMPORTS FROM EUROPE    IMPORTS FROM REST OF WORLD

EXPORTS FOR EUROPE    EXPORTS FOR REST OF WORLD

FIG. 409 — The United States is coming to resemble Europe more and more and therefore has less basis for trading with her. (Courtesy Cleveland Trust Co. *Business Bulletin.*)

wealth. In this doubling of the population, the most conspicuous feature, a feature without a rival in the history of the world, was the increase of the population of the United States from 3.929 millions of people in 1790 to 105.710 millions in 1920. If this rate of increase, 26.9 times in 130 years, should be duplicated in the next 130 years, the population of the United States would be twenty-eight hundred million, and in the next 130 would be seventy-six thousand million, both of which figures are quite ridiculous. Readjustments are due. In fact, they are in progress. The rate of increase in the early decades averaged 35%. It was 21% in 1900–1910, and 14.9% in 1910–1920, and a further decline *must* appear. Otherwise, our numbers will become unbearable. The question of indefinite maintenance has many problems in it and an idea that is unfamiliar to Americans. This idea is "permanent." If we will glance back at the long record of the race and then take a similar look into the *future*, we will realize that western civilization really never thought of it.

Like children and birds, we are living in the day only. The race needs to take hold of itself.

## PART III. HOW LONG CAN INTERDEPENDENCE LAST?

Caesar paused for a whole day on the banks of the Rubicon before he plunged into a course where he had to succeed continuously in the face of enemies or die. Western civilization splashed across its Rubicon into the new and dangerous territory of interdependence without a moment's hesitation, indeed without even realizing the fact. We do, indeed, live in a new world and we have given our lives as hostages to its continuance. If the trains stop running, the wheels stop turning, the ships stop sailing, millions of us will perish as helplessly as the animals in an abandoned zoo — a dangerous world in which to live, as well as a wonderful world.

It is a fact that the increase of population in the United States from 3.9 million in 1790 to 105 million in 1920 saw us start poor and wind up rich.[6] Can we increase our numbers somewhat and maintain them indefinitely in a static or an increasing standard of consumption? The pathway of history is strewn with wrecks of civilizations[7] that developed large populations and wide-reaching trade — Babylon,

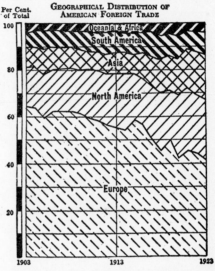

FIG. 410 — The percentage of *value* of our foreign trade also shows how rapidly we, like Europe, are becoming dependent on all the world. (Courtesy Guaranty Trust Co. of New York.)

Nineveh, Persia, Egypt, Crete, Greece, Rome, the Italian cities and Granada, not to mention later examples. Are races like men? It has been well said of families that it takes three generations from shirt-sleeves to shirt-sleeves because prosperity undermines personal staying power. The task confronting North America is to stand its present prosperity and maintain the racial staying power. As a people we seem to be strangely

[6] The National Industrial Conference Board reports, September 1924, that in seventy years between 1850 and 1920 the United States population increased 3.6-fold, manufacturing 28-fold and mining 77-fold. Therefore, we all have flivvers, radio and phonographs; we have shortened the hours of labor and reduced the output per hour.

[7] Because of its greater size, complexity and interdependence our civilization has greater possibilities of smash than any of the others.

like the family that cannot stand prosperity. Perhaps there is no better evidence of this than the way we waste our resources rather than conserve them. Our great increase of numbers, our great wealth, our whole western civilization, are based on mechanically produced energy, and upon a wasteful use of natural resources limited in amount and often of diminishing supply. Our forests are largely gone. Our natural gas is largely gone. Our oil is rapidly going. Our coal is being wastefully mined in comparison to that of Europe. Our soil is being eroded at a rate never matched in the history of the world. We are the worst of all wasters because our tools and machines give us power which we use alike in construction and in waste. China has maintained a civilization for 4000 years. If we waste as much soil per century for the next forty centuries as we have wasted in the last century[8] we shall only have enough good land to make two or three Belgiums.

## The Place of Eugenics

Even greater problems face us. For the maintenance of our complex civilization on this continent, the apparent degeneration of human stock is more alarming even than the waste of resources. Medical science, sanitation, surgery have done little or nothing to improve human vigor, and have done much to reduce it. The laws of heredity, well worked out and practiced by man in his growth of plants and animals, show very clearly that the way to improve stock is to improve parents — take advantage of heredity. Thus far, medical science has been chiefly occupied with saving human weaklings who have propagated their kind. Civilization has made the world safe for weaklings and is producing them.

Civilization has also " made the world safe for stupidity." (See *The New Decalogue of Science*, A. E. Wiggam.) Every recent study of the American birth-rate points to the disappearance of the stock with brains. We have developed the most amazing institutional systems for the care and preservation and attempted improvement of the feeble in both mind and body. If wayward and weak of mind they have special homes for refuge. Hospitals assist them in giving birth. Skilled physicians care for the young bone-head. Nurses wait upon him. Devoted virgins in special schools strive to inject ideas where ideas will not go. Then we, who breed pigs and pups with great care, turn him loose to increase his kind and give him aid therein. If one of us is born brilliant we have nothing for him but an elaborate educational chain gang where we lock-step him with mediocrity. The man from the Moon might well think that we thought our civilization depended on the weak and the dull. It seems to be a peculiar irony that while we breed our animals up we

[8] See publications H. H. Bennett, U. S. Bureau of Soils.

breed ourselves down. Yet this civilization of interdependence in combination with the recent enormous increase in scientific knowledge and
the complexity of life is putting greater stress upon personal and social
character and demanding a higher grade of intellectual ability, social
vision and constructive imagination. The continuance of this civilization
and its improvement through the utilization of the almost unbelievable
powers now at hand is first of all a problem in eugenics. We need men
big enough to use the new powers. It has been said of man in New York,
which is typical of western civilization:

" His mastery, however, depends upon the preservation of his energy,
vigilance, industry, inventiveness, honesty and other high traits of character. Our constantly growing dependence upon nature makes it more
necessary than ever before that science should play its part in preserving
those traits which alone can render man permanently victorious over his
geographical environment. . . .

" Today we are at last coming to a realization that only by weeding out
the weak-bodied, weak-willed parts of the community through some form
of eugenic selection, and by seeing that people are adjusted to their
physical environment, can we provide proper human material for the
great tasks of civilization. We can scarcely avoid the conclusion that
the building up of character is as much the work of the scientist as of the
preacher, teacher or philanthropist." [9]

The overtowering need of man today is a slight increase each generation in the average hereditary intelligence and self-control. If this can
be built up a little as generations go by, we can put civilization on a
permanent and improving basis. If we go the other way another era of
primitive agriculture and natural selection awaits us.

## Science and the Classic Gods

Science and invention have given man the powers of classic gods. Such
powers were not meant for mental children. The instrumentalities of
science and machinery now within human reach and likely to be developed within a few decades give us almost unbelievable possibilities for
the material basis of a civilization. To name a few of the opportunities
that now seem to be within reach — we can irrigate our dry lands, drain
our swamps, drive out malaria, reduce preventable disease to a low figure,
for all except those of low intelligence and weak will-power. We can
probably get sources of almost unlimited mechanical power, and we can
probably open the tropics to the white race.

Two of these possibilities, power and the tropics, merit a little explanation.

[9] " The Water Barriers of New York City," Ellsworth Huntington in the
*Geographical Review*, September 1916.

## Power—Perpetual and Unlimited

The unlimited power seems to be within our reach in the West Indies, perhaps elsewhere. An engineer has pointed out the fact that ether is turned from a liquid to a gas at a temperature of less than eighty degrees Fahrenheit. Secondly, he points out that the warm surface waters of the South Atlantic, Caribbean and Gulf of Mexico have the necessary eighty degrees, and that 2500 feet down these same seas have a temperature of forty degrees. All that is needed to develop power is to supply an ether engine with both kinds of water. One vaporizes the ether which then runs the engine and is condensed by the cold water. It is then ready to be heated again by the warm water—and so on and on. This process is identical to that by which a condensing marine engine takes a limited amount of boiler-water at New York and repeatedly boils it with fire and condenses it with sea-water as it makes its way across the ocean. The whole West Indies is swept by the trade-wind at a temperature year in and year out warm enough to run ether engines. At places on the Virgin Islands of the United States cold water for condensation can be had a half-mile from shore at a depth of 2500 feet. Apparently there are similar places in the Bahamas and perhaps elsewhere. These islands might become power-plants of an almost unlimited extent and with perpetual supply of the "makings" as long as the sun holds out, the trade-winds blow and the cold water keeps replenishing itself from the abundant supplies at the poles. This opens a wide vista to speculation and invention.

## The Conquest of Tropic Climate

Science is now ready to complete or duplicate half of a job of which one-half was done ages ago. The innovator who first heated his shelter with fire doubtless created a great hubbub in cavedom. Also he opened up the lands of frost to man, who had before been a tropic inhabitant; and his invention has greatly changed the history of the world. If we make a house with a tropic or near-tropic temperature and thereby live in cold lands, why should we not make a house with a cool temperature and live in it in tropic lands? It is strange that we have studied out to perfection the temperature and humidity conditions necessary for the preservation of dead pigs and then practiced the science as a fine art in our cold-storage plants, while we have at the same time done almost nothing to find out what conditions of temperature and moisture in a building best suit the human animal.

A decade ago Mr. Ellsworth Huntington, in his book *Civilization and Climate,* advanced the claim that man's mind does best when the outdoor temperature is about forty degrees and his body does best when the outdoor temperature is sixty to seventy degrees. The same author has since followed this up with other studies (see *Modern Hospital,* vol. 14, no. 1), all tending to show the great improvement of health and vigor that come to human beings at some temperatures and humidities rather than at others.[10]   Thus far we are continuing the practice of temperature and moisture control for dead pigs, but for man it has not become an object of serious experiment.   Great is the resistance of the human mind to new ideas!

It seems to be perfectly clear, as a theoretical proposition, that we can build a large residential structure on a tropic shore in which conditions for health and vigor will be as good as those prevailing in northwestern Europe.   There is no technical difficulty in enclosing a whole town under one roof, including playgrounds, stores and places of public assemblage. Here women and children might spend twenty to twenty-four hours a day. Men would spend the hours of sleep, of eating, of loafing, while in the mornings they might travel by motor-bus a few miles out to the plantations where eight or ten hours a day in the tropic air might do them no more injury than results from eight or ten hours a day in freezing or zero weather in Minnesota.   There are today agricultural villages in Spain of 3000 to 5000 people, four or five miles apart, without a dwelling between.   The land between the villages is cultivated by the villagers, who go forth to their distant fields — without the aid of motor-busses.   They live in the villages because man in a social animal.   The tropic town under one roof, with an ideal climate mechanically made, would have the advantage of social opportunity, perfect conditions for health and greatly multiplied energy.

I mention these possibilities not to give a description of the final things that may be achieved in America, but merely to indicate the great things that await us if we can keep up the supply of brains, kindness and constructive imagination.   Everything else is in our hands.   Only a few of these things can be attained until we get more people of a new type, the type *not* described by the Frenchman who said, " I don't believe your average American business man is interested in anything but business." For too long we have had as a hero the man who wanted to buy more land to raise more corn to raise more pigs to buy more land to raise more corn, and so on.   Science has produced wealth.   Its next task is the social reconstruction and social righteousness for which North America offers splendid resources.

[10] Mr. Huntington may not be exactly right in his figures, but theoretically he is right in his main point — that there must be some degrees of temperature and humidity that give more human effectiveness than others, and if he has not found them we are able to find them by experimentation.

# INDEX

Meat industry, Chicago, 384, 385 (ill.),
387 (ill.); Cincinnati, 329; Corn Belt,
303; location, 317
Medford, Ore., 618
Mediterranean Sea, early New England
trade with, 69
Melons, California, 581
Merida, Yucatan, 743
Merrill, L. A., 517
Merrimac River, 74, 83
Merrimac Valley, 85
Merritt, R. P., 583, 585
Mesa Verde, 459
Mesas, 21; example near Denver, 477
(ill.); Hopi Indians and, 479
Mescal, 463
Mesquite, 432, 487
Mestizos, 12, 670; Mexico, 783
Metropolitan districts, growth, 546
Mexicali, 504
Mexican drawn work, 786
Mexicans, character as workers, 793; on
the Lower Rio Grande, 435; soldiers
traveling, 794 (ill.)
Mexico, 456; American grievances, 688;
average annual rainfall (map), 776;
border towns, 461; cotton, 464; dictatorships, 676; eastern lowlands, 767;
estates, 462; financing revolutions,
769; fruit-raising, 506; future of the
plateau, 465; governing, question of,
687; government, 674, 677; inaccessibility and the lives of the people, 670;
irrigation, 465, 505, 506; irrigation,
projected, 502; ixtle, 464; labor conditions, 678; Maximilian's empire, 676;
mining, 464; oil-field conditions, 678,
679; petroleum and politics, 769;
revolutions, 465; Rio Grande as
boundary with Texas, 433; rubber,
464; settling her troubles by a group
of nations, 688; Southwestern Plateaus
and, 460; succession of presidents,
678; temperatures for January and for
July (maps), 780, 781; troop train,
672 (ill.); west coast, 773; west coast,
water supply for a town, 774 (ill.).
See also Moist Eastern Lowlands of
Central America and Mexico; Pacific
Coast of Central America and Southern
Mexico; Uplands of Central America
and Mexico
Mexico Central Plateau, 777; cities, 777,
785; climate, 779; crops and local
markets, 783; cross-section (diagr.),
777; education campaign, 782; foreign
capital, 784, 785; formation, 777;
future, 787; handicrafts, 786; land
problem, 781; land question and education, 782; mining and foreign capital,

784; peons and low diet, 783 (with
ill.); people and civilizations, 779;
ruins and ancient figures, 782 (ills.);
small tradesman's booth, 785 (ill.)
Mexico City, 778, 779, 780; description,
785
Mexico Cordillera regions, 788; eastern
Sierra, 790; Mexican workmen, 793;
minerals, 792; populous and isolated
valleys, 790; Vera Cruz to Orizaba,
789; western Sierra, 791
Mexico, Gulf of, 274, 662. See also Gulf
and Caribbean peoples
Miami, Fla., 279; climate (graph), 59;
golf course, 279 (ill.); negroes in,
277
Miami Basin, 252
Miami Valley, 294
Mice and Truckee settlers, 516
Michigan, 296; apples, 393; beans, 392;
cherries in Leelanau County, 391;
furniture industry, 383; lakes, 367;
lower peninsula, 366; lumber, 368;
lumber cut (graph), 393; sugar beets,
392; upper peninsula, 366
Michigan, Lake, 292, 377; fruit-raising
near, 390; shores, temperature, 390
Michigan's Ice Box, 374
Middle class, 674
Middle West, Chicago as its capital, 384;
literature, 307
Migration, Canada, 352; from the Corn
Belt, 309
Miles City, Mont., 429
Milk, 612; average production per cow
(map), 334; Canada's production per
cow (chart), 51; St. Lawrence Valley,
50; Wisconsin, 332. See also Dairying
Milk tester, 334
Miller and Lux lands, 580, 586
Millinocket, Me., 148, 149
Millville, N. J., 177
Milwaukee, 337, 388, 389, 390
Minadoka irrigation unit, 519
Minerals, Arctic tundra, 657; Arizona
hill with steam shovels, 481 (ill.);
Great Basin, 511; Great Northern
Forest, 406; Great Plains, 430; Mexico,
western Sierra, 792; New England-
Canadian Maritime Region, 94; Northeastern Highlands, 151; resources, 18
Miners, Appalachian Plateau, 226; gold-
miner in Alaska, 640 (with ill.); Penn-
sylvania, 210
Mining industry, 210; Alaska, 631; Appalachian Plateau, 225; Central America, 753; concentrator in Mexico, 792
(ill.); gold in the Rockies, 438; Mexico Central Plateau, 464, 784; Pennsylvania, western, and W. Virginia,